1994

PHYSICS LABORATORY EXPERIMENTS

PHYSICS LABORATORY EXPERIMENTS

Fourth Edition

JERRY D. WILSON
Lander University

D. C. Heath and Company
Lexington, Massachusetts Toronto

Address editorial correspondence to
D. C. Heath and Company
125 Spring Street
Lexington, MA 02173

Acquisitions Editor: Kent Porter Hamann
Developmental Editor: Joanne Williams
Production Editors: Heather L. Garrison and Jennifer Raymond
Designer: Alwyn R. Velásquez
Photo Researcher: Billie Porter
Production Coordinator: Charles Dutton

Published simultaneously in Canada.

Printed in the United States of America.

International Standard Book Number: 0-669-35074-5

10 9 8 7 6 5 4 3 2

"What is the meaning of it all, Mr. Holmes?"
"Ah. I have no data. I cannot tell," he said.

Arthur Conan Doyle, *The Adventures of the Copper Beeches*, 1892

Preface

Physics Laboratory Experiments was written for students of introductory physics. The major purpose of laboratory exercises is to augment and supplement the learning and understanding of basic physical principles while introducing laboratory procedures, techniques, and equipment. Toward this end, each experiment is generally organized into the following sections:

- Advance Study Assignment
- Introduction and Objectives
- Equipment Needed
- Theory
- Experimental Procedure
- Laboratory Report
- Questions

In this fourth edition, material has been revised based on comments and suggestions from instructors and students who used the third edition. The result is clearer explanations of experimental procedures and improvements. For example, experimental Objectives have been added for each experiment and computer-assisted experimental procedures are cited. Those features that proved to be successful in previous editions have been retained. For example, laboratory safety is continually expressed and highlighted in the manual. A major supplemental improvement made available with this edition is an in-lab computer check of data and calculations (*Lab-Check*) described on p. viii.

For the fourth edition, a critical survey of the experiments most often performed was made, and based on the interest of economy and utilization, the number of experiments has been reduced from 57 to 49—still an ample number for a 2-semester or 3-quarter laboratory physics course. A summary of the pedagogical and practical features in this edition is as follows:

Advance Study Assignments. Students often come to the laboratory unprepared, even though they should have read the experiment before the lab period to become familiar with it. To address this problem, an Advance Study Assignment precedes each experiment. These assignments consist of questions drawn from the Theory and Experimental Procedures sections of the experiment. To answer the questions, students must read the experiment before the lab period, and as a result, are better prepared. It is recommended that the Advance Study Assignment be collected at the beginning of the laboratory period.

New Experiments. Two new experimental procedures have been added in this edition:

Experiment 13 Addendum *The Ballistic Pendulum: Conservation of Angular Momentum and Energy*

Experiment 26 *The Voltmeter and Ammeter*

The first is an addendum to Experiment 13 *Rotation Motion and Moment of Inertia*. It takes into account the rigid body properties of the ballistic pendulum, and may be compared to Experiment 8 *Projectile Motion: The Ballistic Pendulum* where the velocity of a projectile is found using the approximation of the conservation of linear momentum and energy. The second new experiment, contributed by Fred B. Otto, has the students essentially build and test meters and multimeters.

Instructor's Resource Manual. The *Instructors Resource Manual* with this edition is a special feature and resource for the instructor. It has been written by Fred. B. Otto of the Maine Maritime Academy, who brings the benefits of 20 years of teaching and laboratory experience. The general format of the previous edition has been retained. For each experiment, there are (1) Comments and Hints, (2) Answers to Experiment Questions, and (3) Post-lab Quiz Questions (completion, multiple-choice, and essay).

Fred's experience has helped expand the Comments and Hints sections, which are intended to assist the instructor. Helpful tips on experimental procedures and common mistakes are given. Also, Fred has given the answers to *all* of the end-of-lab-report questions.

The *Instructor's Resource Manual* includes: general descriptions of and references to computer-assisted experiments, laboratory safety references, lists of scientific equipment suppliers and physics software suppliers, and graph paper copy masters.

Illustrations. Over 200 photographs and diagrams illustrate experimental procedures and equipment. Some of these illustrations have been updated to reflect the changes and improvements that have been made in equipment, and to make procedures more clear.

Example Calculations. In the Theory section of some experiments, sample calculations that involve the formulas and mathematics used in the experiment have been included where appropriate. These show the student how experimental data is applied.

Maximum Application to Available Equipment. Laboratory equipment at many institutions is limited, and often only standard equipment, purchased from scientific equipment suppliers, is available. The experimental procedures in this manual are described for different types of common laboratory apparatus, thus maximizing the application of the manual. For example, in Experiment 4, *Uniformly Accelerated Motion,* three procedures for measurement are described.

Economical Experiments. Many experiments may be done with readily available, economical equipment and materials. See, for example:

Experiment 3 *The Scientific Method: The Simple Pendulum* (investigates system variables—dependent and independent)

Experiment 15 *Hooke's Law and Simple Harmonic Motion* (includes elongation of rubber band)

Experiment 38 *Reflection and Refraction* (plane mirror characteristics and index of refraction of glass plate)

Experiment 40 *Polarized Light* (investigation of methods of polarization, optical activity, and LCDs)

Experiment 44 *The Mass of an Electron:* e/m *Measurement* (does not require expensive Helmholtz coils)

Computer-assisted Experiments. With the increasing use of computers in the laboratory and the development of computer-assisted experiments with data taking and analysis, references have been given for applicable experiments. Because of the variety of programs and equipment, no laboratory procedures are given. You are referred to the suppliers of such computer-assisted experiments for specific laboratory procedures.

Data Analysis and Lab-Check. Experiment 1, *Experimental Error and Data Analysis,* serves as an introduction to laboratory investigation and discusses data uncertainty and analysis, as well as proper graphing procedures. In subsequent experiments, students are usually asked to analyze a set of data before proceeding to the next part of the experiment, thus gaining a better understanding of the purposes of various procedures and of the total experiment. If students delay analysis until they have taken all of the experimental data, they tend to rush through the experiments and simply generate numbers.

To promote better experimental calculation procedures, an innovative feature with this fourth edition is a laboratory calculation self-check computer program for use by students. It is difficult for the instructor to check the validity of data taken by students and the calculations made during various phases of an experiment. All too often, incorrect data and calculations propagate through an experiment, making the results erroneous and far from the desired values on which conclusions are to be drawn. This problem usually comes to light long after the laboratory period, when the busy instructor has time to review the lab reports. Students' grades suffer as a result.

To help students identify very incorrect data and improve experimental procedures, Fred B. Otto and Robert M. Otto have written a computer program (*Lab-Check*) designed for the specific calculation requirements of each lab in this edition of *Physics Laboratory Experiments*. *Lab-Check* allows the students to check many calculations on the computer without the computer giving them the answer. When students enter a set of measurement data, it is checked to see that it is within reasonable limits set by the instructor, and then their calculated results are checked against their data.

The features of *Lab-Check* are as follows:

- Rapid feedback to students so they learn from their mistakes.
- Faster grading of lab reports by the instructor.
- Menu and on-screen prompts guide the user through the program. An F1 help screen is also available.
- Students are given indentifying numbers by which they may reenter the system to continue their checking.
- Student entries are saved for use by the student and instructor.
- Student responses may be printed by the instructor at the end of the lab period for use in grading.
- *Program may be customized by the instructor.*

Laboratory Reports. Since a standardized laboratory report greatly facilitates grading by the instructor, a laboratory report is provided for each experiment. These are separate from the Procedure sections, for recording data, calculations, and experimental results. Only the laboratory report and questions pertaining to the experiment need be handed in for grading. The laboratory report tables are organized for easy data recording and analysis. Blank parentheses to remind the student to not forget the units of measurement are included.

Acknowledgments
I wish to express my sincere thanks to all of the people and companies whose helpful suggestions and assistance were so important in the preparation of this manual. Through four editions, the manual material has been reviewed by various professors.

My gratitude goes to the following users of the third edition who reviewed the manual in preparation for the revision: Michael L. Broyles, Collin County Community College; Stanley D. Cloud, University of Nevada, Las Vegas; Pamela R. Justice, Collin County Community College; Michael J. Matkovich, Oakton Community College; Harold B. McCord, University of Tulsa; Windsor A. Morgan, Morgan State University; Jacob Neuberger, Queens College; Kenneth C. Stuart, San Antonio College.

For their assistance in providing photographs of equipment, I thank Central Scientific Company, Sargent-Welch, and PASCO Scientific.

I hope you find this fourth edition improved. Further suggestions and comments are welcome.

Jerry D. Wilson

Contents

Introduction

Why We Make Experimental Measurements

When you can measure what you are speaking about and express it in numbers, you know something about it; but when you cannot measure it, when you cannot express it in numbers, your knowledge is of a meager and unsatisfactory kind.

LORD KELVIN

As Lord Kelvin so aptly expressed, we measure things to know something about them—so that we can describe objects and understand phenomena. Experimental measurement is the cornerstone of the *scientific method,* which holds that no theory or model of nature is tenable unless the results it predicts are in accord with experiment.

The main purpose of an introductory physics laboratory is to provide "hands-on" experiences of various physical principles. In so doing, one becomes familiar with laboratory equipment and procedures and with the scientific method.

In general, the theory of a physical principle will be presented in an experiment, and the predicted results will be tested by experimental measurements. Of course, these well-known principles have been tested many times before, and there are accepted values for certain physical quantities. Basically you will be comparing your experimentally measured values to accepted theoretical or measured values. Even so, you will experience the excitement of the scientific method. Imagine that you are the first person to perform an experiment to test a scientific theory.

General Laboratory Procedures

Safety

The most important thing in the laboratory is your safety and that of others. Experiments are designed to be done safely, but proper caution should always be exercised.

A potential danger comes from a lack of knowledge of the equipment and procedures. Upon entering the physics lab at the beginning of the lab period, you will probably find the equipment for an experiment on the laboratory table. Restrain your curiosity and do not play with the equipment. You may hurt yourself and/or the equipment. A good general rule is:

> *Do not touch or turn on laboratory equipment until it has been explained and permission has been given by the instructor.*

Also, certain items used in various experiments can be particularly dangerous, for example, hot objects, electricity, mercury lamps, and radioactive sources. In some instances, such as with hot objects and electricity, basic common sense and knowledge are required.

However, in other instances, such as with mercury lamps and radioactive sources, you may not be aware of the possible dangers. Mercury lamps may emit ultraviolet radiation that can be harmful to your eyes. Consequently, some sources need to be properly shielded. Some radioactive sources are solids and are encapsulated to prevent contact. Others are in liquid form and are transferred during an experiment, so there is a danger of spillage. Proper handling is therefore important.

In general, necessary precautions will be given in the experiment descriptions. *Note them well.* When you see the arrow symbol in the margin as illustrated here, you should take extra care to follow the procedure carefully and adhere to the precautions described in the text. As pointed out earlier, experiments are designed to be done safely. Yet a common kitchen match can be dangerous if used improperly. Another good rule for the laboratory is:

> *If you have any questions about the safety of a procedure, ask your instructor before doing it.*

The physics lab is a place to learn and practice safety.

Equipment Care

The equipment provided for the laboratory experiment is often expensive and in some instances quite delicate. If used improperly, certain pieces of apparatus can be damaged. The general rules given above concerning personal safety also apply to equipment care.

Even after familiarizing oneself with the equipment, it is often advisable or required to have an experimental setup checked and approved by the instructor before putting it into operation. This is particularly true for electrical experiments. Applying power to improperly wired circuits can cause serious damage to meters and other pieces of apparatus.

If a piece of equipment is broken or does not function properly, it should be reported to the laboratory instructor. Also, after you complete an experiment, the experimental setup should be disassembled and left neatly as found, unless you are otherwise instructed.

If you accidentally break some equipment or the equipment stops working properly during an experiment, *report it to your instructor*. Otherwise, the next time the equipment is used, a great deal of time may be wasted trying to get good results.

Laboratory Reports

A Laboratory Report is provided for each experiment in which experimental data are recorded. This should be done *neatly*. Calculations of experimental results should be included. Remember, the neatness, organization, and explanations of your measurements and calculations in the Laboratory Report represent the quality of your work.

Name ______________________ Section ______________ Date ______________

Lab Partner(s) ____

EXPERIMENT 1

Experimental Error and Data Analysis

Advance Study Assignment

Read the experiment and answer the following questions.

1. Do experimental measurements give the true value of a physical quantity? Explain.

2. Distinguish among the types and causes of experimental errors. Give a specific example of each.

3. How can each type of experimental error be reduced or minimized?

4. What is the difference between measurement accuracy and precision? Explain their general dependence on the various types of errors.

(continued)

5. What determines the number of significant figures in reporting measurement values? What would be the effect of reporting more or fewer figures or digits than are significant?

6. In expressing experimental error or uncertainty, when does one use (a) experimental error and (b) percent difference?

7. (Optional) For a series of experimentally measured values, distinguish among (a) the average or mean value, (b) the deviation from the mean, and (c) the mean deviation.

8. (Optional) What is the statistical significance of one standard deviation? Two standard deviations?

9. How could the function $y = 3t^2 + 4$ be plotted on a Cartesian graph to produce a straight line? What would be the numerical values of the slope and intercept of the line?

Experimental Error and Data Analysis

I. Introduction and Objectives

Laboratory investigations involve taking measurements of physical quantities, and the process of taking any measurement always involves some uncertainty or experimental error. Suppose that you and another person independently took several measurements of a physical quantity (e.g., the length of an object). It is unlikely that you both would come up with exactly the same results. Therefore, questions such as the following arise:

- How do you compare your experimental result to the accepted value of a physical quantity?
- Whose data are better, or how does one express the degree of uncertainty or error in experimental measurements?
- How does one graphically analyze and report experimental data?

In this introductory study experiment we examine the types of experimental errors and some methods of error and data analysis that will be used in subsequent experiments.

After performing this experiment and analyzing the data, you should be able to do the following:

1. Categorize the types of experimental errors and explain how they may be reduced.
2. Distinguish between measurement accuracy and precision and understand how they may be experimentally improved.
3. Explain the meaning and importance of significant figures (or digits) in reporting measurement values and in computations with these values.
4. Express experimental results and errors in appropriate numerical values so someone reading your report will know how valid your measurements are.
5. Represent measurement data in graphical form so as to illustrate experimental data and error visually.

II. Equipment Needed

- Pencil and ruler
- 3 sheets of Cartesian graph paper

(Optional)

- Hand calculator and/or computer program
- French curve

III. Theory

A. Types of Errors

Experimental errors can be generally classified as being of three types: personal, systematic, and random.

Personal Error

Personal errors arise from personal bias or carelessness in reading an instrument, in recording observations, or in mathematical calculations. Examples of personal errors (sometimes called illegitimate errors) include:

1. In performing a series of measurements, an observer may become biased in favor of the first observation. Falsely assuming this observation to be correct, the observer attempts to make other measurements agree with it, for example, through biased estimations of fractional scale divisions, and rejects measurements that greatly deviate. This incorrectly gives more significance to one reading than to others. All observations taken under the same experimental condition are equally valid and should be retained for analysis.
2. Errors in reading scales. Reading a value from a scale generally involves lining up something, such as the edge of an object, with a mark on the scale. The alignment, and hence the value of the reading, depends on the position of the eye. A reading may appear to be different when viewed from one eye or the other, or when the head is moved from side to side (for a horizontal scale) or up and down (for a vertical scale).

   This apparent change in position due to a change in the position of the eye is called *parallax*. For example, the position of the mercury meniscus on a thermometer scale may appear different if viewed from above or below a line of sight perpendicular to the scale (Fig. 1.1a). Also, when measuring length with a meterstick placed flat against the object, the thickness of the meter stick holds the scale about 0.7 cm from the object, and readings may vary considerably due to parallax (Fig. 1.1b). Such errors can be minimized by using a line of sight perpendicular to the scale and placing the meterstick edgewise against the object.

3. Not observing significant figures in calculations. (This is discussed below.)

Systematic Error

Systematic errors are associated with particular measurement instruments or techniques, such as an improperly calibrated instrument or bias on the part of the observer. Conditions from which systematic errors can result include:

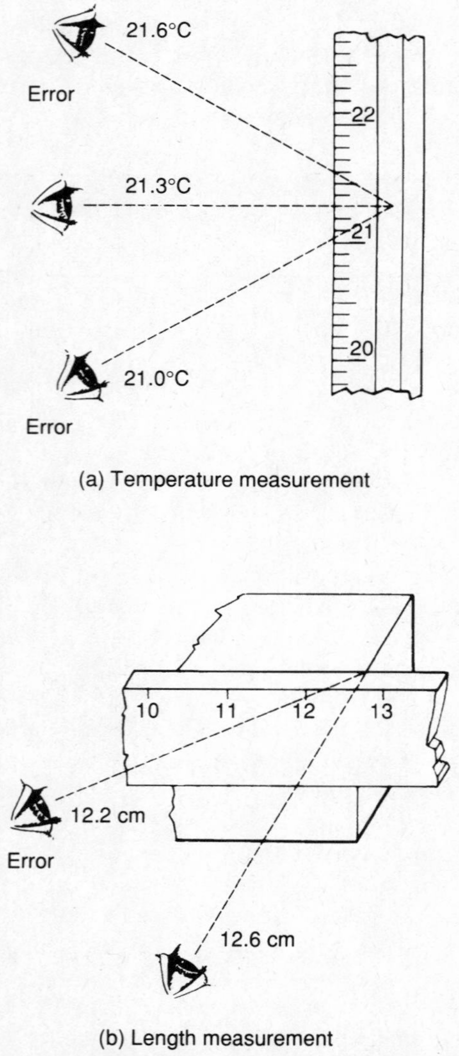

Figure 1.1 Personal error. Examples of personal error due to parallax in reading a scale.

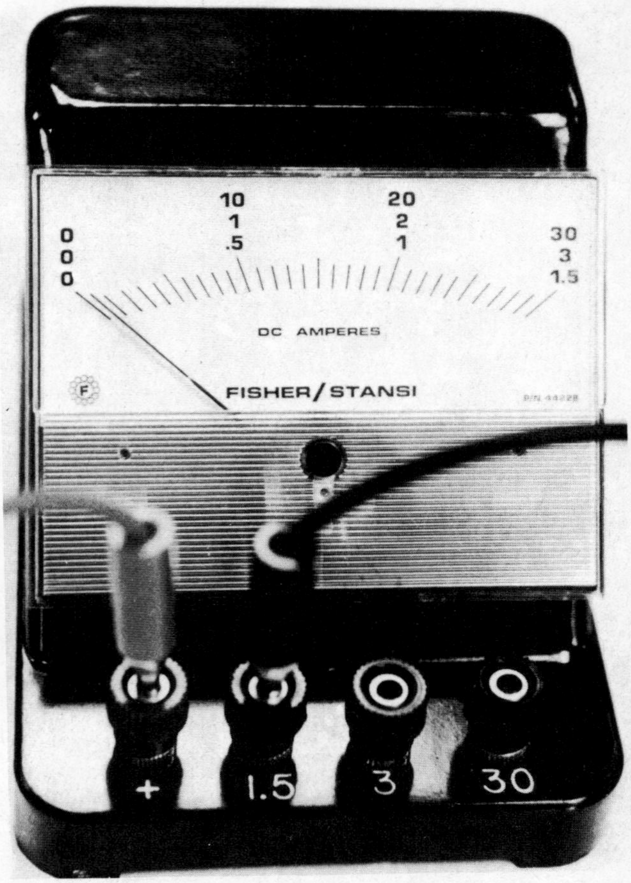

Figure 1.2 Systematic error. An improperly zeroed instrument gives rise to systematic error. In this case, the ammeter would systematically give an incorrect reading larger than the true value.

1. An improperly "zeroed" instrument (e.g., a micrometer or ammeter, Fig. 1.2).
2. A faulty instrument, such as a thermometer that reads 101 °C when immersed in boiling water at standard atmospheric pressure. This thermometer is improperly calibrated, since the reading should be 100 °C.
3. Human reaction time (0.15–0.20 s) when timing is done by an observer who is starting or stopping a clock.
4. Personal bias of an observer, who, for example, always takes a low reading of a scale division. Thus, a personal error may be a systematic error.

Avoiding systematic errors depends on the skill of the observer to detect and to prevent or correct them.

RANDOM ERROR

Random errors result from unknown and unpredictable variations in experimental situations. Random errors are also referred to as accidental errors and are sometimes beyond the control of the observer. Conditions in which random errors can result include:

1. Unpredictable fluctuations in temperature or line voltage.
2. Mechanical vibrations of the experimental setup.
3. Unbiased estimates of measurement readings by the observer.

The effect of random errors can be reduced and minimized by improving and refining experimental techniques and repeating the measurement a sufficient number of times, so that the erroneous readings become statistically insignificant.

B. Accuracy and Precision

Accuracy and precision are commonly used synonymously, but in experimental measurements there is an important distinction.

The **accuracy** of a measurement signifies how close it comes to the true (or accepted) value, i.e., how correct it is.

Example 1.1 Two independent experiments result in the determination of the value of π to be 3.140 and 3.143. The second result is more accurate than the first because the true value of π is 3.142 (to four significant figures).

Precision refers to the agreement among repeated measurements, i.e., the "spread" of the measurements, or how close together they are. The more precise a group of measurements, the closer together they are. However, a large degree of precision does not necessarily imply accuracy, as illustrated in Fig. 1.3.

Example 1.2 Two independent experiments give two sets of data with the expressed results and uncertainties of 2.5 ± 0.1 cm and 2.5 ± 0.2 cm, respectively. The first result is more precise than the second because the spread in the first measurements is between 2.4 and 2.6 cm, whereas the spread in the second measurements is between 2.3 and 2.7 cm. That is, the measurements of the first experiment are less uncertain than those of the second.

Obtaining greater accuracy for an experimental value depends in general on minimizing systematic errors. Obtaining greater precision for an experimental value depends on minimizing random errors.

C. Significant Figures

In general, there are *exact* numbers and *measured* numbers (or quantities). Factors such as the 100 used in calculating percentage or the 2 in $2\pi r$ are examples of exact numbers. Measured numbers, as the name implies, are those obtained from measurement instruments and generally involve some error or uncertainty.

The degree of accuracy or degree of uncertainty of a measured number depends on the quality of the instrument and the fineness of its measuring scale. For example, we might read that an object has a mass of 0.15 kg on one balance and 0.154 kg on another. The latter measurement has more certainty.

The degree of uncertainty of a measurement is implied by the way the result is written or reported.

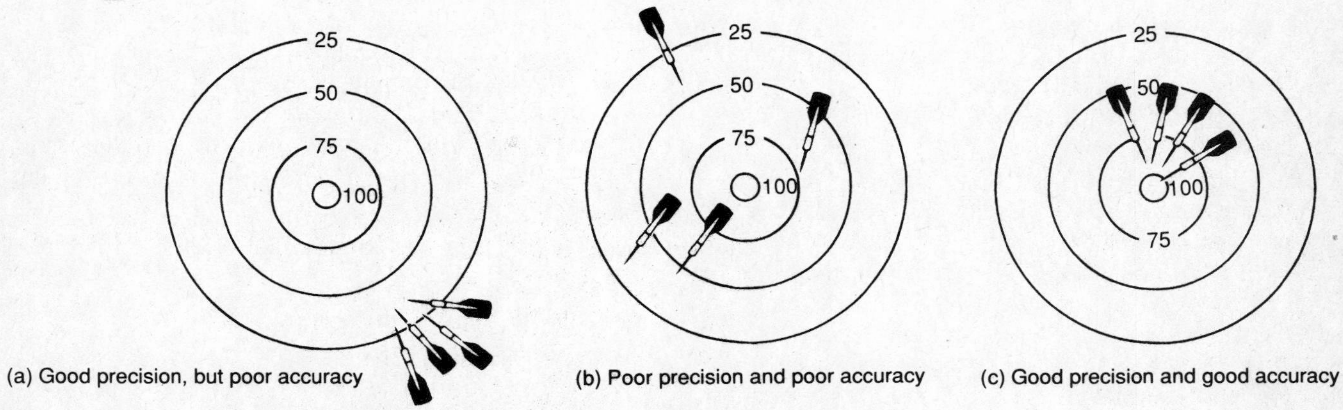

Figure 1.3 Accuracy and precision. The true value in this analogy is the bull's-eye. The degree of scattering is an indication of precision—the closer together a dart grouping, the greater the precision. A group (or symmetric grouping with average) close to the true value represents accuracy.

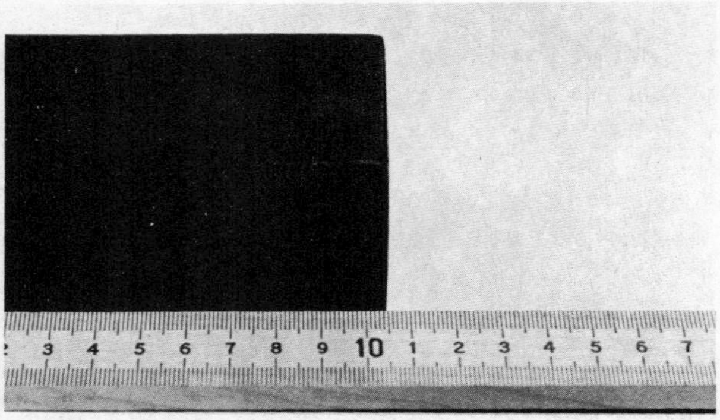

Figure 1.4 Significant figures. The edge of the object is reported to be at the 10.45-cm position of the meterstick. This reading has four significant figures, with the 5 being the estimated or doubtful (least significant) figure.

When reading the value of an experimental measurement from a calibrated scale, only a certain number of figures or digits can be obtained or read. That is, only a certain number of figures are significant.

The **significant figures** (sometimes called **"significant digits"**) of an experimentally measured value include all the numbers that can be read directly from the instrument scale plus one doubtful or estimated number (Fig. 1.4). Thus, measured values contain inherent uncertainty or doubtfulness because of the estimated figure. However, the greater the number of significant figures, the greater the reliability of the measurement the number represents. For example, the length of an object may be read as 2.54 cm (three significant figures) on one instrument scale and 2.5405 cm (five significant figures) on another. The latter reading from an instrument with a finer scale (why?) gives more information and reliability.

Zeros and the decimal point must be properly dealt with in determining the number of significant figures in a result. This is accomplished as follows:

1. The leftmost nonzero digit is the most significant. For example, the 1 in 105.8 and the 7 in 0.0073 are the most significant digits. The zeros before the 7 merely locate the position of the first number.
2. If there is no decimal point, the rightmost nonzero digit is the least significant. For example, the 4 in 240 is the least significant digit.
3. If there is a decimal point, the rightmost digit is the least significant, even if it is zero. For example, the 3 in 1.03 and the 0 in 24.90 are the least significant digits.
4. All digits between the least and most significant digits are considered to be significant.

Example 1.3 Each of the following numbers has four significant figures: 1000.; 11.10; 2783; 278,300; 0.001230; 10.01; 10.00.

In practice, a problem sometimes arises if the decimal point is omitted and the rightmost digit is zero. For example, by the rules given above, the number 4820 has only three significant figures, but the last zero digit may be physically significant in a measurement (the estimated or doubtful figure). With four significant figures, this should have been written 4820. (by rule 3 above). We tend not to include the decimal point at the end of whole numbers. However, this problem is easily resolved by writing the number in powers-of-10 or scientific notation, 4.820×10^3, which shows explicitly that the rightmost zero is significant.

This procedure is also helpful in expressing the significant figures in large numbers. For example, suppose that the average distance from the Earth to the Sun, 93,000,000 miles, is known to only four significant figures. This is easily expressed in powers-of-10 notation: 9.300×10^7 mi.

D. Computations with Measured Values

Calculations are often performed with measured values, and error and uncertainty are "propagated" by the mathematical operations, for example, multiplication or division. The error can be computed by statistical methods; however, a widely used procedure for *estimating* the uncertainty of a mathematical result involves the use of significant figures.

The number of significant figures in a measured value gives an indication of the uncertainty or reliability of a measurement. Hence, you might expect that the result of a mathematical operation can be no more reliable than the quantity with the least reliability or smallest number of significant figures used in the calculation. (That is, you can't *gain* reliability through a mathematical operation.) We have the following rules for basic math operations:

Multiplication and Division

In the multiplication or division of two or more numerical measurements, the number of significant figures in the final answer in general equals the number of significant figures in the measurement with the least number of significant figures.

Example 1.4 (a) To illustrate how doubtful figures are carried through a multiplication process, the doubtful figures are underlined in the following example:

$$\begin{array}{r} 6.2\,\underline{7} \\ 5.\underline{5} \\ \hline \underline{3\,1\,3\,5} \\ 31\;\underline{3\,5}\;\; \\ \hline 3\underline{4}.\underline{4\,8\,5} \rightarrow 3\underline{4}. \end{array}$$

Only the first doubtful figure from the left is reported. The result is rounded off to this figure. (Rounding off procedures are discussed below.) The result of any operation with a doubtful figure is doubtful.

Notice that in the multiplication of the $5 \times \underline{7}$ for the second 5 in the example that when a doubtful figure is carried into the next column, the figure in that column is doubtful, i.e., [$5 \times \underline{7} = \underline{35}$ and $(5 \times 2) + \underline{3} = 1\underline{3}$].

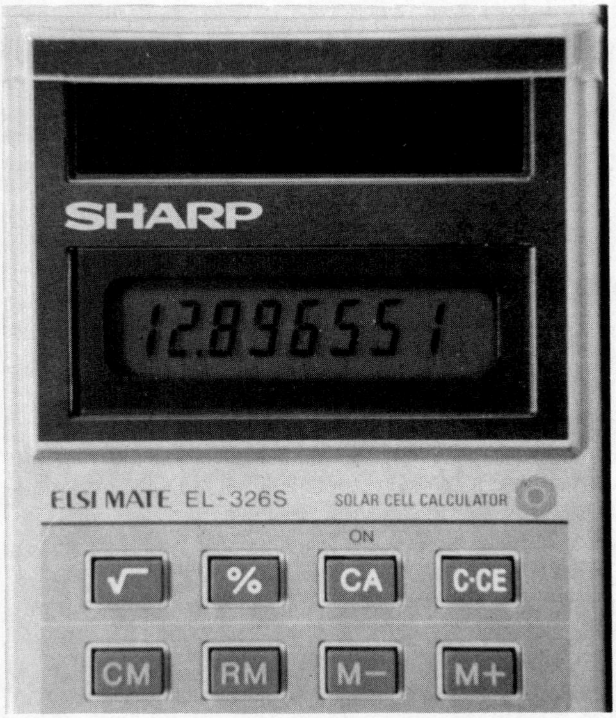

Figure 1.5 Insignificant figures. The calculator shows the result of the division operation 374/29. Since there are only two significant figures in the 29, the result can have no more than this, and the calculator display value should be rounded off to 13.

(b) The division of $37\underline{4}/2\underline{9} = 1\underline{3}$ is shown in Fig. 1.5 as done on a hand calculator. The result must be rounded off to two significant figures. (Why?) Reporting more figures would imply greater significance than given by the measurements, and **a result cannot be made more significant by a mathematical operation.**

Rounding Off

The nonsignificant figures are dropped from a result if they are to the right of the decimal point (as in Example 1.4) and are replaced by zeros if they are to the left of the decimal point. The last significant figure retained should be rounded off. The procedure for doing this is as follows:

Rules for Rounding Off Numbers
Locate the first number to the right of the appropriate number of significant figures, which is the first digit of those to be removed. (For example, in rounding off 5.247 to two significant figures, this is the 4.) If this digit is

1. *less than 5, then the preceding digit remains the same (e.g., 5.247 rounds to 5.2), or*
2. *equal to 5 or greater, then the preceding digit is increased by 1 (e.g., 2.257 rounds to 2.3).**

When doing a multiple-step calculation on a calculator, only the result should be rounded off. Rounding intermediate steps can introduce error.

Example 1.5
Rule 1. In Example 1.4a, the result can have only two significant figures, which are the $3\underline{4}$ since the number on the right of the $\underline{4}$ (another $\underline{4}$) is less than 5.

24.5709 → 24.57 (to four significant figures)
0.0304 → 0.030 (to two significant figures)

Rule 2.

1.025 → 1.03 (to three significant figures)
487.56 → 490 (to two significant figures)

* Notice that in this method, five digits (0, 1, 2, 3, and 4) are rounded down and five digits (5, 6, 7, 8, and 9) are rounded up.

Rounding off a result to zero
Notice that when rounding of a result to a zero, the zero may or may not be significant (the last cases in the above Rule 1 and Rule 2 examples, respectively). Any confusion may be removed by using scientific (powers-of-ten) notation:

$0.0304 \rightarrow 3.0 \times 10^{-2}$ (to two significant figures)
$487.56 \rightarrow 4.9 \times 10^{2}$ (to two significant figures)

ADDITION AND SUBTRACTION

In addition and subtraction, begin with the first column from the left that contains a doubtful figure. Round off all numbers to this column and drop all digits to the right.

Example 1.6 Adding a column of numbers:

$$\begin{array}{r} 42.3\underline{1} \\ 0.062\underline{1} \\ 512.\underline{4} \\ 2.5\underline{7} \\ \hline \end{array} \quad \rightarrow \quad \begin{array}{r} 42.3 \\ 0.1 \\ 512.4 \\ 2.6 \\ \hline 557.4 \end{array}$$

since the $\underline{4}$ in the $512.\underline{4}$ defines the first column from the left with a doubtful figure.

E. Expressing Experimental Error and Uncertainty

PERCENT ERROR

The object of some experiments is to determine the value of a well-known physical quantity, for example, the value of π.

The **accepted or "true" value** of such a quantity found in textbooks and physics handbooks is the most accurate value (usually rounded off to a certain number of significant figures) obtained through sophisticated experiments or mathematical methods.

The **absolute difference** between the experimental value E and the accepted value A, written $|E - A|$, is the positive difference in the values, e.g., $|2 - 4| = |-2| = 2$ and $|4 - 2| = 2$. Simply subtract the smaller value from the larger, even though the symbols may be written in reverse order. For a set of measurements, E is taken as the average value of the experimental measurements.

The **fractional error** is the ratio of the absolute difference to the accepted value:

$$\text{fractional error} = \frac{\text{absolute difference}}{\text{accepted value}}$$

or

$$\text{fractional error} = \frac{|E - A|}{A} \tag{1.1}$$

The fractional error is commonly expressed as a percentage to give the **percent error** of an experimental value.

$$\text{percent error} = \frac{\text{absolute difference}}{\text{accepted value}} \times 100\%$$

or

$$\text{percent error} = \frac{|E - A|}{A} \times 100\% \tag{1.2}$$

Example 1.7 A cylindrical object is measured to have a diameter d of 5.25 cm and a circumference c of 16.38 cm. What is the experimental value of π and the percent error of the experimental value if the accepted value of π is 3.14?

Solution $d = 5.25$ cm, $c = 16.38$ cm:

$$c = \pi d \quad \text{or} \quad \pi = \frac{c}{d} = \frac{16.38}{5.25} = 3.12$$

Then $E = 3.12$ and $A = 3.14$, so

$$\begin{aligned} \text{percent error} &= \frac{|E - A|}{A} \times 100\% \\ &= \frac{|3.12 - 3.14|}{3.14} \times 100\% \\ &= \frac{0.02}{3.14} \times 100\% = 0.6\% \end{aligned}$$

Note: To avoid rounding errors, the preferred order of operations is addition and subtraction before multiplication and division.*

If the uncertainty in experimentally measured values as expressed by the percent error is large, you should suspect and check for possible sources of error. Additional measurements should then be made to reduce the uncertainty. Your instructor may wish to set a maximum percent error for experimental results.

PERCENT DIFFERENCE

It is sometimes instructive to compare the results of two measurements when there is no known or ac-

* Although percent error is generally defined using the absolute difference $|E - A|$, some instructors prefer to use $(E - A)$, which results in positive (+) or negative (−) percent errors, e.g., −0.6% in Example 1.7. In the case of a series of measurements and computed percent errors, this gives an indication of systematic error.

cepted value. The comparison is expressed as a **percent difference**, which is the ratio of the absolute difference between the experimental values E_2 and E_1 to the average or mean value of the two results, expressed as a percent.

$$\text{percent difference} = \frac{\text{abs. difference}}{\text{average}} \times 100\%$$

or

$$\text{percent difference} = \frac{|E_2 - E_1|}{(E_2 + E_1)/2} \times 100\% \quad \textbf{(1.3)}$$

Dividing by the average or mean value of the experimental values is logical, because there is no way of deciding which of the two results is better.

Example 1.8 What is the percent difference between two measured values of 4.6 cm and 5.0 cm?

Solution With $E_1 = 4.6$ cm and $E_2 = 5.0$ cm:

$$\text{percent difference} = \frac{|E_2 - E_1|}{(E_2 + E_1)/2} \times 100\%$$

$$\text{percent difference} = \frac{|5.0 - 4.6|}{(5.0 + 4.6)/2} \times 100\%$$

$$= \frac{0.4}{4.8} \times 100\% = 8\%$$

As in the case of percent error, when the percent difference is large, it is advisable to check the experiment and make more measurements.

In many instances there will be more than two measurement values.

When there are three or more measurements, the percent difference is found by dividing the absolute value of the difference of the extreme values (i.e., the values with greatest difference) by the average or mean value of all the measurements.

Average (Mean) Value

Most experimental measurements are repeated several times, and it is very unlikely that identical results will be obtained for all trials. For a set of measurements with predominantly random errors (i.e., the measurements are all equally trustworthy or probable), it can be shown mathematically that the true value is most probably given by the average or mean value.

The **average** or **mean value** $\bar{x}$ of a set of N measurements is

$$\bar{x} = \frac{x_1 + x_2 + x_3 + \cdots + x_N}{N} = \frac{1}{N}\sum_{i=1}^{N} x_i \quad \textbf{(1.4)}$$

where the summation sign Σ is a shorthand notation indicating the sum of N measurements from x_1 to x_N. ($\bar{x}$ is commonly referred to simply as the *mean*.)

Example 1.9 What is the average or mean value of the set of numbers 5.42, 6.18, 5.70, 6.01, and 6.32?

$$\bar{x} = \frac{1}{N}\sum_{i=1}^{N} x_i$$

$$= \frac{5.42 + 6.18 + 5.70 + 6.01 + 6.32}{5}$$

$$= 5.93$$

Deviation from the Mean (Optional)

Having obtained a set of measurements and determined the mean value, it is helpful to report how widely the individual measurements are scattered from the mean. A quantitative description of this scatter or dispersion of measurements will give an idea of the precision of the experiment.

The **deviation** d_i from the mean of any measurement with a mean value $\bar{x}$ is

$$d_i = x_i - \bar{x} \quad \textbf{(1.5)}$$

(d_i is sometimes referred to as the **residual** rather than the deviation.)

As defined, the deviation may be positive or negative, since some measurements are larger than the mean and some are smaller. The average of the deviations of a set of measurements is always zero, so the mean of the deviations is not a useful way of characterizing the dispersion.

Mean Deviation (Optional)

To obtain what is called the **mean** or **average deviation** of a set of N measurements, the absolute deviations $|d_i|$ are determined; that is,

$$|d_i| = |x_i - \bar{x}| \quad \textbf{(1.6)}$$

The *mean deviation* $\bar{d}$ is then

$$\bar{d} = \frac{|d_1| + |d_2| + |d_3| + \cdots + |d_N|}{N}$$

$$= \frac{1}{N}\sum_{i=1}^{N} |d_i| \quad \textbf{(1.7)}$$

(Although $\bar{d}$ is commonly called the mean deviation, a more appropriate term would be the **mean absolute deviation.**)

Example 1.10 What is the mean deviation of the set of numbers given in Example 1.9?

Solution First find the absolute deviation of each of the numbers using the determined mean of 5.93.

$$|d_1| = |5.42 - 5.93| = 0.51$$
$$|d_2| = |6.18 - 5.93| = 0.25$$
$$|d_3| = |5.70 - 5.93| = 0.23$$
$$|d_4| = |6.01 - 5.93| = 0.08$$
$$|d_5| = |6.32 - 5.93| = 0.39$$

Then

$$\bar{d} = \frac{1}{N}\sum_{i=1}^{N} |d_i|$$

$$= \frac{0.51 + 0.25 + 0.23 + 0.08 + 0.39}{5} = 0.29$$

The mean deviation is a measure of the dispersion of experimental measurements about the mean (i.e., a measure of precision). It is common practice to report the experimental value E of a quantity in the form

$$E = \bar{x} \pm \bar{d}$$

In Example 1.10, this would be $E = 5.93 \pm 0.29$. It is also common practice to express the dispersion of the mean deviation as a percent of the mean:

$$E = \bar{x} \pm \frac{\bar{d}}{\bar{x}} \times 100\%$$

For Example 1.10, we have

$$E = 5.93 \pm \frac{0.29}{5.93} \times 100\% = 5.93 \pm 4.9\%$$

The $\pm$ term gives a measure of the *precision* of the experimental value. The *accuracy* of the mean value of a set of experimental measurements (5.93 in the above example) may be expressed in terms of percent error or percent difference.

The dispersion of an experimental measurement may be expressed by other means (see below), so the method should be specified when reporting.

Standard Deviation (Optional)

To avoid the problem of negative deviations and absolute values, it is statistically convenient to use the square of the deviation.

The **variance** σ^2 of a set of measurements is the average of the squares of the deviations:

$$\sigma^2 = \frac{(x_1 - \bar{x})^2 + (x_2 - \bar{x})^2 + (x_3 - \bar{x})^2 + \cdots + (x_N - \bar{x})^2}{N}$$

$$= \frac{d_1^2 + d_2^2 + d_3^2 + \cdots + d_N^2}{N}$$

$$= \frac{1}{N}\sum_{i=1}^{N} (x_i - \bar{x})^2 = \frac{1}{N}\sum_{i=1}^{N} d_i^2 \qquad \textbf{(1.8)}$$

The square root of the variance σ is called the **standard deviation***:

$$\sigma = \sqrt{\frac{1}{N}\sum_{i=1}^{N} (x_i - \bar{x})^2} = \sqrt{\frac{1}{N}\sum_{i=1}^{N} d_i^2} \qquad \textbf{(1.9)}$$

Because we take the average of the squares of the deviations and then the square root, the standard deviation is sometimes called the **root-mean-square deviation**, or simply the **root-mean-square**. Notice that σ always has the same units as x_i and that it is always positive.

Example 1.11 What is the standard deviation of the set of numbers given in Example 1.9?

Solution First find the square of the deviation of each of the numbers

$$d_1^2 = (5.42 - 5.93)^2 = 0.26$$
$$d_2^2 = (6.18 - 5.93)^2 = 0.06$$
$$d_3^2 = (5.70 - 5.93)^2 = 0.05$$
$$d_4^2 = (6.01 - 5.93)^2 = 0.01$$
$$d_5^2 = (6.32 - 5.93)^2 = 0.15$$

Then

$$\sigma = \sqrt{\frac{1}{N}\sum_{i=1}^{5} d_i^2}$$

$$= \left(\frac{0.26 + 0.06 + 0.05 + 0.01 + 0.15}{5}\right)^{1/2}$$

$$= 0.33$$

The experimental value E is then commonly reported as

$$E = \bar{x} \pm \sigma = 5.93 \pm 0.33$$

The standard deviation is used to describe the precision of the mean of a set of measurements. For a normal distribution of random errors,† it can be statistically shown that the probability that an individual

* For a small number of measurements, it can be statistically shown that a better value of the standard deviation is given by $\sigma = \sqrt{[1/(N - 1)]\Sigma d_i^2}$, where N is replaced by $N - 1$. Your instructor may wish you to use this form of the standard deviation.

† This *normal*, or *Gaussian, distribution* is represented by a "bell-shaped" curve (Fig. 1.6). That is, the scatter or dispersion of the measurements is assumed to be symmetric about the true value of a quantity.

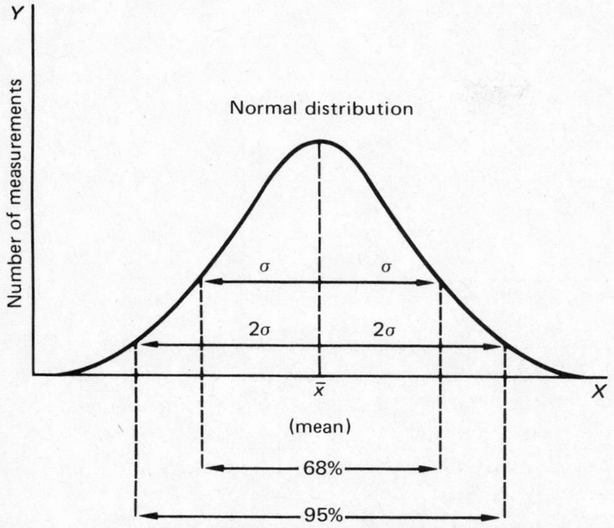

Figure 1.6 Normal or Gaussian distribution. The distribution gives a "bell-shaped" curve. If random errors follow this distribution, there is a 68% chance that a measurement will be within one standard deviation of the mean value, $x = \pm \sigma$. The probability of a measurement falling within two standard deviations of the mean, $x = \pm 2\sigma$, is 95%.

measurement will fall within one standard deviation of the mean, which is assumed to be the true value, is 68% (Fig. 1.6). The probability of a measurement falling within two standard deviations is 95%.

F. Graphical Representation of Data

It is often convenient to represent experimental data in graphical form, not only for reporting, but also to obtain information.

Graphing Procedures

Quantities are commonly plotted using rectangular Cartesian axes (X and Y). The horizontal axis (X) is called the *abscissa*, and the vertical axis (Y), the *ordinate*. The location of a point on the graph is defined by its coordinates x and y, written (x, y), referenced to the origin O, the intersection of the X and Y axes.

When plotting data, choose axis scales that are easy to plot and read. The graph in Fig. 1.7A shows an example of scales that are too small. This "bunches up" the data, making the graph too small, and the major horizontal scale values make it difficult to read intermediate values. Choose scales so that most of the graph paper is used. The graph in Fig. 1.7B shows the data plotted with more appropriate scales.†

When the data points are plotted, draw a smooth line described by the points. "Smooth" means that the line does not have to pass exactly through each point but connects the general areas of significance of the data points. The graph in Fig. 1.7B with an approximately equal number of points on each side of the line gives a "curve of best fit."

In cases where several determinations of each experimental quantity are made, the average value is plotted and the mean deviation or the standard deviation may be plotted as *error bars*. For example, the data in Table 1.1 are plotted in Fig. 1.8. A smooth line is drawn so as to pass within the error bars. (Your instructor may want to explain the use of a French curve at this point.)

Table 1.1 Data for Figure 1.8

Mass (kg)	Period	±	$\bar{d}$ (s)
0.01	0.63	±	0.17
0.05	1.40	±	0.21
0.10	1.99	±	0.25
0.20	2.81	±	0.20
0.40	3.97	±	0.31
0.60	4.87	±	0.13
0.75	5.44	±	0.20
0.90	5.96	±	0.18
1.00	6.28	±	0.14
1.20	6.88	±	0.29

Graphs should have (see Fig. 1.8):

1. Each axis labeled with the quantity plotted.
2. The units of the quantities plotted.
3. The title of the graph on the graph paper (commonly listed as the y coordinate versus the x coordinate).
4. Your name and the date.

Straight-Line Graphs

Two quantities (x and y) are often linearly related; that is, they have an algebraic relationship of the form $y = mx + b$, where m and b are constants. When the values of such quantities are plotted, the graph is a straight line, as shown in Fig. 1.9.

The m in the algebraic relationship is called the **slope** of the line and is equal to the ratio of the intervals $\Delta y/\Delta x$. Any set of intervals may be used to

† As a general rule, it is convenient to choose the unit of the first major scale division to the right or above the origin or zero point as 1, 2, or 5 (or multiples or submultiples thereof, e.g., 10 or 0.1) so the minor (intermediate) scale divisions can be easily interpolated and read.

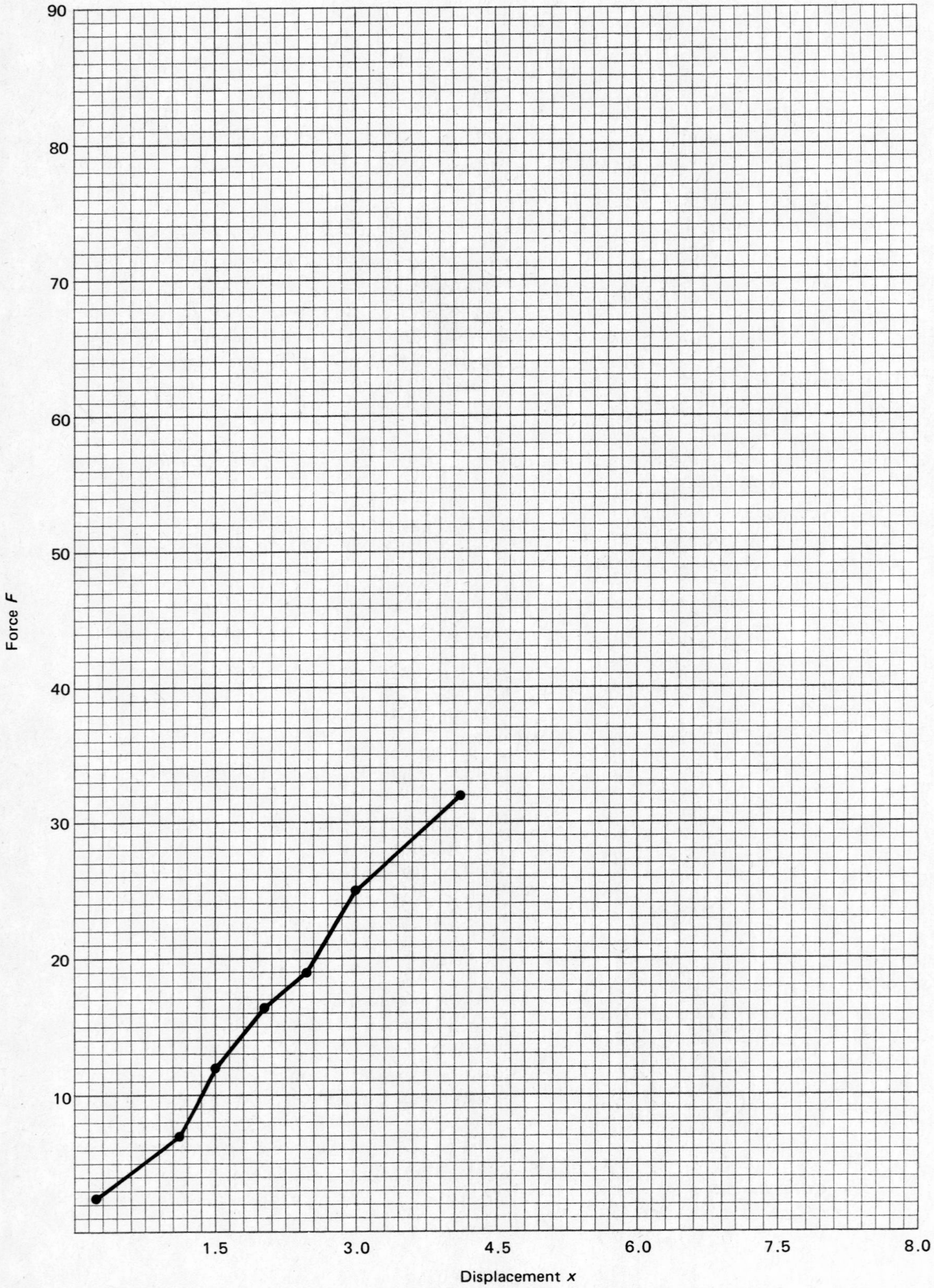

Figure 1.7A Poor graphing. Example of improperly labeled and plotted graph. See text for description.

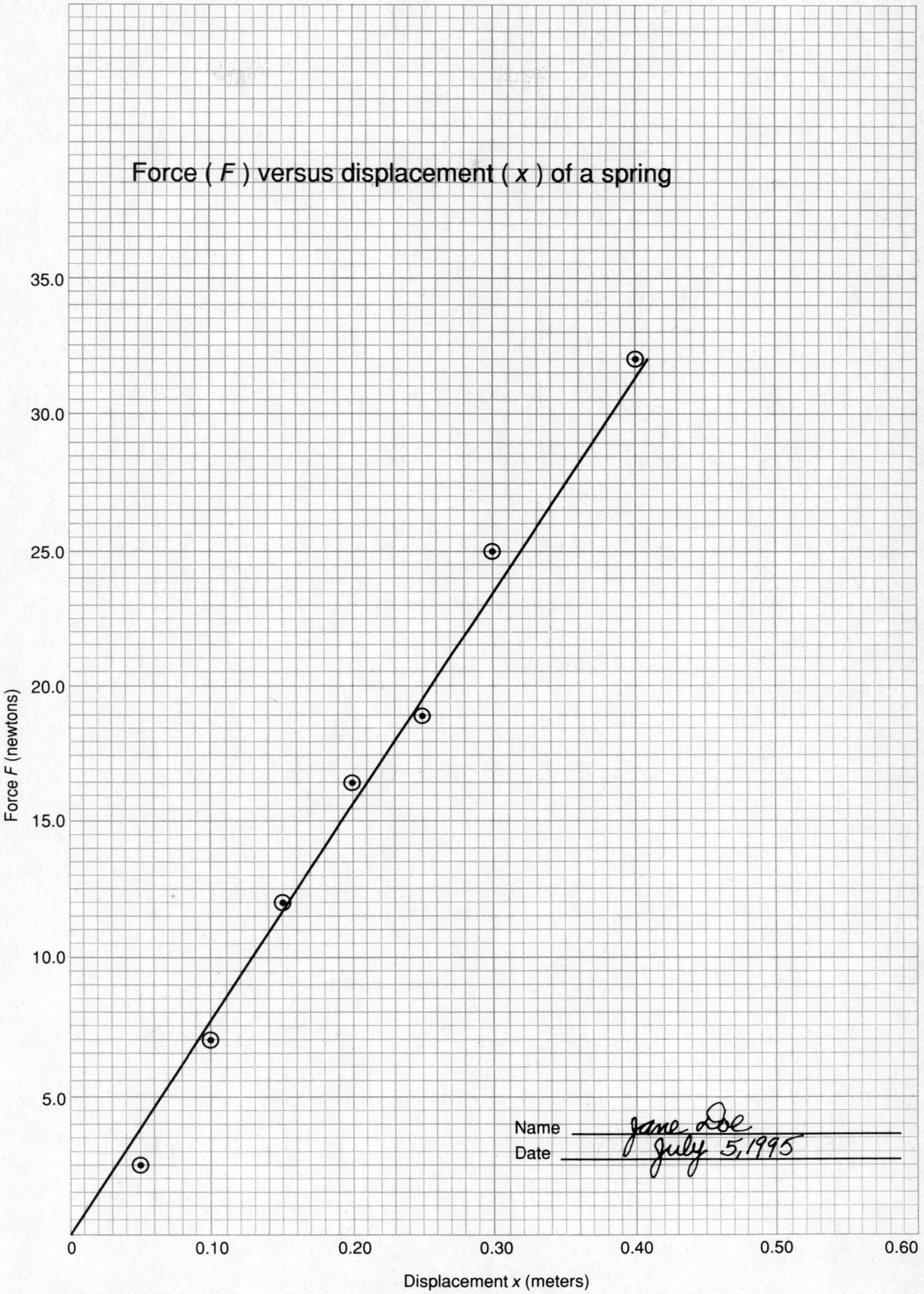

Figure 1.7B Good graphing. Example of properly labeled and plotted graph. See text for description.

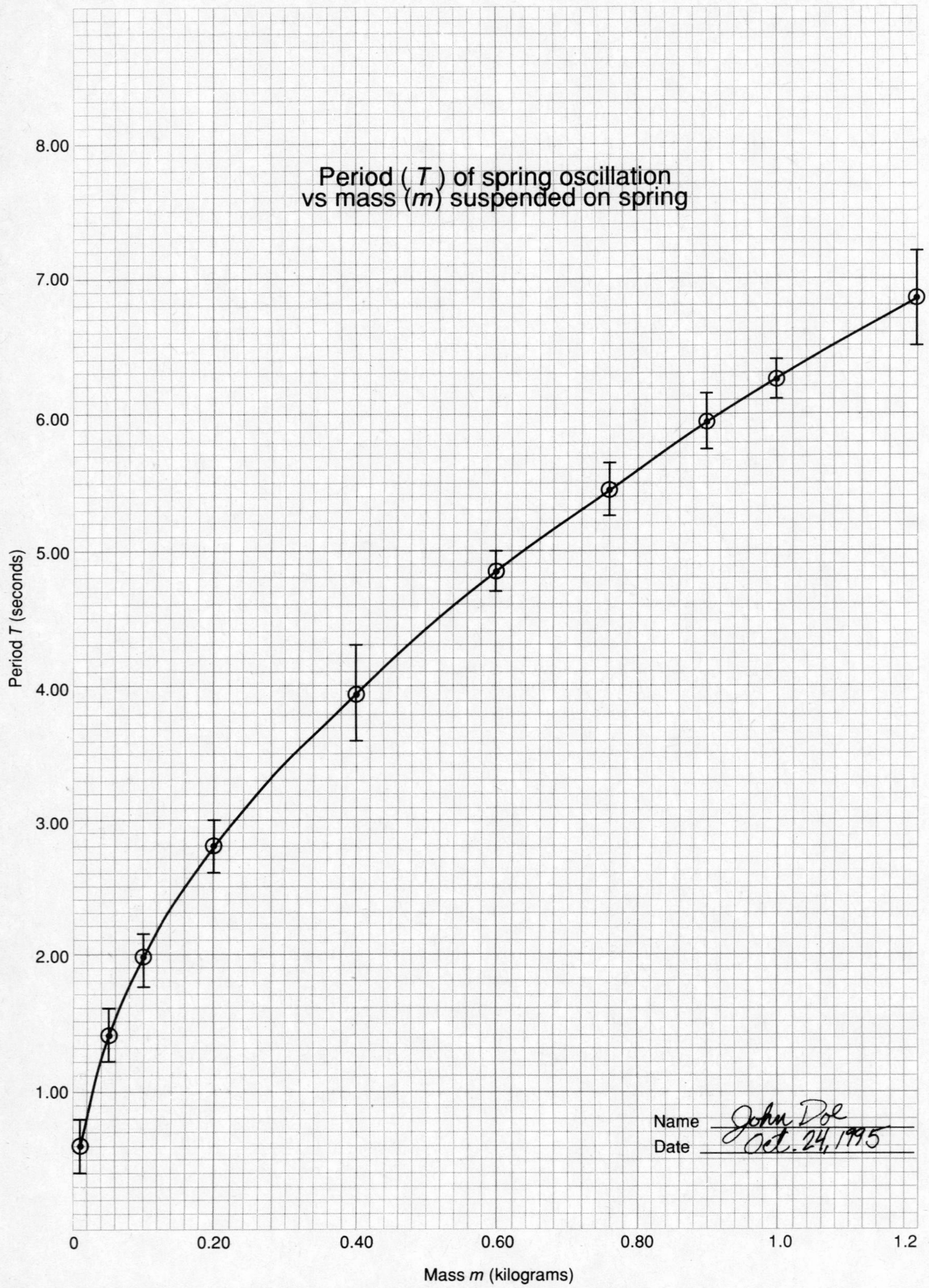

Figure 1.8 Error bars. An example of graphical data with error bars. An error bar indicates the precision of a measurement. In this case, the error bars indicate mean deviations.

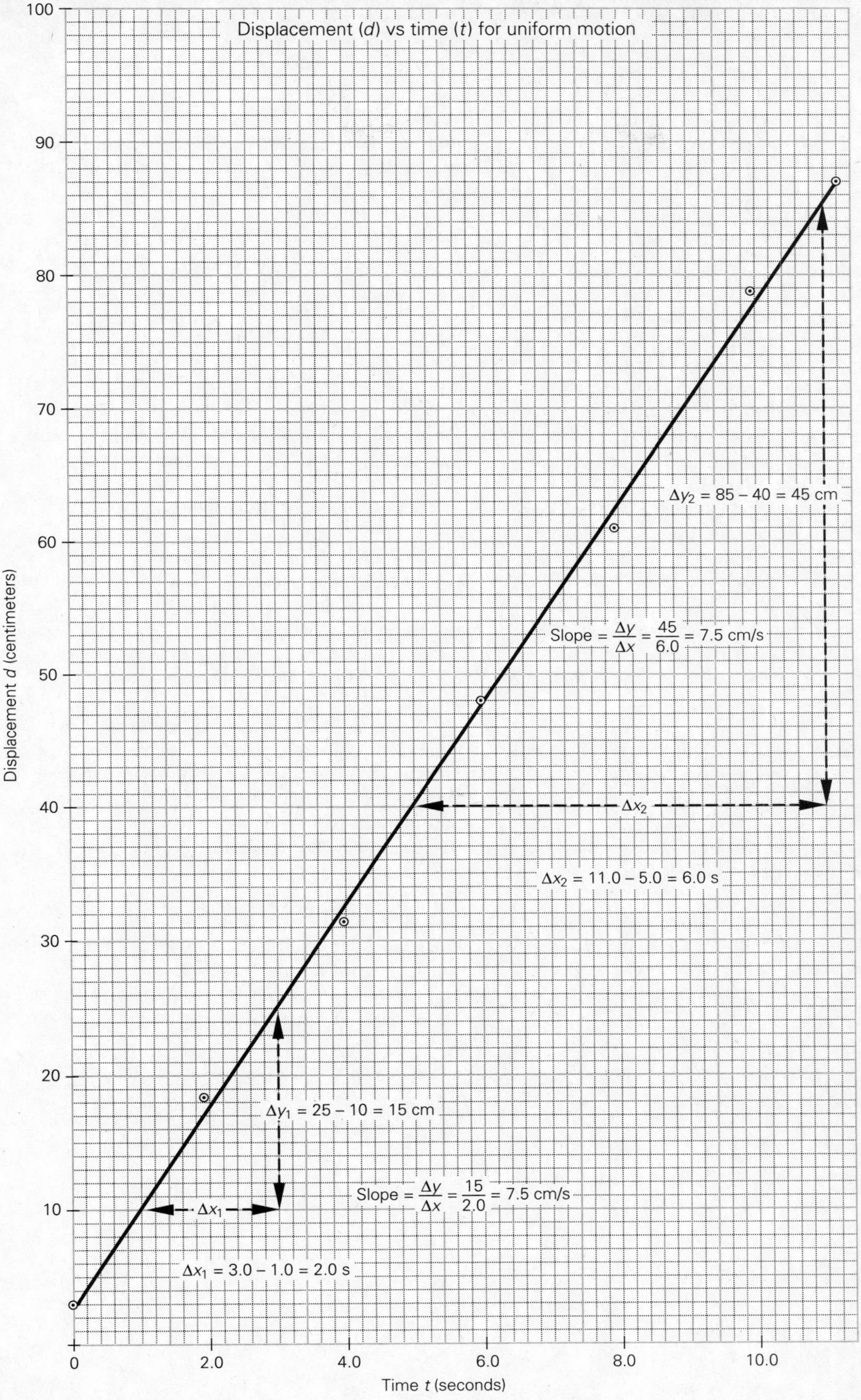

Figure 1.9 Straight-line slope. Examples of intervals for determining the slope of a straight line. The slope is the ratio of $\Delta y/\Delta x$ (or $\Delta d/\Delta t$). Any set of intervals may be used, but the end points of an interval should be relatively far apart, as for $\Delta y_2/\Delta x_2$. Thus, the determination using $\Delta y_2/\Delta x_2$ is preferable.

determine the slope of a straight-line graph; for example, in Fig. 1.9:

$$m = \frac{\Delta y_1}{\Delta x_1} = \frac{15 \text{ cm}}{2.0 \text{ s}} = 7.5 \text{ cm/s}$$

$$m = \frac{\Delta y_2}{\Delta x_2} = \frac{45 \text{ cm}}{6.0 \text{ s}} = 7.5 \text{ cm/s}$$

However, in practice, points should be chosen relatively far apart on the line. For best results, points corresponding to data points should not be chosen, even if they appear to lie on the line.

The b in the algebraic relationship is called the **intercept** and is equal to the value of the y coordinate where the graph line intercepts the Y axis. In Fig. 1.9, $b = 3$ cm. Notice from the relationship that $y = mx + b$, so that when $x = 0$, then $y = b$. If the intercept is the origin (0, 0), then $b = 0$.

The equation of the line in the graph in Fig. 1.9 is $d = 7.5t + 3$. The general equation for uniform motion has the form $d = vt + d_o$. Hence, the initial displacement $d_o = 3$ cm and the speed $v = 7.5$ cm/s.

Some forms of nonlinear functions that are common in physics can be represented as straight lines on a Cartesian graph. This is done by plotting nonlinear values. For example, if you plotted

$$y = ax^2 + b$$

on a regular y versus x graph, you would get a parabola. But, letting $x^2 = x'$, the equation is then

$$y = ax' + b$$

which has the form of a straight line.

This means that if you plotted y versus x', you would get a straight line. Since $x' = x^2$, you must plot the squared values of x: Square all the values of x in your data table and plot these numbers with the corresponding y values.

Other functions can be "straightened out" by this procedure, including

$$y = Ae^{ax}$$

and

$$\ln y = \ln A + \ln e^{ax}$$

or

$$\ln y = ax + \ln A$$

Plotting the values of the natural (base e) logarithm versus x gives a straight line with slope a and an intercept $\ln A$.

Similarly, for

$$y = ax^n$$

using the common (base 10) logarithm,

$$\log y = \log a + \log x^n$$

and

$$\log y = n \log x + \log a$$

Plotting the values of $\log y$ versus $\log x$ gives a straight line with slope n and intercept $\log a$.

Linear Regression and Method of Least Squares (Optional)

The straight line of "best fit" for a set of data points on a graph can be determined by a statistical procedure called **linear regression**, using what is known as the **method of least squares**. This method determines the best-fitting straight line by means of differential calculus, which is beyond the scope of this manual.

Your instructor may wish to explain the resulting equations (Appendix C) and the procedure for determining the slope and intercept of the best-fitting straight line, particularly since they can be computed automatically by some hand calculators and by computers with the appropriate software.*

IV. Experimental Procedure

Complete the exercises in the Laboratory Report, showing calculations and attaching graphs as required. (*Note:* In this experiment and throughout, attach an additional sheet for calculations if necessary.)

* For example, Vernier Software's *Graphical Analysis*.

Name ______________________ Section ______________ Date ______________

Lab Partner(s) ____

E X P E R I M E N T 1

Experimental Error and Data Analysis

Laboratory Report

1. Significant Figures
   (a) Express the numbers listed in Data Table 1 to three significant figures, writing the numbers in normal notation in the first column and the numbers in powers-of-10 (scientific) notation in the second column.

DATA TABLE 1

Purpose: To practice expressing significant figures.

1.065	______________	67,000	______________
2347	______________	0.3140	______________
10.07	______________	29.35	______________
0.1133	______________	0.007865	______________
26,302	______________	970,000,000	______________

   (b) A rectangular block of wood is measured to have the dimensions 11.2 cm × 3.4 cm × 4.10 cm. Compute the volume of the block, showing explicitly how doubtful figures are carried through the calculation (by underlining), and report the final answer with the correct number of significant figures.

Calculations
(show work)

Computed volume (in powers of 10) ______________
(units)

Don't forget units

(continued)

(c) In an experiment to determine the value of π, a cylinder is measured to have an average value of 4.25 cm for its diameter and an average value of 13.39 cm for its circumference. What is the experimental value of π to the correct number of significant figures?

Calculations (show work)

Experimental value of π ________________
(units)

2. Expressing Experimental Error

(a) If the accepted value of π is 3.1416, what is the fractional error and the percent error of the experimental value found in 1(c)?

Calculations (show work)

Fractional error ________________

Percent error ________________

(b) In an experiment to measure the acceleration g due to gravity, two values, 9.96 m/s^2 and 9.72 m/s^2, are determined. Find (1) the percent difference of the measurements, (2) the percent error of each measurement, and (3) the percent error of their mean. (Accepted value: $g = 9.80$ m/s^2.)

Calculations (show work)

Percent difference ________________

Percent error of E_1 ________________

Percent error of E_2 ________________

Percent error of mean ________________

Name ______________________ Section ______________ Date ______________

Lab Partner(s) ____

EXPERIMENT 1 **Laboratory Report**

(c) Data Table 2 shows data taken in a free-fall experiment. Measurements were made of the distance of fall (y) at each of four precisely measured times. Complete the table. Use only the proper number of significant figures in your table entries, even if you carry extra digits during your intermediate calculations.

DATA TABLE 2

Purpose: To practice analyzing data.

Time t (s)	Distance (m)						(Optional)		t^2
	y_1	y_2	y_3	y_4	y_5	$\bar{y}$	$\bar{d}$	σ	( )
0	0	0	0	0	0				
0.50	1.0	1.4	1.1	1.4	1.5				
0.75	2.6	3.2	2.8	2.5	3.1				
1.00	4.8	4.4	5.1	4.7	4.8				
1.25	8.2	7.9	7.5	8.1	7.4				

(d) Plot a graph of $\bar{y}$ *versus* t (optional: with $2\bar{d}$) error bars for the free-fall data in part (c). Remember that $t = 0$ is a known point.

(e) The equation of motion for an object in free fall starting from rest is $y = \frac{1}{2}gt^2$, where g is the acceleration due to gravity. This is the equation of a parabola, which has the general form $y = ax^2$.

Convert the curve to a straight line by plotting $\bar{y}$ versus t^2. That is, plot the square of the time on the abscissa. (Optional: Use regional circles rather than error bars: Around each data point place a circle with a diameter the size of the error bar dispersion.) Determine the slope of the line and compute the experimental value of g from the slope value.

Calculations
(show work)

Experimental value of g from graph ______________
(units)

(continued)

(f) Compute the percent error of the experimental value of g determined from the graph in part (e). (Accepted value: $g = 9.8$ m/s^2.)

Calculations (show work)

Percent error ________________

(g) The relationship of the applied force F and the displacement x of a spring has the general form $F = kx$, where the constant k is called the *spring constant* and is a measure of the "stiffness" of the spring. Notice that this equation has the form of a straight line. Find the value of the spring constant k of the spring used in determining the experimental data plotted in the Fig. 1.7B graph. (*Note:* Since $k = F/x$, the units of k in the graph are N/m.)

Calculations (show work)

Value of spring constant of spring in Fig. 1.7B graph ________________ (units)

(h) The general relationship of the period of oscillation T of a mass suspended on a spring is $T = 2\pi\sqrt{m/k}$, where k is the spring constant. Replot the data in Fig. 1.8 so as to obtain a straight-line graph, and determine the value of the spring constant used in the experiment. [*Hint:* Square both sides of the equation and plot in a manner similar to that used in part (e).] Show the final form of the equation and calculations.

Calculations (show work)

Value of spring constant of spring in Fig. 1.8 ________________ (units)

(continued)

Name ______________________ Section ______________ Date ______________

Lab Partner(s) ____

3. (Optional) Linear Regression
   A linear regression exercise may be found in Appendix C.

QUESTIONS

1. Were the measurements on the block in section 1b above all done with the same instrument? Explain.

2. Referring to the dart analogy in Fig. 1.3, draw a dart grouping that would represent poor precision, but good accuracy with an average value.

3. Do percent error and percent difference give indications of accuracy or precision. Discuss each.

4. (Optional) Why is the average of the deviations of a set of measurement values always zero?

Name ______________________ Section ______________ Date ______________

Lab Partner(s) ____

EXPERIMENT 2

Mass, Volume, and Density

Advance Study Assignment

Read the experiment and answer the following questions.

1. What is the least count of a measurement instrument?

2. Does a laboratory balance measure weight or mass? Explain.

3. What is the function of the vernier scale on the vernier caliper? How does it extend precision?

4. What is meant by a negative zero error, and how is the zero correction made in this case? What kind of error does a zero correction correct for?

(continued)

5. What is the purpose of the ratchet mechanism on a micrometer caliper?

6. Explain how readings from 0.00 through 1.00 mm are obtained from the micrometer thimble scale when it is calibrated only from 0.00 through 0.50 mm.

7. What is the density of a material, and what does it indicate?

8. How may the volume of a heavy, irregularly shaped object be determined experimentally?

Mass, Volume, and Density

I. Introduction and Objectives

Common laboratory measurements involve the determination of the fundamental properties of mass and length. Most people are familiar with the use of scales and rulers or metersticks. However, for more accurate and precise measurements, laboratory balances and vernier calipers or micrometer calipers are often used, particularly in measurements involving small objects. In this initial experiment on measurement you will learn how to use these instruments and their advantages. Also, density, which is the ratio of mass to size (volume), will be considered, and the densities of several materials will be determined experimentally.

After performing this experiment and analyzing the data, you should be able to do the following:

1. Explain how the number of significant figures in a measured value depends on the least count of the measurement instrument.
2. Use the vernier caliper and read the vernier scale.
3. Use the micrometer caliper and read its scale.
4. Distinguish between mass and density and know how to determine experimentally the density of an object or substance.

II. Equipment Needed

- Laboratory balance
- Vernier caliper
- Micrometer caliper (metric)
- Meterstick
- Graduated cylinder
- Cylindrical metal rod (e.g., aluminum, brass, or copper)
- Sphere (metal or glass, e.g., ball bearing or marble)
- Short piece of solid copper wire
- Rectangular piece of metal sheet (e.g., aluminum)
- Irregularly shaped metal object

III. Theory

A. Least Count of an Instrument Scale

The **least count** of an instrument is the smallest subdivision marked on its scale. This is the unit of the smallest reading that can be made without estimating. For example, the least count or smallest subdivision of a meterstick is usually the millimeter (mm). We commonly say "the instrument is calibrated in centimeters (numbered major divisions) with a millimeter least count" (see Fig. 2.1).

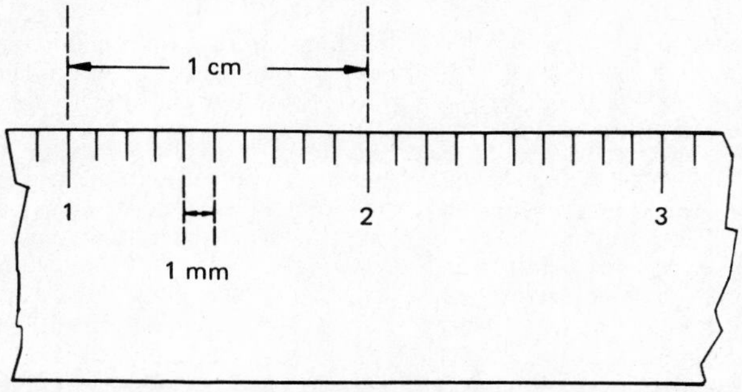

Figure 2.1 Least count. Metersticks are commonly calibrated in centimeters (numbered major divisions) with a least count, or smallest marked subdivision, of millimeters.

A measurement reading generally has one more significant figure than the least count reading of the instrument scale. This is the estimated fractional part (doubtful figure) of the smallest subdivision. In the case of a meterstick with the least count of 1 mm, a reading can be estimated to 0.1 mm (or 0.01 cm or 0.0001 m).

B. Laboratory Balances

Some common types of laboratory balances are shown in Fig. 2.2. Mechanical balances or "scales" are used to balance the weight of an unknown mass m against that of a know mass m_1 (i.e., $mg = m_1g$ or $m = m_1$), and the mass of the unknown is read directly in mass units, usually grams. The weight w of an object is its mass m times a constant g, the acceleration due to gravity; $g = 32\ \text{ft/s}^2 = 9.8\ \text{m/s}^2 = 980\ \text{cm/s}^2$ (i.e., $w = mg$ or $m = w/g$). Some scales, such as bathroom scales, are calibrated in weight (force) units (pounds) rather than in mass units.

A set of known masses is used to balance an unknown mass on a pan balance (Fig. 2.2a). On a beam balance the riders on the beams are used to balance the unknown mass on the platform (Fig.

(a)

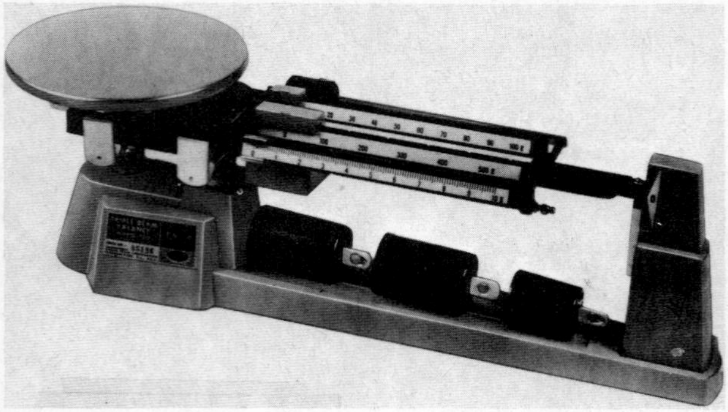

(b)

(c)

Figure 2.2 Laboratory balances. (a) A double-beam, double platform (pan) Harvard trip balance. (b) A single-platform, triple-beam balance. (c) A digital electronic balance. (Photos (a) and (c) courtesy of Sargent-Welch Scientific Co. Photo (b) courtesy of Central Scientific Co., Inc.)

2.2b). The common laboratory beam balance is calibrated in grams. In this case, the least count is 0.1 g and a reading can be made to 0.01 g.*

Before making a mass determination, check to see if the balance is zeroed. Adjustments can be made by various means on different scales.

Electronic balances with digital readouts are becoming increasingly common (Fig. 2.2c). They have the advantage of accuracy and ease of operation; however, electronic balances are much more delicate. The mass value is read out automatically, with the accuracy or number of significant figures depending on the particular balance. Some electronic balances have auto-calibration and others have a keypad for calibration by the user.†

Because of the wide variety of electronic balances available, if you are using one in this experiment you should first familiarize yourself with its operation. Your instructor may brief you, or an operation manual should be available. (When first using an electronic instrument, it is always advisable to read the operation manual supplied by the manufacturer.)

C. The Vernier Caliper

In 1631, A Frenchman, Pierre Vernier, devised a way to improve the precision of length measurements. The **vernier caliper** (Fig. 2.3), commonly called a **vernier**, consists of a rule with a main engraved scale and a movable jaw with an engraved vernier scale. The span of the lower jaw is used to measure length and is particularly convenient for measuring the diameter of a cylindrical object. The span of the upper jaw is used to measure distances between two surfaces (e.g., the inside diameter of a hollow cylindrical object).

The main scale is calibrated in centimeters with a millimeter least count, and the movable vernier scale

* The official abbreviation of the gram unit is g (in roman type). The standard symbol for acceleration due to gravity is *g* (in italic type), where weight is given by *mg*. Look closely so as to avoid confusion with these symbols.

† In general, an electronic balance has a suspended beam, and the balancing force on the end of the beam opposite the weighing pan is electromagnetic. The force is supplied by a current-carrying coil of wire in the field of a permanent magnet. The force is directly proportional to the current, which is controlled automatically by a photosensitive diode whose resistance is a function of the light incident on it.

Any tilting of the beam increases the light from a source on the diode, and a feedback circuit calls for more current in the coil. The increase in current (and hence in force) is adjusted so as to keep the beam in horizontal equilibrium. The current that balances the beam is read out on a digital ammeter calibrated in grams or milligrams.

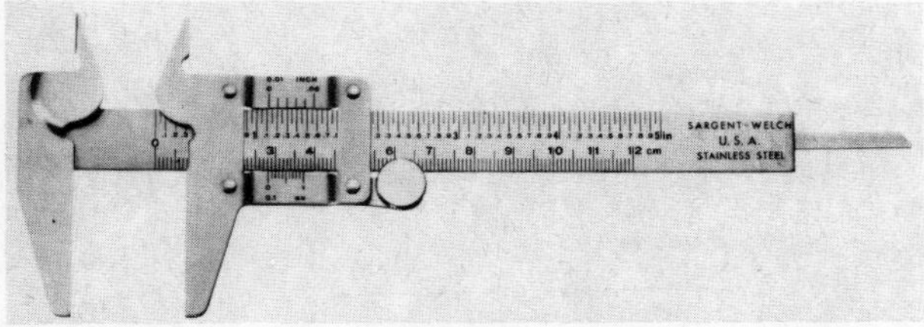

Figure 2.3 The vernier caliper. A good instrument for measuring rectangular dimensions or circular diameters. See text for description. (Photo courtesy of Sargent-Welch Scientific Co.)

has 10 divisions that cover 9 divisions on the main scale. When making a measurement with a meterstick, it is necessary to estimate or "eyeball" the fractional part of the smallest scale division (the tenth of a millimeter). The function of the vernier scale is to assist in the accurate reading of the fractional part of the scale division, thus increasing the precision.

The leftmost mark on the vernier scale is the zero mark (lower scale for metric reading and upper scale for inches). The zero mark is often unlabeled. A measurement is made by closing the jaws on the object to be measured and reading where the zero mark on the vernier scale falls on the main scale (see Fig. 2.4).

The first two significant figures are read directly from the main scale. The vernier zero mark is past the 2 mm line after the 1 cm major division mark, so we have 1.2 cm for both readings in Fig. 2.4. The next significant figure is the fractional part of the smallest subdivision on the main scale. This is obtained by referring to the vernier scale markings. If a vernier mark coincides with a mark on the main scale (Fig. 2.4a), then the mark number is the fractional part of the main-scale division. In the figure, this is the third mark to the right of the vernier zero, so the third significant figure is 3 (0.03 cm). Finally, since the 0.03 cm reading is known exactly, a zero is added as the doubtful figure for a reading of 1.230 cm or 12.30 mm. Note how the vernier scale gives more significant figures or extends the precision.

However, a mark on the vernier scale may not always line up exactly with one on the main scale (Fig. 2.4b). In this case, there is more uncertainty in the 0.001 cm or 0.01 mm figure. There will be a change of "phase" between two successive vernier markings. Notice how in Fig. 2.4b the second vernier mark after the zero is to the right of the closest main-scale mark and the third vernier mark is to the left of the closest main-scale mark. Hence, the marks change phase between the 2 and 3 marks, and the reading is between 1.22 cm and 1.23 cm. Most vernier scales are not fine enough to make an estimate of the doubtful figure, so a suggested method is to

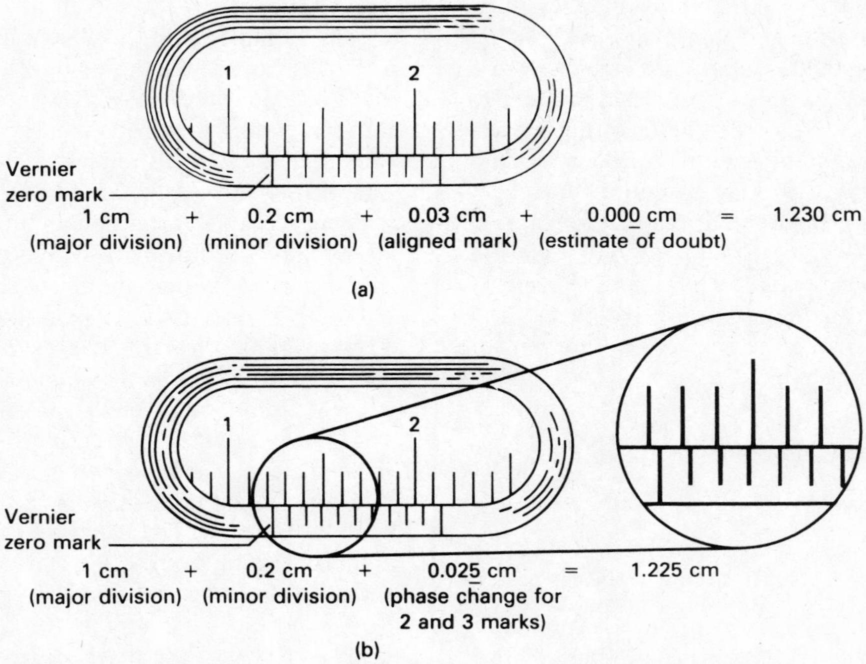

Figure 2.4 Vernier scale. An example of reading the vernier scale on a caliper. See text for description.

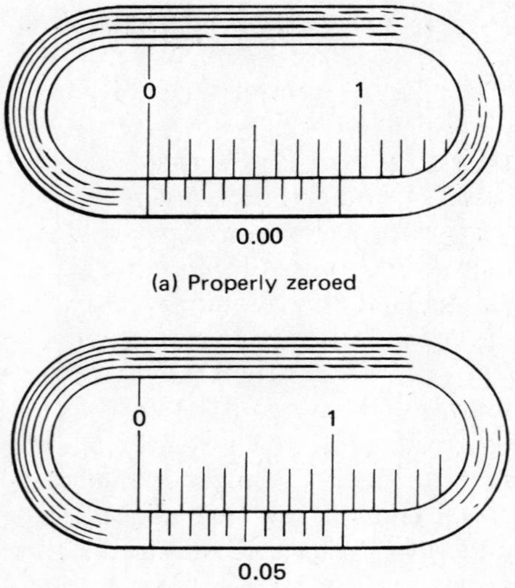

(a) Properly zeroed

(b) Positive error +0.05 cm
(subtracted from measurement reading)

Figure 2.5 Zeroing and error. Zeroing the vernier caliper with the jaws closed. (a) Zero error. (b) Positive error, + 0.05 cm.

take the middle of the range or to put a 5 in the thousandth-of-a-centimeter digit for a reading of 1.225 cm.*

Before making a measurement, the zero of the vernier caliper should be checked with the jaws completely closed. It is possible that through misuse the caliper is no longer zeroed and thus gives erroneous readings (systematic error). If this is the case, a zero correction must be made for each reading. If the vernier zero lies to the right of the main-scale zero, measurements will be too large and the error is said to be *positive*. In this case, the zero correction is made by subtracting the zero reading from the measurement reading. For example, the "zero" reading in Fig. 2.5 is +0.05 cm, and this amount must be subtracted from each measurement reading for more accurate results.

Similarly, if the error is *negative*, or the vernier zero lies to the left of the main-scale zero, measurements will be too small and the zero correction must be added to the measurement readings.

Summarizing these corrections in equation form,

$$\text{Corrected reading} = \text{actual reading} - \text{zero reading}$$

For example, for a *positive* error of +0.05 cm as in Fig.2.5,

$$\text{Corrected reading} = \text{actual reading} - 0.05 \text{ cm}$$

* E. S. Oberhofer, "The Vernier Caliper and Significant Figures," *The Physics Teacher*, Vol. 23 (November 1985), 493.

If there is a *negative* correction of −0.05 cm, then

$$\begin{aligned}\text{Corrected reading} &= \text{actual reading} - (-0.05) \text{ cm}\\ &= \text{actual reading} + 0.05 \text{ cm}\end{aligned}$$

D. Micrometer Caliper

The **micrometer caliper** (Fig. 2.6), commonly called a **mike**, provides for accurate measurements of small lengths and is particularly convenient in measuring the diameters of thin wires and the thicknesses of thin sheets. It consists of a movable spindle (jaw) that is advanced toward another, parallel-faced jaw (called an anvil) by rotating the thimble. The thimble rotates over an engraved sleeve (or "barrel") mounted on a solid frame.

Most micrometers are equipped with a ratchet (ratchet handle to far right) which allows slippage of the screw mechanism when a small and constant force is exerted on the jaw. This permits the jaw to be tightened on an object with the same amount of force each time. Care should be taken not to force the screw (particularly if the micrometer does not have a ratchet mechanism), so as not to damage the measured object and/or the micrometer.

The axial main scale on the sleeve is calibrated in millimeters, and the thimble scale is calibrated in 0.01 mm (hundredths of a millimeter). The movement mechanism of the micrometer is a carefully machined screw with a pitch of 0.5 mm. The pitch of a screw, or the distance between screw threads, is the lateral linear distance the screw moves when turned through one rotation.

The axial line on the sleeve main scale serves as a reading line. Since the pitch of the screw is 0.5 mm and there are 50 divisions on the thimble, when the thimble is turned through one of its divisions, the thimble moves (and the jaws open or close) $\frac{1}{50}$ of 0.5 mm or 0.01 mm ($\frac{1}{50} \times 0.5 \text{ mm} = 0.01 \text{ mm}$).

One complete rotation of the thimble (50 divisions) moves it through 0.5 mm, and a second rotation moves it through another 0.5 mm, for a total of 1.0 mm, or one scale division along the main scale. That is, the first rotation moves the thimble from 0.00 through 0.50 mm and the second rotation moves the thimble from 0.50 through 1.00 mm.

It is sometimes instructive to think of the 1-mm main-scale divisions as being analogous to dollar ($) divisions and the thimble scale divisions as being cents ($0.01) The first rotation of the thimble corresponds to going from $0.00 to $0.50 (50 cents) and the second rotation corresponds to going from $0.50 to $1.00, so that two complete rotations go through 100 cents or $1.00 of the main scale.

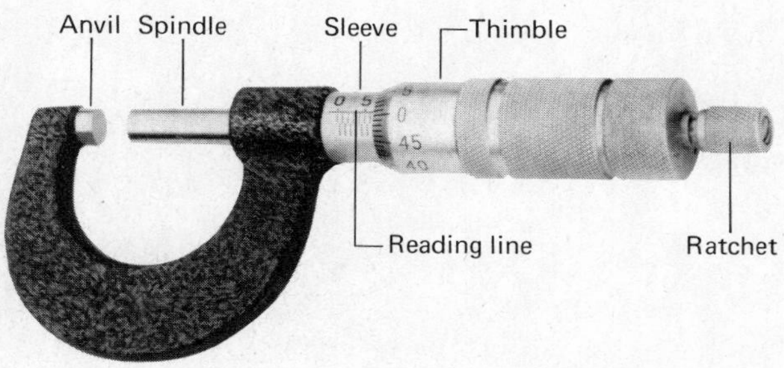

(a)

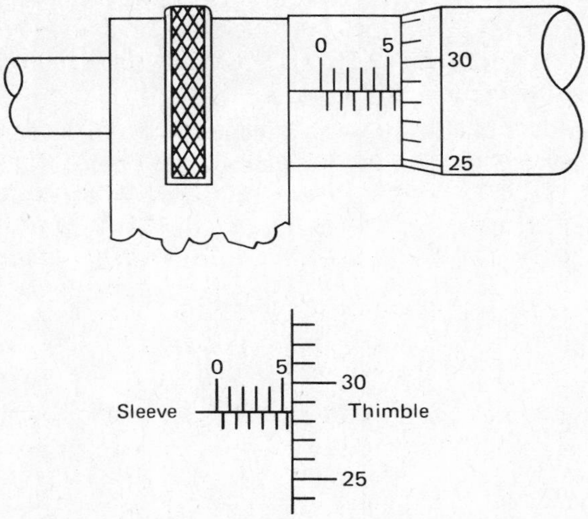

(b) Reading of 5.785 mm

Figure 2.6 Micrometer caliper. A micrometer caliper and an example of a micrometer reading. (a) This particular mike has the 1.0-mm and 0.5-mm scale divisions below the reading line. (b) In this diagram, as on some mikes, the 1.0-mm divisions are above the reading line and the 0.5-mm divisions are below it. The thimble in the diagram is in the second rotation of a mm movement, as indicated by its being past the 0.5-mm mark. The reading is 5.500 + 0.285 mm, or 5.785 mm, where the last 5 is the estimated figure. (Photo courtesy of Sargent-Welch Scientific Co.)

Some micrometers have a scale that indicates the 0.5-mm marks of the main-scale divisions and hence tells which rotation the thimble is in (Fig. 2.6). Cheaper mikes do not have this extra graduation and the main scale must be closely examined to determine which rotation the thimble is in.

If a mike does not have the 0.5-mm scale, you must determine whether the thimble is in its first rotation, in which case the thimble reading is between 0.00 and 0.50 mm (corresponding to the actual engraved numbers on the thimble), or in the second rotation, in which case the reading is between 0.50 and 1.00 mm (the actual thimble scale reading plus 0.50).

This can be determined by judging whether the edge of the thimble is in the first or the second half of the main-scale division. Notice that the zero mark on the thimble is used to indicate both 0.00 mm (beginning of the first rotation) and 0.50 mm (beginning of the second rotation).

Measurements are taken by noting the position of the edge of the thimble on the main scale and the position of the reading line on the thimble scale. For example, for the drawing in Fig. 2.6, the mike has a reading of 5.785 mm. On the main scale is a reading of 5.000 mm plus one 0.500-mm division (scale below reading line), giving 5.500 mm. That is, in the figure, the thimble is in the second rotation of a main-scale division.

The reading on the thimble scale is 0.285 mm, where the 5 is the estimated or doubtful figure (i.e., the reading line is estimated to be midway between the 28 and the 29 marks). Some mikes have vernier scales on the sleeves to help read this last significant figure and further extend the precision.

A zero check should be made and a zero correction applied to each reading if necessary as described in Section III.C. A zero reading is made by rotating the screw until the jaw is closed or the spindle comes into contact with the anvil. The contacting surfaces of the spindle and anvil should be clean and free of dust. (Micrometers can be adjusted to zero readings by means of a spanner wrench. Do not attempt to do this without your instructor's permission or supervision.)

E. Density

The **density** ρ of a substance is defined as the mass m per unit volume V (i.e., $\rho = m/V$). This may be determined experimentally by measuring the mass and volume of a sample of a substance and calculating the ratio m/V. The volume of regularly shaped objects may be calculated from length measurements; for example:

Rectangle
$V = l \times w \times h$ (length × width × height)

Cylinder
$V = Al = (\pi r^2)l$ (circular cross-sectional area $A = \pi r^2$, where r is the radius, times the length l of the cylinder)

Sphere
$V = \frac{4}{3}\pi r^3$ (where r is the radius of the sphere)

Density is commonly expressed in grams per cubic centimeter (g/cm^3) or kilograms per cubic meter (kg/m^3).

Density provides a measure of the compactness of matter in a substance. For example, the marble and Styrofoam ball in Fig. 2.7 have the same mass (5.0 g), but the marble has greater density. With measured radii of $r_m = 0.75$ cm and $r_b = 6.0$ cm for the marble and ball, respectively, the calculated densities are

$$\rho_m = \frac{m_m}{V_m} = \frac{m_m}{\frac{4}{3}\pi r_m^3} = \frac{5.0\text{ g}}{\frac{4}{3}\pi(0.75\text{ cm})^3} = 2.8\text{ g/cm}^3$$

$$\rho_b = \frac{m_b}{V_b} = \frac{m_b}{\frac{4}{3}\pi r_b^3} = \frac{5.0\text{ g}}{\frac{4}{3}\pi(6.0\text{ cm})^3} = 0.0055\text{ g/cm}^3$$

(Notice that the calculated results have only two significant figures. Why?)

To find the density of a heavy, irregularly shaped object, its volume may be determined by immersing it in water (or some other liquid) in a graduated cylinder. Since the object will displace a volume of water equal to its own volume, the difference in the cylinder readings before and after immersion is the volume of the object. Cylinders commonly have scale divisions of milliliters (mL)* and 1 mL = 1 cc (cubic centimeter) = 1 cm^3.

The physical property of density can be used to identify substances in some cases. If a substance is not pure or it is inhomogeneous (mass not evenly distributed), an average density is obtained, which is generally different from that of a pure or homogeneous substance.

Figure 2.7 Density, mass, and volume. The marble and the Styrofoam ball have equal masses, but different densities ($\rho = m/V$). Since the volume of the ball is larger than that of the marble, its density is less.

IV. Experimental Procedure

A. *Least Count of an Instrument Scale*

1. List the least count and the estimated fraction of the least count of each of the measuring instruments in Data Table 1. For example, for a meterstick, these would be 1 mm and 0.1 ($\frac{1}{10}$) mm, respectively.

B. *Thickness Measurements*

2. Using the micrometer caliper, take a zero reading and record in Data Table 3. Then, take several measurements of a single page of this manual, incorporating the zero correction, to determine the average thickness per page. Record the data and result in Data Table 2.

3. With the micrometer, take thickness measurements of a group of several pages together [e.g., 10 pages (sheets of paper)] and record the data in Data Table 2. Calculate the average thickness per page.

4. With the vernier caliper, take several measurements of the total thickness of the manual (*excluding* covers).* Record the data in Data Table 2, and compute the average overall thickness of the manual.

5. Using the values of the average thickness per page determined in procedures 1 and 2 and the overall average thickness of the manual from procedure 3, compute the number of pages (sheets of paper) in your manual. For example, if the average thickness per page is 0.150 mm and the average overall thickness is 35.5 mm (3.55 cm), the calculated number of papers is

$$\frac{35.5\text{ mm}}{0.150\text{ mm/page}} = 236.6666 = 237\text{ pages}$$

6. Determine the actual number of pages (sheets of paper) in the manual. (Remember to subtract any pages handed in from Experiment 1, the Advance Study Assignment for this experiment, and any others that might be missing.) Compute the percent error for each of the two experimentally determined values.

* Milliliter is abbreviated both ml and mL. The mL abbreviation is generally preferred in order to avoid confusion of a lowercase l ("ell") with the number one.

* Be sure the pages are compacted as much as possible before the measurements are taken.

C. Density Determinations

7. The densities of the materials of the various objects are to be determined from mass and volume (length) measurements. The mass and length measurements will give you experience in using the laboratory balance and the vernier and micrometer calipers.

8. Using the appropriate measuring instrument(s), take several measurements to determine the average dimensions of the regularly shaped objects so that their volumes can be calculated. Record the data in Data Table 3. Remember to make a zero correction for each reading if necessary.

9. Calculate the volume of each of the objects and record in Data Table 4.

10. Determine the volume of the irregularly shaped metal object by the method described in Section III.E. Record the volume in Data Table 4.

11. Using a laboratory balance, determine the mass of each object and record the results in Data Table 4.

12. Calculate the density of the material of each object and find the percent error of each experimental result. (Accepted density values are given in Appendix A, Table A1.)

Name ______________________ Section ______________ Date ______________

Lab Partner(s) ____

EXPERIMENT 2

Mass, Volume, and Density

Laboratory Report

A. Least Count of an Instrument Scale

DATA TABLE 1

Purpose: To practice determining least count and estimated fraction of least count.

Instrument	Least count	Estimated fraction
Meterstick		
Vernier caliper		
Micrometer caliper		
Balance		
Graduated cylinder		

Don't forget units

(continued)

B. Thickness Measurements

DATA TABLE 2

Purpose: To practice using calipers.

Reading	Thickness of single page ( )	Thickness of ______ pages ( )	Average page thickness ( )	Thickness of manual, excluding covers ( )
1				
2				
3				
4				
Average				

Actual number of pages (sheets) in manual ______

Percent error

Computed number of pages (from single-page measurement) ______ ______

(from multiple-page measurement) ______ ______

Calculations
(show work)

Name ______________________ Section ______________ Date ______________

Lab Partner(s) ____

C. Density Determination

DATA TABLE 3

Purpose: To record dimensional measurements.

Zero reading: Vernier caliper ______________ Micrometer caliper ______________

	Rod		Wire		Sphere	Rectangular sheet		
Instrument used								
Reading	Diameter ( )	Length ( )	Diameter ( )	Length ( )	Diameter ( )	Length ( )	Width ( )	Thickness ( )
1								
2								
3								
4								
Average								

Calculations
(show work)

(continued)

DATA TABLE 4
Purpose: To compare experimental and accepted density values.

Object	Mass ( )	Volume ( )	Experimental density ( )	Accepted density (from Table A1)	Percent error
Rod Type of material: __________					
Wire Type of material: __________					
Sphere Type of material: __________					
Rectangular sheet Type of material: __________					
Irregularly shaped object Type of material: __________					

Calculations
(attach additional sheet if necessary)

Name ______________________ Section ______________ Date ______________

Lab Partner(s) ____

EXPERIMENT 2 — *Laboratory Report*

Questions

1. Explain the probable source of error(s) in the experimental determination of the number of manual pages.

2. Based on your general experience, do you see any advantage to using the metric system? Explain.

3. Suppose that you were given an irregularly shaped object that floats. Describe how you would experimentally determine its volume.

4. When determining the volume of the irregularly shaped object, any air bubbles sticking to the surface of the object when it is submerged cause systematic errors. Will this error give an experimental density that is too high, or too low? Explain.

(continued)

5. A thin circular sheet of aluminum has a radius of 20 cm and a thickness of 0.50 mm. Find the mass of the sheet.

6. Archimedes, a famous Greek scientist, was given a problem by King Hieron II of Syracuse (Sicily). The king suspected that his crown, which was supposed to be made of pure gold, contained some silver alloy, and he asked Archimedes to prove or disprove his suspicion. (The crown did contain silver.) How would you have experimentally determined whether or not the crown was pure gold?

Name ______________________ Section ______________ Date ______________

Lab Partner(s) ____

E X P E R I M E N T 3

The Scientific Method: The Simple Pendulum

Advance Study Assignment

Read the experiment and answer the following questions.

1. What is the scientific method, and how is it applied?

2. What are the physical parameters of a simple pendulum?

3. What is meant by the period of a pendulum?

4. Distinguish between independent and dependent variables.

(continued)

5. How does the period of a pendulum vary, theoretically, with (a) length; (b) mass of bob; (c) angular displacement?

6. What is meant by a "small-angle approximation"?

The Scientific Method: The Simple Pendulum

I. Introduction and Objectives

The laboratory is a place for the investigation of physical phenomena and principles. Originally, scientists studied physical phenomena in the laboratory in the hope that they might discover relationships and principles involved in the phenomena. This might be called a **trial-and-error approach**. Today, the physics laboratory is used in general to apply what is called the **scientific method**. This principle states that no theory or model of nature is tenable unless the results it predicts are in accord with experiment.

Rather than applying the somewhat haphazard trial-and-error approach, scientists now try to predict physical phenomena theoretically, then test their theories against planned experiments in the laboratory. If the experimental results agree with the theoretical predictions, we consider the theory to be valid and believe that we have an accurate description of certain physical phenomena (until some other results demonstrate otherwise).

To illustrate the scientific method, in this experiment a theoretical expression or equation that describes the behavior of a simple pendulum will be given. You will test the validity of this relationship experimentally. In the process you will learn what variable influences the period of a simple pendulum and how the physical relationship and experimental data can be used to determine other useful information (e.g., the value of the acceleration due to gravity).

After performing this experiment and analyzing the data, you should be able to do the following:

1. Apply the scientific method to a hypothesis to check its validity.
2. Understand how physical parameters are varied so as to investigate a hypothesis.
3. Appreciate the use of approximations to facilitate experimental investigations and analyses.

II. Equipment Needed

- Meterstick
- Laboratory timer or stopwatch
- Protractor
- String
- Three or more pendulum bobs of different masses
- Pendulum clamp (if available)
- 1 sheet of Cartesian graph paper

III. Theory

A **pendulum** consists of a "bob" (a mass) attached to a string that is fastened so that the pendulum assembly can swing or oscillate in a plane (Fig. 3.1). For a simple or ideal pendulum, all the mass is considered to be concentrated at a point at the center (of mass) of the bob.

Some of the physical properties or parameters of a simple pendulum are (1) the length L of the pendulum, (2) the mass m of the pendulum bob, (3) the angular displacement θ through which the pendulum swings, and (4) the period T of the pendulum, which is the time it takes for the pendulum to swing through one complete oscillation (e.g., from A to B and back to A in Fig. 3.1).

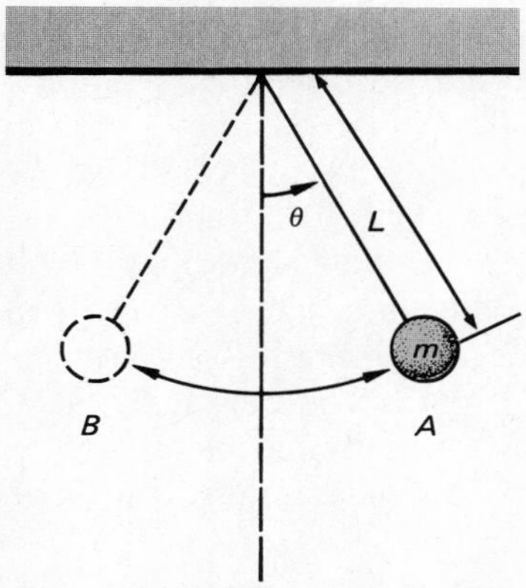

Figure 3.1 Simple pendulum. The physical parameters of a pendulum are the mass m of its bob, its length L, and the angle of swing θ. The period T of a pendulum is the time it takes for one completed oscillation, for example to swing from A to B back to A.

From experience or preliminary investigation, it should be evident that the period of a pendulum is proportional to its length (i.e., the longer the pendulum, the greater its period). How do you think the other parameters (m and θ) affect the period?

From physical principles and advanced mathematics, the theoretical expression for the period of a simple pendulum oscillating in a plane is

$$T = 2\pi\sqrt{\frac{L}{g}}\left(1 + \frac{1}{4}\sin^2\frac{\theta}{2} + \frac{9}{64}\sin^4\frac{\theta}{2} + \cdots\right) \qquad \textbf{(3.1)}$$

where g is the acceleration due to gravity and the terms in parentheses are part of an infinite series. In calculating T for a given angular distance θ, the more terms of the series that are evaluated, the greater the accuracy of the theoretical result.

For small angles ($\theta \lesssim 20°$), the θ terms in the series are small compared to unity (i.e., $<<1$), and in this case, to a good approximation,

$$T = 2\pi\sqrt{\frac{L}{g}} \qquad \textbf{(3.2)}$$

(This is called the **first-order approximation**. If the second term in the series is retained, the approximation is to second order, and so on.)

Notice that even without an approximation (Eq. 3.1), the period is theoretically independent of the mass of the pendulum bob. Also, within the limits of the small-angle approximation (Eq. 3.2), the period is independent of the displacement angle.

It is sometimes helpful to visualize a physical system as a "black box" with inputs and outputs.* The black box is the relationship connecting the input and output parameters. The term parameter refers to anything in the physical system that can be measured.

The input parameters are the physical variables that may *control* or *influence* the behavior of the output parameters (the physical quantities that are measured and that *describe* the resulting behavior of the system). The input parameters are often called **independent variables** because they can (and should) be varied independently of each other. The output parameters, on the other hand, may be called **dependent variables** because their values depend on the inputs. In any given system, some of the inputs may have little or no effect on the outputs.

In the case of a simple pendulum, with a little insight a black box diagram might look like this:

Input

$m \quad \theta \quad L$

$\downarrow \quad \downarrow \quad \downarrow$

Simple Pendulum

$$T = 2\pi\sqrt{\frac{L}{g}}\left(1 + \frac{1}{4}\sin^2\frac{\theta}{2} + \cdots\right)$$

$\downarrow$

T

Output

You may find drawing black box diagrams helpful in understanding the physical systems to be investigated in later experiments.

IV. Experimental Procedure

1. Set up a simple pendulum arrangement. If a pendulum clamp is not available and the string must be tied around something (e.g., a lab stand arm), make sure that the string is secure and does not slip on the support.

2. Experimentally investigate the small-angle approximation (Eq. 3.2) and the theoretical prediction (Eq. 3.1) that the period increases with larger angles. Do this by determining the pendulum period for the several angles listed in Data Table 1, keeping the length and mass of the pendulum constant.

   [Rather than timing only one oscillation, time several (e.g., four or five) and determine the average period. Timing is generally more accurate if you start the pendulum oscillating before the timing begins. Also, it is usually best to take the timing reference point as the lowest point of the swing.]

   Measure and record the pendulum length. The length should be measured to the center of the pendulum bob.

   Compute the percent error of the period for each angle θ using Eq. 3.2 as the accepted value. (In this case, do not use the absolute difference, so that each percent error will have signs, + or −. (Further analysis will be done in the Questions section.) Proceed to the next step.

3. Experimentally investigate whether the period is independent of the mass of the pendulum bob.

* Suggested by Professor I. L. Fischer, Bergen Community College, New Jersey.

Using the three masses provided, determine the periods of a pendulum with each mass as the bob (keeping length L and the small angle of oscillation constant). Record your results in Data Table 2 and draw a conclusion from the data.

4. Experimentally investigate the relationship between the length and period of a pendulum. Using five different lengths (e.g., 0.20, 0.40, 0.60, 0.80, 1.00 m), determine the average period of a pendulum of each length (keeping mass and the small angle of oscillation constant). Record the data in Data Table 3.

5. Compute the theoretical period for each pendulum length (Eq. 3.2) and enter the results in Data Table 3. ($g = 9.80\ \text{m/s}^2 = 980\ \text{cm/s}^2$)

6. Compute the percent error between the experimental and the theoretical values of the period for each pendulum length and record in Data Table 3. Draw conclusions about the validity or applicability of Eq. 3.2.

7. The object of the preceding experimental procedures was to determine the validity or applicability of Eq. 3.2, that is, whether the experimental results agree with the theoretical predictions as required by the scientific method. Once found acceptable, a theoretical expression can then be used to determine experimentally other quantities occurring in the expression. For example, Eq. 3.2 provides a means for experimentally determining g, the acceleration due to gravity, by measuring the pendulum parameters of length and period as was done previously.

Squaring both sides of Eq. 3.2, we have

$$T^2 = \frac{4\pi^2}{g} L \qquad (3.3)$$

or

$$L = \frac{g}{4\pi^2} T^2$$

Hence, the equation has the form $y = ax^2$, that of a parabola. As was learned in Experiment 1, this can be plotted as a straight line with the general form $y = mx'$ by letting $L = y$ and $x' = T^2$, or plotting T^2 on the X axis. The line will have a slope of $m = g/4\pi^2$.

8. Plot L versus T^2 from the experimental data in Data Table 3, determine the slope of the graph, and compute the experimental value of g. Record this in the Laboratory Report and compute the percent error of the result.

Name ______________________ Section ______________ Date ______________

Lab Partner(s) ____

EXPERIMENT 3

The Scientific Method: The Simple Pendulum

Laboratory Report

DATA TABLE 1

Purpose: To investigate the small-angle approximation.

Mass, m ______________ Pendulum length, L ______________

Angle θ	Period, T ( ) Experimental	Theoretical	Percent error
5°			
10°			
20°			
30°			
45°			
60°			

Conclusion:

DATA TABLE 2

Purpose: To investigate period dependence on mass.

θ ______________ L ______________

m ( )	T ( ) Experimental	Theoretical	Percent error

Conclusion:

Don't forget units

(continued)

DATA TABLE 3
Purpose: To investigate period dependence on length.

θ ________________ *m* ________________

L ( )	*T* ( )		Percent error	T^2 ( )
	Experimental	Theoretical		

Conclusion:

Value of *g* from experimental data (slope of graph) ________________ (units)

Percent error ________________

QUESTIONS

1. It was suggested that the time for several periods be measured and the average period determined, rather than timing only one period.
   (a) What are the advantages of this method?

   (b) How and why would the result be affected if a large number of periods were timed?

Name ______________________ Section ______________ Date ______________

Lab Partner(s) ____

2. In general, the results of Procedure 2 may not have shown clear-cut evidence that the period increases as dramatically with the angle as might be indicated by Eq. 3.1. To understand why, write Eq. 3.1 as

$$T = T_1\left(1 + \frac{1}{4}\sin^2\frac{\theta}{2} + \frac{9}{64}\sin^4\frac{\theta}{2}\right)$$

and compute T in terms of $T_1 \left(= 2\pi\sqrt{\frac{L}{g}}\right)$ for angles of 5°, 20°, and 60°.
Comment on the theoretical predictions and experimental accuracy in relation to your results in Data Table 1.

3. Is air resistance or friction a systematic or a random source of error? Would it cause the period to be larger or smaller than the theoretical value? (*Hint:* Consider what would happen if the air resistance were much greater, e.g., as though the pendulum were swinging in a liquid.)

4. Thomas Jefferson once suggested that the period of a simple pendulum be used to define the standard unit of length. What would be the length of a "2-second" pendulum (a pendulum with a period of 2 s)?

5. Suppose Jefferson's 2-second pendulum were operated on the moon. What would its period be there?

Name ______________________ Section ______________ Date ______________

Lab Partner(s) ____

E X P E R I M E N T 4

Uniformly Accelerated Motion

Advance Study Assignment

Read the experiment and answer the following questions.

A. Object in Free Fall

1. From what height should you drop the object to obtain good experimental results?

2. Should the person dropping the object or a lab partner do the timing? Explain.

3. Suppose that the initial height of the object were measured from the top of the object at the release point to the floor. How would this affect your experimental result? Is this a random or a systematic error?

B. Free-Fall Spark-Timer Apparatus

4. How are data recorded on the tape strip, and what information does the data tape give?

(continued)

5. What precautions should be taken in using the apparatus?

6. What equation describes the instantaneous velocity of an object in free fall, and what is the shape of the graph of the instantaneous velocity versus time?

7. What is the difference between average velocity and instantaneous velocity?

8. Describe how the instantaneous velocity of an object in free fall can be calculated from displacement and time data.

C. Linear Air Track

9. What is the function of the air in the air-track operation?

Name ______________________ Section ______________ Date ______________

Lab Partner(s) ____

10. How is the air track positioned to study uniformly accelerated motion? Explain.

11. How is the accelaration of a car traveling on an elevated air track related to (a) the angle of elevation; (b) the height of elevation?

12. (Omit if question 6 answered.) What is the equation describing the instantaneous velocity of a car on an elevated air track, and what is the shape of the graph of the instantaneous velocity versus time?

13. (Omit if question 7 answered.) What is the difference between the average velocity and instantaneous velocity?

14. (Omit if question 8 answered.) Describe how the instantaneous velocity of a car traveling on an elevated air track can be calculated from displacement and time data.

EXPERIMENT 4

Uniformly Accelerated Motion

I. Introduction and Objectives

An important case in kinematics is that of an object in uniformly accelerated motion, that is, an object moving with a uniform or *constant* acceleration. Probably the most common example of an object moving with a constant or uniform acceleration is a falling object. An object falling solely under the influence of gravity is said to be in free fall, and it falls with g, the acceleration due to gravity. Near the Earth's surface, the acceleration due to gravity is essentially constant, with a common value of

$$g = 9.80 \text{ m/s}^2 = 980 \text{ cm/s}^2 = 32.2 \text{ ft/s}^2$$

Of course, air resistance affects the acceleration of a falling object. But for relatively dense objects over short distances of fall, the effects of air resistance are negligible and objects fall with an acceleration of g. In this experiment we make use of the acceleration due to gravity to investigate an object undergoing uniformly accelerated motion to see how its velocity and displacement change with time. Conversely, with displacement and time measurements, the value of g can be determined. The experiment data and its analysis will provide a better understanding of the kinetic equations describing the motion. Investigations will be made using one or more of the following: (1) an object in free fall, (2) a free-fall spark-timer apparatus, and/or (3) a linear air track.

After performing this experiment and analyzing the data, you should be able to do the following:

1. Clearly distinguish between average and instantaneous velocity.
2. Express how the velocity of a uniformly accelerated object changes with time.
3. Express how the distance traveled by a uniformly accelerated object changes with time.
4. Explain how the uniform acceleration of an object may be determined from distance and time measurements.

II. Equipment Needed

A. *Object in Free Fall*

- Lead weight or small wooden block
- Meterstick
- Laboratory timer or stopwatch

(*Optional*)

- Automatic electric timer. May have computer interface as in Pasco Series 6500
- Pasco "picket fence" for computer-assisted free-fall analysis

B. *Free-Fall Timer Apparatus*

- Free-fall timer apparatus
- Meterstick
- 1 sheet of Cartesian graph paper

C. *Linear Air Track*

- Linear air track
- Several laboratory timers or stopwatches
- Wooden blocks of two different heights
- 1 sheet of Cartesian graph paper

(*Optional*)

- Air track system with photogates and computer interfacing

Note: If electronic timers and computer-assisted data analysis are available, your instructor will give you instruction on their use. Electronic timing greatly improves the accuracy and precision of the experimental results. (Why?)

III. Theory

A. *Object in Free Fall*

An object in free fall (air resistance neglected) falls under the influence of gravity, or with an acceleration g. The distance y an object falls in a time t is given by

$$y = v_o t + \tfrac{1}{2}gt^2 \qquad \textbf{(4.1)}$$

where v_o is the initial velocity.

If an object is dropped from rest ($v_o = 0$), then

$$y = \tfrac{1}{2}gt^2 \qquad \textbf{(4.2)}$$

(downward taken as positive to avoid minus signs). Hence, by measuring the time t it takes for an object to fall a distance y, the acceleration g due to gravity can be easily calculated.

The time it takes for a released object to fall a distance y to the floor may be measured manually or electronically (Fig. 4.1a). An electronic method for

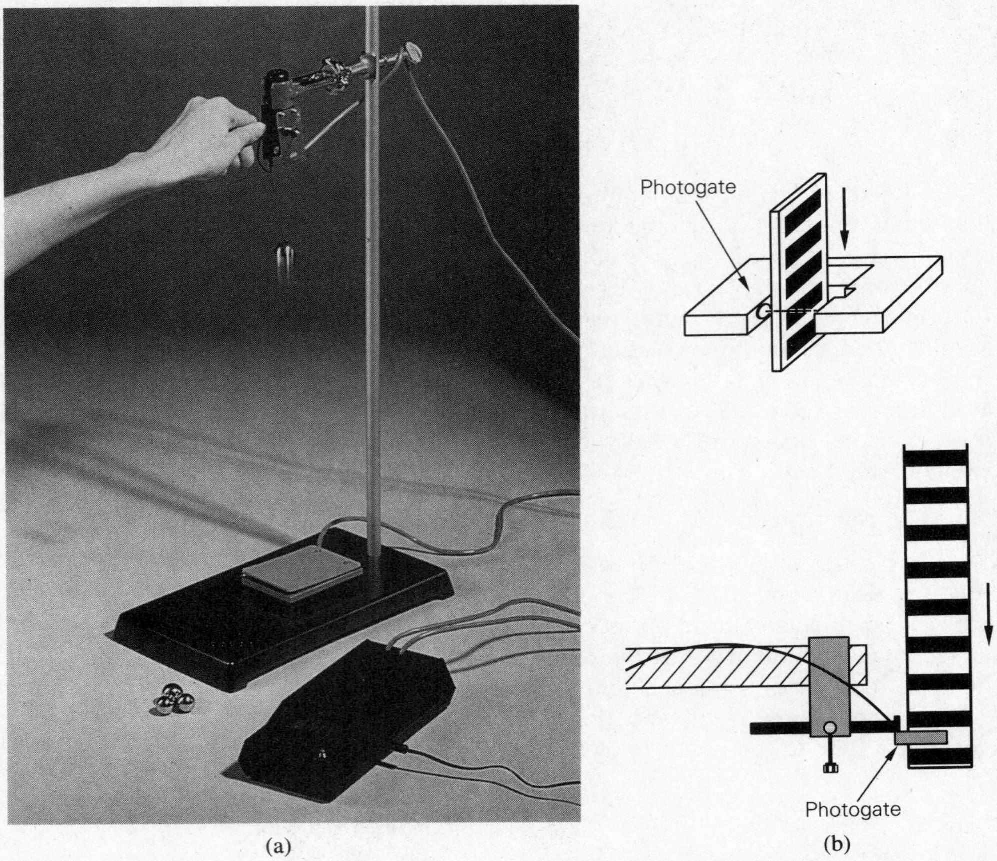

Figure 4.1 Distance-time measurements. (a) A digital free-fall apparatus. The time of fall is electronically recorded. (b) Picket fence method. The photogate times the motion of evenly spaced bars on a transparent piece of plastic. (Photo courtesy of Central Scientific Co., Inc. Basis of drawing courtesy of PASCO Scientific.)

time and distance measurements is illustrated in Fig. 4.1b.

B. Free-Fall Timer Apparatus

Some free-fall timer apparatuses are shown in Fig. 4.2. Other types are available, but we will focus on the spark-timer. The free-fall spark-timer assembly consists of a metal object that falls freely between two wires with a tape strip of specially treated paper between the object and one of the wires. The spark timer is a fast timing device that supplies a high voltage across the wires periodically for preset time intervals (e.g., a frequency of 60 Hz or time interval of $\frac{1}{60}$ s, since $t = 1/f$). The free-fall apparatus is equipped with an electromagnet that releases the metal object when the spark timer is activated.

A high voltage causes a spark to jump between two electrical conductors in close proximity. The wires are too far apart for a spark to jump directly from one wire to the other. However, as the metal object falls between the wires, the spark (electrical current) jumps from one wire to the metal object, travels through the object, and jumps to the other wire. In so doing, the spark burns a spot on the paper tape strip.

The spots on the tape are then a certain time interval apart, as selected and usually preset on the spark timer. The series of spots on the tape gives the vertical distance of fall as a function of time, from which can be measured the distance y_i the object falls in a time t_i.

The instantaneous velocity v_i of a free-falling object (neglecting air resistance) at a time t is given theoretically by

$$v_i = v_o + gt \tag{4.3}$$

(where downward is taken as the positive direction). Hence, a graph of v versus t is a straight line

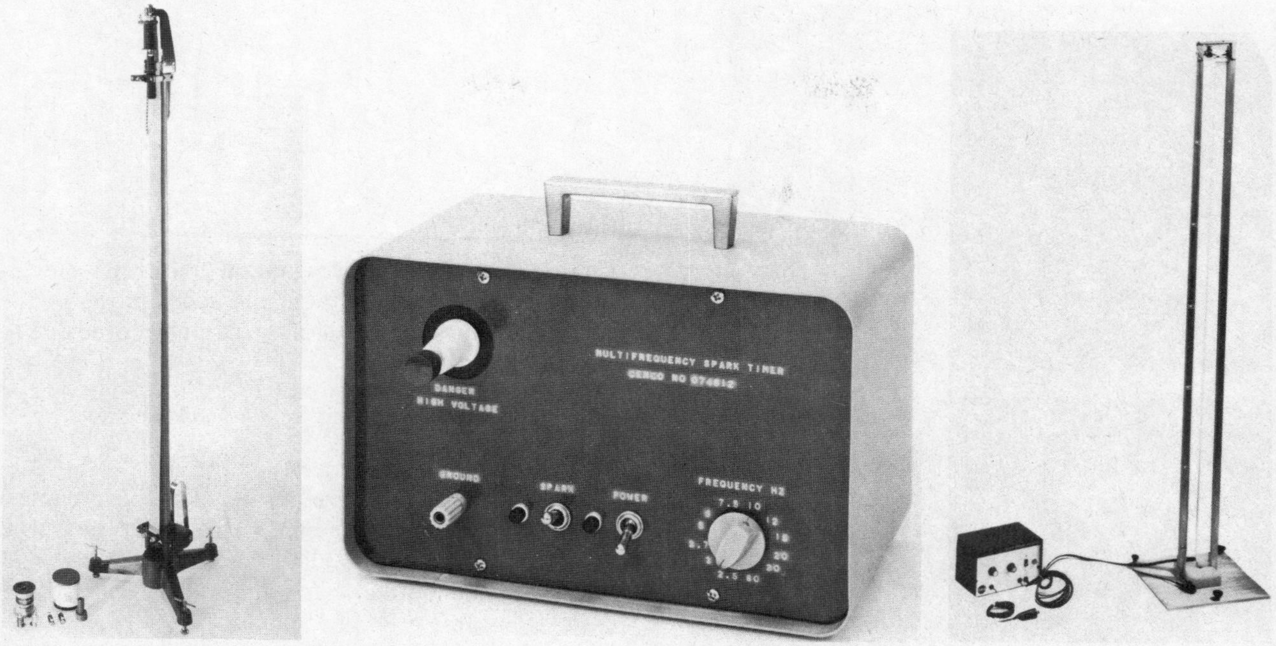

Figure 4.2 Spark timers. Types of free-fall spark-timer apparatuses. (Photos courtesy of (left and center) Central Scientific Co., Inc.; (right) Harvard Apparatus, Inc., S. Natick, MA 01760)

($y = mx + b$) with a slope $m = \Delta v/\Delta t = g$ and an intercept $b = v_o$, the initial velocity. Recall that t in Eq. 4.3 is really a time *interval* measured from an arbitrary starting time $t_o = 0$. At this time, the velocity of the object is v_o, which may or may not be zero.

The motion of the falling object as recorded on the experimental data tape is analyzed as follows. The average velocity $\bar{v}$ of an object traveling a distance y_i in a time t_i is defined as

$$\bar{v} = \frac{y_i}{t_i} \tag{4.4}$$

Keep in mind that y_i and t_i are really length and time *intervals* or the differences between corresponding instantaneous lengths and times. Referenced to an initial position and time (y_o and t_o), $\Delta y_i = y_i - y_o$ and $\Delta t_i = t_i - t_o$. Arbitrarily taking $y_o = 0$ and $t_o = 0$, we have $\Delta y_i = y_i$ and $\Delta t_i = t_i$. (It is these intervals that will be measured from the data tape.)

For a uniformly accelerated object (moving with a constant acceleration) as in the case of free fall, the average velocity is given by

$$\bar{v} = \frac{v_i + v_o}{2} \tag{4.5}$$

where v_i and v_o are the instantaneous velocities at times t_i and t_o, respectively. (Why is this? Consult your textbook.) Then, equating the expressions for $\bar{v}$ given by Eq. 4.4 and Eq. 4.5 and solving for v_i, we have

$$\frac{v_i + v_o}{2} = \frac{y_i}{t_i}$$

and

$$v_i = \frac{2y_i}{t_i} - v_o \tag{4.6}$$

If $v_o = 0$ (i.e., the object falls from rest), then

$$v_i = \frac{2y_i}{t_i} \tag{4.7}$$

C. Linear Air Track

Types of linear air tracks are shown in Fig. 4.3. Air is supplied to the interior of the hollow track and emerges through a series of small holes in the track. This provides a cushion of air on which a car or glider travels along the track with very little friction (an example of the use of a gaseous lubricant).

To have the car move under the influence of gravity, one end of the air track is elevated on a block. The acceration of the car along the air track is then due to a component of the force due to gravity,

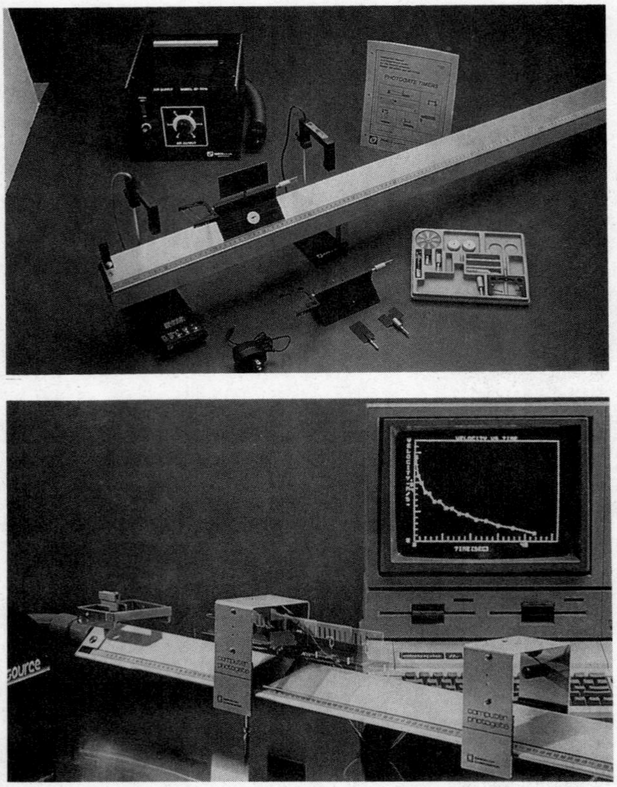

Figure 4.3 Air track systems. A blower supplies air to the track. The cars or gliders travel on a thin cushion of air with friction greatly reduced. These systems are equipped with photogates for automatic timing. (Photos courtesy of (top) PASCO Scientific; (bottom) Central Scientific Co., Inc.)

$F = ma = mg \sin \theta$ (Fig. 4.4). The acceleration a of the glider along the air track is

$$a = g \sin \theta \qquad \textbf{(4.8)}$$

and from the geometry, $\sin \theta = h/L$ (side opposite the angle over the hypotenuse). Hence,

$$a = \frac{gh}{L} \qquad \textbf{(4.9)}$$

The instantaneous velocity v of the uniformly accelerating glider at a time t is given theoretically by

$$v = v_o + at \qquad \textbf{(4.10)}$$

Hence, a graph of v versus t is a straight line ($y = mx + b$) with a slope $m = a = \Delta v/\Delta t$ and an intercept $b = v_o$. If the car starts from rest, the initial velocity v_o is zero, and

$$v = at \qquad \textbf{(4.11)}$$

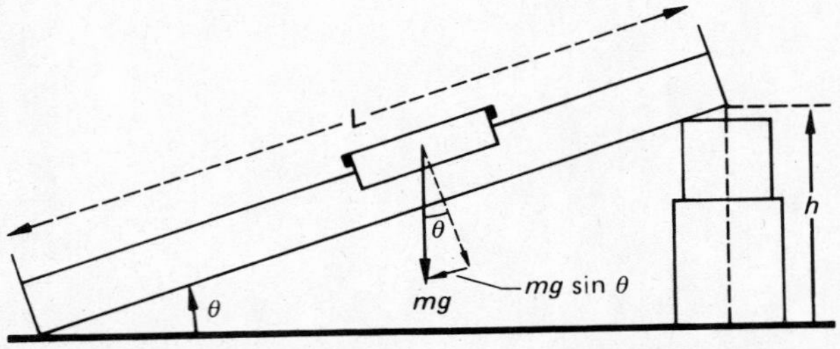

Figure 4.4 Acceleration along the air track. By elevating one end of the air track, the acceleration of the car is due to a component of the (weight) force due to gravity, $a = g \sin\theta$.

The instantaneous velocities of the car can be found from the experimental data of the measured displacements y_i of the glider along the air track at times t_i by the method given in Section III.B. In this case ($v_o = 0$), Eq. 4.6 becomes

$$v_i = \frac{2y_i}{t_i} \qquad \textbf{(4.12)}$$

IV. Experimental Procedure

A. Object in Free Fall

1. One person should drop the object and another do the timing. When someone measures time intervals with a stopwatch or timer, each measurement includes that person's reaction times in starting and stopping the clock. This will be corrected for later.

2. Drop a lead weight or a small wooden block from a fixed height y above the floor and measure its time of fall. Drop it with the arm held horizontally or with the arm held upward. Record the data for five trials in Data Table 1.

3. See Question 3 at the end of the experiment for a procedure to measure reaction time. Determine this for the person doing the timing and add to the fall times.

4. Compute the acceleration g due to gravity from Eq. 4.2 using the corrected times of fall. Find the average or mean value and the average deviation of your results from the mean (see Experiment 1). *Note:* The results obtained by this procedure may have very poor accuracy and precision. (Why?)

B. *Free-Fall Spark-Timer Apparatus*

5. Your laboratory instructor will make a data tape for you or assist you in obtaining one. Care must be taken in aligning the apparatus.

Caution: *When working with high voltages, one must be careful so as not to receive an electrical shock. Do not touch metal parts when the spark timer is on.*

6. Record the time interval of the spark timer used on the data tape and draw small circles around the burn spots so that their locations can be easily seen. Occasionally, a spot of the sequence may be missing (e.g., due to local misalignment of the wires). However, it is usually easy to tell that a spot is missing by observation of the tape. Do not try to guess where the spot should be. Simply make a mark on the tape to indicate that a spot is missing.

7. Draw a straight line through each spot perpendicular to the length of the tape. Using the line through the beginning spot as a reference ($y_o = 0$), measure the distance of each spot line from the reference line (y_1, y_2, y_3, etc.). Write the measured value of the distance on the tape by each respective spot line.

Making use of the known spark-timer interval, write the time taken for the object to fall a given distance on the tape by each spot line taking $t_o = 0$ at $y_o = 0$. For example, if the timer interval is $\frac{1}{60}$ s, the time interval between the reference line ($y_o = 0$) and the first spot line (y_1) is $t_1 = \frac{1}{60}$ s, and the time taken to fall to the second spot line (y_2) is $t_2 = \frac{1}{60} + \frac{1}{60} = \frac{2}{60} = \frac{1}{30}$ s. (Do not forget to account for the time intervals associated with missing spots, if any.)

8. Record the data measured from the tape in Data Table 2. Using Eq. 4.7, compute the instantaneous velocity of the falling object at each spot line from the experimental data and record.

9. At this point, you should realize that the instantaneous velocities given by Eq. 4.7 ($v_i = 2y_i/t_i$) are *not* the actual instantaneous velocities of the falling object, since it had a nonzero initial velocity or was in motion at the first spot line (y_o). Equation 4.6 really applies to the situation, and $2y_i/t_i = v_i + v_o$. Note that the instantaneous velocities you computed ($2y_i/t_i$) included v_o.

Even so, plot the computed v_i's on a v versus t graph and determine the slope. This will still be an experimental value of g. Compute the percent error of your experimental result. (Accepted value, $g = 9.80\ \text{m/s}^2 = 980\ \text{cm/s}^2$.)

10. You will notice on your graph that the line does not intercept the Y axis at the origin ($t = 0$). This is because $t = 0$ usually was not measured at the actual time of release, but at some time later. From Eqs. 4.6 and 4.3 we see that at $t = 0$ in the measurement time frame

$$\frac{2y_o}{t_o} = 2v_o\ [= v_{i_{(t\,=\,0)}}]$$

where y_o and t_o are the distance and time measured by the zero values *from* the point of release.

The initial velocity at the first line spot is then $v_o = y_o/t_o$. This gives you the extra bonus of being able to determine v_o from your graph, since

$$v_o = \frac{v_{i_{(t\,=\,0)}}}{2}$$

where $v_{i_{(t\,=\,0)}}$ is the intercept value. Compute the initial velocity the falling object had at your first line spot and record in Data Table 2.

C. *Linear Air Track*

11. The air track should be set up and leveled by the instructor or laboratory assistant. *Do not* attempt to make any adjustments of the air track. Ask your instructor for assistance if you need it.

12. Turn on the air supply and place the car in motion by applying a small force on the car in a direction parallel to the air track. *Do not* attempt to move the car on the air track if the air supply is not turned on. Use the same force for each trial, for example, by compressing a spring attached to the car.

13. Using laboratory timers or stopwatches, determine the times required for the car to travel several convenient distances, such as 0.20 m, 0.40 m, 0.50 m, 0.75 m, and so on. Record the times and distances in Data Table 3.*

* If electronic photogate timers are available, your instructor will give you instruction in their use. Electronic timing greatly improves the accuracy and precision of the results. (Why?)

Several students should work together, each with a timer, taking a time reading as the car passes his or her assigned distance mark. Make several practice trials before taking actual data. (Remember that the distances are length intervals and need not be measured from the end of the air track. Make use of as much of the air track as is conveniently possible.)

14. After completing procedure 13, ask the instructor to elevate one end of the air track on a block or obtain permission to do so. Measure h and L (See Fig. 4.4) and enter in Data Table 3.

15. Start the car from rest near the elevated end of the air track. (To minimize error, it is better to put a block or pencil in front of the car and pull this away smoothly rather than releasing the car by hand.) Measure and record the times required for the car to travel the distances listed in Data Table 3. Use the experimental method described in procedure 13.

16. Have the end of the air track elevated to a different height and repeat the time measurements for this height.

17. Using Eq. 4.12, compute the instantaneous velocity of the car for each of the times in the three experimental sets of data in Data Table 3.

18. Plot v versus t for each case on the same graph, and determine the slope of each line.

19. Using Eq. 4.9, compute an experimental value of the acceleration due to gravity, g, for each of the elevated air-track cases. Compute the percent error for each experimental result.

Name ______________________ Section ____________ Date ____________

Lab Partner(s) ______________________________________

EXPERIMENT 4

Uniformly Accelerated Motion

Laboratory Report

A. Object in Free Fall

DATA TABLE 1

Purpose: To determine *g* experimentally.

y ____________

Trial	Time of fall, *t* ( )	Time with reaction time correction ( )	Calculated *g* ( )	Deviation ( )
1				
2				
3				
4				
5				
	Mean (average) value			

Calculations
(show work)

Result (average value ± mean deviation) ____________

Don't forget units

(continued)

B. Free-Fall Timer Apparatus

DATA TABLE 2
Purpose: To determine g experimentally.

Spark-timer interval ________________

Distance, y_i ( )		Time, t_i ( )		Computed velocity, $v_i = 2y_i/t_i$ ( )	
y_1		t_1		v_1	
y_2		t_2		v_2	
y_3		t_3		v_3	
y_4		t_4		v_4	
y_5		t_5		v_5	
y_6		t_6		v_6	
y_7		t_7		v_7	
y_8		t_8		v_8	
y_9		t_9		v_9	
y_{10}		t_{10}		v_{10}	
y_{11}		t_{11}		v_{11}	
y_{12}		t_{12}		v_{12}	
y_{13}		t_{13}		v_{13}	
y_{14}		t_{14}		v_{14}	
y_{15}		t_{15}		v_{15}	

Calculations
(show work)

Value of g from graph ________________
(attach graph to lab report) (units)

Percent error ________________

Initial velocity at y_o ________________

Name ______________________ Section ______________ Date ______________
Lab Partner(s) ____

EXPERIMENT 4 **Laboratory Report**

C. Linear Air Track

DATA TABLE 3
Purpose: To determine g experimentally.

Distances ( )					
1. Time, t_i ( ) 1					
Level air track 2					
3					
Average					
Computed v_i ( )					
2. Time, t_i ( ) 1					
Elevated air track 2					
h_1 ______ 3					
Average					
Computed v_i ( )					
3. Time, t_i ( ) 1					
Elevated air track 2					
h_2 ______ 3					
Average					
Computed v_i ( )					

Calculations
(show work)

(continued)

Length of air track, L ________________

Slopes of graphs 1. ________________

2. ________________

3. ________________

Experimental values of g *(computed from data)* 1. ________________

2. ________________

3. ________________

Percent error 1. ________________

2. ________________

3. ________________

QUESTIONS

A. *Object in Free Fall*

1. In the experiment, the air resistance is considered to be negligible. Suppose that it were not. How would this affect the experimentally determined value of g?

2. What is probably the greatest source of error in the experimental procedure? Is it random or systematic error?

3. (a) Have someone hold a meterstick (or ruler) vertically by one end. The person who did the timing should stand close by, with the thumb and fingers of one hand on either side of the meterstick, ready to grasp it when it is dropped. The person holding the meterstick should not warn the other person when the stick is going to be released; he or she should simply be told to grasp the stick as soon as he or she can.

   Note the mark on the meterstick at the top of the grasper's hand before release. From the distance of fall as measured on the caught meterstick and the accepted value of g, obtain an estimate of the reaction time of the person grasping the meterstick. Since $v_o = 0$, then $y = \frac{1}{2}gt^2$, and if the stick falls the distance y before being grasped, the reaction time is on the order of $t = (2y/g)^{\frac{1}{2}}$. (Several trials should be made to obtain an average reaction time.)

(b) Explain how reaction time would affect the experimental results if one person does the releasing and timing, and if one person releases and a second person times.

B. Free-Fall Spark-Timer Apparatus

1. Suppose that a different spark-timer interval were used. How would this affect the slope of the graph of v versus t?

2. What would be the shape of the curve of a graph y versus t of the experimental data?

3. If $t = 0$ were taken to be associated with some line spot other than y_o (for example, y_3 instead), how would this affect the v versus t graph?

(continued)

4. Calculate v_o directly from the first two measurement entries in Data Table 2, using the equation $v_o = 2y_1/t_1 - y_2/t_2$. (Your instructor can derive this for you.) How does this compare with the value determined from your graph?

C. Linear Air Track

1. What are the major sources of error in this procedure?

2. What would be the shapes of the curves of a graph of y versus t of the data in each experimental case? How would you determine the value of the car's acceleration from a graph using only y and t values (i.e., not computing v_i)?

3. What is the physical significance of the slope of the graph for the case of the level air track?

4. What is the maximum possible value of the slope of a v versus t curve for a car released from rest on an air track elevated at one end? Describe the experimental setup in this case.

Name ______________________ Section ______________ Date ______________
Lab Partner(s) ____

E X P E R I M E N T 5

The Addition and Resolution of Vectors: The Force Table

Advance Study Assignment

Read the experiment and answer the following questions.

1. What is the difference between a scalar and a vector?

2. How are vectors represented graphically, and how may they be distinguished from scalars when written?

3. What is meant by drawing a vector to scale? Give an example.

4. Describe the parallelogram method of vector addition.

5. How may the resultant of two vectors be computed analytically from a vector parallelogram?

(continued)

6. What is the cosine of 225° (cos 225°)?

7. What is the polygon method of vector addition?

8. What is meant by resolving a vector into components?

9. Describe the component method of vector addition.

10. On the force table, what is the difference between the equilibrant and the resultant? Why is only one actually determined experimentally?

EXPERIMENT 5

The Addition and Resolution of Vectors: The Force Table

I. Introduction and Objectives

A **vector** is a mathematical concept to represent quantities that have magnitude *and* direction. Such quantities include displacement, velocity, acceleration, and force. Because vectors have the property of direction, the common method of addition, scalar addition, is not applicable to vector quantities. A scalar is a quantity with only magnitude (and units), such as speed or temperature.

To find the resultant or **vector sum** of two or more vectors, special methods of vector addition must be used. The basic methods of vector addition are the graphical parallelogram and triangle methods and the analytical component method. In this experiment we shall investigate these methods in the addition of force vectors. The results of the graphical and analytical methods will be compared with experimental results obtained from a force table. The experimental arrangements of forces (vectors) will physically illustrate the principles of the methods of vector addition.

After performing this experiment and analyzing the data, you should be able to do the following:

1. Add a set of vectors graphically to find the resultant.
2. Add a set of vectors analytically to find the resultant.
3. Appreciate the differences between graphical and analytical methods of vector addition.

II. Equipment Needed

- Force table with four pulleys
- Four weight hangers
- Set of slotted weights (masses), including three of 50 g and three of 100 g
- String
- Protractor
- Ruler
- Level
- 3 sheets of Cartesian graph paper

III. Theory

A. *Methods of Vector Addition: Graphical*

Parallelogram Method

Vectors are represented graphically by arrows. The length of a vector arrow (drawn to scale on graph paper) is proportional to the magnitude of the vector, and the arrow points in the direction of the vector. The length scale is arbitrary and usually selected for convenience and so that the vector graph fits nicely on the graph paper. A typical scale for a force vector might be 1 cm:10 N. That is, each centimeter of vector length represents ten newtons. The *scaling factor* in this case in terms of force/unit length is 10 N/cm. (Note the similarity with the common food cost factor of price/lb, for example, 10 ¢/lb.)

To add two vectors $\mathbf{A} + \mathbf{B}$ (Fig. 5.1a), the parallelogram of which **A** and **B** are adjacent sides is formed. The arrow diagonal of the parallelogram **R** is the resultant or vector sum of $\mathbf{A} + \mathbf{B}$ or, by vector addition, $\mathbf{R} = \mathbf{A} + \mathbf{B}$. The magnitude R of the resultant vector is proportional to the length of the diagonal arrow, and the direction of the resultant vector is that of the diagonal arrow **R**. The direction of **R** may be specified as being at an angle θ relative to **A**.

Triangle Method

An equivalent method of finding **R** is to place the vectors to be added "head to tail" (head of **A** to tail of **B**, Fig. 5.1b). Vector arrows may be moved as long as they remain pointed in the same direction. The head-to-tail method gives the same resultant as the parallelogram does.

Polygon Method

If more than two vectors are added, the head-to-tail method forms a polygon (Fig. 5.1c). For three vectors, the resultant $\mathbf{R} = \mathbf{A} + \mathbf{B} + \mathbf{C}$ is the vector arrow from the tail of the **A** arrow to the head of the **C** vector. The length (magnitude) and the angle of orientation of **R** can be measured from the vector diagram. Note that this is equivalent to applying the head-to-tail method (two vectors) twice (**A** and **B** are added to give $\mathbf{R}_1$, then **C** is added to $\mathbf{R}_1$ to give **R**).

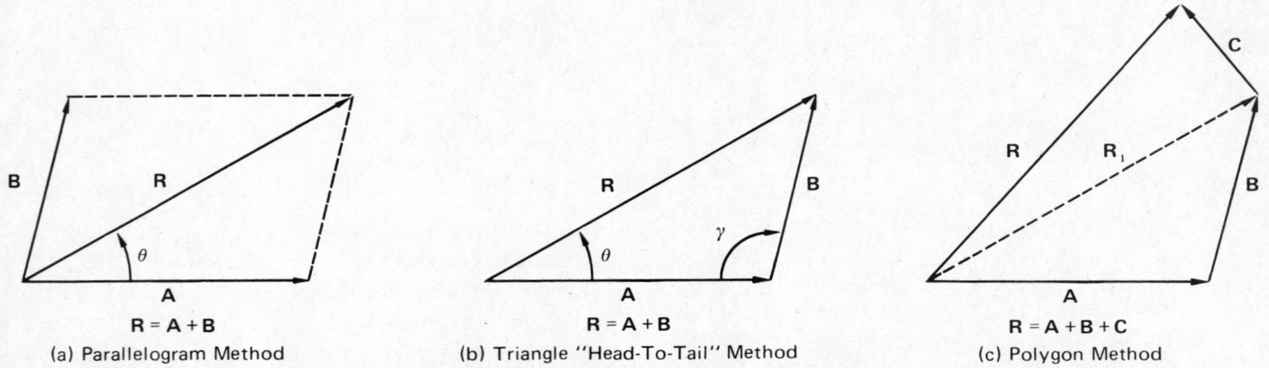

Figure 5.1 Vector addition. Different methods of vector addition. See text for descriptions.

The magnitude (length) R and the orientation angle θ of the resultant vector **R** in a graphical method can be measured directly from the vector diagram using a ruler and a protractor.

Example 5.1 To illustrate scaling and the graphical triangle method, let **A** and **B** represent weight forces (*mg*) with masses of 0.250 kg and 0.150 kg at angles of 0° and 60°, respectively. That is, the vectors have magnitudes of

$$A = m_A g = (0.250 \text{ kg})g = 2.45 \text{ N}$$
$$B = m_B g = (0.150 \text{ kg})g = 1.47 \text{ N}$$

where $g = 9.80 \text{ m/s}^2$ is the acceleration due to gravity.*

Then, choosing a scaling factor, say 0.50 N/cm, we find a vector length by dividing its magnitude by the scaling factor (magnitude/scaling factor). Note the unit cancellation:

$$A\text{:} \quad 2.45 \text{ N}/(0.50 \text{ N/cm}) = 4.9 \text{ cm}$$
$$B\text{:} \quad 1.47 \text{ N}/(0.50 \text{ N/cm}) = 2.9 \text{ cm}$$

Here, the 0.50 N/cm scaling factor was chosen so as to keep Fig. 5.2 an appropriate size. In drawing your vector diagrams, you should choose a scaling factor that will use most of the space provided on the graph paper—much as in plotting a graph in Experiment 1. Also, a factor with two significant figures was chosen because graph paper grids are usually not fine enough to plot more digits accurately.

The triangle has been drawn in Fig. 5.2, where **R** = **A** + **B**. The **R** vector is measured (with ruler and protractor) to have a length of 6.8 cm and a direction angle of θ = 22° relative to the **A** vector. The magnitude of **R** in newtons is found using the scaling factor:

$$\begin{aligned} R &= (\text{scaling factor})(\text{measured length}) \\ &= (0.50 \text{ N/cm})(6.8 \text{ cm}) = 3.4 \text{ N} \end{aligned}$$

B. Analytical

TRIANGLE METHOD

The magnitude of **R** in Fig. 5.2 can be computed from the law of cosines if the angle γ (angle opposite **R**) is known. Knowing γ and with the given magnitudes of **A** and **B**,

$$R^2 = A^2 + B^2 - 2AB \cos \gamma \qquad \textbf{(5.1)}$$

The angle θ (between **R** and **A**) can then be computed using the law of sines because the magnitudes of sides **B** and **R** are known, and

$$\frac{B}{\sin \theta} = \frac{R}{\sin \gamma} \qquad \textbf{(5.2)}$$

From Example 5.1, the magnitudes of **A** and **B** are $(0.250)g$ N and $(0.150)g$ N, respectively; and as can be seen directly from Fig. 5.2, γ = 120°. (Why?) Then, using the law of cosines (Eq. 5.1):

$$\begin{aligned} R^2 &= A^2 + B^2 - 2AB \cos \gamma \\ &= [(0.250)g]^2 + [(0.150)g]^2 \\ &\quad - 2[(0.250)g]\,[(0.150)g] \cos 120° \\ &= (0.0625)g^2 + (0.0225)g^2 \\ &\quad - (0.0750)g^2\,(-0.500)^* \\ &= (0.1225)g^2 \end{aligned}$$

and

* The magnitude of the (weight) force vectors are in general given in the form $R = mg = (0.150)g$ N, for example, where it is understood that the mass is in kilograms and g is the acceleration due to gravity. It is convenient to leave g in symbolic form so as to avoid numerical calculations until necessary. This is similar to carrying along π in symbolic form in equations. Also, note that the masses of the laboratory "weights" usually have values stamped in grams. Don't forget to change grams to kilograms when working in the SI: for example, 150 g = 0.150 kg.

* Value obtained by calculator, or from trig table with cos 120° = cos (180° − 120°) = −cos 60° using the trigonometric identity cos $(A - B)$ = cos A cos B + sin A sin B.

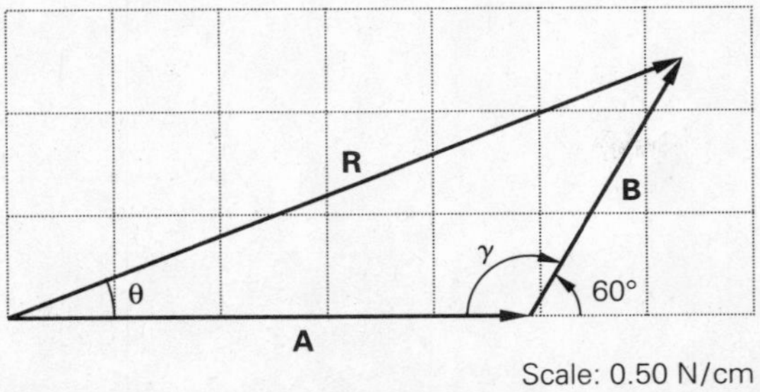

Figure 5.2 Drawing to scale. Figures are often scaled down so as to maintain an appropriate size. Here, the vector triangle is drawn to scale, with a scaling factor of 0.50 N/cm.

$$R = (0.350)g = (0.350 \text{ kg}) (9.80 \text{ m/s}^2) = 3.43 \text{ N}$$

(Units were neglected in the initial calculation for convenience.)

The directional angle θ may be found using the law of sines (Eq. 5.2):

$$\theta = \sin^{-1}\left(\frac{B \sin \gamma}{R}\right)$$

$$= \sin^{-1}\left(\frac{0.150g \sin 120°}{0.350g}\right) = 21.8°$$

Remember that this is the angle between vectors **R** and **A**.

Component Method

If two vectors **A** and **B** are at right (90°) angles (Fig. 5.3a), then the magnitude of their resultant is given by the **Pythagorean theorem**, $R = \sqrt{A^2 + B^2}$ (the hypotenuse of a right triangle is equal to the square root of the sum of the squares of the legs of the triangle). Notice that the law of cosines reduces to this formula with $\gamma = 90°$ (because $\cos 90° = 0$). The angle of orientation is given by $\tan \theta = B/A$, or $\theta = \tan^{-1}(B/A)$.

By the inverse process, we may resolve a vector into x and y components (Fig. 5.3b). That is, the vector **R** is the resultant of $\mathbf{R}_x$ and $\mathbf{R}_y$, and $\mathbf{R} = \mathbf{R}_x + \mathbf{R}_y$, where $R_x = R \cos \theta$ and $R_y = R \sin \theta$. The magnitude of R is given by

$$R = \sqrt{R_x^2 + R_y^2}$$

and

$$\tan \theta = \frac{R_y}{R_x}$$

or

$$\theta = \tan^{-1}\left(\frac{R_y}{R_x}\right)$$

The vector sum of any number of vectors can be obtained by adding the x and y components of the vectors. This is illustrated in Fig. 5.4. The magnitude of the resultant is given by $R = \sqrt{R_x^2 + R_y^2}$, where $\mathbf{R}_x = \mathbf{A}_x + \mathbf{B}_x$ and $\mathbf{R}_y = \mathbf{A}_y + \mathbf{B}_y$, and $\theta = \tan^{-1}(R_y/R_x)$.

However, rather than placing the vectors head to tail as in Fig. 5.4, it is usually more convenient to

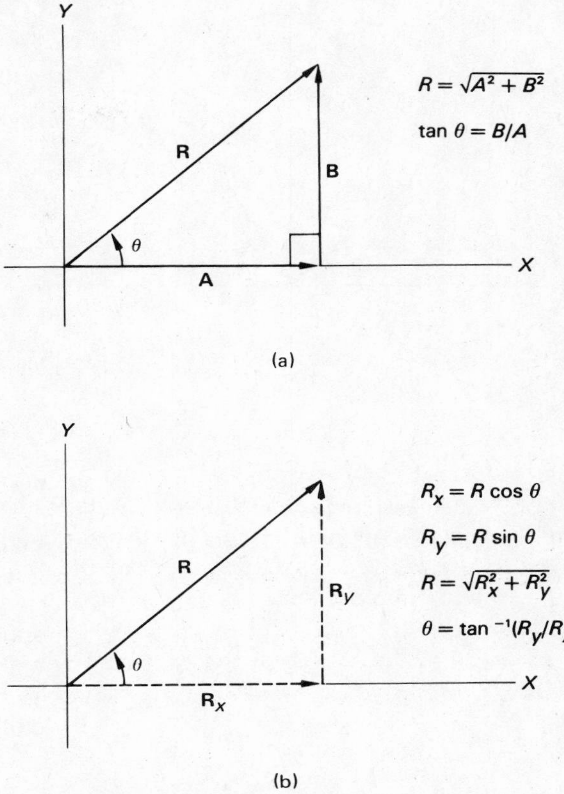

Figure 5.3 Vector resultant and components. (a) The vector addition of **A** and **B** gives the resultant **R**. (b) A vector **R** can be resolved into x and y (rectangular) components, $\mathbf{R}_x$ and $\mathbf{R}_y$, respectively.

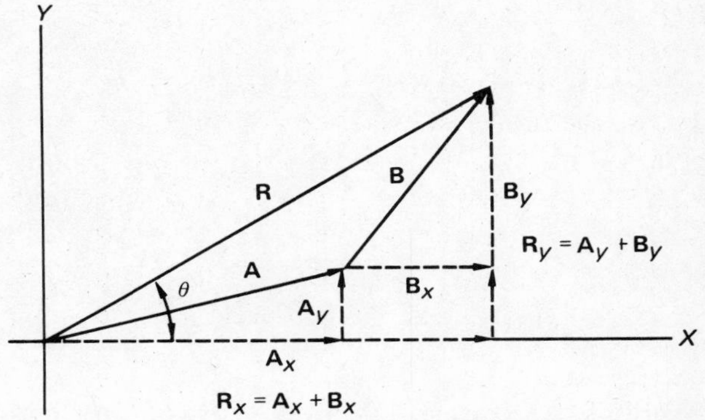

Figure 5.4 Component addition. The resultant or vector sum of any number of vectors can be obtained by adding the x and y components of the vectors, as illustrated here for two vectors. Here $\mathbf{R} = \mathbf{R}_x + \mathbf{R}_y$, where $\mathbf{R}_x = \mathbf{A}_x + \mathbf{B}_x$ and $\mathbf{R}_y = \mathbf{A}_y + \mathbf{B}_y$.

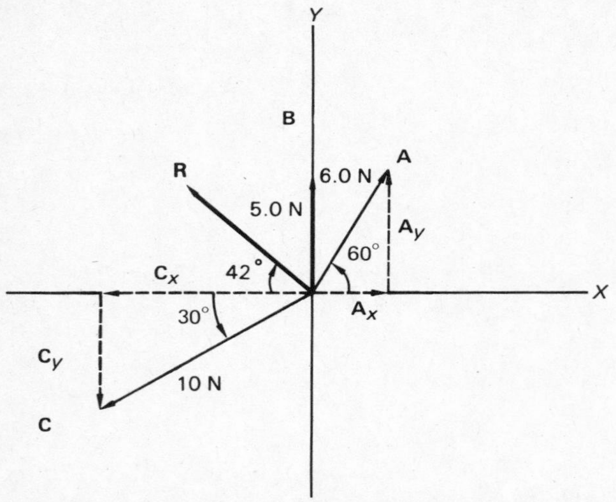

Figure 5.5 Common component method. Rather than using the head-to-tail method, it is usually more convenient to have all vectors originating from the origin when resolving into components.

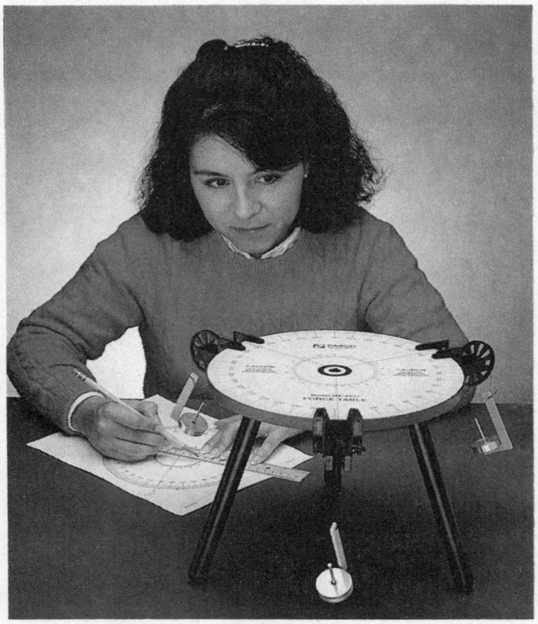

(b)

(a)

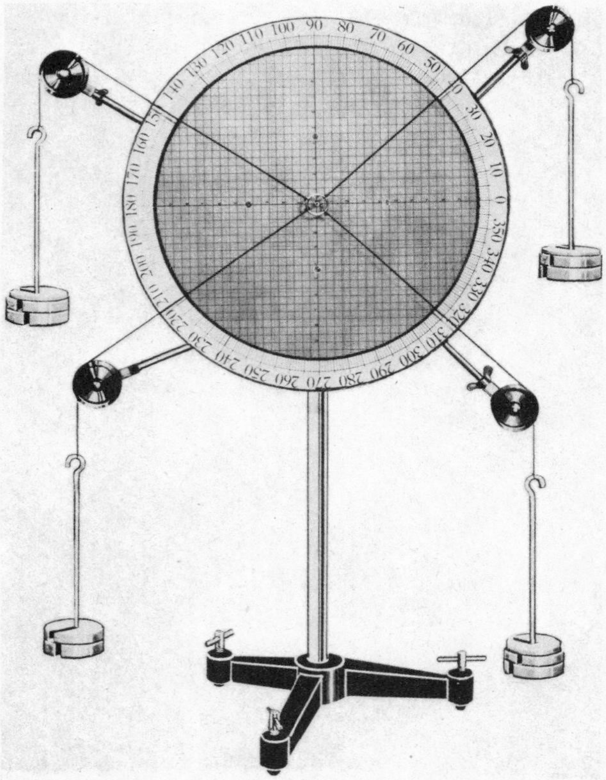

(c)

Figure 5.6 Force tables. Various types of force tables are available. The table in (c) may be used vertically for demonstration as shown, or horizontally in the laboratory. (Photos courtesy of (a) Central Scientific Co., Inc.; (b) PASCO Scientific; (c) Sargent-Welch Scientific Co.)

have all the vectors originate from the origin when resolving them into components. Applying this method analytically to **R** = **A** + **B** + **C** in Fig. 5.5, we have

$$\mathbf{R}_x = \mathbf{A}_x + \mathbf{B}_x + \mathbf{C}_x$$
$$= 6.0 \cos 60° + 0 - 10 \cos 30°$$
$$= -5.7 \text{ N}$$
$$\mathbf{R}_y = \mathbf{A}_y + \mathbf{B}_y + \mathbf{C}_y$$
$$= 6.0 \sin 60° + 5.0 - 10 \sin 30°$$
$$= 5.2 \text{ N}$$

where the component directions are indicated by the positive and negative signs (arbitrary units). Note that **B** has no x component and $\mathbf{C}_x$ and $\mathbf{C}_y$ are in the negative x and y directions, as indicated by the minus signs. Then the magnitude of **R** is (Eq. 5.3):

$$R = \sqrt{R_x^2 + R_y^2} = \sqrt{(5.7)^2 + (5.2)^2} = 7.7 \text{ N}$$

and by Eq. 5.4:

$$\theta = \tan^{-1}\left|\frac{R_y}{R_x}\right| = \tan^{-1}\left(\frac{5.2}{5.7}\right) = 42°$$

relative to the $-X$ axis (or 180° − 42° = 138° relative to the $+X$ axis). It is customary to measure all component angles from the X axis. The minus R_x and positive R_y indicate that the resultant is in the second quadrant.

C. Experimental

The Force Table

The **force table** is an apparatus that allows the experimental determination of the resultant of force vectors (Fig. 5.6). The rim of the circular table is calibrated in degrees. Weight forces are applied to a central ring by means of strings running over pulleys and attached to weight hangers. The magnitude of a force (vector) is varied by adding or removing slotted weights, and the direction is varied by moving the pulley.

The resultant of two or more forces (vectors) is found by balancing the forces with another force (weights on a hanger) so that the ring is centered around the central pin. The balancing force is *not* the resultant **R**, but rather the *equilibrant* **E**, or the force that balances the other forces and holds the ring in equilibrium.

The equilibrant is the vector force of equal magnitude, but in the *opposite direction*, to the resultant (i.e., **R** = −**E**). See Fig. 5.7. For example, if an equilibrant has a magnitude of (0.30)g N in a direction of 225° on the circular scale, the resultant of the forces has a magnitude of (0.30)g N in the opposite

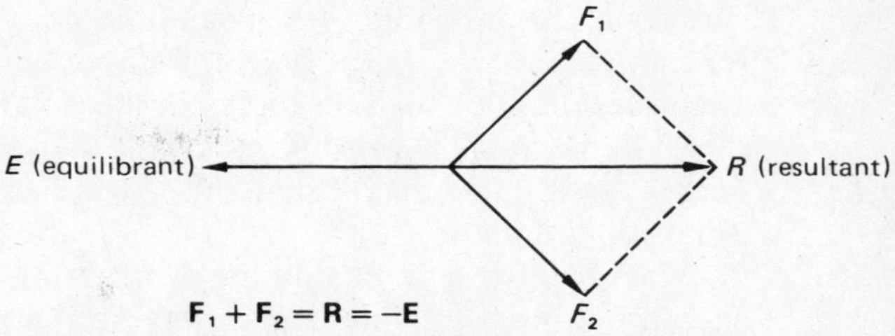

Figure 5.7 Resultant and equilibrant. On the force table, the magnitude and direction of the equilibrant **E** are measured, rather than those of the resultant **R**, and **R** = −**E**.

direction, 225° − 180° = 45°. It should be evident that the resultant cannot be determined directly from the force table. (Why?)

IV. Experimental Procedure

1. Set up the force table with strings and suspended weights and perform the following cases of vector addition.

2. *Vector addition 1.* Given two vectors with magnitudes F_1 = (0.200)g N and F_2 = (0.200)g N at 30° and 120°, respectively, find their vector sum or resultant $\mathbf{F} = \mathbf{F}_1 + \mathbf{F}_2$ by each of the following procedures. (*Note:* Orientation angles of vectors are given relative to the 0° reference line or positive X axis.)
   (a) *Graphical.* Using the parallelogram method of vector addition, draw a vector diagram to scale. Use a scale such that the finished vector diagram fills about half a sheet of graph paper. Measure the magnitude and direction of the resultant (with ruler and protractor) and record the results in the data table. Save your graphical sheets to attach to the Laboratory Report.
   (b) *Analytical.* Using the law of cosines, compute the magnitude of the resultant force. Compute the angle of orientation from the relationship $\tan\theta = F_2/F_1$. (Why can you use $\tan\theta$? Remember that θ is the angle between **F** and $\mathbf{F}_1$.) Record the results in the data table.
   (c) *Experimental.* On the force table, clamp pulleys at 30° and 120° and add enough weights to each weight hanger to total 0.200 kg, so as to give weight forces of $F_1 = F_2$ = (0.200)g N in these directions. (The weight hangers usually have masses of 50 g or 0.050 kg.)

   Using a third pulley and weights, determine the magnitude and direction of the equilibrant force that maintains the central ring centered in equilibrium around the center pin. Record the magnitude and direction of the resultant of the two forces in the data table. Remember, the resultant has the same magnitude as the equilibrant but is in the opposite direction.

(*Note:* The string knots on the central ring should be of a nontightening variety so that the strings will slip freely on the ring and allow the strings to pull directly away from the center. Pulling the center ring straight up a short distance and releasing it helps adjust the friction in the pulleys as the ring vibrates up and down. When the forces are balanced, the pin may be carefully removed to see if the ring is centered around the central hole.)

3. *Vector addition 2.* Repeat procedure 2 for $F_1 = (0.200)g$ N at 20° and $F_2 = (0.150)g$ N at 80°. Use the other half sheet of graph paper from procedure 1 (a) for the graphical analysis. Be careful in the analytical analysis. Can you use $\tan\theta = F_2/F_1$ in this case?

4. *Vector addition 3.* Repeat procedure 2 with $F_1 = F_x = (0.200)g$ N (at 0°) and $F_2 = F_y = (0.150)g$ N (at 90°). In this case, $\mathbf{F} = \mathbf{F}_x + \mathbf{F}_y$, where $\mathbf{F}_x$ and $\mathbf{F}_y$ are the x and y components of $\mathbf{F}$, respectively. That is, the resultant can be resolved into these components. Use one-half of another sheet of graph paper for the graphical method.

5. *Vector resolution.* Given a force vector of $F = (0.300)g$ N at 60°, resolve the vector into its x and y components and find the magnitudes of $\mathbf{F}_x$ and $\mathbf{F}_y$ by the following procedures:

(a) *Graphical.* Draw a vector diagram to scale (on the other half sheet of graph paper used in procedure 3) with the component vectors (see Fig. 5.3b) and measure the magnitudes of $\mathbf{F}_x$ and $\mathbf{F}_y$. Record the results in the data table.

(b) *Analytical.* Compute the magnitudes of $\mathbf{F}_x$ and $\mathbf{F}_y$ (see Section III). Record the results in the data table.

(c) *Experimental.* Clamp pulleys at 240°, 90°, and 0° on the force table. Place a *total* of 0.300 kg on the 240° pulley string using a weight hanger. This force is then the equilibrant of $F = (0.300)g$ N at 60° (since 60° + 180° = 240°), which must be used on the force table rather than the force itself. Add weights to the 0° and 90° hangers until the system is in equilibrium. The 0° and 90° forces are then the $\mathbf{F}_x$ and $\mathbf{F}_y$ components, respectively, of $\mathbf{F}$. Record their magnitudes in the data table.

6. *Vector addition 4.* Given the force vectors $F_1 = (0.100)g$ N at 30°, $F_2 = (0.200)g$ N at 90°, and $F_3 = (0.30)g$ N at 225°, find the magnitude and direction of their resultant $\mathbf{F} = \mathbf{F}_1 + \mathbf{F}_2 + \mathbf{F}_3$ by the following procedures:

(a) *Graphical.* Use the polygon method.

(b) *Analytical.* Use the component method.

(c) *Experimental.* Use the force table. Record the results in the data table.

7. *Vector addition 5.* Instructor's choice (optional). Your instructor will give you a set of vectors to add. Record the results in the data table as you did for previous procedures.

Name ______________________ Section ______________ Date ______________

Lab Partner(s) ____

EXPERIMENT 5

The Addition and Resolution of Vectors: The Force Table

Laboratory Report

Note: Attach graphical analyses to Laboratory Report.

DATA TABLE

Purpose: To analyze results of different methods of vector addition.

	Forces ( )	Resultant R (magnitude and direction)		
		Graphical	Analytical*	Experimental
Vector addition 1	$F_1 = (0.200)g$ N, $\theta_1 = 30°$ $F_2 = (0.200)g$ N, $\theta_2 = 120°$			
Vector addition 2	$F_1 = (0.200)g$ N, $\theta_1 = 20°$ $F_2 = (0.150)g$ N, $\theta_2 = 80°$			
Vector addition 3	$F_1 = F_x = (0.200)g$ N, $\theta_1 = 0°$ $F_2 = F_y = (0.150)g$ N, $\theta_2 = 90°$			
Vector resolution	$F = (0.300)g$ N, $\theta = 60°$	F_x F_y	F_x F_y	F_x F_y
Vector addition 4	$F_1 = (0.100)g$ N, $\theta_1 = 30°$ $F_2 = (0.200)g$ N, $\theta_2 = 90°$ $F_3 = (0.300)g$ N, $\theta_3 = 225°$			
Vector addition 5				

* Show analytical calculations below.

Calculations
(attach additional sheet if necessary)

Don't forget units

(continued)

QUESTIONS

1. Considering the graphical and analytical methods for obtaining the resultant, which method is more accurate? Give the probable sources of error for each method.

2. Vector subtraction (**A** − **B**) is a special case of vector addition, since **A** − **B** = **A** + (−**B**). Suppose that the cases of Vector Addition 1, 2, and 3 in this experiment were vector subtraction ($\mathbf{F}_1 - \mathbf{F}_2$).
   (a) What effect would this have on the directions of the resultants? (Do not calculate explicitly. Simply state in which quadrant the resultant would be in each case.)

   (b) Would the magnitude of the resultant be different for vector subtraction than for vector addition in each case? If so, state whether the subtractive resultant would be greater or less than the additive resultant.

3. A picture hangs on a nail as shown in Fig. 5.8. If the tension T in each string segment is 3.5 N,
   (a) what is the equilibrant or the upward reaction force of the nail;
   (b) what is the weight of the picture?

Name ______________________ Section ______________ Date ______________

Lab Partner(s) ______________________

EXPERIMENT 5 *Laboratory Report*

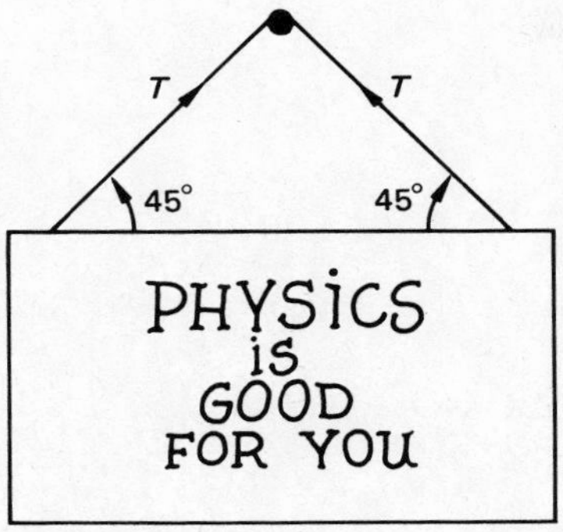

Figure 5.8 See Question 3.

4. A hospital traction device is shown in Fig. 5.9. What is (a) the horizontal force; (b) the vertical force exerted on the foot by the arrangement? (The cord transmits an undiminished tension T of 10 lb.)

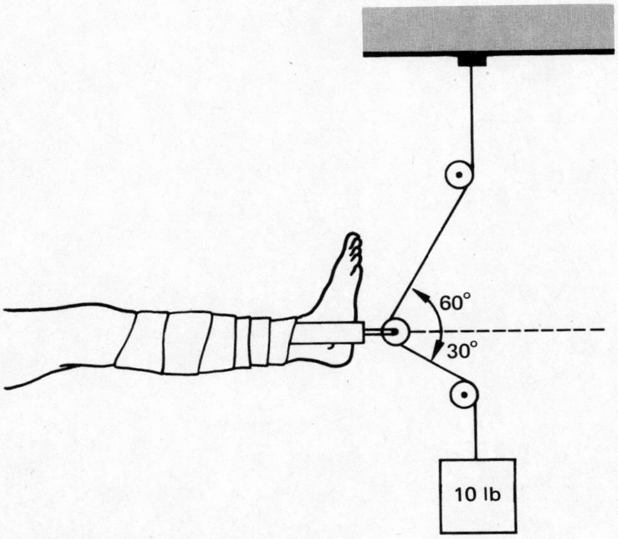

Figure 5.9 See Question 4.

Name ______________________ Section ______________ Date ______________

Lab Partner(s) ____

EXPERIMENT 6

Newton's Second Law: The Atwood Machine

Advance Study Assignment

Read the experiment and answer the following questions.

1. Write Newton's second law in mathematical form, and describe how the acceleration of an object or system varies with the unbalanced force and mass of the system.

2. What is the advantage of using an Atwood machine in measuring the acceleration of a system experimentally?

3. How does the frictional force of the pulley affect the acceleration of the system?

(continued)

4. How can the frictional force be experimentally determined, and how is this used in calculations?

5. What are F and m in Newton's second law in terms of the Atwood machine?

6. How is the acceleration of the Atwood system determined experimentally in terms of general physical principles?

Newton's Second Law: The Atwood Machine

I. Introduction and Objectives

Newton's second law of motion states that the acceleration a of an object or system is directly proportional to the unbalanced or net force $\mathbf{F}_{net}$ acting on the system and inversely proportional to the total mass m of the system ($\mathbf{a} \propto \mathbf{F}_{net}/m$), or in equation form with standard units, $\mathbf{a} = \mathbf{F}_{net}/m$ (or $\mathbf{F}_{net} = m\mathbf{a}$).

This relationship will be investigated using an **Atwood machine**, which consists of two masses connected by a string looped over a pulley (see Fig. 6.1). The Atwood machine, named after George Atwood (1746–1807), was originally used before the development of fast timing devices to determine the acceleration g due to gravity by experimentally measuring the relatively slow uniform acceleration of the system. In this experiment, however, the acceleration of the masses will be used to investigate Newton's second law. By varying the unbalanced weight force and the total mass of the system, the resulting accelerations may be determined experimentally from distance and time measurements and compared with the predictions of Newton's law.

After performing this experiment and analyzing the data, you should be able to do the following:

1. Tell how the acceleration of a system varies with changes in net force and/or mass—in particular, for
   (a) mass variations with a constant (unbalanced) force, and
   (b) force variations with constant mass.
2. Articulate the precise meanings of the variables (F, m, and a) in Newton's second law.
3. Explain how the acceleration of the masses of an Atwood machine may be determined experimentally.

II. Equipment Needed

- Pulley (preferably low-inertia, precision ball-bearing type)
- Clamps and support rods
- Two weight hangers
- Set of slotted weights, including small 5-, 2-, and 1-g weights
- Paper clips
- String
- Laboratory timer or stopwatch
- Meterstick
- 2 sheets of Cartesian graph paper

- (*Optional*) A system such as PASCO's Smart Pulley for automatic computer-interfaced measurements

III. Theory

The light string is considered to be of negligible mass. With masses m_1 and m_2 as the ascending and descending sides of the system, respectively, (Fig. 6.1), the unbalanced (net) force is

$$F_{net} = m_2 g - m_1 g = (m_2 - m_1)g \quad \textbf{(6.1)}$$

where the friction and inertia of the pulley are neglected.

By Newton's second law,

$$F_{net} = ma = (m_1 + m_2)a \quad \textbf{(6.2)}$$

where $m = m_1 + m_2$ is the total mass of the moving system. Then, equating Eqs. 6.1 and 6.2, we have

$$(m_2 - m_1)g = (m_1 + m_2)a$$

or

$$a = \frac{(m_2 - m_1)g}{m_1 + m_2} \quad \textbf{(6.3)}$$

In the experimental arrangement, there may be an appreciable frictional force f associated with the pulley that opposes the motion. Also, the pulley has inertia. In an attempt to take this inertia into account, we will add an equivalent mass m_{eq} to the total mass being accelerated. Hence, for better accuracy, the equation for the acceleration of the system should be modified as follows:

$$\begin{aligned} F_{net} &= F - f = (m_2 - m_1)g - f \\ &= ma = (m_1 + m_2 + m_{eq})a \end{aligned}$$

or

$$a = \frac{(m_2 - m_1)g - f}{m_1 + m_2 + m_{eq}} \quad \textbf{(6.4)}$$

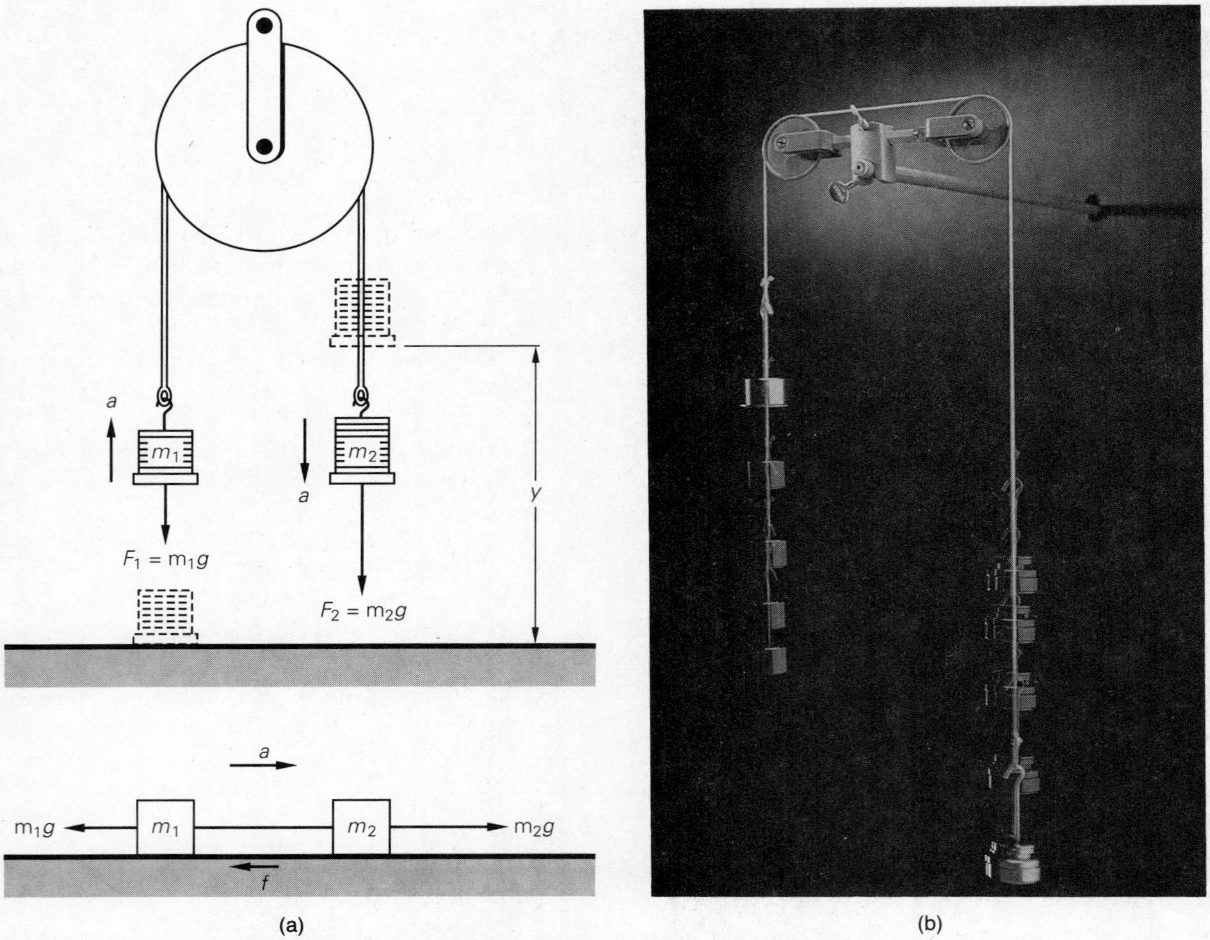

Figure 6.1 The Atwood machine. The dynamics of the Atwood machine are shown in diagram (a). A double or a single fixed pulley system is simply a "direction changer" and it is sometimes convenient to draw a horizontal diagram for analysis. The force f represents the pulley friction. A double-pulley system as in (b) eliminates the possibility of the passing weights hitting each other which may occur with a single pulley of small diameter.

If the masses of the Atwood machine move with a constant speed, the magnitude a of the acceleration of the system is zero, and

$$a = 0 = \frac{(m_2 - m_1)g - f}{m_1 + m_2 + m_{eq}}$$

or

$$f = (m_2 - m_1)g = m_f g \qquad \textbf{(6.5)}$$
(uniform speed)

which provides a method of determining the magnitude of the frictional force of the pulley, or the mass m_f needed to provide the weight to balance the frictional force.

Hence, the expression for the theoretical acceleration of the system (Eq. 6.4) may be written

$$a_t = \frac{(m_2 - m_1 - m_f)g}{m_1 + m_2 + m_{eq}} \qquad \textbf{(6.6)}$$

where a_t is used to distinguish the theoretical acceleration from the experimentally measured acceleration a_m. Thus, part of the weight of m_2 goes into balancing or canceling the frictional force of the pulley. In the experimental acceleration trials, the m_f determined in each case is left on the descending hanger as part of m_2 to compensate for the frictional force.

To determine the acceleration of the system experimentally so that it may be compared to that predicted by Eq. 6.6, the time t for the descending mass to fall through a given distance y is measured. Then, using the kinematic equation

$$y = v_o t + \tfrac{1}{2}at^2$$

with the mass starting from rest ($v_o = 0$), we have

$$y = \tfrac{1}{2}at^2$$

or

$$a_m = \frac{2y}{t^2} \tag{6.7}$$

where a_m is the experimentally measured acceleration.

When a_m is determined experimentally using distance and time measurements, friction and pulley inertia are involved. These are taken into account in the theoretical expression (Eq. 6.6), so the experimental and theoretical values of a will be more comparable. Even so, keep in mind that these are approximations and the percent differences may be large. The main purpose of the experiment is to demonstrate how the acceleration of a system depends on the net force and total mass.

IV. Experimental Procedure*

1. Set up the Atwood machine as shown in Fig. 6.1. Use enough string so that the distance of travel (y) is slightly less than 1m for convenient measuring. (To measure y, hold one hanger against the floor and measure from the floor to the bottom of the other hanger.)

As noted in the Theory section, the pulley contributes to the inertia of the system as though an "equivalent mass," m_{eq}, were part of the total mass being accelerated. The instructor will provide the value of m_{eq} or tell you how to measure it (*Instructor's Resource Manual*). Record the value of m_{eq} in the data tables.

A. *Varying the Total Mass (Unbalanced Force Constant)*

2. Begin with the descending mass (m_2) and the ascending mass (m_1) each equal to 50 g, i.e., the masses of the hangers alone. With $m_1 = m_2$, the system is in equilibrium—equal forces, $m_1g = m_2g$. In the absence of friction, a slight tap or momentary force applied to m_2 should set the system in uniform motion (constant speed). Why? However, because of the opposing frictional force, the motion will not persist.

3. Add small masses to m_2 until a downward push causes m_2 to descend with a uniform (constant) velocity. (See "Comments on Experimental Technique" at the end of the Procedure section.) Apply a sufficient push so the masses move at a reasonable speed; they should not move too slowly. You may find it easier to recognize uniform motion by observing the rotating pulley rather than the masses.

Record m_1 and m_2 in Data Table 1 in the first column marked (*). These values are used to calculate the frictional mass, $m_f = m_2 - m_1$, needed in the theoretical calculation of the acceleration of the system (Eq. 6.6).

4. **(a)** Add 10 g to m_2, leaving m_f in place. This creates an unbalanced force that should cause the system to accelerate from rest. Measure the distance y. Record y, m_1, and the new value of m_2 in Data Table 1 (Trial 1).*

(b) Make three independent measurements of the time it takes for m_2 to travel the distance y from rest. Record the data under Trial 1. (See "Comments on Experimental Technique" at the end of the Procedure section.)

(c) Remove m_f and the 10-g mass before proceeding to the next trial.

5. **(a)** Add 100 g to each hanger for a total of 150 g each.

(b) Repeat procedure 3 (measurement of frictional mass) and record data in the next (*) column in Data Table 1.

(c) Repeat procedure 4 (measurement of acceleration with a net 10-g mass imbalance). Record the data in the Trial 2 column. The calculations for Trial 2 should utilize the value of m_f obtained for the immediately preceding (*) column. *Note:* The values of m_f and y should be remeasured for each of the trials in Data Table 1. As the total mass is changed, the friction will change likewise. Even the length of the string (y distance) may vary noticeably because of stretching.

6. Repeat procedures 3 and 4 with another 100 g added to each hanger for a total of 250 g each. (The mass of m_1 should be 250 g for this trial.)

7. Repeat procedures 3 and 4 with another 100 g added to each hanger for a total of 350 g each. (The mass of m_1 should be 350 g for this trial.)

* Refinements in the Experimental Procedure were developed by Professor I. L. Fischer, Bergen Community College, New Jersey.

* The data tables are arranged to facilitate data taking and analysis. The upper (seven) rows include all the experimental measurements, while the lower (six) rows are for calculations based on these measurements.

B. *Varying the Unbalanced Force (Total Mass Constant)*

8. Begin with an ascending mass $m_1 = 260$ g (50-g hanger + 200 + 5 + 2 + 2 + 1-g masses) and a similar descending mass $m_2 = 260$ g (50-g hanger + 200 + 10-g masses).*

9. Measure the frictional mass as in procedure 3. Record the data in the (*) column in Data Table 2. The value of m_f from these data may be used in the calculations for all trials in Data Table 2, since the total mass (and presumably the friction) will now be constant.

10. Leaving m_f in place, transfer 1 g from m_1 to m_2 in order to create a net unbalanced force without affecting the total mass. Make three measurements of the travel time as in procedure 4. Record all pertinent data in the Trial 5 column.

11. Leaving m_f and the previously transferred 1-g mass in place,
(a) transfer an additional 2 g for Trial 6;
(b) transfer an additional 2 g for Trial 7;
(c) transfer an additional 5 g for Trial 8. (The final net unbalanced mass, $m_2 - m_1 - m_f$, should be 20 g.)

* Mass increments larger than 1 g and 2 g may have to be used, depending on the pulley friction. The friction may not be uniform, so a greater mass difference may be needed to initiate motion in procedures 10 and 11.

C. *Comments on Experimental Technique*

12. Measure the frictional mass to a precision of $\pm \frac{1}{2}$ g. Fine adjustment of the descending mass may be made by using small "custom" masses (paper clips) as needed. These paper clips can be attached to the cord just above the m_2 hanger. Good precision is necessary for good results because the frictional force is comparable in magnitude to the accelerating force. Small errors in the frictional masses may create large experimental errors.

13. The masses must start from rest during the acceleration trials. A good technique is as follows:
(a) Hold m_1 down against the floor;
(b) Simultaneously release m_1 and start the timer;
(c) Stop the timer at the instant m_2 strikes the floor.
The best results are obtained when the same person releases m_1 and operates the timer.

14. Some of the masses may be jolted off the hangers by the impact on hitting the floor. It may be helpful to place a shock-absorbing pad on the floor. Also one lab partner should attend to the upper weight to prevent it, or some of it, from falling.

15. Take turns at each task.

Name ______________________ Section ______________ Date ______________

Lab Partner(s) ____

E X P E R I M E N T 6

Newton's Second Law: The Atwood Machine

Laboratory Report

DATA TABLE 1

Purpose: To investigate $a = F/m$ by holding F constant.

m_{eq} ________ ( )		Trial							
		*	1	*	2	*	3	*	4
Descending mass m_2 ( )									
Ascending mass m_1 ( )									
Distance of travel y ( )									
Time of travel t ( )	Run 1								
	Run 2								
	Run 3								
	Average								
Measured acceleration $a_m = 2y/t^2$ ( )									
Total mass $= m_1 + m_2 + m_{eq}$ ( )									
Measured frictional mass $m_f = m_2 - m_1$									
Net force $= (m_2 - m_1 - m_f)g$ ( )									
Theoretical acceleration $a_t = \frac{\text{Net force}}{\text{Total mass}}$									
Percent difference between a_m and a_t									

*Measurement of frictional mass, m_f. Masses move with constant velocities when given an initial push.

Calculations
(show work)

Don't forget units

(continued)

Calculations
(show work)

DATA TABLE 2
Purpose: To investigate $a = F/m$ by holding m constant.

m_{eq} ________ ( )		Trial				
		*	5	6	7	8
Descending mass m_2 ( )						
Ascending mass m_1 ( )						
Distance of travel y ( )						
Time of travel t ( )	Run 1					
	Run 2					
	Run 3					
	Average					
Measured acceleration $a_m = 2y/t^2$ ( )						
Total mass $= m_1 + m_2 + m_{eq}$ ( )						
Measured frictional mass $m_f = m_2 - m_1$						
Net force $=$ $(m_2 - m_1 - m_f)g$ ( )						
Theoretical acceleration $a_t = \frac{\text{Net force}}{\text{Total mass}}$						
Percent difference between a_m and a_t						

*Measurement of frictional mass, m_f. Masses move with constant velocities when given an initial push.

Name ______________________ Section ______________ Date ______________

Lab Partner(s) ____

EXPERIMENT 6 *Laboratory Report*

Calculations
(show work)

QUESTIONS

1. In the experiment, should the mass of the string be added to the total mass moved by the unbalanced force for better accuracy? Explain.

2. Complete the following sentences:
   (a) When the unbalanced force increases (total mass remaining constant), the acceleration of the system ______________.
   (b) When the total mass that is accelerating increases (unbalanced force remaining constant), the acceleration of the system ______________.

(Questions 3 and 4 provide practice in plotting straight-line forms.)

3. Using the data in Data Table 2 (constant total mass), plot a_m versus $(m_2 - m_1)$ for each trial and draw a straight line that best fits the data. Find the slope and intercept of the line and enter the values below.

   Rewrite Eq. 6.6 in slope-intercept form ($y = mx + b$) and, using the data in Trial 6, compute the slope and intercept. (Show calculations.) Compare and comment on your results.

	From graph	From Eq. 6.6
Slope	______________ (units)	______________ (units)
Intercept	______________ (units)	______________ (units)

(continued)

4. Using the Data Table 1 (constant unbalanced force), plot $1/a_m$ versus $(m_1 + m_2)$ for each trial and draw a straight line that best fits the data. Perform the same kind of analysis as in Question 3 using the data in Trial 2 for computing the slope and intercept.

	From graph	From Eq. 6.6
Slope	______ (units)	______ (units)
Intercept	______ (units)	______ (units)

Name ______________________ Section ______________ Date ______________

Lab Partner(s) ____

EXPERIMENT 7

Conservation of Linear Momentum

Advance Study Assignment

Read the experiment and answer the following questions.

1. What is the condition for the conservation of linear momentum of a system?

2. What is meant when it is said that a quantity, such as linear momentum, is conserved?

3. Is linear momentum conserved in common applications? Explain.

4. Is the conservation of linear momentum consistent with Newton's first and third laws of motion? Explain.

(continued)

5. In a system of particles for which the total linear momentum is conserved, is the linear momentum of the individual particles constant? Explain.

6. Suppose that a particle of mass m_1 approaches a stationary mass m_2 and $m_2 >> m_1$.
   (a) Describe the velocity of m_2 after an elastic collision; that is, one in which both momentum and kinetic energy are conserved. Justify your answer mathematically.

   (b) What is the approximate momentum of m_1 after collision?

Conservation of Linear Momentum

I. Introduction and Objectives

The conservation of linear momentum ($\mathbf{p} = m\mathbf{v}$) is an important physical concept. However, the experimental investigation of this concept in an introductory physics laboratory is hampered by ever-present frictional forces.

An air track provides one of the best methods to investigate linear momentum (see Fig. 4.3). Aluminum cars or gliders riding on a cushion of air on the track approach frictionless motion—a necessary condition for the conservation of linear momentum.

In the absence of friction (and other external forces), the total linear momentum of a system of two cars will be conserved during a collision of the cars. That is, the total linear momentum of the system should be the same after collision as before collision. By measuring the velocities of cars of the same and different masses before and after collision, the total momentum of a system can be determined and the conservation of linear momentum investigated.

After performing this experiment and analyzing the data, you should be able to do the following:

1. Explain when linear momentum is conserved and what this means in terms of force and motion.
2. Apply the conservation of linear momentum to a system.
3. Describe two-body collisions in terms of the conservation of linear momentum.

II. Equipment Needed

- Air track
- Three cars (two of similar mass)
- Four laboratory timers
- Laboratory balance
- Masking tape
- Meterstick (if no length scale on air track)
- Velcro (optional)

(Optional)

- Air track system with photogates/timers and computer interfacing*
- PASCO's Dynamics System with Magnetic Collision Carts

III. Theory

The linear momentum $\mathbf{p}$ of a particle or object is defined as

$$\mathbf{p} = m\mathbf{v} \tag{7.1}$$

where m is the mass of the object and $\mathbf{v}$ its velocity. Since velocity is a vector quantity, so is linear momentum.

Newton's second law of motion, commonly expressed in the form $\mathbf{F} = m\mathbf{a}$, can also be written in terms of momentum:

$$\mathbf{F} = \frac{\Delta\mathbf{p}}{\Delta t} \tag{7.2}$$

If there is no net or unbalanced external force acting on the object ($F = 0$), then

$$\mathbf{F} = \frac{\Delta\mathbf{p}}{\Delta t} = 0$$

or

$$\Delta\mathbf{p} = 0$$

That is, the change in the momentum is zero, or the momentum is conserved. By "conserved" is meant that the momentum remains constant (in time).

$$\Delta\mathbf{p} = \mathbf{p}_f - \mathbf{p}_i = 0$$

or

$$\mathbf{p}_f = \mathbf{p}_i \tag{7.3}$$

and the "final" momentum $\mathbf{p}_f$ at any time t_f is the same as the initial momentum $\mathbf{p}_i$ at time t_i.

Notice that this is consistent with Newton's first law of motion, since

$$\mathbf{p}_f = \mathbf{p}_i \quad \text{or} \quad m\mathbf{v}_f = m\mathbf{v}_i$$

and

$$\mathbf{v}_f = \mathbf{v}_i$$

That is, an object remains at rest ($\mathbf{v}_i = 0$) or in uniform motion ($\mathbf{v}_i = \mathbf{v}_f$) unless acted on by some external force.

* If electronic photogates/timers and computer-assisted data analysis are available, your instructor will give you instruction on their use.

The previous development also applies to the total momentum of a system of particles or objects. For example, the total linear momentum of a system of two objects m_1 and m_2 is $\mathbf{P} = \mathbf{p}_1 + \mathbf{p}_2$, and if there is no net external force acting on the system, then

$$\Delta\mathbf{P} = 0$$

In the case of a collision between two objects of a system (with only internal forces acting), the initial momentum before the collision is the same as the final momentum after the collision. That is,

$$\underset{\text{(before)}}{\mathbf{p}_{1_i} + \mathbf{p}_{2_i}} = \underset{\text{(after)}}{\mathbf{p}_{1_f} + \mathbf{p}_{2_f}} \qquad \textbf{(7.4)}$$

or

$$m_1\mathbf{v}_{1_i} + m_2\mathbf{v}_{2_i} = m_1\mathbf{v}_{1_f} + m_2\mathbf{v}_{2_f}$$

In one dimension, the directions of the velocity and momentum vectors are commonly indicated by plus and minus signs, i.e., $+v$ and $-v$.*

The internal forces do not change the total momentum because, according to Newton's third law, $\mathbf{F}_{12} = -\mathbf{F}_{21}$ (the force on object 1 due to object 2 is equal and opposite [−] to the force on object 2 due to object 1). Thus, the change in momentum for one object will be equal in magnitude and opposite in direction to the change in momentum for the other object, and the total momentum will be unchanged.

IV. Experimental Procedures

1. Determine the mass of each car and record it in the Trial Data Table. Let the masses of the two cars of nearly equal mass be m_1 and m_2 and the mass of the third car be m_3.

2. Mark off two equal and convenient lengths (for example, $\frac{1}{2}$ or 1 m) on both sides of the center position of the air track. Make full use of the length of the track, but leave some space near the ends of the track. Place the four tape reference marks at the lower edges of the track so as not to interfere with the car motion. *Do not* mark the air track surface itself with tape or anything else.

3. *Time trials*. By measuring the time interval Δt it takes a car to move the reference mark length d, one can determine the velocity $v = d/\Delta t$ of the car, where $\Delta t = t_2 - t_1$. The actual timing of the motion of a car moving between the two sets of reference marks is done by either method (A), involving four observers, each with a timer and assigned to an individual reference mark, or method (B), involving two observers, each with a timer and assigned to one set of reference marks, as described below. Time trials will be done to determine the better method.*

In addition to giving timing practice and determining the better method of timing, the time trials check out the experimental setup for possible systematic errors. The time intervals for the individual cars to travel the equal distances between the reference marks should be very similar for any one trial. If not, the air track may need leveling and/or there may be some frictional problem with part of the track. Should this be the case, call your instructor. *Do not* attempt to level the air track on your own.

Experimentally carry out each of the following timing methods to determine which is better.

Method A—Four Timers. Set one of the cars in motion with a *slight* push so that it moves with moderate speed up and down the track. (A few practice starts help.) As the car hits the bumper at one end of the track, all four observers should start their timers. As the leading edge of the car passes the reference marks, each respective observer stops his or her timer. (A dry run or two to become familiar with the timing sequence is helpful.) Carry out this procedure twice for each of the three cars, and record the data in the Trial Data Table.

Method B—Two Timers. Set the car in motion. The two observers should start and stop their individual timers as the leading edge of the car passes their respective reference marks. Carry out this procedure twice for each of the three cars, and record the data in the Trial Data Table.

4. Compute the Δt's for each trial and calculate the percent difference for each trial set. From the data, decide which timing method should be used based on consistency or precision.

Case 1: Collision Between Two Cars of (Nearly) Equal Mass, with One Initially at Rest

5. With one of the cars (m_2) of nearly equal mass stationary at the center position of the air track,

* In two (or three) dimensions, the momentum is conserved in both (or all) directions. That is, $\mathbf{P} = \mathbf{P}_x + \mathbf{P}_y = 0$, and $\mathbf{P}_x = 0$ and $\mathbf{P}_y = 0$. Why? Note: $\mathbf{P}_x = \Sigma\mathbf{p}_x$ and $\mathbf{P}_y = \Sigma\mathbf{p}_y$.

* If electronic photogate timers are available, your instructor will give you instruction in their use. Electronic timing greatly improves the accuracy and precision of the results. (Why?)

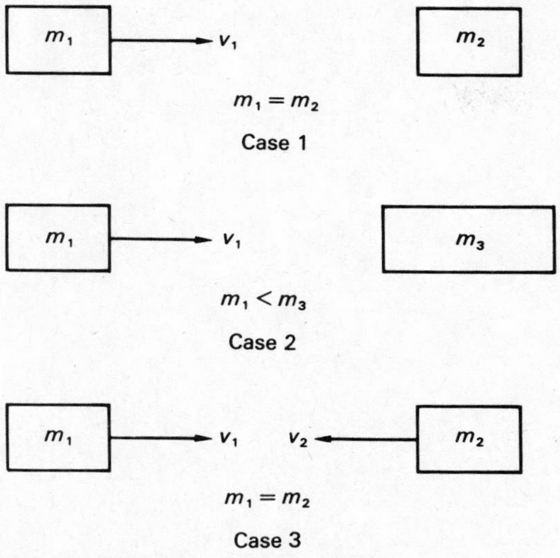

Figure 7.1 Experimental collision cases.

start the other car (m_1) moving toward the stationary car. See Fig. 7.1. (It may be more convenient to start m_1 moving away from m_2 and take measurements as m_1 returns from rebounding from the end of the track.) A trial run should show that m_1 remains at rest, or nearly at rest, after collision and that m_2 is in motion.

Determine the time it takes for m_1 to travel between the reference marks as it approaches m_2 and the time it takes for m_2 to travel between the other set of reference marks after collision. Carry out this procedure three times and record the data in Data Table 1.

Compute the velocities and the total momentum before and after collision and the percent difference in these values for each trial.

Case 2: Collision Between Two Cars of Unequal Mass, with the More Massive Car Initially at Rest

6. Repeat procedure 5 with m_2 replaced by m_3 (more massive than m_1 and m_2). See Fig. 7.1. In this case, m_1 will travel in the opposite direction after collision, as a trial run will show. Make appropriate adjustments in the timing procedure to measure the velocity of m_1 before *and* after collision. Record the data and the required calculations in Data Table 2. Be careful with the directional signs of the velocities and momenta.

Case 3: Collision Between Two Cars of (Nearly) Equal Mass Initially Traveling in Opposite Directions

7. With m_1 and m_2 initially moving toward each other (Fig. 7.1), determine the total momentum before and after collision. (*Note:* Speeds do not have to be, and probably won't be, equal.)

   Make appropriate adjustments in the timing procedure to measure the velocities of m_1 and m_2 before and after collision. Carry out the procedure three times and record the data in Data Table 3.

   Compute the percent difference for the total momentum before and after collision for each trial.

(Optional Procedure)

Another procedure, which may be done at the instructor's option, is as follows:

8. Attach pieces of Velcro to the collision bumpers of both cars, and repeat one or more of the preceding cases as directed by your instructor. Make up a data table, and analyze your results as previously. (*Hint:* read in your textbook about elastic and inelastic collisions—in particular, completely inelastic collisions.)

Name ____________________ Section ____________ Date ____________

Lab Partner(s) ____

E X P E R I M E N T 7

Conservation of Linear Momentum

Laboratory Report

Distance between marks ____________

TRIAL DATA TABLE

Purpose: To determine better method of timing.

		Method A							Method B		
Car mass ( )		t_1 ( )	t_2 ( )	Δt_{12} ( )	t_3 ( )	t_4 ( )	Δt_{34} ( )	Percent diff.	Δt_{12} ( )	Δt_{34} ( )	Percent diff.
m_1											
m_2											
m_3											

DATA TABLE 1

Purpose: To analyze $m_1 = m_2$ case, with $v_{2_i} = 0$.

Trial	Before collision			After collision			
	m_1			m_2			
	Δt_1 ( )	v_{1_i} ( )	p_{1_i} ( )	Δt_2 ( )	v_{2_f} ( )	p_{2_f} ( )	Percent diff.
1							
2							
3							

Don't forget units

(continued)

DATA TABLE 2

Purpose: To analyze $m_3 > m_1$ case, with $v_{3_i} = 0$.

Trial	Before collision			After collision							Percent diff.
	m_1			m_1			m_3				
	Δt_{1_i} ( )	v_{1_i} ( )	Total momentum ( )	Δt_{1_f} ( )	v_{1_f} ( )	p_{1_f} ( )	Δt_{3_f} ( )	v_{3_f} ( )	p_{3_f} ( )	Total momentum ( )	
1											
2											
3											

DATA TABLE 3

Purpose: To analyze $m_1 = m_2$ case, initial motions in opposite directions.

Trial	Before collision						
	m_1			m_2			Total momentum ( )
	Δt_{1_i} ( )	v_{1_i} ( )	p_{1_i} ( )	Δt_{2_i} ( )	v_{2_i} ( )	p_{2_i} ( )	
1							
2							
3							

Trial	After collision							
	m_1			m_2			Total momentum ( )	Percent diff. ( )
	Δt_{1_f} ( )	v_{1_f} ( )	p_{1_f} ( )	Δt_{2_f} ( )	v_{2_f} ( )	p_{2_f} ( )		
1								
2								
3								

Name ______________________ Section ______________ Date ______________

Lab Partner(s) ____

QUESTIONS

1. Do the results of the experiment support the conservation of linear momentum? Consider possible sources of error.

2. Was it necessary to have equal length intervals in the experiment to investigate properly the conservation of momentum? Explain.

3. In Cases 1 and 2 one of the cars was initially at rest, so it must have received an acceleration. Is the car accelerating as it passes between the reference marks? Explain.

4. In each of the three cases, was kinetic energy conserved? Justify your answers with a sample calculation for a trial from each case. If the kinetic energy is not conserved, where did it go?

Name ______________________ Section ______________ Date ______________

Lab Partner(s) ____

EXPERIMENT 8

Projectile Motion: The Ballistic Pendulum

Advance Study Assignment

Read the experiment and answer the following questions.

A. The Ballistic Pendulum

1. What conservation laws are involved in the computation of the initial velocity of a projectile using the ballistic pendulum?

2. Why is it justified to say that the momentum in the horizontal direction is conserved over the collision interval? Is momentum conserved before and after the collision? Explain.

3. Is the center of mass of the pendulum-ball system at the center of the ball? If not, where and how is the center of mass located?

(continued)

B. Determination of the Initial Velocity of a Projectile from Range-Fall Measurements

4. What is the range of a projectile, and what affects it?

5. After the projectile leaves the gun, what are the accelerations in the x and y directions?

6. How is the location where the ball strikes the floor determined?

C. Projectile Range Dependence on the Angle of Projection

7. How does the range of a projectile vary with the angle of projection θ?

8. Theoretically, at what angle of projection is the range a maximum? How could you increase the range?

Projectile Motion: The Ballistic Pendulum

I. Introduction and Objectives

Projectile motion refers to the motion of an object in a plane (two dimensions) under the influence of gravity. The kinematic equations of motion describe the components of such motion and may be used to analyze projectile motion. In most textbook cases, the initial velocity of a projectile is given and the motion is described through the equations of motion. However, in this laboratory experiment, the unknown initial velocity will be determined from experimental measurements. This will be done (1) through the use of the ballistic pendulum and (2) from range-fall distance measurements. The dependence of the projectile range on the angle of projection will also be investigated so as to get an experimental indication of the angle of projection that gives the maximum range.

These procedures will greatly assist you in understanding some of the most basic physical principles. After performing the experiment and analyzing the data, you should be able to do the following:

1. Explain the use of conservation laws (linear momentum and energy) in determining the initial velocity of a projectile using the ballistic pendulum.
2. Describe the components of motion and how they are used in determining the velocity of a projectile with range-fall measurements.
3. Tell how the range of a projectile varies with the angle of projection.

II. Equipment Needed

- Ballistic pendulum
- Sheets of plain paper (and carbon paper)*
- Meterstick
- Protractor
- Laboratory balance
- Masking tape
- Wooden blocks
- 1 sheet of Cartesian graph paper
- Safety glasses

III. Theory

A. The Ballistic Pendulum

Types of ballistic pendula apparatus are shown in Fig. 8.1. The ballistic pendulum is used to measure the initial velocity of a horizontally projected object (a metal ball) fired from a spring gun. The projectile is fired into a stationary, hollow pendulum bob suspended by a rod, and the pendulum and the embedded projectile swing upward. A catch mechanism stops the pendulum at its highest position of swing. By measuring the vertical distance that the center of mass of the pendulum-ball system rises, one can compute the initial velocity of the projectile through the use of the conservation of linear momentum and the conservation of mechanical energy (neglecting rotational considerations).

Consider the schematic diagram of a ballistic pendulum shown in Fig. 8.2. A projectile of mass m with an initial horizontal velocity of v_{x_o} is fired into and becomes embedded in a stationary pendulum of mass M.

The horizontal momentum is conserved during collision (if the external forces are vertical). To a good approximation, this applies over the time interval of the collision; therefore, the horizontal component of total momentum is taken to be the same immediately before and after collision. The velocity of the pendulum bob is initially zero and the combined system $(m + M)$ has a velocity of magnitude V just after collision. Hence, we may write for the horizontal direction

$$\underset{\text{(before)}}{mv_{x_o}} = \underset{\text{(after)}}{(m + M)V} \qquad \textbf{(8.1)}$$

After the collision, the pendulum with the embedded projectile swings upward (momentum of the system no longer conserved) and stops. The center of mass of the system is raised a maximum vertical distance $h = h_2 - h_1$. By the conservation of mechanical energy, the increase in potential energy is equal to the kinetic energy of the system just after

* may or may not be needed

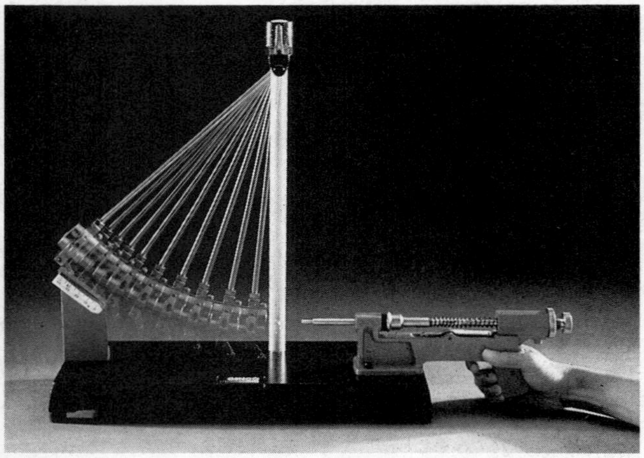

(a)

(c)

(b)

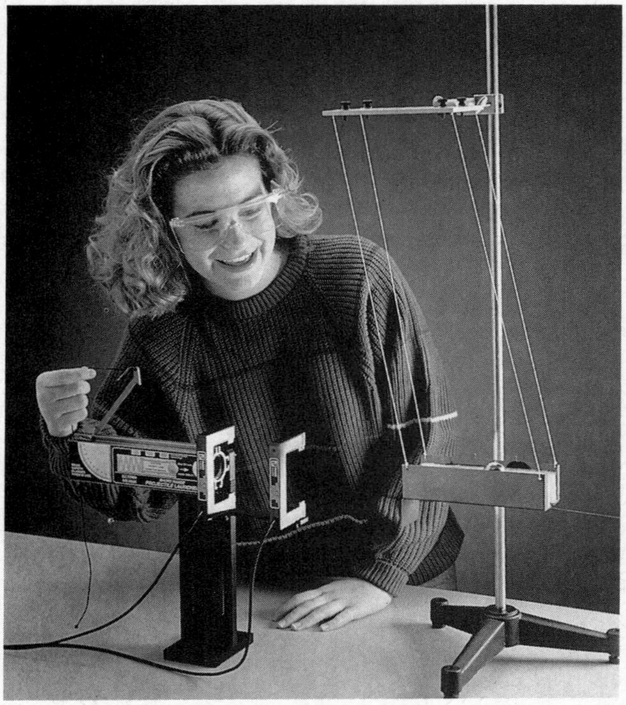

(d)

Figure 8.1 Ballistic pendula. Types of ballistic pendula. (a) Courtesy of Central Scientific Co., Inc. (b) Courtesy of Sargent-Welch Scientific Co. (c) Courtesy of Bernard O. Beck & Co. (d) Courtesy of PASCO Scientific.

collision (the friction of the support is considered negligible). Hence,

$$\underset{\text{kinetic energy just after collision}}{\tfrac{1}{2}(m + M)V^2} = \underset{\text{change in potential energy}}{(m + M)gh} \quad \textbf{(8.2)}$$

Solving Eq. 8.2 for V, we obtain

$$V = \sqrt{2gh} \quad \textbf{(8.3)}$$

Substituting this expression into Eq. 8.1 and solving for v_{x_o} yields

$$v_{x_o} = \frac{m + M}{m}\sqrt{2gh} \quad \textbf{(8.4)}$$

Hence, by measuring m, M, and h, the initial velocity of the projectile can be computed.

B. Determination of the Initial Velocity of a Projectile from Range-Fall Measurements

If a projectile is projected horizontally with an initial velocity of magnitude v_{x_o} from a height of y, it will

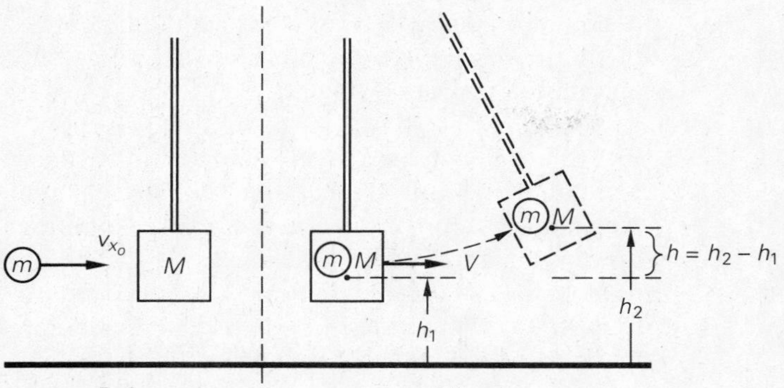

Figure 8.2 Ballistic pendulum action. Ideally, the horizontal momentum is conserved during collision. After collision, work is done against gravity, and kinetic energy is converted to potential energy. (Rotational considerations neglected.)

describe an arc as illustrated in Fig. 8.3. The projectile will travel a horizontal distance x (called the *range* of the projectile) while falling a vertical distance y.

The initial vertical velocity is zero, $v_{y_o} = 0$, and the acceleration in the y direction has a magnitude of $a_y = g$ (acceleration due to gravity—downward taken as positive in this case for convenience). There is no horizontal acceleration, $a_x = 0$; hence the components of the motion are described by

$$x = v_{x_o} t \tag{8.5}$$

and

$$y = \tfrac{1}{2} g t^2 \tag{8.6}$$

Eliminating t from these equations and solving for v_{x_o}, we have (neglecting air resistance):

$$v_{x_o} = \sqrt{\frac{gx^2}{2y}} = \left(\frac{g}{2y}\right)^{1/2} x \tag{8.7}$$

Hence, by measuring the range x and the distance of fall y, one can compute the initial velocity of the projectile.

C. *Projectile Range Dependence on the Angle of Projection*

The projectile path for a general angle of projection θ is shown in Fig. 8.4. The components of the initial velocity have magnitudes of

$$\begin{aligned} v_{x_o} &= v_o \cos\theta \\ v_{y_o} &= v_o \sin\theta \end{aligned} \tag{8.8}$$

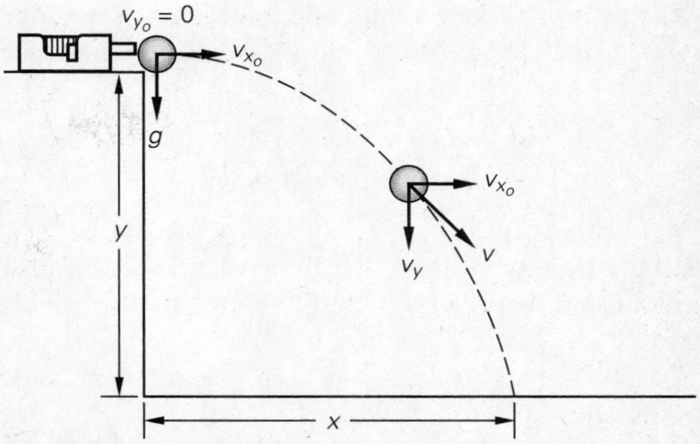

Figure 8.3 Range-fall. The configuration for range-fall measurements.

At the top of the arc path, $v_y = 0$, and since

$$\begin{aligned} v_y &= v_{y_o} - gt \\ &= v_o \sin\theta - gt \end{aligned}$$

(downward taken as negative), we have

$$v_o \sin\theta - g t_m = 0$$

or

$$t_m = \frac{v_o \sin\theta}{g} \tag{8.9}$$

where t_m is the time for the projectile to reach the maximum height of y_m. If the projectile returns to the same elevation as that from which it was fired, the total time of flight t is then

$$t = 2t_m = \frac{2v_o \sin\theta}{g} \tag{8.10}$$

During the time t, the projectile travels a distance R (range) in the x direction:

$$R = v_{x_o} t = \frac{2v_o^2 \sin\theta \cos\theta}{g}$$

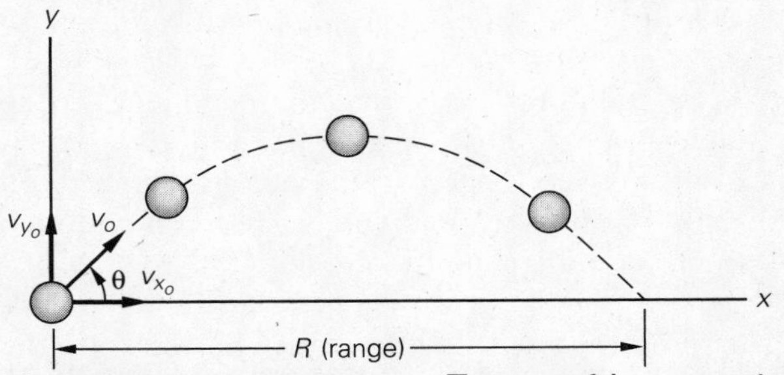

Figure 8.4 Projectile motion. For an arbitrary projection angle, the range R depends on the initial velocity, that is, speed and angle of projection.

But using the trigonometric identity $2 \sin \theta \cos \theta = \sin 2\theta$, the **range** or maximum distance in the x direction is

$$R = \frac{v_o^2 \sin 2\theta}{g} \qquad \textbf{(8.11)}$$

From Eq. 8.11, we see that the range of the projectile depends on the angle of projection θ. The maximum range R_{max} occurs when $\sin 2\theta = 1$. Since $\sin 90° = 1$, by comparison

$$2\theta = 90° \quad \text{or} \quad \theta = 45°$$

Hence, a projectile has a maximum range for $\theta = 45°$, and

$$R_{max} = \frac{v_o^2}{g} \qquad \textbf{(8.12)}$$

which provides another convenient method to determine experimentally the initial speed of a projectile.

(*Note*: this development neglects air resistance, but the equations give the range to a good approximation for relatively small initial speeds and short projectile paths. Why?)

IV. Experimental Procedure

Caution: *With projectiles involved, it is recommended that safety glasses be worn when doing all procedures.*

A. The Ballistic Pendulum

1. Obtain the projectile ball, which may be in the pendulum bob. (*Note*: When removing the ball from the pendulum bob of some types of ballistic pendula, be sure to push up on the spring catch that holds the ball in the pendulum so as not to damage it.) Place the projectile ball on the ball rod of the spring gun, and cock the gun by pushing on the ball. Both the ball and rod may move backward, or the ball may slip over the rod, depending on the type of ballistic pendulum. ***Caution**: In either case, be careful not to bruise or hurt your hand when cocking the gun. Also, keep your fingers away from the projectile end of the gun.*

   Fire the projectile into the pendulum to see how the apparatus operates. If the catch mechanism does not catch on the notched track, you should adjust the pendulum suspension to obtain the proper alignment.

2. A preset pointer or a dot on the side of the pendulum bob indicates the position of the center of mass of the pendulum-ball system. With the pendulum hanging freely, measure the height h_1 of the pointer above the base surface (Fig. 8.2) and record in Data Table 1.

3. Fire the ball into the freely hanging stationary pendulum and note the notch at which the catch mechanism stops on the curved track. Counting upward on the curved track, record the notch number in Data Table 1. Repeat this procedure four times and for each trial record the notch number in the data table. (Alternately, the height may be measured each time. See Procedure 4.)

4. Determine the average of these observations, which is the average highest position of the pendulum. Place the catch mechanism in the notch corresponding most closely to the average and measure the height h_2 of the pointer or dot above the base surface used for the h_1 measurement (Fig. 8.2).

   Note: To minimize frictional losses, the catch mechanism may be disabled by tying it up with thread or using a rubber band. The mechanism then acts as a pointer to indicate the highest notch, which is observed by a lab partner. Holding some reference object, e.g., a pencil, by the notched track helps to determine the proper notch number.

5. Loosen the screw of the pendulum support and carefully remove the pendulum. Weigh and record the masses of the ball (m) and the pendulum (M). *Note*: The mass of the pendulum is that of the bob and the support rod. Do not attempt to remove the support rod from the bob. Consult your instructor for an explanation if a different model is used.

6. From the data, compute the magnitude of the initial velocity using Eq. 8.4 ($g = 9.80$ m/s^2 = 980 cm/s^2).

B. Determination of the Initial Velocity of a Projectile from Range-Fall Measurements

7. With the pendulum removed or in the upper catch mechanism notch so as not to interfere with the projectile, position the apparatus near one edge of the laboratory table as shown in Fig. 8.3. Fire the ball from the gun and note where the ball strikes the floor. (The range of the ball is appreciable, so you will probably have to shoot

the ball down an aisle. Be careful not to hit anyone with the ball, particularly the instructor.)

8. Place a sheet of paper where the ball hit the floor. Tape the paper to the floor (or weight it down) so that it will not move. When the ball strikes the paper, the indentation mark made will allow you determine the range of the projectile.* Also, mark the position of the apparatus on the table (e.g., using a piece of tape as a reference). It is important that the gun be fired from the same position each time.

9. Fire the ball five times and measure the horizontal distance or range x the ball travels for each trial (see Fig. 8.3). [If the faint indentation marks are not able to be found, cover the paper on the floor with a sheet of carbon paper (carbon side down). The ball will then make a carbon mark on the paper on impact.]

Record the measurements in Data Table 2 and find the average range. Also, measure the height y of the ball rod from the floor and record it in the data table. The height y is measured from the bottom of the ball (as it rests on the gun) to the floor.

10. Using Eq. 8.7, compute the magnitude of the initial velocity of the ball ($g = 9.80$ m/s^2 = 980 cm/s^2). Compare this to the velocity determined in part A, and compute the percent difference.

C. Projectile Range Dependence on the Angle of Projection

11. With the ballistic pendulum apparatus on the floor (with pendulum removed), elevate the front end so that it can be fired at an angle θ relative to the horizontal. Your instructor will tell you how to do this. Aim the projectile down an aisle or hallway, being careful not to aim at anything or anybody.

12. Using a protractor to set the angles of projection, fire the projectile at angles of 20°, 30°, 40°, 45°, 50°, 60°, and 70° with two or three trials for each angle. The projectile should be aimed so that it lands as close as possible to the same spot for the trials of a particular angle. Station one or more lab partners near where the projectile strikes the floor. They are to judge the average range of the two or three trials. Measure the average range for each angle of projection and record the data in Data Table 3.

Suggestion: It is convenient to measure the distance from the gun to a position near where the ball lands and to mark this position. The range measurement then can be made relative to the measured mark, instead of from the starting point each time. Also, it is convenient to shoot toward a wall at the end of the hall or aisle or to lay a meterstick on the floor perpendicularly to the line of flight, in order to stop the ball from rolling.

13. Plot the range versus the angle of projection, and draw a smooth curve that fits the data best. As you might expect, the points may be scattered widely because of the rather crude experimental procedure. Even so, you should be able to obtain a good idea of the angle for the maximum range. Determine this angle from the graph and record it in Data Table 3.

* The range will be measured from the position below the center of the ball just as it leaves the gun to the marks that are on the paper on the floor. This will be determined by putting the ball on the gun without loading the spring.

Name ______________________ Section ______________ Date ______________

Lab Partner(s) ____

EXPERIMENT 8

Projectile Motion: The Ballistic Pendulum

Laboratory Report

A. The Ballistic Pendulum

DATA TABLE 1

(Modify Data Table if it does not apply to your ballistic pendulum.)

Purpose: To determine the magnitude of initial projectile velocity.

Trials	Notch number of pendulum catch	
		Height of h_2 of pointer with pendulum catch in closest-to-average notch number ______
1		Height h_1 of pointer with pendulum freely suspended ______
2		
3		$h = h_2 - h_1$ ______
4		Mass of ball m ______
5		
		Mass of pendulum M (bob and support) ______
Average		

Calculations
(show work)

Computed v_{x_o} ______ (units)

Don't forget units

(continued)

B. Determination of the Initial Velocity of a Projectile from Range-Fall Measurements

DATA TABLE 2

Purpose: To determine the magnitude of initial projectile velocity.

Trial	Range
1	
2	
3	
4	
5	
Average	

Vertical distance of fall, y ______________

Computed v_{x_o} ______________ (units)

Percent difference between results of parts A and B ______________

Calculations
(show work)

C. Projectile Range Dependence on the Angle of Projection

DATA TABLE 3

Purpose: To investigate projection angle from maximum range.

Angle of projection	Average range
20°	
30°	
40°	
45°	
50°	
60°	
70°	

Angle of projection for maximum range from graph ______________

Name ______________________ Section ______________ Date ______________

Lab Partner(s) ____

EXPERIMENT 8 *Laboratory Report*

QUESTIONS

A. The Ballistic Pendulum

1. Is the collision between the ball and the pendulum elastic or inelastic? Justify your answer by calculating the kinetic energy of the system before collision using the value of v_{x_o} found in the experiment and the kinetic energy just after collision using the experimental value of h in Eq. 8.2.

2. Using the results of Question 1, find the fractional kinetic energy loss during collision. Express the "loss" as a percent. What became of the "lost energy"?

3. Expressing the kinetic energy in terms of momentum (i.e., $K = \frac{1}{2}mv^2 = p^2/2m$), prove using symbols, not numbers, that the fractional loss during the collision is equal to $M/(m + M)$.

4. Compute the fractional energy loss from the experimental mass values using the equation developed in Question 3, and compare this to the result in Question 2. Explain the difference, if any.

(continued)

5. Is the friction of the pendulum (pointer, support axis, etc.) a random or systematic error? Will this source of error cause your calculated velocity to be less than or greater than the actual velocity?

B. Determination of the Initial Velocity of a Projectile from Range-Fall Measurements

6. What effect does the force of gravity have on the horizontal velocity of the projectile? Explain.

C. Projectile Range Dependence on the Angle of Projection

7. Using experimental data, compute the magnitude of the initial velocity v_o of the projectile from Eq. 8.12 and compare this to the results of parts A and B of the procedure.

8. What effect does air resistance have on the range of a projectile?

Name ______________________ Section ______________ Date ______________
Lab Partner(s) ____

EXPERIMENT 8 *Laboratory Report*

9. Show that the range in part B cannot be computed from Eq. 8.11, and explain why.

Name ______________________ Section ______________ Date ______________

Lab Partner(s) ____

EXPERIMENT 9

Centripetal Force

Advance Study Assignment

Read the experiment and answer the following questions.

1. Define centripetal force.

2. What supplies the centripetal force for (a) a satellite in orbit around the Earth; (b) the mass in uniform circular motion in this experiment?

3. An object moving in *uniform* circular motion is accelerating. How can this be, since uniform motion implies constant motion?

4. For an object in uniform circular motion, on what parameters does the determination of the centripetal force depend when using $F = ma$?

(continued)

5. If the centripetal force acting on an object in uniform motion suddenly ceased to act or went to zero, what would happen to the object? That is, what would be its subsequent motion?

6. Suppose that the centripetal force acting on an object in circular motion were increased and the object remained in a circular path with the same radius. How would its motion be affected?

7. Explain how the centripetal force is directly determined for each apparatus described in the experiment.

Centripetal Force

I. Introduction and Objectives

The Earth revolves about the Sun, and atomic electrons move around the nucleus. What keeps these objects in orbit? The answer is **centripetal (center-seeking) force**. The centripetal force is supplied by gravitational and electrical interactions, respectively, for each of these cases.

The study of centripetal force in the laboratory is simplified by considering objects in uniform circular motion. An object in uniform circular motion moves with a constant speed (a scalar) but has a changing velocity (a vector) because of the continuing change in direction. This change in velocity results from centripetal acceleration due to a centripetal force.

In the experimental situation(s) of this experiment, the centripetal force will be supplied by a spring and can be readily measured. However, the magnitude of the centripetal force can also be determined from other experimental parameters (e.g., the frequency of rotation of the object, its mass, and its radius of orbit). Centripetal force will be experimentally investigated by measuring these parameters and comparing the calculated results with the direct measurement of the spring force, which mechanically supplies the center-seeking centripetal force.

After performing the experiment and analyzing the data, you should be able to do the following:

1. Explain why a centripetal force is necessary for circular motion.
2. Describe how the magnitude of the centripetal force for uniform circular motion may be determined from motional parameters.
3. Summarize what determines the magnitude of the centripetal force necessary to keep an object in uniform circular motion.

II. Equipment Needed

A. *Centripetal Force Apparatus with Variable-Speed Rotor and Counter*

- Laboratory timer or stopwatch
- Weight hanger and slotted weights
- Vernier caliper
- Support rod and clamp
- String
- Safety glasses

B. *Manual Centripetal Force Apparatus*

- Laboratory timer or stopwatch
- Meterstick
- Weight hanger and slotted weights
- String
- Laboratory balance
- Safety glasses

III. Theory

An object in uniform circular motion requires a centripetal or center-seeking force to "hold" it in orbit. For example, when one swings a ball on a rope in a horizontal circle around one's head (Fig. 9.1), the **centripetal force** $F_c = ma_c$ is supplied by the person and transmitted to the ball through the rope. In the

Figure 9.1 Centripetal acceleration. An object in uniform circular motion must have a centripetal acceleration with a magnitude $a_c = v^2/r$ directed toward the center of the circular path. In the case of swinging a ball on a rope around one's head, the centripetal force, $F_c = ma_c$, is supplied by the person and transmitted through the rope. (Courtesy of PhotoEdit/Tony Freeman.)

absence of the centripetal force (e.g., if the rope breaks or if the person releases the rope), the ball would no longer be held in orbit, and would initially fly off in the direction of its tangential velocity v.

An object in uniform circular motion moves with a constant speed. Even though the object's speed is constant, its velocity is changing because the direction of the motion is continually changing. This change in velocity results from a centripetal acceleration a_c that is due to the applied centripetal force F_c. The direction of the acceleration (and force) is always toward the center of the object's circular path, and it can be shown (see your text) that the magnitude of the acceleration is given by

$$a_c = \frac{v^2}{r} \qquad \textbf{(9.1)}$$

where v is the tangential or orbital speed of the object and r the radius of the circular orbit. By Newton's second law, $F = ma$, the magnitude of the centripetal force is

$$F_c = ma_c = \frac{mv^2}{r} \qquad \textbf{(9.2)}$$

where m is the mass of the object. In terms of distance and time, the orbital speed v is given by $v = 2\pi r/T$, where $2\pi r$ is the circumference of the circular orbit and T is the period.

Notice that this general expression describes the centripetal force acting on an object in uniform circular motion in terms of the properties of the motion and orbit. It is equal to the expression of a physical force that actually supplies the centripetal action. For example, in the case of a satellite in uniform circular motion around the Earth, the centripetal force is supplied by gravity, which is generally expressed $F_g = Gm_1m_2/r^2$, and $F_c = F_g$. Similarly, for an object being held in uniform circular motion by the tension force of a string, the tension force is equal to Eq. 9.2 (i.e., tension $T = mv^2/r$).

The centripetal force given by Eq. 9.2 can also be expressed in terms of the angular speed ω or frequency f of rotation using the expressions $v = r\omega$ and $\omega = 2\pi f$:

$$F_c = \frac{mv^2}{r} = \frac{m(r\omega)^2}{r} = mr\omega^2$$

and

$$F_c = mr(2\pi f)^2 = 4\pi^2 mrf^2 \qquad \textbf{(9.3)}$$

where ω is in radians per second and f is in hertz (cycles per second). In this experiment it is convenient to think of f as being in revolutions per second.

IV. Experimental Procedure

A. *Centripetal Force Apparatus with Variable-Speed Rotor*

1. The centripetal force apparatus mounted on a variable-speed rotor is shown in Fig. 9.2.* **Before turning on the rotor,**

(a) By means of the threaded collar on the centripetal force apparatus, adjust the spring to a minimum tension (0–5 on the scale above the threaded collar).

(b) By means of the milled screw head near the base of the rotor, move the rubber friction disk to near the center of the driving disk. (The driving disk can be pushed back so that the friction disk can be moved freely.) This will give a low angular starting speed when the rotor is turned on (but don't turn it on yet!).

The speed of the rotor is increased or decreased by moving the friction disk in (up) or out (down), respectively, along the radius of the driving disk.

Caution: *Excessive speeds can be dangerous. Do not go beyond the speeds needed.*

(c) *Make certain* that the force apparatus is locked securely in the rotor mount by means of the locking screw. Have the instructor check your setup at this point.

2. Referring to Fig. 9.3: When the motor is turned on and adjusted to the proper speed, the cylindrical mass m in the centripetal force apparatus in contact with pointer P will cause the pointer to rise and horizontally point toward the index screw I. In this condition, the mass will be in uniform circular motion around the axis of rotation through I.

Caution: *When taking measurements, be careful not to come in contact with the rotating apparatus. The rotor should* **not** *be operated without a belt guard covering the belt and pulleys. See* Fig. 9.2(c).

3. Put on your safety glasses and turn on the rotor. Adjust the speed until the pointer rises and is opposite the head of the index screw I (Fig. 9.3). Observe this with your eyes on a level with the index screw. (***Caution***: *Why is it a good precaution to wear safety glasses while doing this?*) The

* The following procedures apply particularly to the belt-driven rotor model.

(a)

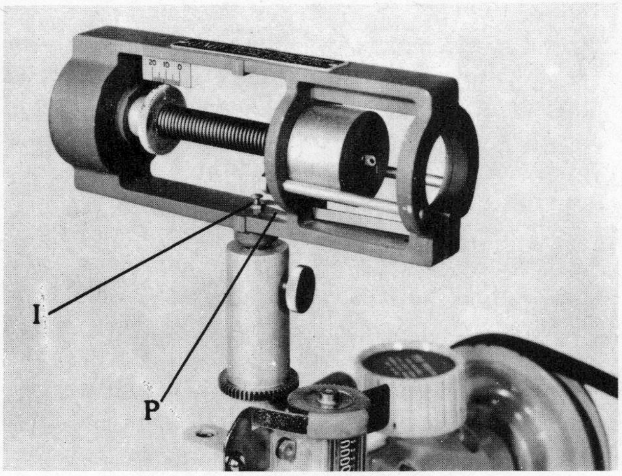

(b)

(c)

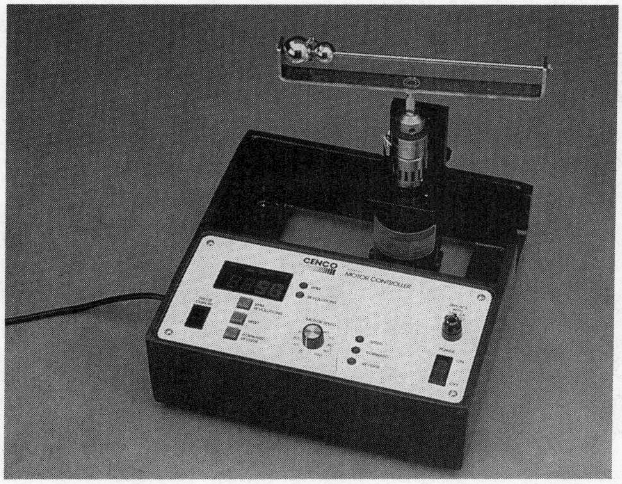

(d)

Figure 9.2 Centripetal force apparatus. (a) A model for which the speed of the rotor is adjusted by moving a rubber friction disk by means of a milled screw head, as illustrated in the photo. (b) When the centripetal force is equal to the spring force, the pointer *P* will rise and point horizontally toward the tip of the index screw *I*. The pointer and screw may be seen more clearly in (a) on the lower horizontal frame of the rotor. See also Figure 9.3. (c) Motor with belt guard and rotating arm in horizontal storage position. The belt guard has been removed in (a) and (b) to provide a clearer illustration. ***Caution***: *When in operation, the motor should always be equipped with a belt guard for safety*. (d) A newer, self-contained centripetal force apparatus that eliminates any belt-guard problem. The apparatus has a digital readout. (Photos courtesy of Central Scientific Co., Inc.)

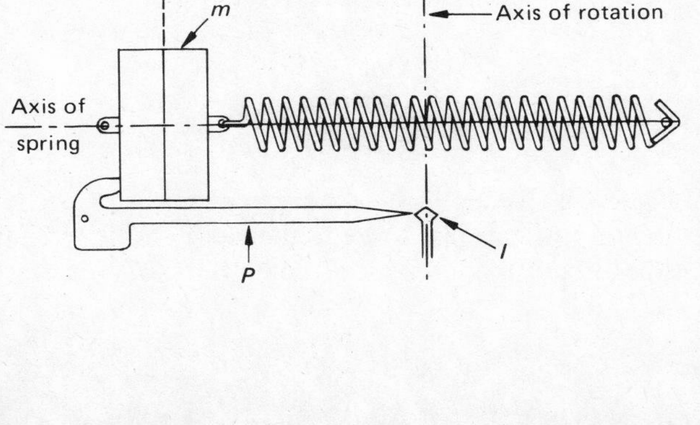

Figure 9.3 Pointer and index screw. When the apparatus is rotating, the mass acting against the pointer *P* will cause it to rise and point toward the index screw *I*.

pointer will be slightly erratic, and as a particular speed is reached, it will "jump" and point horizontally toward the index screw *I*. Do not exceed this speed. The pointer would be aimed at the head of the index screw when the rotor is spinning at higher speeds, too. (Why?)

Do not lock the friction disk. Rather, observe and adjust the speed of the rotor *continuously* during each timed interval in order to keep the pointer as steady as possible. Continuous adjustment is necessary because the rotor speed varies when the counter is engaged. Because the pointer will point horizontally at excessive speeds and induce experimental error, an alternate technique is to adjust the rotor speed continually so that the pointer is not quite horizontal, that is, aimed midway or just below the head of the index screw.

Experiment with your apparatus and see which technique is better, trying to maintain the pointer horizontally at the critical "jump" speed or aiming the pointer at a lower position on the screw at a slightly slower speed.

4. Practice engaging the counter and adjusting the rotor speed. (*Do not* engage the counter too forcefully or you will overly slow down the rotor, yet don't engage the counter so lightly that you accidentally cause the rotor to lose contact with the rotor gear.) When you are satisfied with your technique, record the (initial) counter reading in Data Table 1.

   Then, using a laboratory timer or stopwatch, measure (count) the number of rotations for a 1-min interval. One lab partner should engage the counter for the timing interval while the other adjusts the rotor speed.

   Repeat this procedure for four more 1-min intervals, but *do not* use the previous final counter reading for the next initial interval reading. Advance the counter to a new arbitrary initial reading for each trial.

   Also, share the action. One lab partner should be the "speed controller" who constantly watches and adjusts the rotor speed as described in procedure 3. Another partner should be the "timer" who engages the counter and times the interval. If there are three lab partners, the third may handle the counter engagement and disengagement in response to the timer's instructions. Rotate team responsibilities periodically. (Why might such rotation produce better experimental results?)

5. Subtract the counter readings to find the number of rotations for each timed interval. (They should be similar.) Then, compute the average number of rotations *N* of the five 1-min intervals (average rotations per minute).

   Divide the average value by 60 (1 min = 60 s) to obtain the average rotation frequency in rotations (cycles) per second or hertz (Hz).

6. Without altering the spring tension setting, remove the centripetal force apparatus from the rotor and suspend it from a support as shown in Fig. 9.4. Suspend enough mass on the hanger to produce the same extension of the spring as when on the rotor (pointer aimed at the index screw position). Record this mass M' (includes mass of hanger) in the Laboratory Report below Data Table 1. Also, record the mass of the cylinder m in the force apparatus (stamped on the end of the cylinder).

   Add the masses to find the total suspended mass, $M = M' + m$, and compute the direct measure of F_c = weight of total suspended mass $= Mg$.

   With the spring at the same tension setting and the apparatus still hanging from the support with the same mass M' suspended, use a vernier caliper to measure the distance r, or the radius of the circular rotational path, and record. This is

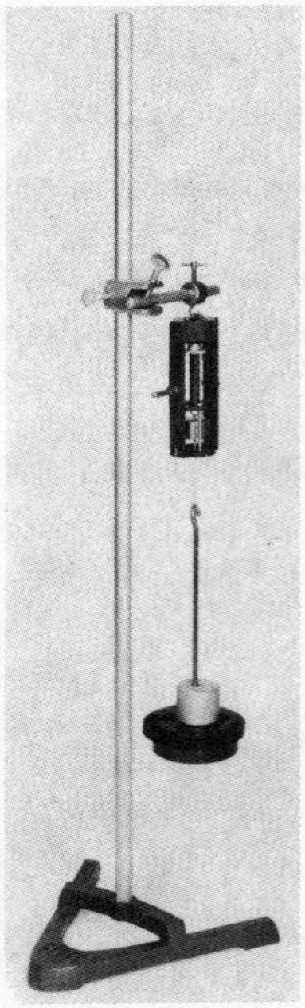

Figure 9.4 Spring tension. Arrangement for application of gravitational force to measure spring tension. (Photo courtesy of Central Scientific Co., Inc.)

the distance between the axis of rotation (line through the index screw) and the center of mass of the cylinder (see Fig. 9.3). The distance is conveniently measured between a line scribed on the upper part of the force apparatus frame above the index screw and a line scribed on the center of the cylinder.

7. Using Eq. 9.3, compute the magnitude of the centripetal force. Compare this with the directly measured value given by the weight force required to produce the same extension of the spring by computing the percent difference.

8. Change the spring tension to a maximum setting (about the 20 mark on the scale above the threaded collar) and repeat procedures 3 through 7, recording your results in Data Table 2.

B. Manual Centripetal Force Apparatus

9. A type of hand-operated centripetal force apparatus is shown in Fig. 9.5. By rolling the rotor between the thumb and fingers, a suspended mass bob is set into circular motion, with the centripetal force being supplied by a spring. The horizontal support arm is counterbalanced for ease of operation, with the position of the counterbalance not being critical.

   A pulley mounted to the base of the apparatus is used to make direct measurement of the spring tension supplying the centripetal force for uniform circular motion of a particular radius indicated by the distance between the vertical pointer rod P and the axis of rotation.

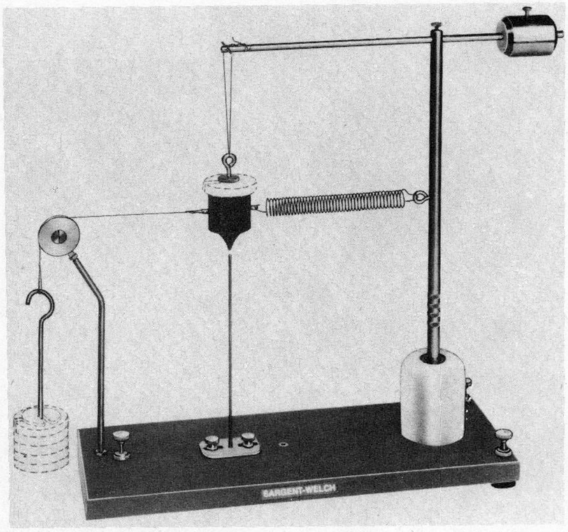

Figure 9.5 Hand-operated centripetal force apparatus. The suspended weights used to determine the centripetal force supplied by the spring are not attached to the bob when the apparatus is operationally rotated. See text for description. (Courtesy of Sargent-Welch Scientific Co.)

10. Remove the bob and determine its mass on a laboratory balance. Record the mass value in Data Table 3. Adjust the position of the vertical pointer rod, if possible, to the smallest possible radius (distance between pointer tip and the center of vertical rotor shaft). Measure this distance and record.

11. Attach the bob to the string on the horizontal support arm, and with the bob hanging freely (spring unattached), adjust the support arm so that the bob is suspended directly over the pointer. Attach the spring to the bob and practice rolling the rotor between your thumb and fingers so that the bob revolves in a circular path and passes over the pointer on each revolution in uniform circular motion. (Adjust the position of the counterbalance on the support arm if necessary for ease of operation.) Make sure the locking screws are tight, and be careful of the rotating counterweight.

   ***Caution**: Safety glasses should be worn. This is always a good practice in a laboratory with moving equipment.*

   While one lab partner operates the rotor, another lab partner with a laboratory timer or stopwatch times the interval for the bob to make about 25 revolutions. The number of counted revolutions may have to be varied depending on the speed of the rotor. Count enough revolutions for an interval of at least 10 s. Record the data in Data Table 3. Practice the procedure before making an actual measurement.

12. Repeat the counting-timing procedure twice. Compute the time per revolution of the bob for each trial and determine the average time per revolution of the three trials.

   From the data, calculate the average speed of the bob. Recall $v = c/t = 2\pi r/T$, where c is the circumference of the circular orbit, r is the radius of the orbit, and T is the average time per revolution or period. Then, using Eq. 9.2, calculate the centripetal force.

13. Attach a string to the bob opposite the spring and suspend a weight hanger over the pulley. Add weights to the hanger until the bob is directly over the pointer. Record the weight Mg in the data table. (Do not forget to add the mass of the

weight hanger.) This weight is a direct measure of the centripetal force supplied by the spring during rotation. Compare this with the calculated value and compute the percent difference of the two values.

14. *Variation of mass*. Unscrew the nut on the top of the bob, insert a slotted mass of 100 g or more under it, and retighten the nut. Repeat procedures 11 through 13 for determining the period of rotation and comparing the computed value of the centripetal force with the direct measurement of the spring tension. (*Question*: Does the latter measurement need to be repeated?) Record your findings in Data Table 4.

15. *Variation of radius*. Remove the slotted masses from the bob and if pointer *P* is adjustable, move it farther away from the axis of rotation to provide a larger path radius. Measure and record this distance in Data Table 5. Repeat procedures 11 through 13 for this experimental condition.

16. *Variation of spring tension (optional)*. Replace the spring with another spring of different stiffness. Repeat procedures 11 through 13, recording your findings in Data Table 6.

Name ______________________ Section ______________ Date ______________

Lab Partner(s) ____

E X P E R I M E N T 9

Centripetal Force

Laboratory Report

A. Centripetal Force Apparatus with Variable-Speed Rotor

DATA TABLE 1

Purpose: To determine rotational frequency for computation of centripetal force.

Minimum spring tension: scale reading ______________

Trial	Counter readings		Difference in readings (rotations/min)
	Final	Initial	
1			
2			
3			
4			
5			
		Average number of rotations N	

Computation of centripetal force (show work)

Average rotational frequency ($f = N/60$) ______________

Suspended mass M' ______________

Cylinder mass m ______________

Total suspended mass ($M = M' + m$) ______________

Direct measure of F_c ($F_c = Mg$) ______________

Radius of circular path r ______________

Computed F_c ______________

Percent difference ______________

Don't forget units

(continued)

DATA TABLE 2

Purpose: To determine rotational frequency for computation of centripetal force.

Maximum spring tension:
scale reading ____________

Trial	Counter readings		Difference in readings (rotations/min)
	Final	Initial	
1			
2			
3			
4			
5			
		Average number of rotations N	

Computation of centripetal force (show work)

Average rotational frequency ($f = N/60$) ____________

Suspended mass M' ____________

Cylinder mass m ____________

Total suspended mass ($M = M' + m$) ____________

Direct measure of F_c ($F_c = Mg$) ____________

Radius of circular path r ____________

Computed F_c ____________

Percent difference ____________

Name ______________________ Section ____________ Date ____________

Lab Partner(s) ______________________

B. Manual Centripetal Force Apparatus

DATA TABLE 3

Purpose: To determine period of revolution for computation of centripetal force.

	Trial 1	Trial 2	Trial 3
Number of revolutions			
Total time ( )			
Time/revolution ( )			

Mass of bob ____________

Radius of circular path ____________

Average time per revolution ____________

Average speed of bob (v) ____________

Computed value of centripetal force ____________

Direct measurement of centripetal force ____________

Percent difference ____________

Computation of centripetal force (attach additional sheet)

DATA TABLE 4

Purpose: To observe the effect of varying mass.

	Trial 1	Trial 2	Trial 3
Number of revolutions			
Total time ( )			
Time/revolution ( )			

Mass of bob plus slotted mass ____________

Radius of circular path ____________

Average time per revolution ____________

Average speed of bob (v) ____________

Computed value of centripetal force ____________

Direct measurement of centripetal force ____________

Percent difference ____________

Computation of centripetal force (attach additional sheet)

(continued)

DATA TABLE 5
Purpose: To observe the effect of varying radius.

	Trial 1	Trial 2	Trial 3
Number of revolutions			
Total time ( )			
Time/revolution ( )			

Mass of bob ______

Radius of circular path ______

Average time per revolution ______

Average speed of bob (v) ______

Computed value of centripetal force ______

Direct measurement of centripetal force ______

Percent difference ______

Computation of centripetal force (attach additional sheet)

DATA TABLE 6 (optional)
Purpose: To observe the effect of varying spring tension.

	Trial 1	Trial 2	Trial 3
Number of revolutions			
Total time ( )			
Time/revolution ( )			

Mass of bob ______

Radius of circular path ______

Average time per revolution ______

Average speed of bob (v) ______

Computed value of centripetal force ______

Direct measurement of centripetal force ______

Percent difference ______

Computation of centripetal force (attach additional sheet)

Name ______________________ Section ______________ Date ______________

Lab Partner(s) ____

EXPERIMENT 9 *Laboratory Report*

QUESTIONS

1. How does the centripetal force vary with the radius of the circular path? Consider (a) constant frequency; and (b) constant speed. Was this substantiated by experimental results?

2. If the centripetal force on an object in uniform circular motion is increased, what is the effect on (a) the frequency of rotation f (with r constant); and (b) f and r when both are free to vary?

3. Does the centripetal force acting on an object in uniform circular motion do work on the object? Explain.

(continued)

4. In part A of the experimental procedure, the counter was advanced to a new arbitrary initial reading for the time interval trials. This is because if consecutive counter readings had been used (i.e., final reading for one interval taken as the initial reading for the next interval), then in averaging the differences all readings except the first and last would have been "thrown out" by the averaging process. That is, the result is essentially one 5-min interval. Prove this explicitly. (*Hint*: Let the counter readings be n_0, n_1, n_2, . . . , and then $\Delta n_1 = n_1 - n_0$, $\Delta n_2 = n_2 - n_1$, etc. Perform the averaging process on these values.)

5. Figure 9.1 shows a student swinging a ball in a circle about his head. (a) Is the rope between the hand and the ball horizontal? (b) Is the force applied by the student on the rope equal to the centripetal force? (Use a diagram to illustrate and justify your answers.)

Name ______________________ Section ______________ Date ______________

Lab Partner(s) ____

EXPERIMENT 10

Friction

Advance Study Assignment

Read the experiment and answer the following questions.

1. State the three general empirical rules used to describe friction.

2. What is the normal force, and why is it used instead of the load?

3. Why is it important to have the string parallel to the horizontal surface in the procedures where suspended weights are used?

4. What is the coefficient of friction, and in what units is it expressed? Distinguish between μ_s and μ_k. Which is generally greater?

(continued)

5. When is (a) $f_s < \mu_s N$; and (b) $f_s = \mu_s N$?

6. Explain how graphs of weight versus normal force in procedures A and B give the coefficients of friction.

Friction

I. Introduction and Objectives

In general, **friction** refers to the resistance to motion between contacting material surfaces. (Internal friction occurs in liquids and gases.) The friction between unlubricated solids is a broad and complicated topic, since it depends on the contacting surfaces and the material properties of the solids. Three general empirical "rules" often used to describe friction between solid surfaces are that the frictional force is:

1. Independent of the surface area of contact.
2. Directly proportional to the **load**, the perpendicular component of the force pressing the surfaces together.
3. Independent of the sliding speed.

Let's take a look at these rules:

1. Intuitively, one would think that friction would depend on the roughness or the irregularities of the surfaces or, more specifically, the *actual* area of contact of the irregularities of the surfaces. This would seem to contradict rule 1.
2. The contact area of the surfaces, however, should depend on the force that presses the surfaces together, specifically, its perpendicular component. That is, increasing this force should increase the amount of contact surface and hence the friction. Rule 2 then seems logical.
3. Is it consistent that the friction between a sliding object and a surface be independent of the sliding speed? It would seem that the rate at which the surface irregularities met, which is dependent on the sliding speed, should have some effect.

With these thoughts in mind, the validity of the foregoing empirical rules will be investigated in this experiment. Although we apply these rules in analyzing friction, you might find experimentally that they are very general and, at best, approximations when applied to all materials and all situations.

After performing the experiment and analyzing the data, you should be able to:

1. Comment on the validity of the empirical rules of friction.
2. Describe how coefficients of friction are determined experimentally.
3. Tell why the normal reaction force of a surface on an object is used to express the frictional force rather than the weight of the object.

II. Equipment Needed

- Board with attached pulley
- Wooden block with hook (e.g., piece of 2 × 4 lumber or commercially available block)
- Weight hanger and set of weights
- String
- Protractor
- Laboratory balance
- Table clamp and support
- Meterstick
- Masking tape
- 2 sheets of Cartesian graph paper

(Optional)

- Phenolic block
- Aluminum block
- Wheel cart
- Lubricating powder

III. Theory

Considering the magnitude of the force of friction f to be proportional to the magnitude of the load or normal force N, we may write

$$f \propto N$$

or

$$f = \mu N \qquad \textbf{(10.1)}$$

where the Greek letter μ (mu) is a dimensionless constant of proportionality called the **coefficient of friction**.

Referring to the case in Fig. 10.1a, the load is the downward weight force of the block (mg). The normal reaction force of the surface on the block is equal ($N = mg$) and opposite to the load. It is customary to write the force of friction in terms of the normal force rather than the load force. As will be seen later, if a block is on an inclined plane, the load force pressing the surfaces together is not the weight of the block but a component of its weight. In any case, the magnitude of the normal force is always equal to the

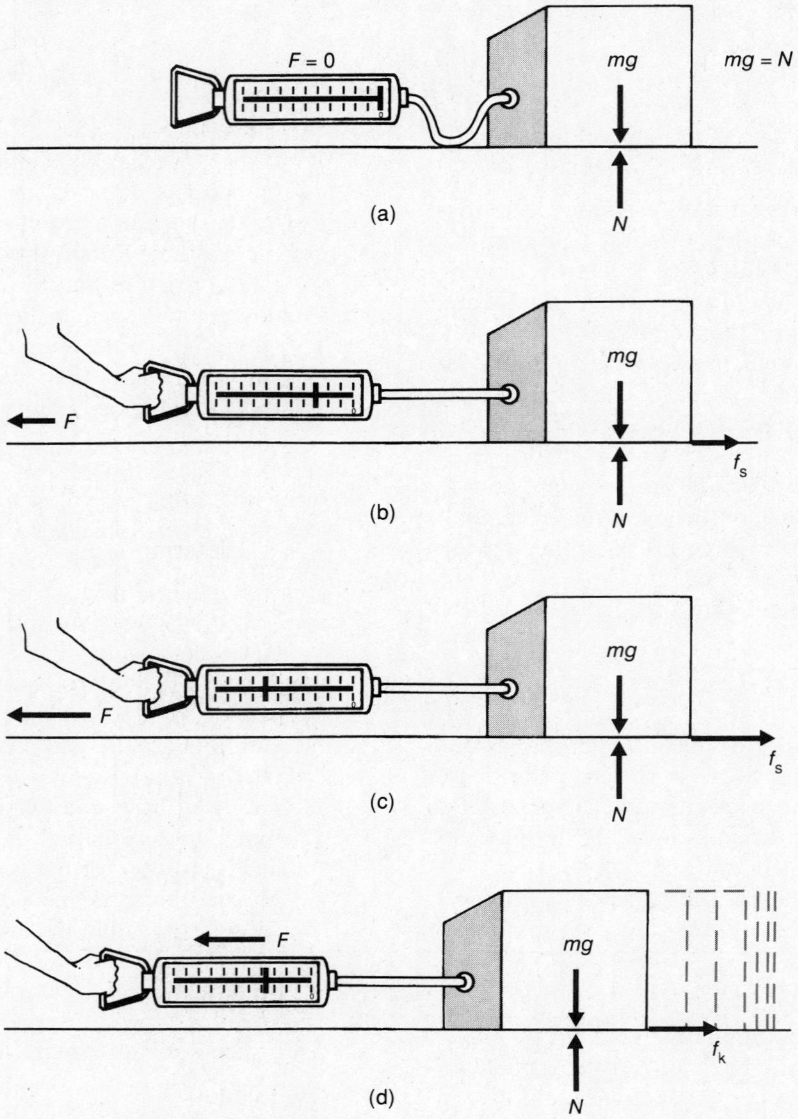

Figure 10.1 Friction. The applied force is balanced by the force of static friction f_s until its maximum value is reached. A slightly greater force sets the block into motion, and the applied force is opposed by the force of kinetic friction f_k.

magnitude of the force that presses the surfaces together.

When a force F is applied to the block parallel to the surface and no motion occurs, we say that the applied force is balanced by an opposite force of static friction, f_s, which is exerted on the block by the table along the surface of contact (Fig. 10.1b). As the magnitude of the applied force is increased, f_s increases to a *maximum* value given by (Fig. 10.1c)

$$f_s = \mu_s N \qquad \textbf{(10.2)}$$

where μ_s is the coefficient of static friction.* The maximum force of static friction is essentially equal and opposite to the smallest force applied parallel to the surface that will set the block into motion.

At the instant F becomes greater than $f_s = \mu_s N$, however slightly, the block is set into motion; the

* These conditions of f_s are sometimes written $f_s \leq \mu_s N$; that is, f_s is less than or equal to $\mu_s N$.

motion is opposed by the force of kinetic (sliding) friction f_k, and (Fig. 10.1d)

$$f_k = \mu_k N \qquad \textbf{(10.3)}$$

where μ_k is the coefficient of kinetic (sliding) friction.

In general, $\mu_k N < \mu_s N$, and the unbalanced force causes the block to accelerate. However, if the applied force is reduced so that the block moves with a uniform velocity, then $F = f_k = \mu_k N$.

Usually, for a given pair of surfaces, $\mu_k < \mu_s$. That is, it takes more force to overcome static friction (get an object moving) than to overcome kinetic friction (keep it moving). Both coefficients may be greater than one, but they are commonly less than one. The actual values depend on the nature and roughness of the surfaces.

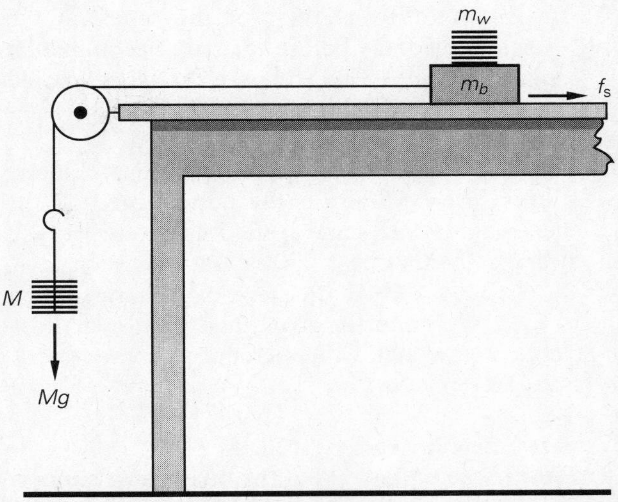

Figure 10.2 Coefficient of static friction. Experimental setup to determine μ_s.

IV. Experimental Procedure

A. *Determination of* μ_s

1. Determine the mass of the wooden block on a laboratory balance and record in the Laboratory Report.

2. Clean the surfaces of the board and block so they are free from dust and other contaminants. Place the board with the pulley near the edge of the table so that the pulley projects over the table's edge. Attach one end of a length of string to the wooden block and the other end to a weight hanger. Place the block flat on the board and run the string over the pulley so that the weight hanger is suspended over the end of the table (Fig 10.2). Be sure that the string is parallel to the board.

3. With the block lying on one of its sides of larger area, add weights to the hanger until the block just begins to move. (*Note*: If the 50-g hanger causes the block to move, add some weights m_w to the block.) Determine the required suspended mass within 1 gram. Record the weight force required to move the block in Data Table 1. (This is equal in magnitude to the normal force N.)

   Suggested experimental technique:

   (a) Keep the block in the middle of the plane.

   (b) Lift the block, gently lower it onto the plane, and *restrain* from moving for a count of five (*do not* press it against the plane), then release the block. If the block moves, the suspended mass M is too large; if it doesn't move, M is too small; if the block moves about half the time, M is about right.

4. Repeat procedure 3 with 100-, 200-, 300-, 400-, and 500-g masses, respectively, added to the block. Record the results in Data Table 1.

5. Plot the weight force just required to move the block (or the maximum force of static friction, $F = f_s$) versus the normal force N of the surface on the block [$N = (m_b + m_w)g$]. Draw a straight line that best fits the data. Include the point (0,0). (Why?)

   Since $f_s = \mu_s N$, the slope of the straight line is μ_s. Determine the slope and record in Data Table 1.

B. *Determination of* μ_k

Horizontal Board

6. When the block moves with a uniform speed, its acceleration is zero. The weight force F and the frictional force f_k are then equal and opposite ($F - f_k = ma = 0$, and $F = f_k$).

7. Using the larger side (surface area) of the block and the series of added masses as in part A, add mass to the weight hanger until a slight push on the block will cause it to move with a uniform speed. It may be helpful to tape the weights to the block. The required weight force for the motion in each case should be less than that for the corresponding case in part A. (Why?) Record the data in Data Table 2.

   Suggested experimental technique:

   (a) Begin with the block at one end of the plane and give it a push so that it slides across the entire plane.

(b) Observe the behavior of the block in the same region as before, namely in the middle of the plane. This is where the block should be observed for constant speed.

8. Plot the weight force (or the force of kinetic friction, $F = f_k$) versus the normal force N for these data on the same graph for part A. Draw a straight line that best fits the data.

Since $f_k = \mu_k N$, the slope of the straight line is μ_k. Determine the slope and record in Data Table 2. Calculate the percent decrease of μ_k from the μ_s value.

Elevated Board (Inclined Plane)

9. Elevate the pulley end of the board on a support to form an inclined plane (Fig. 10.3, see Fig. 11.3 for a similar setup). Note in the figure that the magnitude of the normal force is equal to a *component* of the weight force.

With the block lying on a *side* of its larger surface area, determine the angle θ of incline that will allow the block to slide down the plane with a constant speed after being given a slight tap. (No suspended weight is used in this case.) *Note*: The maximum angle before slipping *without* tapping gives μ_s, while the angle of constant velocity *with* tapping gives μ_k.

10. Using a protractor, measure the angle θ and record in Data Table 3. Also, with a meterstick, measure the length L of the base (along the table) and the height h of the inclined plane. Record the ratio h/L in Data Table 3.

11. Repeat this procedure for the block with the series of added masses as in the previous procedure for the horizontal board and record in Data Table 3. It may be helpful to tape the masses to the block.

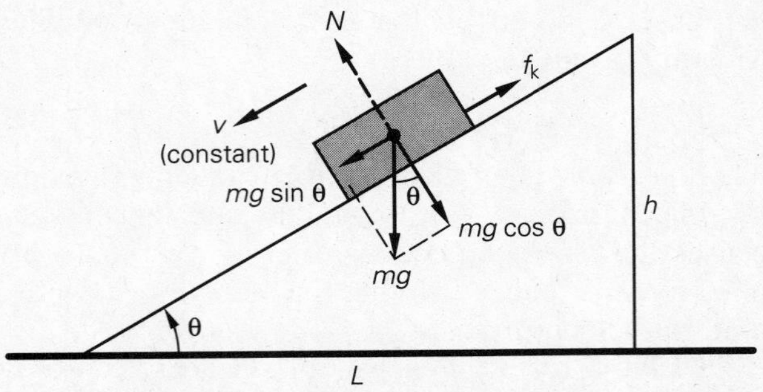

Figure 10.3 Coefficient of kinetic friction. Experimental setup to determine μ_k from the angle of incline.

12. Using your calculator or Table B5 in Appendix B, find the tangents of the θs, and record. Compute the average of these values and the average of the ratios of h/L. These averages should be similar. (Why?)

13. Compare the average value of tan θ with the value of μ_k found in the procedure for the horizontal board. It can be shown theoretically (Question 4) that $\tan\theta = \mu_k$ in this case. Compute the percent difference of the experimental values.

*C. Dependences of μ**

14. Use the *inclined plane method* to investigate the dependence of μ on area, material, velocity, rolling, and lubrication. The experimental setups are described in Data Table 4. Answer the questions listed after the data table.

* This experimental procedure and modifications were suggested by Professor I. L. Fischer, Bergen Community College, New Jersey.

Name ______________________ Section ______________ Date ______________

Lab Partner(s) ____

EXPERIMENT 10

Friction

Laboratory Report

Note: Attach graphs to Laboratory Report

Mass of block, m_b ______________

A. Determination of μ_s

DATA TABLE 1

Purpose: To investigate $f_s = \mu_s N$, where N depends on $m_b + m_w$, by measuring μ_s on a level plane (see Fig. 10.2).

m_w	0					
$N = (m_b + m_w)g$*						
$f_s = F = Mg$						

* It is convenient to express the force in terms of mg, where g is left in symbol form [e.g., $(0.250)g$ N], even when graphing.

Calculations
(show work)

μ_s ______________ (from graph)

Don't forget units

(continued)

B. Determination of μ_k

DATA TABLE 2

Purpose: To investigate $f_k = \mu_k N$, where N depends on $m_b + m_w$, by measuring μ_k on a level plane.

m_w	0					
$N = (m_b + m_w)g$						
$f_k = F = Mg$						

Calculations
(show work)

μ_k ______________
(from graph)

Percent decrease of
μ_k relative to μ_s ______________

DATA TABLE 3

Purpose: To investigate $\mu_k = \tan\theta$, where θ is independent of $m_b + m_w$, by measuring μ_k by inclined plane method (see Fig. 10.3).

m_w	0						
θ							Average
h/L							
$\tan\theta$							

Calculations
(show work)

Percent difference between
$\tan\theta = \mu_k$ and μ_k from Data Table 2 ______________

Name ______________________ Section ______________ Date ______________

Lab Partner(s) ____

EXPERIMENT 10 — *Laboratory Report*

C. Dependences of μ

DATA TABLE 4

Purpose: To investigate dependences of μ by various measurements using inclined plane method and other materials (if available).

No.	Conditions	θ	$\mu = \tan\theta$
1	Wooden block on larger area, static (μ_s)		
2	Wooden block on smaller area, static (μ_s)		
3	Wooden block on smaller area, kinetic (μ_k)		
Other materials			
4	Phenolic block		
5	Aluminum block, moving slowly		
6	Aluminum block, moving faster		
7	Wheeled cart		
8	Aluminum block with dry lubricating powder		
9	Phenolic block with dry lubricating powder		

(a) Compare No. 1 with Data Table 1: Is the inclined plane method valid for μ_s?

(b) Compare No. 2 with No. 1, and No. 3 with Data Table 3: Does μ depend on area?

(c) Compare Nos. 3, 4, and 5: Does μ_k depend on material?

(continued)

(d) Compare No. 5 with No. 6: Does μ_k depend on velocity?

(e) Compare No. 7 with anything: Does rolling friction compare with other types of friction?

(f) Compare Nos. 8 and 9 with Nos. 5 and 4: What is the effect of adding the lubricant?

QUESTIONS

1. Explain why $f_s \leqslant \mu_s N$; that is, why is f_s less than or equal to $\mu_s N$?

2. Speculate in terms of the microscopic surface irregularities as to why $\mu_k < \mu_s$ and what effect a lubricant has on the coefficient of friction.

Name ______________________ Section ______________ Date ______________

Lab Partner(s) ____

3. Why was it experimentally convenient to have the block move along the board with a uniform speed when determining the coefficient of kinetic friction?

4. (a) Prove that tan θ is equal to μ_k when the block slides down the incline with a constant speed. (Use symbols, not numbers.)

   (b) If θ is the maximum angle of incline just before the block moves, what is μ_s in terms of θ?

5. Suppose that the block were made to move up the inclined plane with a uniform speed by suspending masses on a string over the pulley. Derive an equation for the coefficient of kinetic friction for this case in terms of the suspended masses, the mass of the block, and the angle of decline. (Neglect any friction and mass effects of the pulley.)

(continued)

6. Draw and justify conclusions about the validity of the empirical rules for friction based on your experimental results. What does this tell you about applying general rules to all materials and about the nature of friction?

Name ______________________ Section ______________ Date ______________

Lab Partner(s) ____

EXPERIMENT 11

Work and Energy

Advance Study Assignment

Read the experiment and answer the following questions.

1. What is the difference between the conservation of mechanical energy and the conservation of total energy?

2. Is mechanical energy conserved in real situations? Explain.

3. Discuss the relationship of work and energy in pushing a car up an incline (a) with a constant speed and (b) with an acceleration.

4. Discuss the relationship of work and energy when a car rolls down an incline (a) with a constant speed and (b) with an acceleration.

(continued)

5. Under what conditions would the frictional forces be expected to be equal in magnitude for a car moving up an incline and a car moving down an incline?

6. Is the force of friction the same for different angles of incline if all other parameters are equal? Explain by specifically considering the angles used in the experiment.

Work and Energy

I. Introduction and Objectives

Work and **energy** are intimately related, as pointed out in a common definition of energy as being the ability to do work. That is, an object or system possessing energy has the *capability* of doing work. When work is done by a system, energy is expended; that is, the system loses energy. Conversely, when work is input to a system, the system gains energy.

In an ideal conservative system, energy is transferred back and forth between kinetic energy and potential energy. In such a system, the sum of the kinetic and potential energies is constant, as expressed by the law of conservation of mechanical energy. However, in actual systems, friction is always present, and these systems are nonconservative. That is, some energy is lost as a result of the work done against frictional forces. Even so, the *total* energy is conserved.

In this experiment you will make use of the conservation of energy to study the relationship between work and energy in the cases of a car rolling up and down an inclined plane. The ever-present frictional forces and the work done against friction will be investigated and taken into account so as to provide a better understanding of the concept of work-energy. To simplify matters, experimental conditions with constant speeds will be used so that only the relationship between work and changes in gravitational potential energy will have to be considered.

After performing this experiment and analyzing the data, you should be able to:

1. Explain how work and energy are related.
2. Describe how frictional work can be determined experimentally using either force-distance or energy considerations.
3. Better appreciate the nonconservative aspects of real situations and the difference between the conservation of mechanical energy and the conservation of total energy.

II. Equipment Needed

- Inclined plane with pulley and Hall's carriage (car)
- Weight hanger and slotted weights
- String
- Meterstick
- Protractor (if plane not so equipped)
- Laboratory balance

III. Theory

A. Work of Friction: Force-Distance Method

1. The situation for a car moving up an inclined plane with a constant velocity is illustrated in Fig. 11.1. Since the car is not accelerating, the force up the plane must be equal in magnitude to the sum of the forces down (parallel to) the plane:

$$F = F_{\parallel} + f$$

where f is the force of friction and $F_{\parallel} = m_c g \sin \theta$ is the component of the car's weight parallel to the plane.

Since the magnitude of F is equal to that of the weight force w_1, we may write

$$w_1 = F_{\parallel} + f$$

Then, solving for f and expressing the other forces in terms of the experimental parameters,

$$f = m_1 g - m_c g \sin \theta \qquad (11.1)$$

(car moving up)

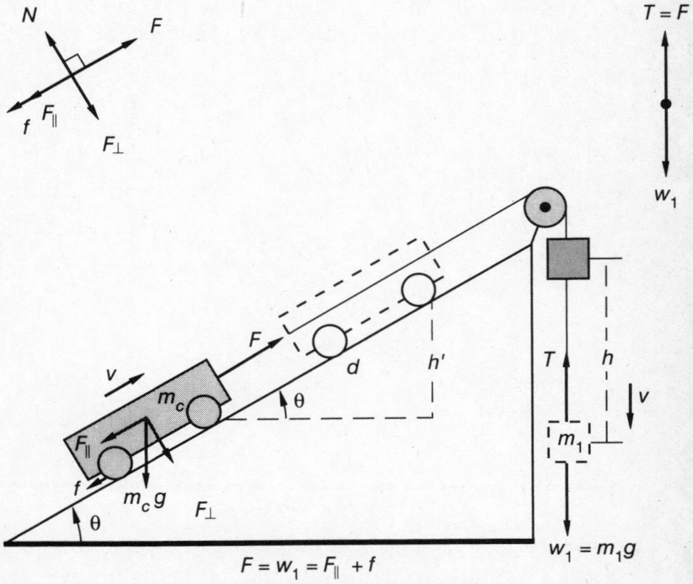

Figure 11.1 Car moving up incline with constant velocity. With no acceleration, the net force on the car is zero, and $F = F_{\parallel} + f = w_1$ (see free-body diagrams).

2. The situation for a car moving down an inclined plane with the same constant speed is illustrated in Fig. 11.2. Again, since the car is not accelerating, the sum of the forces up the plane must be equal in magnitude to the force down the plane, and

$$F_{\parallel} = F + f$$

where, in this case, the direction of f is up the plane. Since $F = w_2$,

$$F_{\parallel} = w_2 + f$$

and, expressing f as before,

$$f = m_c g \sin \theta - m_2 g \qquad \textbf{(11.2)}$$

(car moving down)

Then, in either case, the frictional work is given by

$$W_f = fd \qquad \textbf{(11.3)}$$

where d is the distance the car moves.

If the car moves approximately at the same constant speed in each case, it might be assumed that the magnitude of the frictional force f would be the same in each case (same angle of incline and load). This will be investigated experimentally.

B. *Work of Friction: Energy Method*

Another way of looking at the frictional work is in terms of energy.

1. For the case of the car moving up the plane, by the conservation of energy, the *decrease* in the potential energy of the descending weight on the weight hanger $\Delta U_w = m_1 gh$ is equal to the *increase* in the potential energy of the car $\Delta U_c = m_c gh'$ *plus* the energy lost to friction, which is equal to the work done against the force of friction W_f. That is,

$$\Delta U_w = \Delta U_c + W_f$$

or

$$W_f = \Delta U_w - \Delta U_c$$
$$= m_1 gh - m_c gh' \qquad \textbf{(11.4)}$$

(car moving up)

2. Similarly, for the case of the car moving down the plane, by the conservation of energy, the *decrease* in the potential energy of the descending car is equal to the *increase* in the potential energy of the ascending weight *plus* the work done against the force of friction:

$$\Delta U_c = \Delta U_w + W_f$$

or

$$W_f = \Delta U_c - \Delta U_w$$
$$= m_c gh' - m_2 gh \qquad \textbf{(11.5)}$$

(car moving down)

In terms of the experimental parameters, the methods for determining W_f are equivalent.

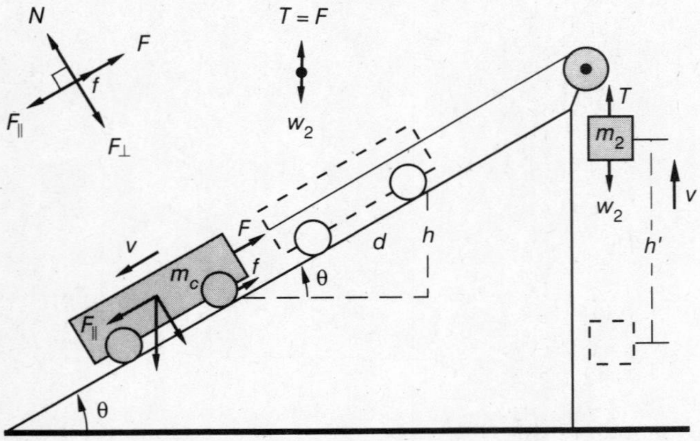

Figure 11.2 Car moving down incline with same constant speed. With no acceleration, the net force on the car is zero, and $F_{\parallel} = F + f = w_2 + f$ (see free-body diagrams).

IV. Experimental Procedure

1. Using a laboratory balance, determine the mass of the car m_c and record in the Laboratory Report.

2. Arrange the inclined plane and the car as shown in Fig. 11.3, with an angle of incline of $\theta = 30°$. Make certain that the pulley is adjusted so that the string attached to the car is parallel to the plane. (Should the car accelerate up the plane by the weight of the weight hanger alone, place some weights in the car so that the car is initially stationary. Add the additional mass to that of the car in Data Table 1.)

3. Add enough weights to the weight hanger so that the car moves up the incline with a slow uniform speed when the car is given a slight tap. Record the total suspended mass in Data Table 1.

4. With the car positioned near the bottom of the incline, mark the position of the car's front wheels and give the car a slight tap to set it into motion. Stop the car near the top of the plane after it moves up the plane (with a constant

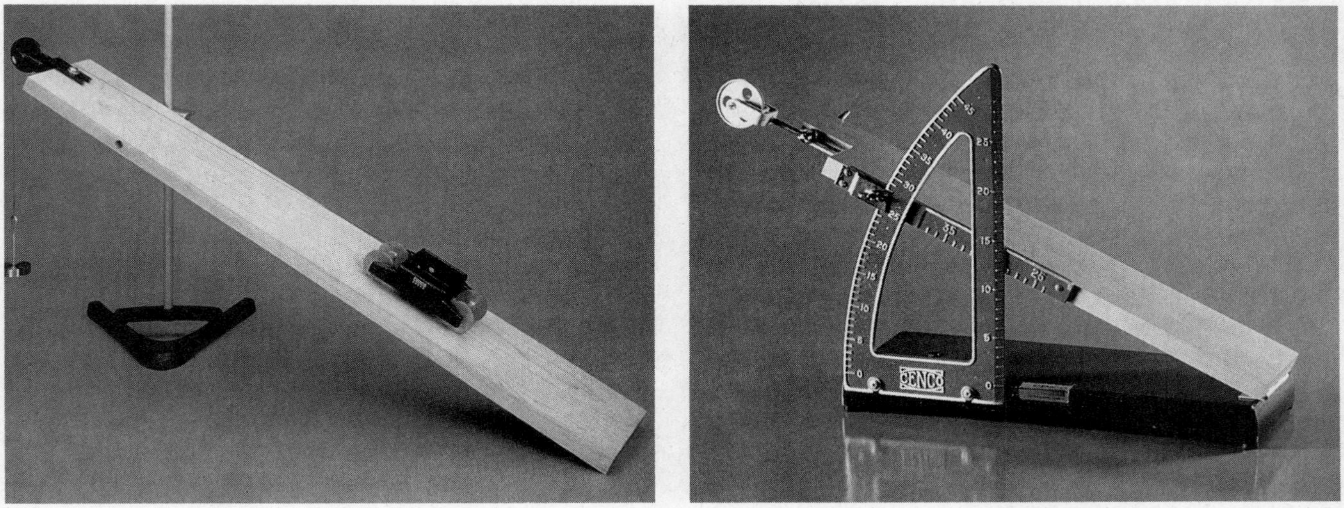

(a) (b)

Figure 11.3 Types of inclined plane apparatus. (a) Inclined plane board and stand. (b) Calibrated inclined plane. (Photos courtesy of Central Scientific Co., Inc.)

speed), and measure the distance of d it moved up the plane as determined by the stopped position of the car's front wheels. Or measure the height h the weight hanger descends. This corresponds to the situation in Fig. 11.1. The lengths d and h are the same. Record in Data Table 1.

5. With the car near the top of the plane, remove enough weights from the weight hanger so that the car rolls down the inclined plane with a slow uniform speed on being given a slight tap. Use as close to the same speed as for the upward case as is possible. This corresponds to the situation in Fig. 11.2. Record the total suspended mass in Data Table 1. For convenience, use the same d (or h) as in procedure 4.

6. Compute the frictional force f (Eqs. 11.1 and 11.2) and work done against friction W_f (Eq. 11.3) for each case. Show your calculations and record the results in Data Table 1.

7. Compare the frictional work for the two cases by computing the percent difference.

8. Adjust the angle of the inclined plane to $\theta = 45°$ and repeat procedures 3 through 7, recording your measurements in Data Table 2.

Name ______________________ Section ______________ Date ______________
Lab Partner(s) ____

EXPERIMENT 11

Work and Energy

Laboratory Report

Angle of incline ______________

DATA TABLE 1
Purpose: To determine work done against friction.

Mass of car, m_c ______________

		Suspended mass ( )	d ( )	f ( )	W_f ( )
Car moving up incline	m_1				
Car moving down incline	m_2				

Calculations
(show work)

Percent difference in W_f ______________

Don't forget units

(continued)

Angle of Incline ____________

DATA TABLE 2
Purpose: To determine work done against friction.

Mass of car, m_c ____________

		Suspended mass ( )	d ( )	f ( )	W_f ( )
Car moving up incline	m_1				
Car moving down incline	m_2				

Calculations
(show work)

Percent difference in W_f ____________

QUESTIONS

1. What was the work done by the suspended weight when the car (a) moved up the incline; and (b) moved down the incline? (*Show your calculations.*)

	$\theta = 30°$	$\theta = 45°$
Car moving up incline	____________	____________
Car moving down incline	____________	____________

Name ______________________ Section ______________ Date ______________

Lab Partner(s) ____

EXPERIMENT 11 *Laboratory Report*

2. What was the work done by gravity acting on the car when it (a) moved up the incline; and (b) moved down the incline. (*Show your calculations.*)

	$\theta = 30°$	$\theta = 45°$
Car moving up incline	______	______
Car moving down incline	______	______

3. (a) For the car going up the incline, what percentage of the work done by the suspended weight was lost to friction? (b) For the car moving down the incline, what percentage of the work done by gravity is lost to friction? (*Show your calculations.*)

	$\theta = 30°$	$\theta = 45°$
Car moving up incline	______	______
Car moving down incline	______	______

4. Taking W_f into account, what was the total or net work done by all three forces acting on the car when it (a) moved up the incline; and (b) moved down the incline? Justify your answer.

(continued)

5. Is the assumption justified that f would be the same for both up and down cases for the same constant speed? If not, speculate as to why there is a difference.

6. Assuming that $f = \mu N$ (see Experiment 10), show that the coefficient of (rolling) friction for the car moving down the inclined plane with a constant speed is given by $\mu = \tan\theta - \dfrac{m_2}{m_c \cos\theta}$. (Use symbols, not numbers.)

Name ______________________ Section ______________ Date ______________

Lab Partner(s) ____

EXPERIMENT 12

Torques, Equilibrium, and Center of Gravity

Advance Study Assignment

Read the experiment and answer the following questions.

1. What conditions must be present for (a) translational equilibrium and (b) rotational equilibrium of a rigid body?

2. If these conditions for equilibrium are satisfied, is the rigid body necessarily in static equilibrium? Explain.

3. Write a definition and a mathematical expression for torque.

(continued)

4. What is meant by clockwise and counterclockwise torques, and when are the sums of these torques on a rigid body equal?

5. What defines the center of gravity of a rigid body, and how is it related to the center of mass?

6. Define linear mass density. Also, what is implied if it is assumed that the linear mass density of an object is constant?

Torques, Equilibrium, and Center of Gravity

I. Introduction and Objectives

An important condition of rigid bodies in many practical applications is of **static equilibrium**. Examples include beams in bridges and beam balances. When a rigid body such as a beam or a rod is "in balance," it is at rest, or in static equilibrium. In particular, the beam is in rotational static equilibrium; it does not rotate about some point or axis of rotation.

The criterion for rotational static equilibrium is that the sum of the torques, or moments of force acting on a rigid body, be equal to zero. To study torques and rotational equilibrium, a "beam" balance in the form of a meterstick and suspended weights will be used. By using the "moment-of-force" method, the mass of an object will be determined experimentally and the experimental value compared to the mass of the object as measured on a laboratory balance. Also, the concepts of center of gravity and center of mass will be investigated.

After performing this experiment and analyzing the data, you should be able to:

1. Explain mechanical equilibrium and how it is applied to rigid bodies.
2. Distinguish between center of mass and center of gravity.
3. Describe how a laboratory beam balance measures mass.

II. Equipment Needed

- Meterstick
- Support stand
- Laboratory balance
- String and one knife-edge clamp *or* four knife-edge clamps (three with wire hangers)
- Four hooked weights (50 g, two 100 g, and 200 g)
- Unknown mass with hook

III. Theory

A. *Equilibrium*

The conditions for the mechanical equilibrium of a rigid body are

$$\Sigma \mathbf{F} = 0 \tag{12.1a}$$

$$\Sigma \boldsymbol{\tau} = 0 \tag{12.1b}$$

That is, the (vector) sums of the forces $\mathbf{F}$ and torques $\boldsymbol{\tau}$ acting on the body are zero.

The first condition, $\Sigma \mathbf{F} = 0$, is concerned with **translational equilibrium** and ensures that the object is at a particular location (not moving linearly) or that it is moving with a uniform linear velocity (Newton's first law of motion). In this experiment, the rigid body (the meterstick) is restricted from linear motion and $\Sigma \mathbf{F} = 0$ is automatically satisfied.

To be in static equilibrium, a rigid body must also be in rotational static equilibrium. Although the sum of the forces on the body may be zero and it is not moving linearly, it is possible that it may be rotating about some fixed axis of rotation. However, if the sum of the torques is zero, $\Sigma \boldsymbol{\tau} = 0$, the object is in **rotational equilibrium**, and either it does not rotate (static case) or it rotates with a uniform angular velocity. (Forces produce linear motion, and torques produce rotational motion.)

A **torque**, or **moment of force**, results from the application of a force acting at a distance from an axis of rotation (Fig. 12.1). The magnitude of the torque is equal to the product of the force's magnitude F and the perpendicular distance r from the axis of rotation to the force's line of action (a straight line through the force vector arrow). That is,

$$\tau = rF \tag{12.2}$$*

The perpendicular distance r is called the **lever arm** or **moment arm**. The unit of torque can be seen to be the meter-newton (m-N). Notice that these units are the same as those of work, newton-meter = joule. The units of torque are usually written meter-newton to emphasize the distinction.

Relative to an axis of rotation, a rigid body can rotate in only two senses, clockwise and counterclockwise. It is therefore customary to refer to clockwise torques and counterclockwise torques, that is,

* More fully, $\boldsymbol{\tau} = \mathbf{r} \times \mathbf{F}$, and $\tau = rF \sin\theta$, where θ is the angle between the $\mathbf{r}$ and $\mathbf{F}$ vectors.

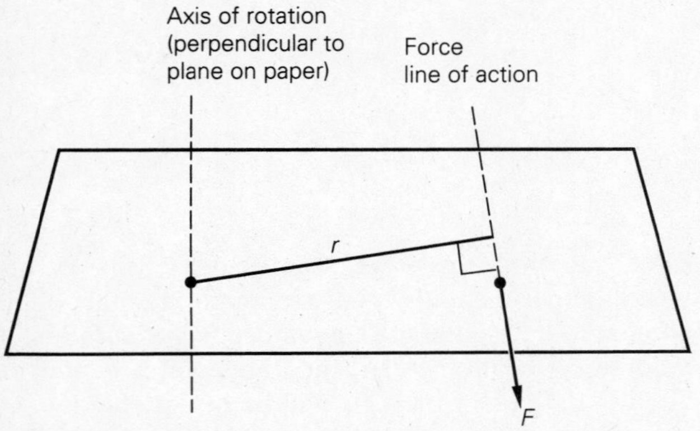

Figure 12.1 Torque. The magnitude of a torque is equal to the product of F and the perpendicular distance r from the axis of rotation to the force's line of action, $\tau = Fr$.

torques that may produce clockwise rotations and torques that may produce counterclockwise rotations about an axis of rotation. For example, in Fig. 12.2, taking the axis of rotation at the 50-cm position, F_1 and F_2 produce counterclockwise torques and F_3 and F_4 produce clockwise torques, but no rotation takes place if the torques are balanced and the system is in rotational static equilibrium.

The condition for rotational equilibrium is

$$\Sigma \boldsymbol{\tau} = \Sigma \boldsymbol{\tau}_{cc} + \Sigma \boldsymbol{\tau}_{cw} = 0 \qquad (12.3)$$

where $\boldsymbol{\tau}_{cc}$ and $\boldsymbol{\tau}_{cw}$ are counterclockwise and clockwise torques, respectively. Designating the directions arbitrarily by plus and minus signs, Equation 12.3 can be written

$$\Sigma \tau_{cc} - \Sigma \tau_{cw} = 0$$

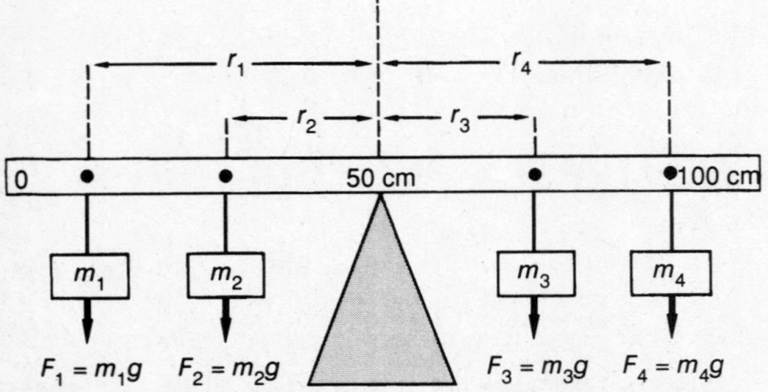

Figure 12.2 Torques in different directions. F_1 and F_2 give rise to counterclockwise torques, and F_3 and F_4 give rise to clockwise torques.

or

$$\Sigma \tau_{cc} = \Sigma \tau_{cw} \qquad (12.4)$$

(sum of counterclockwise torques = sum of clockwise torques.)

For example, for the rod in Figure 12.2, we have

$$\begin{array}{ccc} \textit{Counterclockwise} & & \textit{Clockwise} \\ \tau_1 + \tau_2 & = & \tau_3 + \tau_4 \end{array}$$

or

$$F_1r_1 + F_2r_2 = F_3r_3 + F_4r_4$$

The forces are due to weights suspended from the rod, and with $F = mg$,

$$m_1gr_1 + m_2gr_2 = m_3gr_3 + m_4gr_4 \qquad (12.5)$$

and, cancelling the gs,

$$m_1r_1 + m_2r_2 = m_3r_3 + m_4r_4$$

Example 12.1 Let $m_1 = m_3 = 50$ g,* $m_2 = m_4 = 100$ g in Fig. 12.2, where m_1, m_2, and m_3 are at the 10-, 40-, and 60-cm marks or positions, respectively, on the meterstick. Where would m_4 have to be suspended for the stick to be in static equilibrium?

Solution In static equilibrium, the sum of the torques is zero, or the sum of the counterclockwise torques is equal to the sum of the clockwise torques (Eq. 12.4),

$$\Sigma \tau_{cc} = \Sigma \tau_{cw}$$

In terms of forces and lever arms, we have (writing the forces first),

$$F_1r_1 + F_2r_2 = F_3r_3 + F_4r_4$$

where the forces are $F_i = m_ig$. The lever arms are measured from the 50-cm position of the meterstick, which is the pivot point, or the location of the axis of rotation. In general, $r_i = (50 \text{ cm} - x_i)$, where x_i is the centimeter location of a mass. Hence,

$$m_1g(50 \text{ cm} - 10 \text{ cm}) + m_2g(50 \text{ cm} - 40 \text{ cm}) = m_3g(60 \text{ cm} - 50 \text{ cm}) + m_4gr_4$$

and, cancelling the gs,

$$m_1(40 \text{ cm}) + m_2(10 \text{ cm}) = m_3(10 \text{ cm}) + m_4r_4$$

Then, putting in the mass values,

$$(50 \text{ g})(40 \text{ cm}) + (100 \text{ g})(10 \text{ cm}) = (50 \text{ g})(10 \text{ cm}) + (100 \text{ g})r_4$$

* Unfortunately, the official abbreviation for gram is g, and the commonly used symbol for acceleration due to gravity is also *g*. To help distinguish, the gravity *g* is written in italic and the gram g is not. Look closely to avoid confusion.

and solving for r_4,

$$r_4 = \frac{2500 \text{ g-cm}}{100 \text{ g}} = 25 \text{ cm}$$

Hence, for rotational equilibrium m_4 is 25 cm from the support position (axis of rotation), or at the 75-cm position on the meterstick (measured from the zero end).

B. Center of Gravity and Center of Mass

The gravitational torques due to "individual" mass particles of rigid body define what is known as the body's center of gravity. The **center of gravity** is the point of the body about which the sum of the gravitational torques about an axis through this point is zero. For example, consider the rod shown in Fig. 12.3. If the rod is visualized as being made up of individual mass particles and the point of support is selected such that $\Sigma \tau = 0$, then

$$\Sigma \tau_{cc} = \Sigma \tau_{cw}$$

or

$$\sum_{cc} (m_i g) r_i = \sum_{cw} (m_i g) r_i$$

and

$$(m_1 r_1 + m_2 r_2 + m_3 r_3 + \cdots)_{cc} = (m_1 r_1 + m_2 r_2 + m_3 r_3 + \cdots)_{cw}$$

When the rod is in equilibrium, it is supported by a force equal to its weight, and the support force is directed through the center of gravity. Hence, it is as though all of the object's weight (Mg) is concentrated at the center of gravity. That is, if you were blindfolded and supported an object at its center of gravity on your finger, weightwise you would not be able to tell if it were perhaps a rod or a block of equal mass.

If an object's weight were concentrated at its center of gravity, so would be its mass, and we often refer to an object's **center of mass** instead of its center of gravity. These points are the same as long as the acceleration due to gravity g is constant (uniform gravitational field). Notice how g can be factored and divided out of the previous *weight* equations, leaving *mass* equations.

Also, it should be evident that for a symmetric object with a uniform mass distribution, the center of gravity is located at the center of symmetry. For example, if a rod has a uniform mass distribution, its center of gravity is located at the center of the rod's length. (Why?)

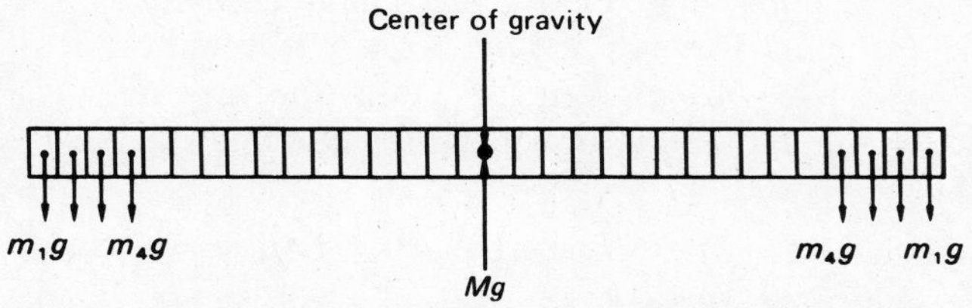

Figure 12.3 Center of gravity. A rod can be considered to be made of individual masses in rotational equilibrium when the vertical support force is directed through the center of gravity.

LINEAR MASS DENSITY

In part of the experiment, the masses of certain lengths of the meterstick will need to be known. These may be obtained from the **linear mass density** μ of the stick, i.e., the mass per unit length

$$\mu = \frac{m}{L} \qquad (12.6)$$

with units of grams/centimeter or kilograms/meter. For example, suppose a meterstick is measured to have a mass of 50 g on a balance. Then, since the stick is 100 cm long (L = 100 cm), the linear mass density of the stick is $\mu = m/L = 50$ g/100 cm = 0.50 g/cm. If the mass distribution of the stick were uniform, then every centimeter would have a mass of 0.50 g. However, metersticks are not uniform, so this is an average value.

Example 12.2 If a meterstick has a linear mass density of 0.50 g/cm, what is the mass of a 16-cm length of the stick?

Solution Since $\mu = m/L$, we have $m = \mu L$, and for $\mu = 0.50$ g/cm and $L = 16$ cm,

$$m = \mu L = (0.50 \text{ g/cm})(16 \text{ cm}) = 8.0 \text{ g}$$

IV. EXPERIMENTAL PROCEDURE

A. Apparatus with Support Point at Center of Gravity

1. A general experimental setup is illustrated in Fig. 12.4, where the masses or weights are suspended by clamp weight hangers. The hooked masses may also be suspended from small loops of string, which can be slid easily along the meterstick. The string allows the position of a mass to be read easily and may be held in place by a small piece of masking tape.
   (a) Determine the mass of the meterstick (without any clamps) and record in the Laboratory Report.

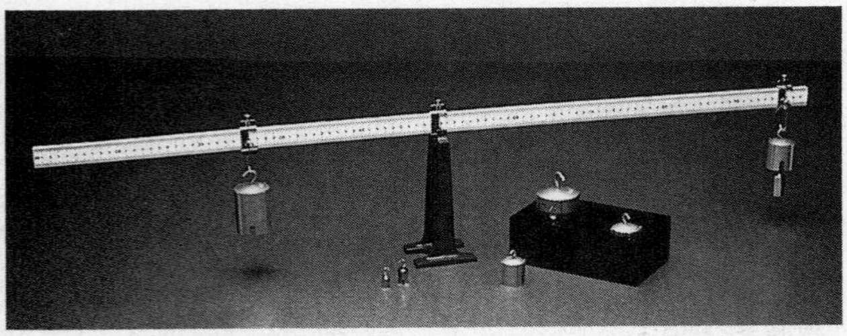

Figure 12.4 Torque apparatus. Example of experimental setup and equilibrium conditions. (Courtesy Sargent-Welch Scientific Co.)

(b) Weights may be suspended by loops of string or clamps with weight hangers. The string method is simpler; however, if you choose or are instructed to use weight hangers, weigh the three clamps together on a laboratory balance and compute the average mass of a clamp. Record in the Laboratory Report.

2. With a knife-edge clamp on the meterstick near its center, place the meterstick (without any suspended weights) on the support stand. Make certain that the knife edges are on the support stand. (The tightening screw head on the clamp will be down.) Adjust the meterstick through the clamp until the stick is balanced on the stand. Tighten the clamp screw and record in Data Table 1 the meterstick reading or the distance of the balancing point x_o from the zero end of the meterstick.

3. *Case 1: Two known masses.*
   (a) With the meterstick on the support stand at x_o, suspend a mass $m_1 = 100$ g at the 15-cm position on the meterstick, that is, 15 cm from the zero end of the meterstick.
   (b) Set up the conditions for static equilibrium by adjusting the moment arm of a mass $m_2 = 200$ g suspended on the side of the meterstick opposite m_1. Record the masses and moment arms in Data Table 1. If clamps are used instead of string, do not forget to add the masses of the clamps. Remember the moment arms are the distances from the pivot point to the masses (i.e., $r_i = |x_i - x_o|$).
   (c) Compute the torques and find the percent difference in the computed values (i.e., compare the clockwise torque with the counterclockwise torque).

4. *Case 2: Three known masses.*
   Case (a)
   (i) With the meterstick on the support stand at x_o, suspend $m_1 = 100$ g at the 30-cm position and $m_2 = 200$ g at the 70-cm position. Suspend $m_3 = 50$ g and adjust the moment arm of this mass so that the meterstick is in static equilibrium. Record the data in Data Table 1.
   (ii) Compute the torques and compare as in procedure 3.

   Case (b)
   (i) Calculate theoretically the lever arm (r_3) for the mass $m_3 = 50$ g for the system to be in equilibrium if $m_1 = 100$ g is at the 20-cm position and $m_2 = 200$ g is at the 60-cm position. (Remember to add the masses of the hanger clamps if used.) Record in the data table.
   (ii) Check your results experimentally, and compute the percent error of the experimental value of r_3, taking the previously calculated value as the accepted value.

5. *Case 3: Unknown mass—The balance principle.* A balance (scale) essentially uses the method of moments to compare an unknown mass with a known mass. Some balances have constant and equal lever arms, and others do not (see Fig. 2.2). This procedure will illustrate the balance principle.
   (a) With the meterstick on the support stand at x_o, suspend the unknown mass (m_1) near one end of the meterstick (e.g., at the 10-cm position). Suspend from the other side of the meterstick an appropriate known countermass m_2 (e.g., 200 g) and adjust its position until the meterstick is "in balance" or equilibrium. Record the value of the known mass and the moment arms in Data Table 1.
   (b) Remove the unknown mass and determine its mass on a laboratory balance.
   (c) Compute the value of the unknown mass by the method of moments and compare with the measured value by calculating the percent error.

6. *Case 4: Instructor's choice (optional).* Your instructor may have a particular case he or she would like you to investigate. If so, the conditions will be given. Space has been provided in the data table for reporting your findings.

B. Apparatus Supported at Different Pivot Points

In the previous cases, the mass of the meterstick was not explicitly taken into account since the fulcrum or the position of the support was at the meterstick's center of gravity or center of mass. In effect, the torques due to the mass of the meterstick on either side of the support position canceled each other. The centers of gravity of the lengths of the stick on either side of the support are equidistant from the support (e.g., at the 25-cm and 75-cm positions) and have equal masses and moment arms.

For the following cases, the meterstick will not be supported at its center-of-gravity position (x_o) but at some other pivot points (designated in general by x'_o, e.g., see Fig. 12.5). In these cases, the mass of the meterstick needs to be taken into account. To illustrate this very vividly, let's start off with a case with only one suspended mass.

7. *Case 5: Meterstick with one mass.* Suspend a mass $m_1 = 100$ g at or near the zero end of the meterstick (Fig. 12.5). If a string loop is used, a piece of tape to hold the string in position helps. Move the meterstick in the support clamp until the system is in equilibrium. (This case is analogous to the solitary seesaw—sitting on one side of a balanced seesaw with no one on the other side.) Record the support position x'_o in Data Table 2.

Since the meterstick is in balance (static equilibrium), the point of support must be at the center of gravity of the system [i.e., the torques (clockwise and counterclockwise) on either side of the meterstick must be equal]. But where is the mass or force on the side of the meterstick opposite the suspended mass? The balancing torque must be due to the mass of length L_2 of the meterstick (Fig. 12.5). To investigate this:

(a) Using the total mass m of the meterstick (measure previously) as m_2, with a moment arm r_2 (see the diagram in Data Table 2), compute the counterclockwise and clockwise torques, and compare by a percent difference. Record in Data Table 2.

(b) Now the masses of the lengths of meterstick will be taken into account. Compute the average linear mass density of the meterstick (see Theory, Section B) and record in the data table.

Assuming the mass of the meterstick to be uniformly distributed, the center of mass (or center of gravity) of the length of meterstick L_2 on the *opposite* side of the support from m_1 would be at its center position (see Fig. 12.5). Compute the mass m_2 of this length of stick (see Example 12.2) and record. Also, record the center position of L_2, where this mass is considered concentrated (x_2), and find the length of the lever arm r_2. It should be evident that $r_2 = L_2/2$.

Compute the torque due to m_2 and record it as τ_{cw}. From the linear mass density compute the m_3 of the portion of the meterstick remaining to the left of the pivot. Calculate the torque due to this portion of the meterstick and add it to the torque due to mass m_1 to find the total counterclockwise torque and record it as τ_{cc}. Compare the torque *differences* with those found in Case 5(a).

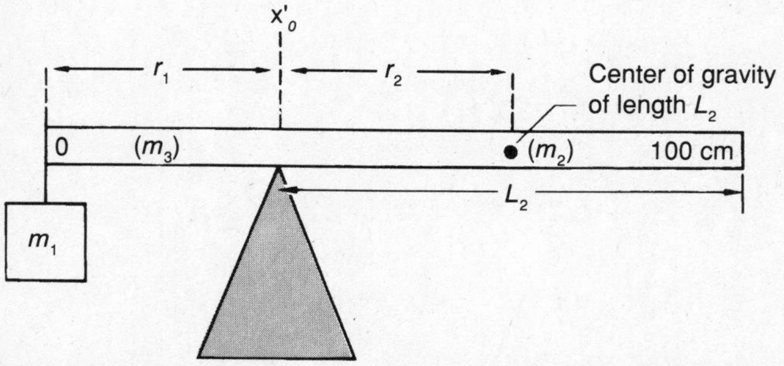

Figure 12.5 Equilibrium. A meterstick in equilibrium with one suspended mass.

8. *Case 6: Center of gravity.*

(a) With a mass $m_1 = 100$ g positioned at or near one end of the meterstick as in Case 5, suspend a mass $m_2 = 100$ g on the opposite side of the support stand at the 60-cm position. Adjust the meterstick in the support-stand clamp until the stick is in balance. This locates the center of gravity x'_o of the system. Record in Data Table 2 and find r_1 and r_2.

(b) Repeat the procedure with m_2 positioned at 70 cm.

(c) Repeat the procedure with m_2 positioned at 80 cm.

Notice how the position of the center of gravity moves as the mass distribution is varied.

(d) Based on the experimental data, what would you predict the position of the center of gravity x'_o of the system to be if m_2 were moved to the 90-cm position? Record your prediction in the data table.

Using your prediction, compute the counterclockwise and clockwise torques, taking into account the mass of the meterstick as in procedure 7(c). Compare the torques by computing the percent difference.

Experimentally determine the position of the center of gravity of the system and compute the percent difference between the experimental and predicted values.

Name ______________________ Section ______________ Date ______________
Lab Partner(s) ____

E X P E R I M E N T 1 2

Torques, Equilibrium, and Center of Gravity

Laboratory Report

A. Apparatus with Point of Support at Center of Gravity

Mass of meterstick ______________ Total mass of clamps ______________

Average mass of one clamp m_c ______________
Balancing position (center of gravity) of meterstick x_o ______________

DATA TABLE 1

Diagram*	Values (add m_c to masses if clamps used)	Moment (lever) arms	Results†
Case 1 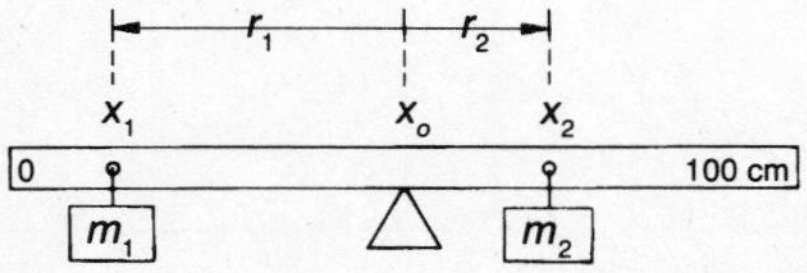	m_1 ______ x_1 = 15 cm m_2 ______ x_2 ______	r_1 ______ r_2 ______	τ_{cc} ______ τ_{cw} ______ Percent diff. ______
Case 2(a)	m_1 ______ x_1 = 30 cm m_2 ______ x_2 = 70 cm m_3 ______ x_3 ______	r_1 ______ r_2 ______ r_3 ______	τ_{cc} ______ τ_{cw} ______ Percent diff. ______
Case 2(b)	m_1 ______ x_1 = 20 cm m_2 ______ x_2 = 60 cm m_3 ______ x_3 ______	r_1 ______ r_2 ______	r_3 ______ (calculated) r_3 ______ (measured) Percent error ______

* Draw a diagram to illustrate each case, using Case 1 diagram as an example.
† Attach a sheet to the Laboratory Report showing calculations for each use.

Don't forget units

(continued)

Diagram*	Values (add m_c to masses if clamps used)	Moment (lever) arms	Results†
Case 3	x_1 ______ (known) m_2 ______ (known) x_2 ______ (from expt.)	r_1 ______ r_2 ______	m_1 ______ (measured) m_1 ______ (calculated) Percent error ______
Case 4 (instructor's option)			

* Draw a diagram to illustrate each case, using Case 1 diagram as an example.
† Attach a sheet to the Laboratory Report showing calculations for each use.

B. Apparatus Supported at Different Pivot Points

DATA TABLE 2 Linear mass density of meterstick, $\mu = m/L$ ______

Diagram*	Values (add m_c if appl.)	Moment (lever) arms	Results†
Case 5(a) 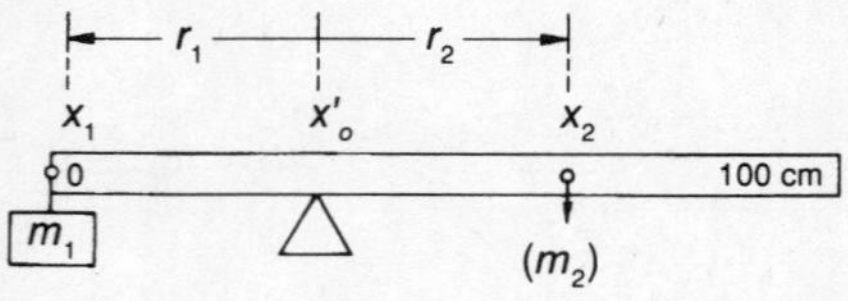	m_1 ______ x_1 ______ m_2 ______ x_2 ______ x'_o ______	r_1 ______ r_2 ______	τ_{cc} ______ τ_{cw} ______ Torque differences (show below table)
Case 5(b)	m_1 ______ x_1 ______ m_2 ______ x_2 ______ m_3 ______ x_3 ______ x'_o ______	r_1 ______ r_2 ______ r_3 ______	τ_{cc} ______ τ_{cw} ______ Torque differences (show below table)

Name ______________________ Section ______________ Date ______________

Lab Partner(s) ____

EXPERIMENT 12 *Laboratory Report*

Diagram*	Values (add m_c if appl.)	Moment (lever) arms	Results†
Case 6(a)	m_1 ______ $x_1 = 0$ cm m_2 ______ $x_2 = 60$ cm x'_o ______	r_1 ______ r_2 ______	
Case 6(b)	same except $x_2 = 70$ cm x'_o ______	r_1 ______ r_2 ______	
Case 6(c)	same except $x_2 = 80$ cm x'_o ______	r_1 ______ r_2 ______	
Case 6(d)	same except $x_2 = 90$ cm x'_o ______ (predicted)	τ_{cc} ______ τ_{cw} ______ Percent diff. ______	x'_o ______ (measured) Percent diff. ______

* Draw a diagram to illustrate each case, using Case 5(a) diagram as an example. Put the mass of a length of stick in parentheses as in that diagram.

† Attach a sheet to the Laboratory Report showing calculations for each use.

QUESTIONS (answer those applicable)

1. Explain how the condition $\Sigma \mathbf{F} = 0$ is satisfied for the meterstick in part A of the experiment.

(continued)

2. In many instances, the balancing position x_o of the meterstick by itself (procedure 2) is not at 50 cm. Explain why this is the case.

3. Explain the principle of the triple-beam laboratory balance (see Experiment 2).

4. Suppose in a situation as in Case 2(a) in the experiment, $m_1 = 200$ g were at the 20-cm position and $m_2 = 100$ g at the 65-cm position. Would there be a problem in experimentally balancing the system with $m_3 = 50$ g? Explain. If so, how might the problem be resolved?

5. Describe the effects of taking the mass of the meterstick into account when the balancing position is not near the 50-cm position.

Name ______________________ Section ______________ Date ______________

Lab Partner(s) ____

EXPERIMENT 12 — *Laboratory Report*

6. (*Optional*) A uniform meterstick is in static rotational equilibrium when a mass of 220 g is suspended from the 5.0-cm mark, a mass of 120 g is suspended from the 90-cm mark, and the support stand is placed at the 40-cm mark. What is the mass of the meterstick?

Name ______________________ Section ______________ Date ______________

Lab Partner(s) ____

EXPERIMENT 13

Rotational Motion and Moment of Inertia

Advance Study Assignment

Read the experiment and answer the following questions.

1. What are the rotational analogs of force, mass, and Newton's second law?

2. Define moment of inertia. How is torque related to moment of inertia?

3. Describe two methods by which the moment of inertia of a body may be experimentally determined.

4. How is the frictional torque of a rotating system experimentally determined or compensated for?

(continued)

5. Explain how tangential and angular velocities and accelerations are related to one another.

6. When a body or system is a composite of regularly shaped bodies, what is the moment of inertia of the system about a coaxis along the component bodies' axes of symmetry?

7. A solid cylindrical object has a mass of 2.0 kg and a diameter and length of 0.10 m and 0.18 m, respectively. What is the moment of inertia of the body about an axis along the axis of the cylinder? Show your work.

Rotational Motion and Moment of Inertia

I. Introduction and Objectives

In the case of linear motion, an unbalanced force **F** acting on an object gives it an acceleration **a**, and by Newton's second law,

$$\mathbf{F} = m\mathbf{a}$$

where m is the mass of the object. For **rotational motion**, an unbalanced torque $\boldsymbol{\tau}$ acting on a body causes it to rotate (i.e., gives it an angular acceleration $\boldsymbol{\alpha}$). The rotational analog of Newton's second law is

$$\boldsymbol{\tau} = I\boldsymbol{\alpha}$$

where I is the moment of inertia of the body.

The **moment of inertia** of a body depends on its mass distribution and shape. For a symmetrical, homogeneous object, the moment of inertia can be derived theoretically using calculus methods and is expressed in terms of the object's total mass and dimensions. By determining these quantities, the moment of inertia can be calculated.

However, the moment of inertia of an object can also be determined experimentally from the dynamical equation $\tau = I\alpha$ by measuring τ and α, or from energy considerations, because the rotational kinetic energy is $\frac{1}{2}I\omega^2$.

In this experiment the theoretical and experimental values of the moments of inertia of some common, regularly shaped objects will be determined and compared. The experimental procedures will provide a good insight into the concepts of rotational motion and the moment of inertia. Several types of apparatus are described. The experiment is rather involved and will test your experimental skills. Read the Theory and Procedure sections well.

After performing this experiment and analyzing the data, you should be able to:

1. Explain the relationships involving torque, rotational motion, and rotational energy.
2. Tell what is meant by the moment of inertia of a rigid body and on what this quantity depends.
3. Describe the parallel axis theorem and how it can be practically applied.

II. Equipment Needed

General

- Meterstick
- String
- Weight hanger and weights
- Laboratory timer or stopwatch
- Laboratory balance (kilogram range)
- Vernier calipers
- Large calipers
- Safety glasses

A. Rotational Inertia Apparatus (Figure 13.6) or Similar Apparatus

- One sheet of Cartesian graph paper

B. Rotating Support with Accessories (Figure 13.4)

- Cylindrical ring
- Disk
- Bar attachment (optional)
- Two cylinders
- Table clamp
- Support rod
- Two right-angle clamps
- One or two pulleys (depending on setup)

C. *Moment of Inertia Accessory (for centripetal force apparatus, see Figure 13.7)*

- Two sheets of Cartesian graph paper

(*Optional*)

- Computer-assisted analysis of rotational motion with PASCO rotational apparatus

III. Theory

An unbalanced force **F** applied any distance from a body's axis of rotation produces an unbalanced torque $\boldsymbol{\tau}$, the magnitude of which is given by

$$\tau = rF \tag{13.1}$$

where r is the perpendicular distance from the axis of rotation to the force's line of action, a line running through the force vector (Fig. 13.1). For a particle of mass m,

$$\tau = rF = r(ma) = mra$$

where a is the tangential acceleration. Using the relationship between the magnitudes of angular acceleration (α) and tangential acceleration, $a = r\alpha$, we obtain

$$\tau = mr(r\alpha) = (mr^2)\alpha = I\alpha$$

where the moment of inertia $I = mr^2$.

A rigid body is a system of particles, and summing this product for all the individual particles yields

$$\tau = (\Sigma_i m_i r_i^2)\alpha$$
$$= I\alpha \tag{13.2}$$

where the **moment of inertia** for a rigid body is $I = \Sigma_i m_i r_i^2$. Calculus methods may be used to evaluate

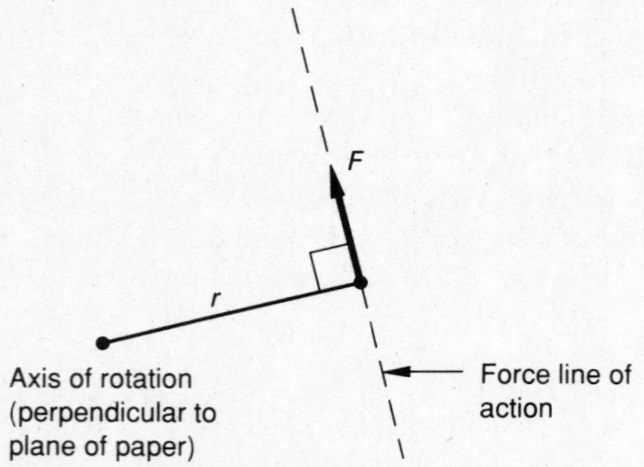

Figure 13.1 Torque. The magnitude of the torque is the product of the force and the perpendicular distance r from the axis of rotation to the force's line of action ($\tau = rF$).

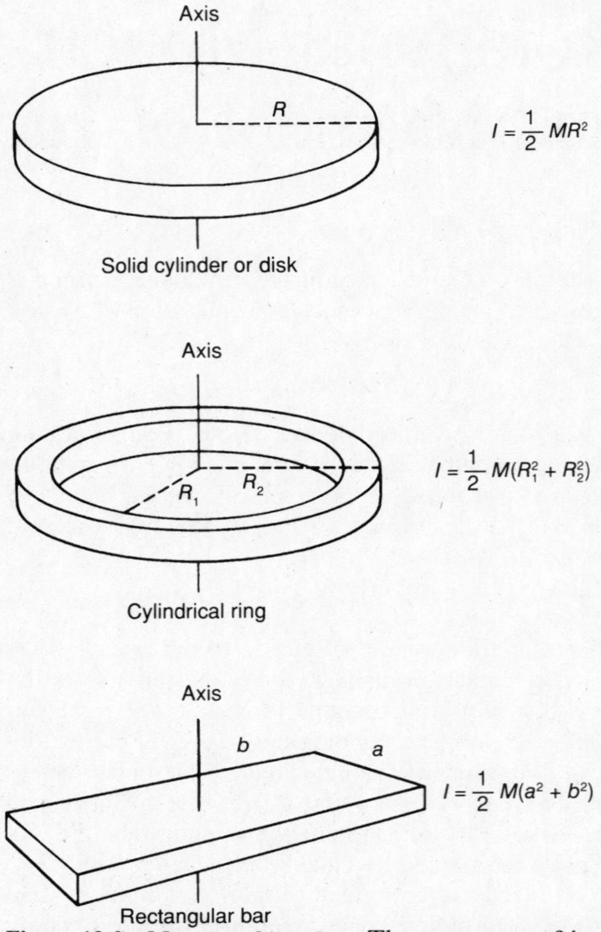

Figure 13.2 Moment of inertia. The moments of inertia for some uniform, regularly shaped objects.

this expression for regularly shaped bodies, and the moments of inertia of several such bodies are given in Fig. 13.2.

When the torque is supplied by a constant-weight force as in Fig. 13.3, the magnitudes of the angular velocity and angular acceleration of the rotating body can be found from measurements of the distance y the weight descends from rest and the time t it takes the weight to travel this distance. The magnitude of the average velocity $\bar{v}$ is given by

$$\bar{v} = \frac{y}{t} \tag{13.3}$$

Using the kinematic equation for average velocity for motion with constant acceleration,

$$\bar{v} = \frac{v + v_o}{2}$$

the magnitude of the final velocity v of the descending weight with $v_o = 0$ is given by

$$\bar{v} = \frac{v}{2}$$

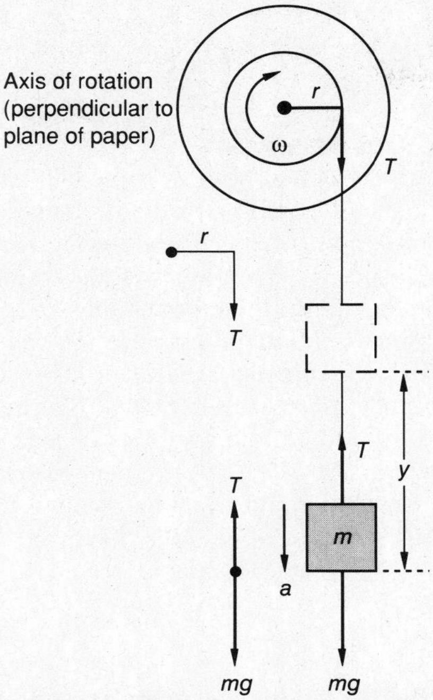

Figure 13.3 Applied torque. A torque being applied by a constant-weight force.

or

$$v = 2\bar{v} = \frac{2y}{t} \qquad \textbf{(13.4)}$$

The angular velocity has a magnitude, then, of

$$\omega = \frac{v}{r} = \frac{2\bar{v}}{r} \qquad \textbf{(13.5)}$$

where r is the radius of the axle. Also,

$$v = at$$

or

$$a = \frac{v}{t}$$

and

$$\alpha = \frac{a}{r} \qquad \textbf{(13.6)}$$

From the forces acting on the descending mass (Fig. 13.3), the acceleration is given by Newton's second law:

$$mg - T = ma$$

or

$$T = mg - ma = m(g - a) \qquad \textbf{(13.7)}$$

where T is the magnitude of the tension force in the string. The magnitude of the applied torque, τ_a is then

$$\tau_a = rT \qquad \textbf{(13.8)}$$

Two torques are acting on the wheel and axle, the applied torque τ_a and an opposing frictional torque τ_f due to the friction on the bearings of the rotating axle. The frictional torque is assumed to be constant. The magnitude of the net torque, $\tau = I\alpha$, may then be written

$$\tau = \tau_a - \tau_f = I\alpha$$

so that

$$\tau_a = I\alpha + \tau_f \qquad \textbf{(13.9)}$$

Determination of I

The moment of inertia I of a system can be found from Eq. 13.9 using experimentally determined values of τ_a, α, and τ_f. The frictional torque can be determined or taken into account as follows:

(a) Determine the suspended mass m_o needed to cause the body to rotate with a constant angular speed ω (i.e., $\alpha = 0$). Then $\tau_f = \tau_a = rT = r(m_o g)$. In this case, the frictional torque is balanced or vectorially canceled by the applied torque due to m_o.

(b) Since I and τ_f are constants, by determining the α's for two or more τ_a's, both I and τ_f can be determined from the set of equations (Eq. 13.9) for the different conditions or determined graphically.

In some instances, the rotating body may be symmetric, but a moment arm cannot be measured for the complete body (e.g., the rotating support in Fig. 13.4). In this case, the moment of inertia can be found from energy considerations, which can also be used to find the moment of inertia of a body with a well-defined moment arm.

The potential energy lost by the descending mass in the setup in Fig. 13.4 goes into the linear kinetic energy of the mass and the rotational kinetic energy of the rotating body (neglecting frictional losses). By the conservation of energy,

$$\text{energy lost} = \text{energy gained}$$

$$mgy = \tfrac{1}{2}mv^2 + \tfrac{1}{2}I\omega^2 \qquad \textbf{(13.10)}$$

where all the quantities except I are known or can be calculated from experimental data.

The energy lost to friction can be accounted for by adding the term $m_o gy$ to the right side of Eq. 13.10, where m_o is the mass determined in (a) above.

When a body is a composite of two or more regular bodies (e.g., a wheel and axle), the moment of inertia of the system about a coaxis along the component bodies' axes of symmetry is the sum of the moments of inertia of each of the component bodies (i.e., $I = I_1 + I_2 + \cdots$).

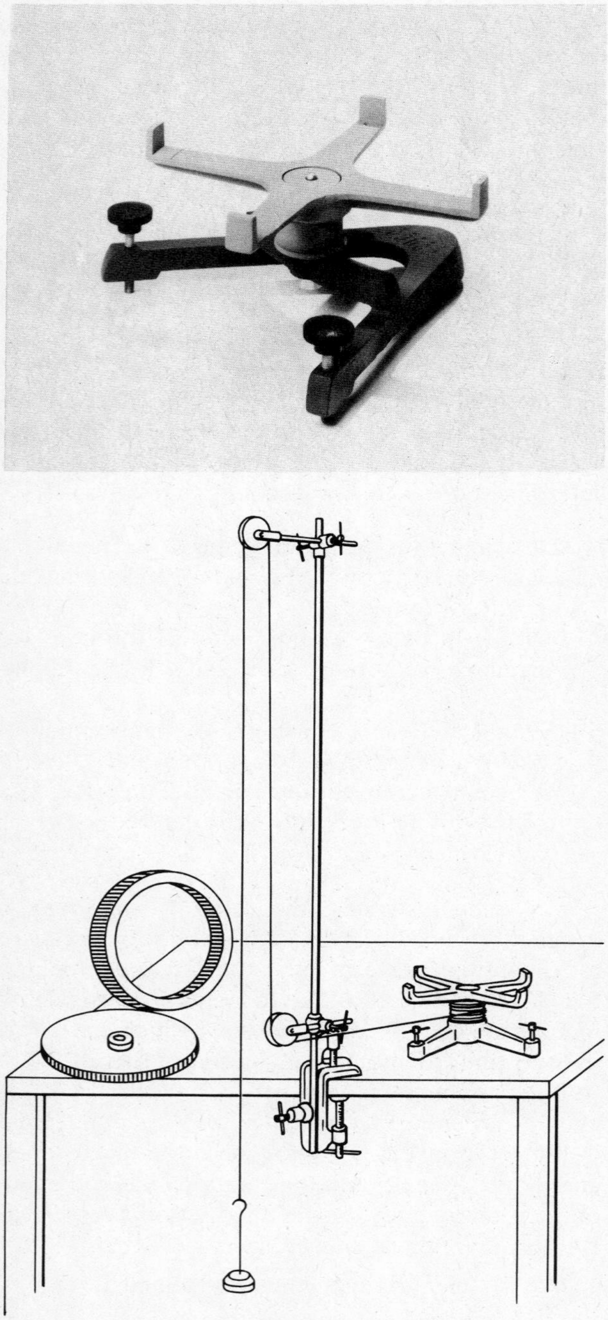

Figure 13.4 **Moment of inertia apparatus.** A rotating support and illustration of experimental setup and accessories. (Courtesy of Central Scientific Co., Inc.)

When the system consists of a regularly shaped accessory body mounted on the rotating support with the axis of rotation through the center of mass (symmetry) of the accessory body, the total moment of inertia I of the system is $I = I_s + I_a$, where I_s and I_a are the moments of inertia of the support and accessory body, respectively. The moment of inertia of the accessory body is then $I_a = I - I_s$, where I and I_s are measured independently by one of the previously described methods.

Parallel Axis Theorem

For a system of regular bodies, some of which do not have the axis of rotation through their centers of mass, the moment of inertia of the system can be calculated using the parallel axis theorem. Such a system is that of the cylindrical masses placed on opposite arms of the metal cross of the rotating support or a bar attachment, as shown in Fig. 13.5.

The **parallel axis theorem** states that the moment of inertia of a body about any axis O' parallel to an axis through the body's center of mass is equal to the moment of inertia about the axis through the center of mass plus the mass of the body times the square of the distance between the axes:

$$I_{o'} = I_{\text{cm}} + Md^2 \tag{13.11}$$

Then the total moment of inertia I for the system shown in Fig. 13.5 (identical cylinders) about an axis through O' is

$$\begin{aligned} I &= I_s + I_b + I_c + I_c \\ &= I_s + I_b + 2I_c \end{aligned}$$

where I_s is the moment of inertia of the rotating support, I_b the moment of inertia of the bar, and I_c the moment of inertia of one of the cylinders.

The axis of rotation is through the centers of mass of the support and the bar, so I_s and I_b can be determined by previously described methods. By the parallel axis theorem,

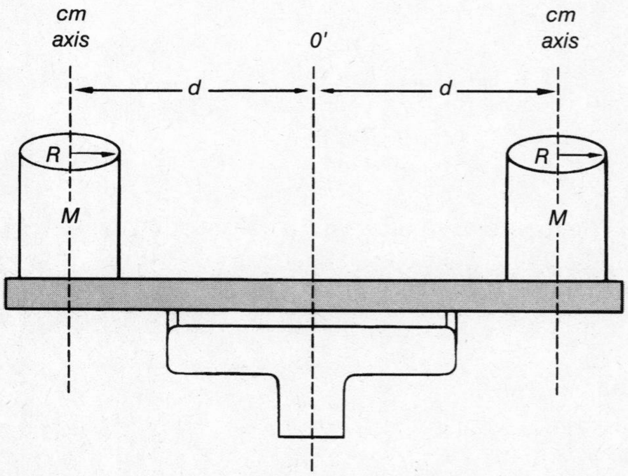

Figure 13.5 Parallel axis theorem. The moment of inertia of a system of regularly shaped objects can be calculated using the parallel axis theorem. See text for description.

$$I_c = I_{cm} + Md^2$$

where I_{cm} for a cylinder is $I_{cm} = \frac{1}{2}MR^2$ (see Fig. 13.2). Although convenient, it is not necessary that the cylinders be placed equal distances from the axis of rotation (different d's are used if they are not at equal distances).

IV. Experimental Procedure

A. *Rotational Inertia Apparatus (Wheel and Axle)*

1. A rotational inertia apparatus is shown in Fig. 13.6. It is essentially a wheel and axle, a large heavy wheel or disk with a concentric axle hub that rotates freely on bearing mounts.*

2. Measure the diameter of the disk with the large calipers and the diameter of the axle hub with the vernier calipers and record in Data Table 1. Also record the total mass of the wheel and axle, which is usually stamped on the wheel.

3. Fix one end of a length of string to the set pin in the axle, and wrap the string around the hub axle in a single layer. The string should be sufficiently long to allow weights attached to the free end of the string to descend to the floor.

   Making a loop in the free end of the string, attach just enough weight to the string so that the disk, when given a slight start, rotates with a uniform angular speed as the weight descends. (The ordinary 50-g weight hanger will probably be too large. Put smaller weights in the string loop.)

   When the disk rotates with a uniform angular speed, the weight descends with uniform linear speed, and this may be easier to judge than the disk's rotational speed.

   Record the mass of the descending weight m_o in Data Table 1. (This will be used in a direct calculation of τ_f.)

4. Remove the weights from the string loop and attach a 0.050-kg (50-g) weight hanger. Measure the distance of the bottom of the weight hanger from the floor with the string wrapped around the smaller axle, and record in Data Table 1.

   Releasing the weight hanger, measure the time it takes to reach the floor and record. [Newer models of the apparatus have a platform on which the mass initially rests. The experimental run is initiated by tripping the platform (Fig. 13.6). Also, some rotational inertia apparatus may be equipped with spark timers. Consult your instructor for operating instructions.] Repeat the timing procedure twice more for the same distance of descent.

* Some older inertia wheels have two concentric axles with different size radii. In this case, record both radii and descend two mass from each in the following procedures.

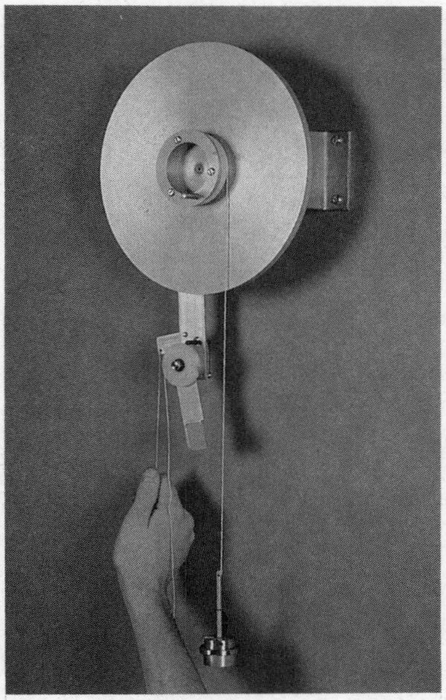

Figure 13.6 Rotational inertia wheel apparatus. Wheel and axle used in experimental setup. (Courtesy Sargent-Welch Scientific Co.)

5. Repeat the timing procedures (three trials) for three more *total* masses of 0.075 kg, 0.10 kg, and 0.125 kg (or different appropriate masses).

6. Compute the average time of descent for each case, and using Eqs. 13.3 through 13.8, calculate the magnitudes of the quantities called for in the Laboratory Report.

7. Notice that Eq. 13.9, $\tau_a = I\alpha + \tau_f$, is of the form of a straight line,

$$y = mx + b$$

   where m is the slope of the line and b its y intercept. Plot τ_a versus α for the data in Data Table 1 and draw the straight line that best fits the data. Determine the slope I and the y intercept τ_f. Compare these values with the computed theoretical values by calculating the percent differences. (See Determination of I in Theory Section.)

8. *Moment of inertia from conservation of energy.* Using Eq. 13.10, find the moment of inertia of the wheel and axle using the data from the final

descending weight case trial. (*Note*: The mass used on the left side of this equation should be the mass of the descending weight *minus* the mass of the descending weight in the constant angular speed case of procedure 3. Why?)

Compare the moment of inertia determined from Eq. 13.10 with the computed theoretical value by calculating the percent difference.

B. Rotating Support and Accessory Bodies

9. A rotating support and some accessories are shown in Fig. 13.4. The rotating support consists of a light metal cross mounted on ball bearings so as to rotate in a horizontal plane about a vertical axis.

10. With the vernier calipers, measure the diameter of the drum of the rotating support and record in Data Table 2. (The string unwinds from the drum.) With the appropriate instruments, measure the linear dimensions of the accessory bodies needed to calculate the theoretical moments of inertia. (Refer to Fig. 13.2.) Also, determine the masses of the accessory bodies on a laboratory balance and record.*

11. Use a pulley arrangement similar to the one in Fig. 13.4 so that the descent distance of the driving weight is at least 1 m. Attach one end of a length of string to the rotating support drum and wrap the string around the drum in a single layer. The length of the string should be sufficient to allow weights attached to the free end of the string to descend to the floor.

Making a loop in the free end of the string, attach just enough weight (mass m_o) to the string so that, when given a slight start, the cross of the rotating support rotates with a uniform speed as the weight descends. (The ordinary 50-g weight hanger will probably be too large. If so, put some smaller weights in the string loop.)

The weight should also descend with a uniform speed, which may be easier to judge. Make certain the string unwinding from the drum is parallel to the table top.

Record the mass of the descending weight m_o in Data Table 2.

12. Remove the weights from the string loop, attach a 50-g weight hanger to the loop, and place the removed weights on the weight hanger. Record the total mass (m_1) in the data table. Measure the distance y from the bottom of the weight hanger to the floor with the string wrapped around the drum and record in the data table.

After releasing the weight hanger, measure the time it takes to reach the floor and record. Repeat the timing procedure twice more for the same distance of descent and record.

13. Using the distance of descent and the average time of descent of the three trials, calculate the magnitude of the final velocity v of the descending weight and the final angular speed ω of the rotating support from the measured data using Eqs. 13.4 and 13.5.

Using Eq. 13.10, calculate the moment of inertia I_s of the rotating support. [*Note*: The mass m in this equation does *not* include the mass on the weight hanger used to determine the constant speed in procedure 111 (i.e., $m = m_1 - m_o$). Why?]

14. Place one of the regularly shaped accessory bodies (e.g., the cylindrical ring) on the metal cross of the rotating support so that the axis of rotation is through the body's center of mass. Add just enough weight to the weight hanger so that the system rotates (or the weight hanger descends) with a constant speed when given a slight start. Record the total mass m_o of the descending weight.

15. Add additional mass (0.10 to 0.20 kg) to the weight hanger so that it descends slowly to the floor when released from rest. Record the total mass m_1 of the descending weight. Measure the time t it takes for the weight hanger to descend a distance y to the floor for three trials and record these data.

16. Repeat procedures 14 and 15 for the other accessory bodies (disk and bar) if available.

17. Compute the average time of descent, and using Eqs. 13.4 and 13.5, find the magnitude of the final velocity of the descending weight and the final angular speed ω of the rotating system for each case.

Calculate the moments of inertia I for the combined accessory-support systems from the experimental data using Eq. 13.10. Determine the moments of inertia of the individual accessory objects ($I_a = I - I_s$), using the previously determined value of I_s.

* The values of the masses may be given to you by your instructor if the masses of the accessories are too large for regular laboratory balances.

18. Using the measured masses and appropriate length measurements of the accessory objects, compute the theoretical values of their moments of inertia (see Fig. 13.2), and compare with the experimentally determined values by calculating the percent differences.

19. *Parallel axis theorem.* Set up the system as shown in Fig. 13.5, using the bar attachment if available. Measure the distance d from the axis of rotation to the parallel axes through the centers of masses of the cylinders and record. Repeat procedures 14, 15, and 17 for this system, where in procedure 17, $I_a = I_c$ and

$$I = I_s + I_b + 2I_c$$

20. Applying the parallel axis theorem (Eq. 13.11), calculate the theoretical moment of inertia of the cylinders about the axis of rotation. Compare this result with the experimentally determined value of I by calculating the percent difference.

C. Moment of Inertia Accessory (for Centripetal Force Apparatus)

21. The moment of inertia accessory for a centripetal force apparatus is shown in Fig. 13.7 (see Fig. 9.5, Experiment 9). Using the vernier calipers, measure the diameter of the vertical shaft and record the radius r in Data Table 3.

Set up the apparatus with 100-g slotted weights about 12 cm from the vertical shaft on the horizontal rod. Secure the weights with the wing nuts, making certain that they are equidistant from the shaft. Record the mass of a single weight (M = 100 g). Measure the distance R from the *center* of the vertical shaft to the *center* of one of the slotted weights and record.

22. Secure one end of a length of string to the screw in the vertical shaft and the other end to a weight hanger. The string should be long enough to allow the weight hanger to reach the floor. Twisting the shaft, wind the string evenly around it, so that the weight hanger is near the base of the

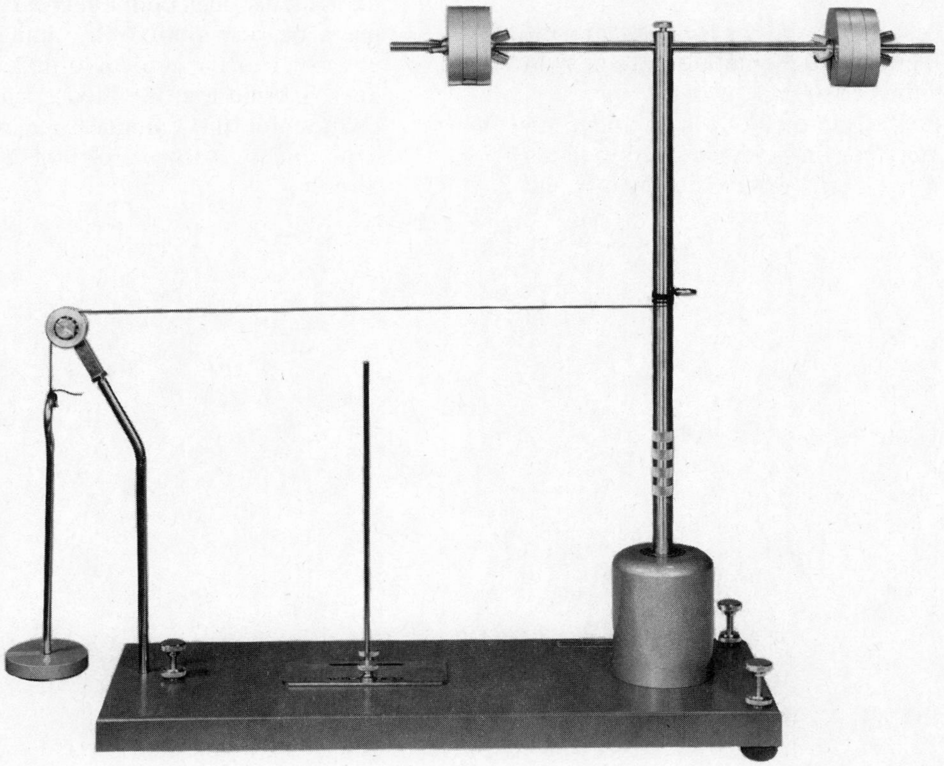

Figure 13.7 Moment of inertia apparatus. A hand-operated centripetal force apparatus (see Experiment 9) with accessory may be used to measure the moment of inertia of rotating masses. Descending weights supply the torque. (Photo courtesy Sargent-Welch Scientific Co.)

apparatus at a convenient distance from the floor. Measure and record the distance y of the bottom of the weight hanger from the floor.

23. Add mass to the weight hanger so that it accelerates at a moderate rate as it descends (e.g., add sufficient mass to make the total $m = 150$ g, including the mass of the weight hanger). Record this mass in the data table.

Rewind the string around the shaft so the bottom of the weight hanger is again at the previous height (y) from the floor. Releasing the weight hanger, measure the time t that it takes to descend to the floor and record. Repeat the timing procedure twice for the same distance of descent in order to get an average.

24. Remove the two 100-g weights from the horizontal arm, leaving the wing nuts on the arm. (The wing nuts should be loosened only slightly and turned back so that they are at their previous positions.) Repeat the timing procedures with no weights (other than wing nuts) on the horizontal arm.

25. Using Eqs. 13.4, 13.5, and 13.10, compute the moments of inertia of the rotating system with the masses on the arm (I) and without them (I_o).

The moment of inertia I of the rotating system with the masses can be considered the sum of two parts, $I = I_1 + I_o$, where I_1 is the moment of inertia of the two-mass system. Subtract the results to obtain the moment of inertia I_1 of the two-mass system alone ($I_1 = I - I_o$).

26. Repeat procedures 22 through 24 for various values of R with constant M. ($M = 100$ g is convenient, since you already have one data point.)

27. Repeat procedures 22 through 24 for various values of M with the same constant R.

28. Using the data from the preceding procedures, plot (a) I_1 versus R, with constant M; and (b) I_1 versus M, with constant R.

29. Considering the slotted weights to be point masses (that is, concentrated at their centers of mass), the moment of inertia of the two-mass system is given theoretically by $I_1 = 2MR^2$. Using this relationship, compute the moment of inertia I_1 for each combination of M and R and record in the data table.

Compare the computed theoretical values with the experimental values by plotting the computed values on the respective graphs. Comment on any noticeable similarities or differences. (Note the general forms of the graphs, and keep in mind that the theoretical I is an approximation for the extended masses and that the experimental values are subject to experimental error.)

Name ______________________ Section ______________ Date ______________

Lab Partner(s) ____

EXPERIMENT 13

Rotational Motion and Moment of Inertia

Laboratory Report

A. Rotational Inertia Apparatus (Wheel and Axle)

DATA TABLE 1

Diameter of axle ______________

Total mass of wheel and axle ______________

Thickness of wheel (needed for some apparatus) ______________

Radius, r ______________

Suspended mass for constant velocity, m_o ______________

Length of axle (beyond wheel) ______________

Diameter of wheel ______________

Suspended mass ( )					
Distance of descent, y ( )					
Time of descent, t ( )	1.				
	2.				
	3.				
	Average				
Magnitudes of: Final velocity, $v = 2y/t$ ( )					
Final angular velocity, $\omega = v/r$ ( )					
Acceleration, $a = v/t = 2y/t^2$ ( )					
Angular acceleration, $\alpha = a/r$ ( )					
Tension, $T = m(g - a)$ ( )					
Applied torque, $\tau_a = rT$ ( )					

(Space for calculations and results on the following pages) *(continued)*

Calculations
(show calculations for all cases, attaching additional sheet if necessary)

1. Magnitudes of final velocity v and angular velocity ω

2. Magnitudes of acceleration a and angular acceleration α

3. Magnitudes of tension in string T and applied torque τ_a

4. Theoretical moment of inertia I (Fig. 13.2) and frictional torque τ_f

5. Moment of inertia I (energy method)

Name ______________________ Section ______________ Date ______________

Lab Partner(s) ____

Results

Using the torque method:

	Experimental value from plotted data	Computed value	Percent difference
Moment of inertia, I	________	________	________
Frictional torque, τ_f	________	________	________

Using the energy method:

Moments of inertia, I ________

Percent of difference (between experimental and theoretical values) ________

B. Rotating Support and Accessory Bodies

DATA TABLE 2

Diameter of support drum ________ Radius, r ________

Accessory object:

1. Cylindrical ring Mass ________ Inner radius, R_1 ________

   Outer radius, R_2 ________

2. Disk Mass ________ Radius, R ________

3. Bar Mass ________ Width ________

   Length ________

4. Solid cylinder Mass ________ Diameter ________ Radius, R ________

   (Both cylinders should be approximately the same)

Procedure 19: Distance from axis of rotation to parallel axis through center of mass of cylinders d ________

Don't forget units

(continued)

		(a) Rotating support	(b) Support with cylindrical ring	(c) Support with disk	(d) Support with bar	(e) Support with (bar and) cylinders
m_o ( )						
m_1 ( )						
$m = m_1 - m_o$						
Distance of descent, y ( )						
Time of descent, t ( )	1.					
	2.					
	3.					
	Average					
Magnitudes: Final velocity, v ( )						
Magnitudes: Final angular velocity, ω ( )						
Calculated I of system ( )		(I_s)				
Moment of inertia of accessory, I_a ($I_a = I - I_s$)		X				($I_a = I_c$)
Theoretical I_a		X				
Percent difference		X				

(Space for calculations on following page)

Name ______________________ Section ______________ Date ______________

Lab Partner(s) ____

EXPERIMENT 13 **_Laboratory Report_**

Calculations
(show calculations for all cases, attaching additional sheet if necessary)

1. Magnitudes of final velocity v and final angular velocity ω

2. I of the system

3. Theoretical I_a

(continued)

C. Moment of Inertia Accessory

DATA TABLE 3

Diameter of shaft ____________________ Radius, r ____________________

			Variable R				Varible M			
Mass, M ( )			Constant M ____________ ( )							
Distance, R ( )							Constant R ____________ ( )			
Height, y ( )										
Mass, m ( )										
Time of descent, t ( ) 1.										
2.										
3.										
Average										
Magnitudes: Velocity, v ( )										
Magnitudes: Angular velocity, ω ( )										
I ( )										
I_o ( )										
$I_1 = I - I_o$ ( )										
$I_1 = 2MR^2$ ( )										

Comments on graphs:

Name ______________________ Section ______________ Date ______________

Lab Partner(s) ____

EXPERIMENT 13 *Laboratory Report*

Calculations
(show calculations for all cases, attaching additional sheet if necessary)

1. Magnitudes of final velocity v and final angular velocity ω

2. I of the system

3. I_1 of the two-mass system

4. I_o of the system without masses

5. I_1 theoretical

(continued)

QUESTIONS

A. Rotational Inertia Apparatus (Wheel and Axle)

1. Discuss the probable sources of error in the experiment. Which are systematic, and which are random? Which are most important?

2. The energy lost by the descending mass m_o is m_ogy. Express this energy loss mathematically in terms of the frictional torque τ_f.

3. In a graph of τ_a versus α, what would be the implications if (a) the line went through the origin; and (b) the y intercept were negative?

B. Rotating Support and Accessory Bodies

4. Answer Question 1 above.

Name ______________________ Section ______________ Date ______________

Lab Partner(s) ____

5. Answer Question 2 above.

6. If the mass for the disk is M_d and the cylinder has a mass M_c, find the expression for the moment of inertia of the system shown in Fig. 13.8 (a) about the axis O'; and (b) about the axis O?

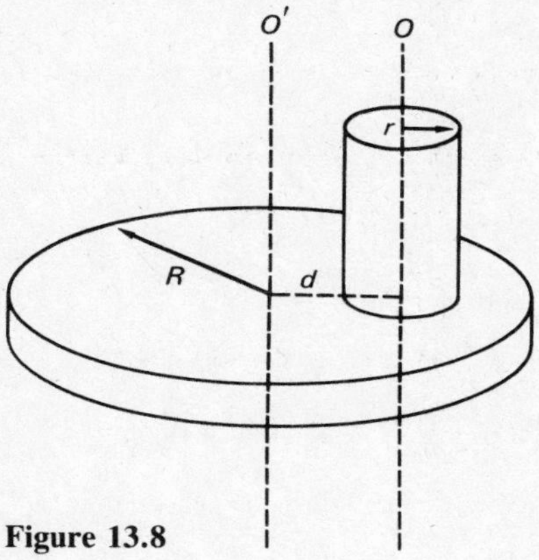

Figure 13.8

C. Moment of Inertia Accessory

7. Answer Question 1 above.

8. The moment of inertia of a two-mass system was approximated by $I_1 = 2MR^2$. Justify this approximation.

(continued)

9. Are the shapes of the curves on the graphs for the experimental values consistent with what would be expected theoretically? (Explain what the theoretical shapes of the curves would be.) For each nonlinear curve, explain how you might obtain a straight-line graph by plotting some function of the dependent variable other than itself (e.g., ln m instead of m).

The Ballistic Pendulum: Conservation of Angular Momentum and Energy

(Experiment 8 Introduction and Theory sections should be read for familiarity.)

I. Introduction

When the projectile collides with the bob of the ballistic pendulum, equal and opposite forces are involved. With no net collision force, it would be expected that the linear momentum would be conserved (in the horizontal direction), as was assumed in Experiment 8. However, during the collision, there is a reaction force on the pendulum's pivotal support, so the horizontal net force is not zero and the linear momentum is not conserved. Also, the pendulum is not a simple one, but rather a rigid body or compound pendulum, so there are rotational considerations.

Taking rotational motion into account, we then look at angular momentum. Summing the collision torques about an axis through the pendulum's pivotal support, the net torque is zero and the angular momentum is conserved; the reaction force on the support acts through the axis of rotation and the projectile-bob forces are equal and opposite.

In this Addendum, we will analyze the ballistic pendulum in terms of angular momentum and rotational kinetic energy to determine the magnitude of the projectile's initial velocity.*

II. Equipment Needed

- Ballistic pendulum
- Meterstick
- Laboratory balance
- Timer or stopwatch
- Protractor
- Knife edge
- Safety glasses

III. Theory

As pointed out in the Introduction, the angular momentum (L) is conserved during collision, and we have

$$\underset{\text{(just before collision)}}{L_1} = \underset{\text{(just after collision)}}{L_2}$$

or

$$mv_{x_o}r_p = I\omega_o \qquad \textbf{(13.A1)}$$

where r_p is the moment arm of the projectile, I the moment of inertia of the projectile-pendulum system, and ω_o the magnitude of the initial angular velocity $L = I\omega$ of the system (see Fig. 13.A1). Solving for v_{x_o},

$$v_{x_o} = \frac{I\omega_o}{mr_p} \qquad \textbf{(13.A2)}$$

Then, after collision, by the conservation of energy we have

$$\underset{\substack{\text{(kinetic energy}\\ \text{just after collision)}}}{\tfrac{1}{2}I\omega_o^2} = \underset{\substack{\text{(change in}\\ \text{potential energy)}}}{(m + M)gh} \qquad \textbf{(13.A3)}$$

where h is the vertical distance the center of mass of the system is raised at the maximum amplitude of the pendulum's swing. Solving for ω_o,

$$\omega_o = \sqrt{\frac{2(m + M)gh}{I}} \qquad \textbf{(13.A4)}$$

and substituting into Eq. 13.A2,

$$v_{x_o} = \frac{I}{mr_p}\sqrt{\frac{2(m + M)gh}{I}} = \frac{1}{mr_p}\sqrt{2I(m + M)gh} \qquad \textbf{(13.A5)}$$

The masses and lengths in the equation are easily measured, and the moment of inertia I of the projectile-pendulum system can be found through its period of oscillation.

* This procedure was included at the suggestion of Professor Kenneth C. Stuart of San Antonio College.

Recall that for small oscillations, the period T of a *simple* pendulum is given (see Experiment 3) by:

$$T = 2\pi\sqrt{\frac{L}{g}} \qquad \textbf{(13.A6)}$$

(A simple pendulum consists of a bob on a flexible string.) A rigid body can also oscillate as a pendulum, and if it does it is called a *compound* or *physical* pendulum. As a rigid body, such a pendulum has a moment of inertia I, and the period of a compound pendulum for small oscillations ($\theta \leq 20°$) can be shown to be, to a good approximation,

$$T = 2\pi\sqrt{\frac{I}{M'gr_{cm}}} \qquad \textbf{(13.A7)}$$

where M' is the total mass ($M' = m + M$ in our case) and r_{cm} is the distance between the pivot point and the center of mass of the pendulum (Fig. 13.A1). Then,

$$I = \frac{T^2M'gr_{cm}}{4\pi^2} = \frac{T^2(m + M)r_{cm}}{4\pi^2} \qquad \textbf{(13.A8)}$$

Thus, by determining r_{cm} and measuring the period T of the pendulum, its moment of inertia I can be found experimentally.

Radius of Gyration

It is sometimes convenient to treat a rotating rigid body as if it were a particle. This is done in terms of a quantity called the *radius of gyration* (r_g), which is defined as the radial distance from the axis of rotation to a point at which the total mass of an object could be considered concentrated as a particle without changing its moment of inertia. The moment of inertia of a particle of mass M' is $I = M'R^2$, so in terms of the radius of gyration, we have

$$I = M'r_g^2 \qquad \textbf{(13.A9)}$$

For example, for a uniform disk, $I = \frac{1}{2}M'R^2$, and since $I = \frac{1}{2}M'R^2 = M'r_g^2$, then $r_g = R/\sqrt{2}$. That is, a particle of mass M' a distance $r_g = R/\sqrt{2}$ from the axis of rotation would have the same moment of inertia as a uniform disk.

Expressing Eq. 13.A5 in terms of r_g, where $I = M'r_g^2 = (m + M)r_g^2$,

$$v_{x_o} = \frac{1}{mr_p}\sqrt{2I(m + M)gh} = \frac{1}{mr_p}\sqrt{2(m + M)^2r_g^2gh}$$

and

$$v_{x_o} = \frac{m + M}{m}\left(\frac{r_g}{r_p}\right)\sqrt{2gh} \qquad \textbf{(13.A10)}$$

which is simpler in form. [Notice that Eq. 13.A10 differs from Eq. 8.4 by a factor of (r_g/r_p).]

The radius of gyration of a compound pendulum may be expressed in terms of its small oscillation period using Eqs. 13.A9 and 13.A8 with $M' = (m + M)$,

$$I = M'r_g^2 = (m + M)r_g^2 = \frac{T^2(m + M)r_{cm}}{4\pi^2}$$

and

$$r_g = \frac{T}{2\pi}\sqrt{r_{cm}} \qquad \textbf{(13.A11)}$$

IV. Experimental Procedure

Caution: *With projectiles involved it is recommended that safety glasses be worn when doing all procedures.*

1. Obtain the projectile ball, which may be in the pendulum bob. (*Note*: When removing the ball from the pendulum bob of some types of ballistic pendula, be sure to push up on the spring catch that holds the ball in the pendulum so as not to damage it.) Place the projectile ball on the ball rod of the spring gun, and cock the gun by pushing on the ball. Both the ball and rod may move backward, or the ball may slip over the rod, depending on the type of ballistic pendulum. ***Caution***: *In either case, be careful not to bruise or hurt your hand when cocking the gun. Also, keep your fingers away from the projectile end of the gun.*

   Fire the projectile into the pendulum to see how the apparatus operates. If the catch mechanism does not catch on the notched track, you should adjust the pendulum suspension to obtain the proper alignment.

2. A preset pointer or a dot on the side of the pendulum bob indicates the position of the center of mass of the pendulum-ball system. With the pendulum hanging freely, measure the height h_1 of the pointer above the base surface (Fig. 13.A1) and record in Data Table 1.

3. Fire the ball into the freely hanging stationary pendulum and note the notch at which the catch mechanism stops on the curved track. Counting upward on the curved track, record the notch number in Data Table A.1. Repeat this procedure four times and for each trial record the notch number in the data table. (Alternately, the height may be measured each time.)

4. Determine the average of these observations, which is the average highest position of the pen-

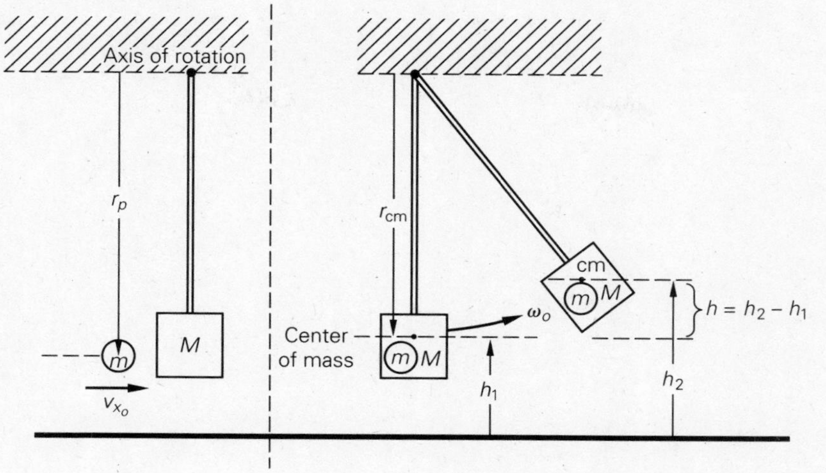

Figure 13.A1 Ballistic pendulum action. On collision, the net torque about the pivot axis is zero (equal and opposite collision forces), and the angular momentum is conserved. After collision, work is done against gravity and rotational kinetic energy is converted into potential energy.

dulum. Place the catch mechanism in the notch corresponding most closely to the average and measure the height h_2 of the pointer or dot above the base surface used for the h_1 measurement (Fig. 13.A1).

Note: To minimize frictional losses, the catch mechanism may be disabled by tying it up with thread or using a rubber band. The mechanism then acts as a pointer to indicate the highest notch, which is observed by a lab partner. Holding some reference object, e.g., a pencil, by the notched track helps to determine the proper notch number.

5. Measure and record the moment arm (r_p) of the projectile. Then, loosen the screw of the pendulum support and carefully remove the pendulum. Weigh and record the masses of the ball (m) and the pendulum (M). *Note*: The mass of the pendulum is that of the bob and the support rod. Do not attempt to remove the support rod from the bob. Consult your instructor for an explanation if a different model is used.

6. With the ball in the pendulum holder, balance the combined system on a knife edge and make a pencil mark on the pendulum indicating the line along which the center of mass (cm) lies. Do this even if there is a mark on the pendulum that may appear to indicate the location of the center of mass. (Why does the center of mass necessarily lie along this line?) Measure the distance r_{cm} from the pendulum's pivot point (axis of rotation) to the center-of-mass line you marked and record it. (*Note*: if the shape of your pendulum prohibits its being balanced on a knife edge, your instructor will provide an alternate suspension method.)

7. Resuspend the pendulum *with the ball in its holder* and adjust it so that it swings freely. Using the timer, determine the period T of the pendulum for small-angle oscillations (e.g., $\theta \simeq 15°$). Use a procedure like the one in Experiment 3. That is, rather than timing only one oscillation, time several (e.g., four or five) and determine the average period. Timing is generally more accurate if you start the pendulum oscillating before the timing begins. Also, it is usually best to take the timing reference at the lowest point of the swing.

   Record the average period in Data Table A.2, and repeat the procedure three times. Use the average value of the four trials as the period, i.e.,

$$T = \sum_i \frac{\overline{T}_i}{4}$$

8. With the experimental values of r_{cm} and T, determine the radius of gyration r_g using Eq. 13.A11.

9. Compute the magnitude of the projectile's initial velocity v_{x_o} using Eq. 13.A10.

Name ______________________ Section ______________ Date ______________

Lab Partner(s) ____

EXPERIMENT 13 ADDENDUM

The Ballistic Pendulum: Conservation of Angular Momentum and Energy

Laboratory Report

A. The Ballistic Pendulum

DATA TABLE A.1

(*Modify Data Table if it does not apply to your ballistic pendulum.*)

Purpose: To determine the maximum height of pendulum swing.

Trials	Notch number of pendulum catch	
		Height h_2 of pointer with pendulum catch in closest to average notch number ______________
1		Height h_1 of pointer with pendulum freely suspended ______________
2		
3		$h = h_2 - h_1$ ______________
4		Mass of ball, m ______________
5		Mass of pendulum, M (bob and support) ______________
Average		Moment arm of projectile, r_p, ______________

Calculations
(show work)

Don't forget units

(continued)

DATA TABLE A.2

Purpose: To determine the moment arm of the center of mass and the period of oscillation.

Moment arm r_{cm} ______________

Trial	Total time for n oscillations ( )	n	Average period $\overline{T}$ ( )
1			
2			
3			
4			
		Experimental period	

$$T = \sum_i \frac{\overline{T}_i}{4}$$ (units)

Calculation of radius of gyration (r_g):
(*show work*)

r_g ______________ (units)

Calculation of v_{x_o}:
(*show work*)

v_{x_o} ______________ (units)

Name ______________________ Section ______________ Date ______________

Lab Partner(s) ____

EXPERIMENT 13 | *Laboratory Report*

QUESTIONS

1. What are the probable sources of error in this experiment?

2. Compare the experimental result for v_{x_o} here with those from Experiment 8 (if done). In particular, compute the ratio r_g/r_p and compare the experimental results for v_{x_o} for the ballistic pendulum procedures using the conservation of linear momentum and the conservation of angular momentum to see if they differ by this factor. (See Eqs. 8.4 and 13.A10.)

Name ______________________ Section ______________ Date ______________

Lab Partner(s) ____

EXPERIMENT 14

Elasticity: Young's Modulus

Advance Study Assignment

Read the experiment and answer the following questions.

1. What is meant by "elasticity"?

2. Define the terms stress, strain, and Young's modulus.

3. Show that Hooke's law has the form of the general equation for a straight line. What would be the slope and y-intercept of this straight-line relationship?

(continued)

4. What is the elastic limit of a material? Does Hooke's law hold for a material stressed beyond its elastic limit?

5. In the experiment, why is it permissible not to include the initial 1-kg weight and weight hanger in the loads for the corresponding elongations?

Elasticity: Young's Modulus

I. Introduction and Objectives

All bodies are deformed to some extent when acted on by forces. If, after deformation, a body returns to its original dimensions, it is said to be **elastic**. Elasticity is a material property and is characterized by an **elastic modulus**, defined as the ratio of the stress to the strain. **Stress** is related to the deforming force, and **strain** is the effect of relative changes in the dimensions of the body when subjected to a stress.

You may not have realized that materials such as steel are elastic. However, this is the case, as will be demonstrated. The deformation and recovery of a steel wire will be observed, and by experimentally determining the longitudinal strain for an applied tensile stress, the elastic modulus, commonly called **Young's modulus**, will be computed.

After performing this experiment and analyzing the data, you should be able to:

1. Clearly distinguish between stress and strain by citing experimental examples.
2. Explain how Young's modulus and Hooke's law are related and how they are limited in describing elasticity.
3. Appreciate that all solids are elastic to some extent, even metal wires.

II. Equipment Needed

- Young's modulus apparatus
- Optical lever attachment (mirror on tripod base and telescope and scale; a desk lamp may be needed to illuminate the scale if laboratory lighting is poor)

or

- Micrometer screw attachment
- Slotted weights (ten 1-kg weights)
- Meterstick and 2-m stick (if available)
- Micrometer calipers
- Safety goggles

III. Theory

Elasticity is characterized by elastic moduli: Young's modulus (linear), shear modulus (two-dimensional), and bulk modulus (three-dimensional). Each modulus describes a different type of elastic deformation. Only Young's modulus will be considered in this experiment.

In general, an elastic modulus is defined as

$$\text{elastic modulus} = \frac{\text{stress}}{\text{strain}} \quad \textbf{(14.1)}$$

For the linear case, the stress is equal to the magnitude of the applied longitudinal force, F, divided by the object's cross-sectional area A normal to the force (Fig. 14.1). This is commonly called a **tensile** or **normal stress**:

$$\text{tensile stress} = \frac{F}{A} \quad \textbf{(14.2)}$$

A **strain** is the effect or relative changes in the dimensions or shape of a body subjected to a stress. For the linear case, this involves a change in length, and the tensile strain is defined as the ratio of the change in length ΔL to the original length L_o (Fig. 14.1):

$$\text{tensile strain} = \frac{\Delta L}{L_o} = \frac{L - L_o}{L_o} \quad \textbf{(14.3)}$$

Longitudinal stresses and strains may be either tensile (elongating) or compressive.

The elastic modulus for the linear case is called *Young's modulus Y*, and

$$Y = \frac{\text{tensile stress}}{\text{tensile strain}} = \frac{F/A}{\Delta L/L_o} \quad \textbf{(14.4)}$$

[It should be noted that it is the increment or change in stress $\Delta(F/A)$ that produces the strain ΔL.]

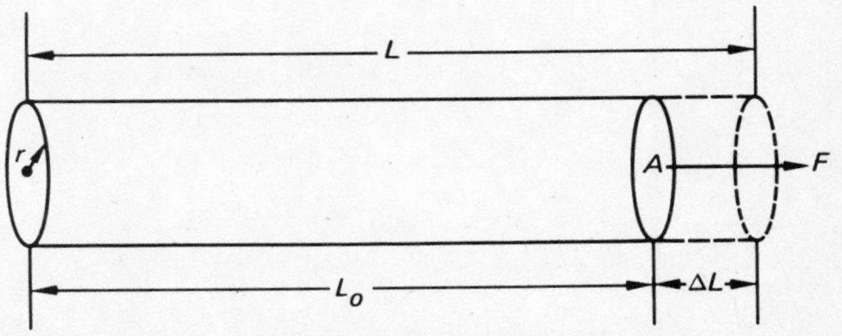

Figure 14.1 Tensile stress. For the linear case, the stress is equal to the magnitude of the applied longitudinal force F divided by the cross-sectional area A normal to the force.

Since the strain is a ratio of lengths, it is dimensionless, and the dimensions of Young's modulus are N/m^2 or lb/in^2. Provided that the elastic limit of the material is not exceeded, the ratio of the stress to the strain—Young's modulus—is often found to be constant and characteristic of a given material. Such materials obey **Hooke's law**, which, for a spring force, is commonly expressed as $F = -k\Delta x$, where k is a constant and the minus sign indicates that the spring force is opposite to the displacement. (See Experiment 15.) Equation 14.4 may be rewritten

$$F = \left(\frac{YA}{L_o}\right)\Delta L$$

A typical plot of stress versus strain is shown in Fig. 14.2. In the Hooke's law region, there is a straight-line relationship with a slope equal to Young's modulus. If the stress is increased beyond the elastic limit (point A), the sample does not return to its original length when the stress is removed, but retains a permanent strain, or is permanently deformed. If enough stress is applied, the sample will break (point B).

For a wire of radius r with an applied longitudinal weight force mg, Young's modulus has the form

$$Y = \frac{F/A}{\Delta L/L_o} = \frac{mg/\pi r^2}{\Delta L/L_o} \qquad \textbf{(14.5)}$$

where ΔL is the elongation of the wire from its original length L_o.

Optical Lever

(For experimental apparatus with elongation measurements made by the optical lever method)

In the optical lever method, small elongations are measured by means of the deflection of a mirror. If the plane of a mirror is originally vertical (MM), as illustrated in Fig. 14.3, then when you look through a telescope, the cross-hairs of the telescope will be on a mark T on the scale. However, if the mirror becomes tilted through an angle θ (due to a change in the length of the wire), a reflected beam is turned through an angle of 2θ.

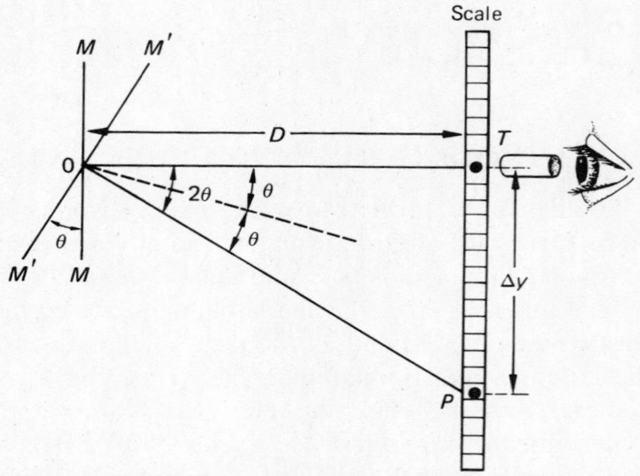

Figure 14.3 Optical lever. An illustration of the optical lever method of determining elongation. See text for description.

The cross-hairs of the telescope will then be on a mark on the scale at point P. That is, looking through the telescope, you would see point P. From Fig. 14.3, it can be seen that the double angle of deflection 2θ can be written in terms of the deflection distance Δy on the scale and the distance D from the mirror to the scale:

$$\tan 2\theta = \frac{\Delta y}{D} \qquad \textbf{(14.6)}$$

The tilting of the mirror results from the lowering of one end of the tripod base of the mirror mount (see Figs. 14.4 and 14.5). As seen in Fig. 14.4, the elongation ΔL is related to the deflection angle by

$$\Delta L = d \sin\theta \qquad \textbf{(14.7)}$$

where d is the apex length of the tripod triangle. For a small angle, as is the case here, $\frac{1}{2}\tan 2\theta \simeq \tan\theta \simeq \sin\theta$. From Eq. 14.6, the elongation becomes

$$\Delta L = \frac{d\Delta y}{2D} \qquad \textbf{(14.8)}$$

and the small elongation can be determined from easily measured experimental parameters.

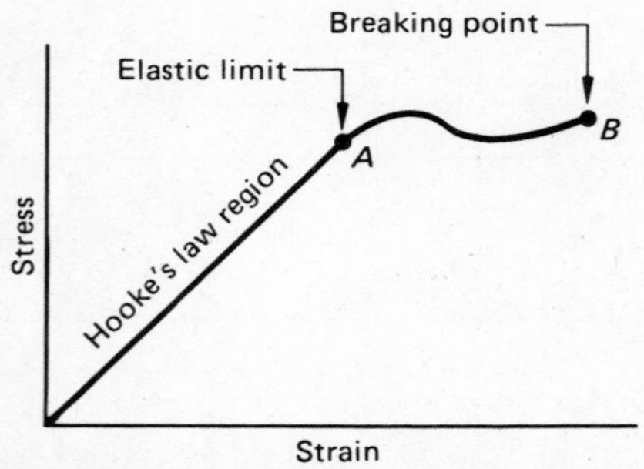

Figure 14.2 Stress versus strain. Typically, in the linear region, where Hooke's law is applicable, the slope of the line is equal to Young's modulus.

IV. Experimental Procedure

1. A common type of Young's modulus apparatus is shown in Fig. 14.6. The wire is supported by a chuck in a clamped yoke at the upper end of the

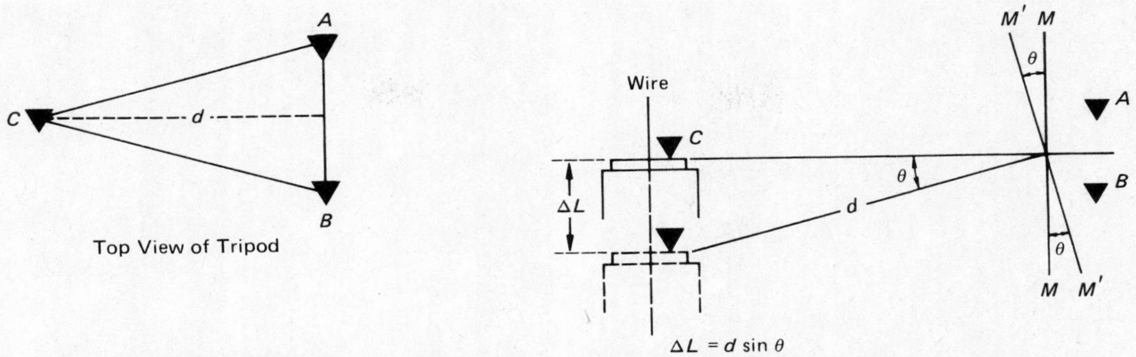

Figure 14.4 Optical lever and elongation. The tilting of the optical lever mirror results from the lowering of one side of the tripod base of the mirror mount due to the elongation of the wire. (See Figure 14.5.)

apparatus support rods. A lower chuck that tightly grips the wire is positioned in the hole of an adjustable platform that is clamped to the support rods. If an optical lever attachment is used, the mount rests in the groove on the platform and on the face of the chuck (Fig. 14.5a).

If a micrometer screw attachment is used (Fig. 14.5b), a lever with a spirit level on one end and a micrometer screw on the other is pivoted on the chuck. The micrometer screw is referenced to the adjustable platform. A weight hanger is suspended from the lower end of the wire, with the bottom of the hanger about 2 or 3 cm above the heavy tripod base of the apparatus.

A direct-reading dial micrometer is also available (Fig. 14.5c).

2. Hang a 1-kg weight on the weight hanger and level the tripod base of the apparatus by means of the leveling screws. The weight should be centered between the support rods when the base is level. Measure the length L_o of the wire from the bottom of the upper chuck to the top of the lower chuck and record in the appropriate data table.

[*Note*: The length of wire between the gripping chuck holders, not the total length of the wire, is taken as L_o. Also, the measurement attachment zero reading, y_o below, is taken with an initial 1-kg mass on the weight hanger. These weights are *not* included as part of the individual load increments since the individual load increments (1 kg each) produce the corresponding ΔL's.]

3. (a) *Optical lever attachment* (if used).

(i) Place the optical lever mount on a piece of paper and press lightly so that the pointed feet make indentations on the paper. Mark the indentations with a pencil. Then, draw a line between the two front points (*AB* in Fig. 14.4), and draw a line perpendicularly from this line to point *C*. With a vernier caliper, measure the length of the latter line (*d* in Fig. 14.4), and record in Data Table 1.

(ii) Carefully place the optical lever on the platform with its two front feet in the platform groove and its rear foot on the chuck (see Fig. 14.5). Rotate the mirror to the vertical position. Set the scale and telescope at least 1 m away, with the telescope at about the same height as the mirror. Adjust the telescope so that a mark on the scale as indicated by the telescope cross-hairs is easily seen. Record the zero reading (y_o).

(iii) Carefully measure the distance between the mirror and the scale with a meterstick (distance *D* in Figure 14.3), and record. It may be necessary to illuminate the scale with a lamp.

(b) *Micrometer screw attachment* (if used). Pivot the micrometer attachment lever on the lower chuck, and adjust the platform and the micrometer screw so that it has a midscale reading when the screw is balanced against the platform with the spirit level in a level position. Record this zero reading (L_o') of the micrometer in Data Table 2. (*Note*: Always move the screw in the same direction just before each reading, e.g., toward the higher numbers, so as to avoid screw thread "backlash" or hysteresis. If direct-reading dial micrometer attachment is used, see Fig. 14.6c for arrangement.)

(a)

(b)

(c)

Figure 14.5 Elongation measurement. (a) Optical lever attachment. (b) Micrometer screw attachment. (c) Direct-reading dial micrometer attachment. (Photos courtesy of Central Scientific Co., Inc.)

(c) *Direct-reading dial micrometer attachment* (if used). The zero reading (L_o') may be read directly from the micrometer and recorded in Data Table 2.

4. Carefully add another 1-kg weight to the load and record in the appropriate data table the scale reading seen through the telescope or the micrometer reading when again brought into level balance. The reading should not be taken immediately after increasing the load. A short time is required for the wire to stretch to equilibrium; this is called **elastic lag**.

   Caution: *If the wire is rusted, kinked, or in some way weakened, it could break and possibly damage the eyes. Safety goggles are suggested when adding weights.*

5. Add 1-kg weights, one at a time, recording in the appropriate data table the scale reading or the micrometer reading after adding each 1-kg weight until there is a total of 10 kg on the hanger. (*Note*: These loads are appropriate for a steel wire. If another kind of wire is used, ask your instructor for the proper maximum load.)

   At some point in this procedure after a 5-kg load is on the wire, measure the diameter of the wire with the micrometer calipers and record in the appropriate data table. With a substantial load, error resulting from kinks in the wire is avoided.

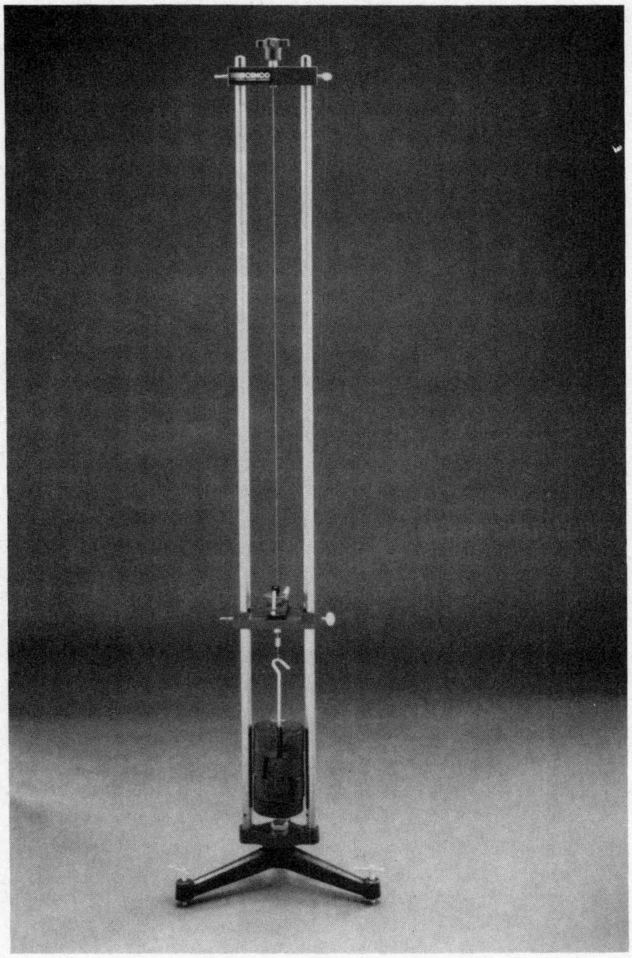

Figure 14.6 A Young's modulus apparatus. A great deal of weight is needed to elongate the wire appreciably. (Photo courtesy of Central Scientific Co., Inc.)

6. Remove the weights one at a time and record the scale reading or balanced micrometer reading after each weight is removed (allowing for the elastic lag). Stop when only one 1-kg weight is left on the weight hanger. At this point, measure L_o again and record.

7. Compute the elongations ΔL_i for each load from

(a) *Optical lever method:* the average of the scale readings for increasing and decreasing loads using Eq. 14.8, where $\Delta y_i = \bar{y}_i - \bar{y}_o$ and $\bar{y}_i$ and $\bar{y}_o$ are the averages of two scale readings (increasing and decreasing). That is, $\bar{y}_o$ is subtracted from each of the other average scale readings.

(b) *Micrometer method*: the average micrometer readings for increasing and decreasing loads, $\Delta L_i = \bar{L}_i - \bar{L}_o'$, where $\bar{L}_i$ and $\bar{L}_o'$ are the averages of two micrometer readings (increasing and decreasing). That is, $\bar{L}_o'$ is subtracted from each of the other average lengths.

Notice in the data table that the initial 1-kg weight and the weight of the weight hanger are not to be included as part of the individual loads.

8. Compute the stress F/A and the strain, $\Delta L_i/L_o$ for each load.

Use an average L_o if the initial and final measurements are different. Plot a graph of stress versus strain. Draw a straight line that best fits the data points, and determine the slope of the line. Compare this result with the value of Young's modulus of the wire material given in Appendix A, Table A2 by calculating the percent error.

Name ______________________ Section ______________ Date ______________

Lab Partner(s) ____

EXPERIMENT 14

Elasticity: Young's Modulus

Laboratory Report

d ______________

D ______________

Wire diameter ______________

L_o (initial) ______________

L_o (final) ______________

DATA TABLE 1

Purpose: To determine Young's modulus using optical lever method.

Load ( )	Increased load scale reading ( )		Decreased load scale reading ( )		Average scale reading	Computed elongation ΔL_i ( )		Strain $\Delta L_i/L_o$	Stress $F/A = mg/\pi r^2$ ( )
*	y_o		y_o			X		X	X
1	y_1		y_1			ΔL_1			
2	y_2		y_2			ΔL_2			
3	y_3		y_3			ΔL_3			
4	y_4		y_4			ΔL_4			
5	y_5		y_5			ΔL_5			
6	y_6		y_6			ΔL_6			
7	y_7		y_7			ΔL_7			
8	y_8		y_8			ΔL_8			
9	y_9		y_9			ΔL_9			

* Initial 1-kg weight and weight hanger not included as part of loads.

Calculations
(continue work on following page)

Slope of graph ______________

Accepted Young's modulus ______________

Percent error ______________

Don't forget units

(continued)

Calculations

Wire diameter ______________

L_o (initial) ______________

L_o (final) ______________

DATA TABLE 2

Purpose: To determine Young's modulus using micrometer method.

Load ( )	Increased load micr. reading ( )		Decreased load micr. reading ( )		Average reading	Elongation $\Delta L_i = L_i - \bar{L}_{o'}$ ( )		Strain $\Delta L_i/L_o$	Stress $F/A = mg/\pi r^2$ ( )
*	L_o'		L_o'						
1	L_1		L_1			ΔL_1			
2	L_2		L_2			ΔL_2			
3	L_3		L_3			ΔL_3			
4	L_4		L_4			ΔL_4			
5	L_5		L_5			ΔL_5			
6	L_6		L_6			ΔL_6			
7	L_7		L_7			ΔL_7			
8	L_8		L_8			ΔL_8			
9	L_9		L_9			ΔL_9			

* Initial 1-kg weight and weight hanger are not included as part of loads.

Name ______________________ Section ______________ Date ______________

Lab Partner(s) ____

EXPERIMENT 14 — *Laboratory Report*

Calculations
(show work)

Slope of graph ______________

Accepted Young's modulus ______________

Percent error ______________

QUESTIONS

1. (a) Why is it proper to take L_o as the length of wire between the chucks rather than the total length of the wire?

   (b) Why aren't the initial 1-kg and weight hanger included as part of the load?

(continued)

2. Suppose that the stress versus strain graph for another wire had a steeper slope than that of the wire used in this experiment. What would this mean physically?

3. If the elastic limit of a material is exceeded, the curve of the graph of stress versus strain may go above or below an extension of the straight line in the Hooke's law region. Explain what each case means physically.

4. (a) Suppose that the length of the wire between the chucks L_o were twice the length used in the experiment (same wire). Would a particular load produce the same elongation as found in the experiment? If not, what would it be?

(b) Suppose that the experiment were repeated (same L_o) with a wire of the same material, but with a diameter twice that of the wire used in the experiment. Would a particular load produce the same corresponding elongation as found in the experiment? If not, what would it be?

5. What should happen to the diameter of the wire as the load on the wire is increased? Why?

6. *Optional (optical lever method)* Prove explicitly that when a mirror is rotated (tilted) through an angle θ, a reflected beam is deflected by an angle 2θ (see Fig. 14.3). *Hint*: Draw reflected rays for the same incident ray for each orientation.

(continued)

7. *(Optional)* In the interest of speed and simplicity, ''raw data'' are often recorded directly on a graph. In this experiment the ''increasing load'' data might have been recorded on a graph where x = load = total mass (2 kg to 11 kg) and y = actual micrometer reading (in mm). Draw such a graph and use it to compute Y. Comment on the speed and validity of this method.

Name ______________________ Section ______________ Date ______________

Lab Partner(s) ____

EXPERIMENT 15

Hooke's Law and Simple Harmonic Motion

Advance Study Assignment

Read the experiment and answer the following questions.

1. What are Hooke's law and simple harmonic motion, and how are they related?

2. How is the "internal" restoring force of a spring measured experimentally?

3. What is the physical significance of the spring constant, i.e., what does it tell you?

4. In the equation of motion for SHM (Eq. 15.2), what physically determines A and T?

5. How is the period of a mass oscillating on a spring related to the spring constant? (Express mathematically and verbally.)

EXPERIMENT 15

Hooke's Law and Simple Harmonic Motion

I. Introduction and Objectives

An elastic material tends to return to its original form or shape after being deformed. Hence, elasticity implies a restoring force that can give rise to vibrations or oscillations. For many elastic materials, the restoring force is proportional to the amount of deformation, if the deformation is not too great. This relationship for elastic behavior is known as **Hooke's law**. In one dimension, the restoring force magnitude F is proportional to that of the deformation displacement x, or $F \propto x$. In equation form, we have

$$F = -kx$$

where k is a constant of proportionality and the minus sign indicates that the displacement and the force are in opposite directions. In the case of the linear restoring force of a coil spring, k is called the **spring constant** and is a relative indication of the "stiffness" of the spring.

A particle or object in motion under the influence of a linear restoring force such as that described by Hooke's law undergoes what is known as **simple harmonic motion (SHM)**. This periodic oscillatory motion is one of the common types found in nature. The period of oscillation of an object in simple harmonic motion is related to the constant of proportionality in Hooke's law.

In this experiment, Hooke's law will be investigated along with the parameters and description of simple harmonic motion.

After performing this experiment and analyzing the data, you should be able to:

1. Tell how Hooke's law is represented graphically, and cite an example of an elastic object that does *not* follow Hooke's law.
2. Explain why simple harmonic motion (SHM) is simple and harmonic.
3. Better understand how the period of a weight oscillating on a spring varies with the weight's mass and the spring constant.

II. Equipment Needed

- Coil spring
- Wide rubber band
- Slotted weights and weight hanger
- Laboratory timer or stopwatch
- Meterstick
- Laboratory balance
- 2 sheets of Cartesian graph paper

III. Theory

A. Hooke's Law

The fact that for many elastic substances the deformation is directly proportional to a restoring force that resists the deformation was first demonstrated by Robert Hooke (1635–1703), an English physicist. For one dimension, this relationship—known as **Hooke's law**—is expressed mathematically as

$$F = -k\Delta x = -k(x - x_o) \qquad \textbf{(15.1)}$$

or

$$F = -kx \qquad (\text{with } x_o = 0)$$

where Δx is the linear deformation or displacement of the spring and x_o is its initial position. The minus sign indicates that the force and displacement are in opposite directions. (For experimental convenience, the minus sign may be neglected.)

In terms of Young's modulus and stress and strain (see Eq. 14.4), Hooke's law has the form

$$F = \left(\frac{YA}{L_o}\right)\Delta L$$

so $k = YA/L_o$. However, for a coil spring, the stress is practically a pure shear, and the constant k, called the spring constant, depends on the shear modulus of the wire, the radius of the wire, the radius of the coils, and the number of coils.

The spring constant is sometimes called the "stiffness constant," since it gives an indication of the relative stiffness of a spring—the greater the k, the greater the stiffness. As can be seen from Eq. 15.1, k may have units of N/m or lb/in.

According to Hooke's law, the elongation of a spring as a whole is directly proportional to the magnitude of the stretching force.* For example, as illustrated in Fig. 15.1, if a spring has an initial length y_o and a suspended weight of mass m stretches the

* The restoring spring force and the stretching force are equal in magnitude and opposite in direction (Newton's third law).

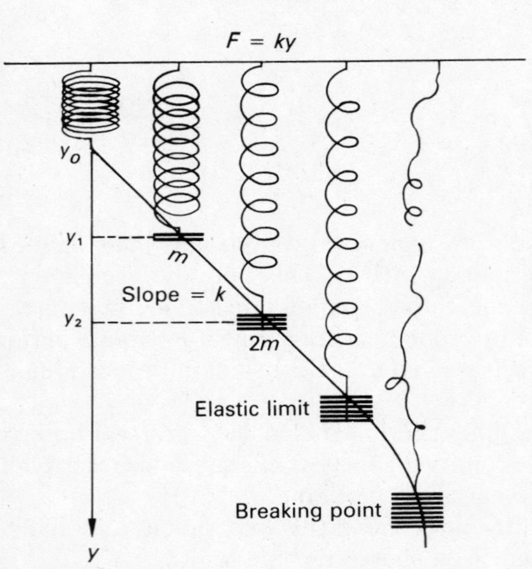

Figure 15.1 Hooke's law. An illustration in graphical form of spring elongation versus force. Hooke's law holds, up to the elastic limit.

spring so that its length is y_1, then in equilibrium the weight force is balanced by the spring force and

$$F_1 = mg = k(y_1 - y_o)$$

Here we use y to indicate the vertical direction instead of x as in Eq. 15.1 which is usually used to mean the horizontal direction. Similarly, if another mass m is added and the spring is stretched to a length y_2,

$$F_2 = 2mg = k(y_2 - y_o)$$

and so on for more added weights. The linear relationship of Hooke's law holds, provided that the deformation or elongation is not too great. Beyond the elastic limit, a spring is permanently deformed and eventually breaks with increasing force (see Fig. 14.2, Experiment 14).

Notice that Hooke's law has the form of an equation for a straight line:

$$F = k(y - y_o)$$

or

$$F = ky - ky_o$$

which is of the general form $y = mx + b$

B. Simple Harmonic Motion

When the motion of an object is repeated in regular time intervals or periods, it is called **periodic motion**. Examples include the oscillations of a pendulum with a path back and forth along a circular arc and a mass oscillating linearly up and down on a spring. The latter is under the influence of the type of force described by Hooke's law, and its motion is called **simple harmonic motion (SHM)**—simple because the restoring force has the simplest form and harmonic because the motion can be described by *harmonic functions* (sines and cosines).

As illustrated in Fig. 15.2, a mass oscillating on a spring would trace out a wavy, time-varying curve on a moving roll of paper. The equation for this curve, which describes the oscillatory motion of the mass, can be written

$$y = A \cos \frac{2\pi t}{T} \quad \textbf{(15.2)}$$

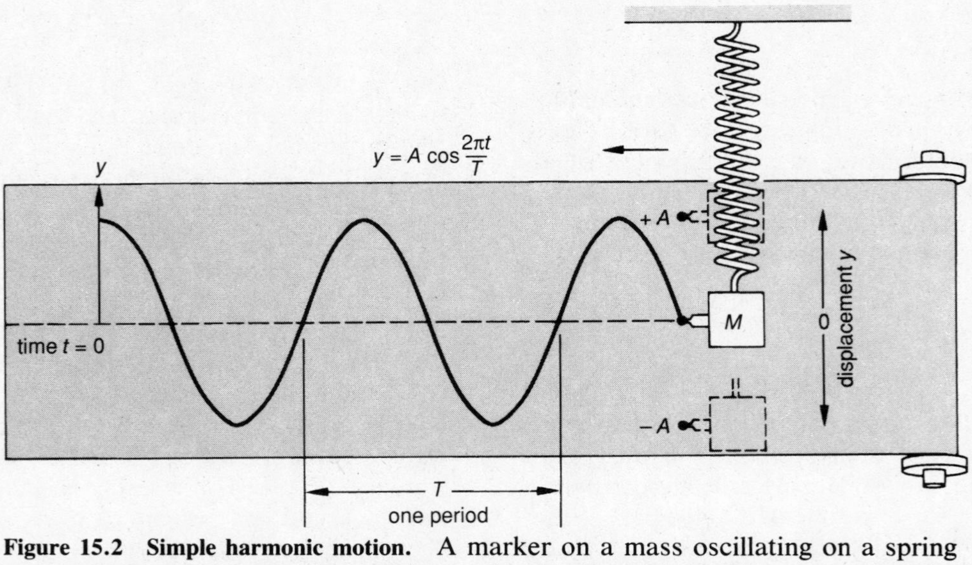

Figure 15.2 Simple harmonic motion. A marker on a mass oscillating on a spring traces out a curve, as illustrated, on the moving paper. The curve may be represented as a function of displacement (magnitude y) versus time.

where T is the period of oscillation and A the amplitude or maximum displacement of the mass. The amplitude depends on the initial conditions of the system (i.e., how far the mass was initially displaced from its equilibrium position). If the mass were initially pulled below its equilibrium position (to $y = -A$) and released, the equation of motion would be $y = -A \cos 2\pi t/T$, which satisfies the initial condition at $t = 0$, that is, $\cos 0 = 1$ and $y = -A$. The argument of the cosine (i.e., $2\pi t/T$) is in radians rather than degrees.

In actual practice, the amplitude decreases slowly as energy is lost to friction, and the oscillatory motion is slowly "damped." In some applications, the simple harmonic motion of an object is intentionally damped (e.g., the spring-loaded needle indicator of an electrical measurement instrument or the dial on a common bathroom scale). Otherwise, the needle or dial would oscillate about the equilibrium position for some time making it difficult to obtain a quick and accurate reading.

The period of oscillation depends on the parameters of the system, and, for a mass on a spring, is given by

$$T = 2\pi \sqrt{\frac{m}{k}} \tag{15.3}$$

IV. Experimental Procedure

A. Rubber-Band Elongation

1. Hang a rubber band on a support and suspend a weight hanger from the rubber band. Add an appropriate weight to the weight hanger (e.g., 100–300 g) and record the total suspended weight ($m_1 g$) in Data Table 1. [It is convenient to leave g the acceleration due to gravity in symbolic form, that is, if $m_1 = 100$ g or 0.100 kg, then weight $= m_1 g = (0.100\text{ kg})g$ N.]* Fix a meterstick vertically alongside the weight hanger and note the position of the bottom of the weight hanger on the meterstick. Record this as y_1 in the data table.

2. Add appropriate weights to the weight hanger one at a time (e.g., 100 g), and record the total suspended weight and the position of the bottom of the weight hanger on the meterstick after each elongation (y_2, y_3, etc.). The weights should be small enough so that seven or eight weights can be added without overstretching the rubber band.

3. Plot the total suspended weight force versus elongation position (mg versus y), and draw a smooth curve that best fits the data points.

B. Spring Elongation

4. Repeat procedures 1 and 2 for a coil spring. A commercially available Hooke's law apparatus is shown in Fig. 15.3. Choose appropriate mass increments for the spring stiffness.

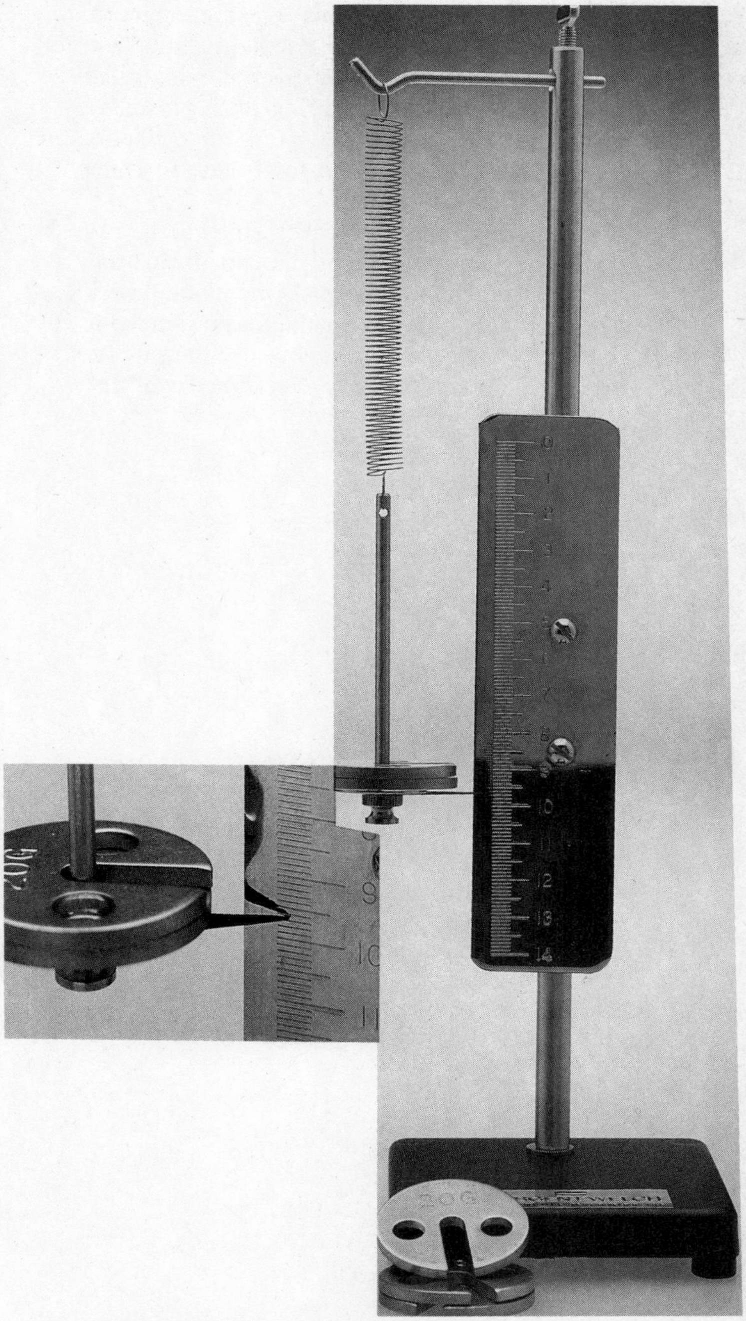

Figure 15.3 A Hooke's law apparatus. (Photos courtesy of Sargent-Welch Scientific Co.)

* Be careful not to confuse the symbol for the acceleration due to gravity, g, and the abbreviation for gram(s), g.

5. Plot mg versus y on the same sheet of graph paper used in procedure 3 (double-label axes if necessary) and draw a straight line that best fits the data. Determine the slope of the line (the spring constant k) and record in the data table. Answer Questions 1 through 3 following the data tables.

C. Period of Oscillation

6. **(a)** On the weight hanger suspended from the spring, place a mass just great enough to prevent the spring from oscillating too fast and to prevent the hanger from moving relative to the end of the spring during oscillations when it is pulled down (e.g., 5 to 10 cm) and released. Record the total mass in Data Table 3.

   (b) Using a laboratory timer or stopwatch, release the spring weight hanger from the predetermined initial displacement and determine the time it takes for the mass to make a number (5 to 10) of complete oscillations or cycles. The number of cycles timed will depend on how quickly the system loses energy or is damped. Make an effort to time enough cycles to get a good average period of oscillation. Record the total time and the number of oscillations in the data table.

   Divide the total time by the number of oscillations to determine the average period.

7. Repeat procedure 6 for four more mass values, each of which is several times larger than the smallest mass, and record the results in Data Table 3. The initial displacement may be varied if necessary. (This should have no effect on the period. Why?)

8. Plot a graph of the period squared (T^2) versus the mass (m) and draw a straight line that best fits the data points. Determine the slope of the line and compute the spring constant k. [Note from Eq. 15.3 that k is not simply equal to the slope; rather, $k = (2\pi)^2/\text{slope}$.] Compare this value of k with that determined from the slope of the spring elongation graph in part B by computing the percent difference, and finish answering the Questions.

Name ______________________ Section ______________ Date ______________

Lab Partner(s) ____

EXPERIMENT 15

Hooke's Law and Simple Harmonic Motion

Laboratory Report

A. Rubber-Band Elongation

DATA TABLE 1

Total suspended weight* ( )		Scale reading ( )	
m_1g		y_1	
m_2g		y_2	
m_3g		y_3	
m_4g		y_4	
m_5g		y_5	
m_6g		y_6	
m_7g		y_7	
m_8g		y_8	

B. Spring Elongation

DATA TABLE 2

Total suspended weight* ( )		Scale reading ( )	
m_1g		y_1	
m_2g		y_2	
m_3g		y_3	
m_4g		y_4	
m_5g		y_5	
m_6g		y_6	
m_7g		y_7	
m_8g		y_8	

* It is convenient to leave g in symbol form, even when graphing.

Calculations
(show work)

k (slope of graph) ______________
(units)

Don't forget units

(continued)

C. Period of Oscillation

DATA TABLE 3

Total suspended mass ( )		Total time ( )	Number of oscillations	Average period T ( )	T^2 ( )
m_1					
m_2					
m_3					
m_4					
m_5					

Calculations
(show work)

Slope of graph ______________

Computed spring constant k ______________

Percent difference (of k's in B and C) ______________

QUESTIONS

1. Interpret the intercepts of the straight line for the spring elongation in the mg versus y graph of part B.

2. Is the elastic property of the rubber band an example of Hooke's law? Explain.

3. Draw a horizontal line through the y-intercept of the straight line graph of part B, and form a triangle by drawing a vertical line through the last data point.
   (a) Prove that the area of the triangle is the work done in stretching the spring. (*Hint*: $W = \frac{1}{2}kx^2$, and area of triangle $A = \frac{1}{2}ab$ or $\frac{1}{2}$ altitude times base.)

   (b) From the graph, compute the work done in stretching the spring.

4. Interpret the x-intercept of the straight line of the T^2 versus m graph of part C.

(continued)

5. For a mass oscillating on a spring, at what positions do the (a) velocity and (b) acceleration of the mass have maximum values?

6. What is the form of the equation of motion for the SHM of a mass suspended on a spring when the mass is initially (a) released 10 cm above the equilibrium position; (b) given an upward push from the equilibrium position, so that it undergoes a maximum displacement of 8 cm; (c) given a downward push from the equilibrium position, so that it undergoes a maximum displacement of 12 cm? (*Hint*: Sketch the curve for the motion as in Fig. 15.2 and fit the appropriate trigonometric function to the curve.)

7. For case (a) in Question 6 only, what is the displacement y of the mass at times (a) $t = T/2$; (b) $t = 3T/2$; (c) $t = 3T$?

Name ______________________ Section ______________ Date ______________
Lab Partner(s) ____

EXPERIMENT 16

Standing Waves in a String

Advance Study Assignment

Read the experiment and answer the following questions.

1. How is wave speed related to frequency and wavelength? How is the period of oscillation related to wave speed?

2. What is a standing wave, and what are nodes and antinodes?

3. What are normal modes?

(continued)

4. How does the wavelength of a standing wave in a vibrating string vary as the tension force in the string or the linear mass density of the string varies?

5. Standing waves in a string can be produced by oscillating the string at the various natural frequencies. However, in this experiment the string vibrator has only one frequency. How, then, are standing waves with different wavelengths produced?

Standing Waves in a String

I. Introduction and Objectives

A **wave** is the propagation of a disturbance or energy. When a stretched cord or string is disturbed, the wave travels along the string with a speed that depends on the tension in the string and its linear mass density. Upon reaching a fixed end of the string, the wave is reflected back along the string.

For a continuous disturbance, the propagating waves interfere with the oppositely moving reflected waves and a standing- or stationary-wave pattern is formed under certain conditions. These standing-wave patterns can be visually observed, and the number of loops in a pattern depends on the length of the string and the wave speed, which is dependent on the tension in the string.

The visual observation and measurement of standing waves serve to provide a better understanding of wave properties and characteristics. In this experiment, the relationship between the tension force and the wavelength in a vibrating string will be studied as applied to the natural frequencies or normal modes of oscillation of the string.

After performing this experiment and analyzing the data, you should be able to:

1. Explain how standing waves are formed.
2. Distinguish between nodes and antinodes.
3. Tell what determines the natural frequencies of a vibrating string system.

II. Equipment Needed

- Electric string vibrator
- Clamps and support rod
- Pulley with rod support
- String
- Weight hanger and slotted weights
- Meterstick
- Laboratory balance
- 1 sheet of Cartesian graph paper

III. Theory

A wave is characterized by its **wavelength** λ, the **frequency of oscillation** f (in Hz or $1/\text{s} = \text{s}^{-1}$), and the **wave speed** v. (See Fig. 16.1.) These quantities are related by the expression

$$\lambda f = v \tag{16.1}$$

(Check to see if the equation is dimensionally correct.)

Waves in a stretched string are transverse waves; that is, the "particle" displacement is perpendicular to the direction of propagation. In longitudinal waves, the particle displacement is in the direction of wave propagation (e.g., sound waves). The maximum displacements of the particle oscillation are $+A$ and $-A$. The magnitude of the maximum displacement, called the **amplitude** (A), is related to the energy of the wave. The **period of oscillation** (T) is related to the frequency of oscillation, $T = 1/f$.

When two waves meet, they interfere and the combined wave form is a superposition of the two interfering waves. The superposition of two waves of equal amplitude and frequency traveling in opposite directions gives rise to what is known as a **standing** or **stationary wave**.

The periodic constructive and destructive interference causes the formation of a standing-wave pattern as illustrated in Fig. 16.2. Notice that some of the "particles" on the axis are stationary. These positions are called **nodal points** or **nodes**, and the points of maximum displacement are called **antinodes**. It might be said that the energy is standing in the wave envelope, alternating between the kinetic and potential energies of the particles.

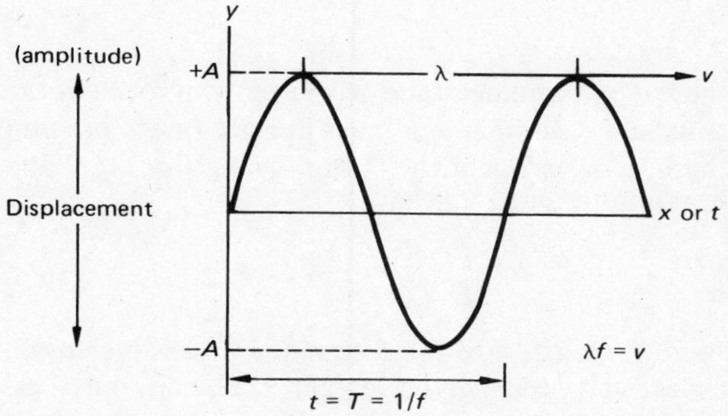

Figure 16.1 Wave description. The parameters involved in wave description.

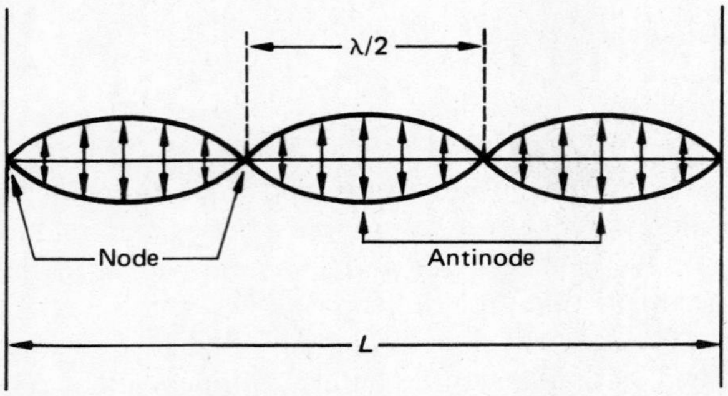

Figure 16.2 Standing wave. Periodic constructive and destructive interference gives rise to a standing-wave pattern, as illustrated here. The length of one loop of the standing wave is equal to one-half of the standing wave's wavelength. Note the positions of nodes and antinodes.

In a stretched string being oscillated or shaken at one end, waves traveling outward from the oscillator interfere with waves that have been reflected at the other fixed end. However, standing waves in a given length of string occur only for certain wave frequencies. That is, for a given stretching tension or force, the string must be driven or oscillated with certain vibrational frequencies to produce standing waves.

Since the st ing is fixed at each end, a standing wave must have a node at each end. As a result, only an integral number of half wave-lengths may "fit" into the length L of the string, $L = \lambda/2, \lambda, 3\lambda/2, 2\lambda$, and so on, such that in general

$$L = \frac{n\lambda}{2} \qquad n = 1, 2, 3, 4, \ldots \qquad \textbf{(16.2)}$$

Figure 16.2 illustrates the case for $L = 3\lambda/2$.

The wave speed in a stretched string is given by

$$v = \sqrt{\frac{F}{\mu}} \qquad \textbf{(16.3)}$$

where F is the magnitude of the tension force in the string and μ is the linear mass density (mass per unit length, $\mu = m/L_o$) of the string. Using Eqs. 16.2 and 16.3 in $\lambda f = v$ (Eq. 16.1),

$$f_n = \frac{v}{\lambda_n} = \frac{n}{2L}\sqrt{\frac{F}{\mu}} \qquad n = 1, 2, 3, \ldots \textbf{(16.4)}$$

where f_n and λ_n are the frequency and wavelength, respectively, for a given integer n. Hence, only certain frequencies produce standing waves for a given string tension, density, and length. These frequencies are called the **natural frequencies** or **normal modes of oscillation** of the string. The lowest frequency f_1 is called the **fundamental frequency** or **first harmonic**. The higher frequencies, f_2, f_3, and so on, are higher harmonics (e.g., f_2 is the second harmonic, etc.).

In this experiment, the electrically driven string vibrator has a fixed frequency, so that the driving frequency cannot be varied to produce different normal-mode standing-wave patterns. However, by varying the string tension, the wave speed can be varied so as to produce different standing-wave patterns. Since $v = \sqrt{F/\mu}$ (Eq. 16.3),

$$\lambda = \frac{v}{f} = \frac{1}{f}\sqrt{\frac{F}{\mu}} \qquad \textbf{(16.5)}$$

where f and μ are constant. Hence, by varying F, one can select the appropriate wavelengths that will "fit" into a given string length L to produce standing waves.

IV. Experimental Procedure

1. If not provided, cut a piece of string long enough to be used in the experimental setup—long enough to be looped at each end so as to be attached to the vibrator and a weight hanger suspended from the end running over the pulley (Fig. 16.3). The vibrator and pulley should be clamped to support posts at the opposite ends of the laboratory table to give an active string length of about 150 cm. (This length may vary for a given setup.)

   Measure the total length of the string, and determine its mass on a laboratory balance. Record these values in the data table and compute the linear mass density $\mu = m/L_o$. (*Note*: L_o is the total length of the string.)

2. Attach the string to the vibrator and suspend a weight hanger from the other end as shown in Fig. 16.3. Make certain that the string is aligned properly and that it is parallel to the table surface. Measure the distance between the vibrator arm and the point of contact of the string on the pulley. Record this length L in the data table.

   Turn on the vibrator. Try to produce different standing-wave patterns in the string by alternatively lifting and carefully pulling down on the weight hanger. It is helpful to fold a thin strip of paper in half and hang it on the string to observe vibrating action. The number of loops should increase with less tension. (Why?) Also, try grasping the string at a node and antinode of a given pattern to see what happens.

3. When you are familiar with the operation of the apparatus, add enough weights to the weight

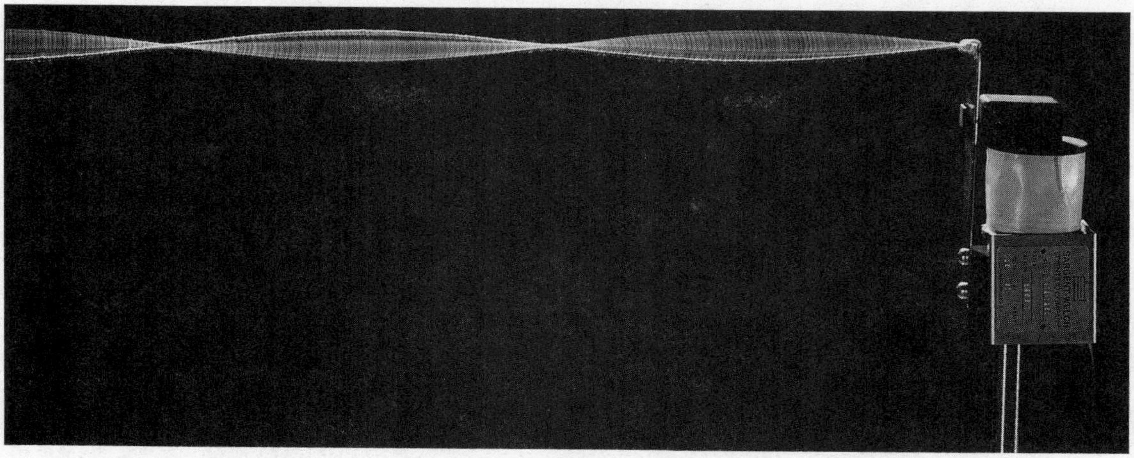

(a)

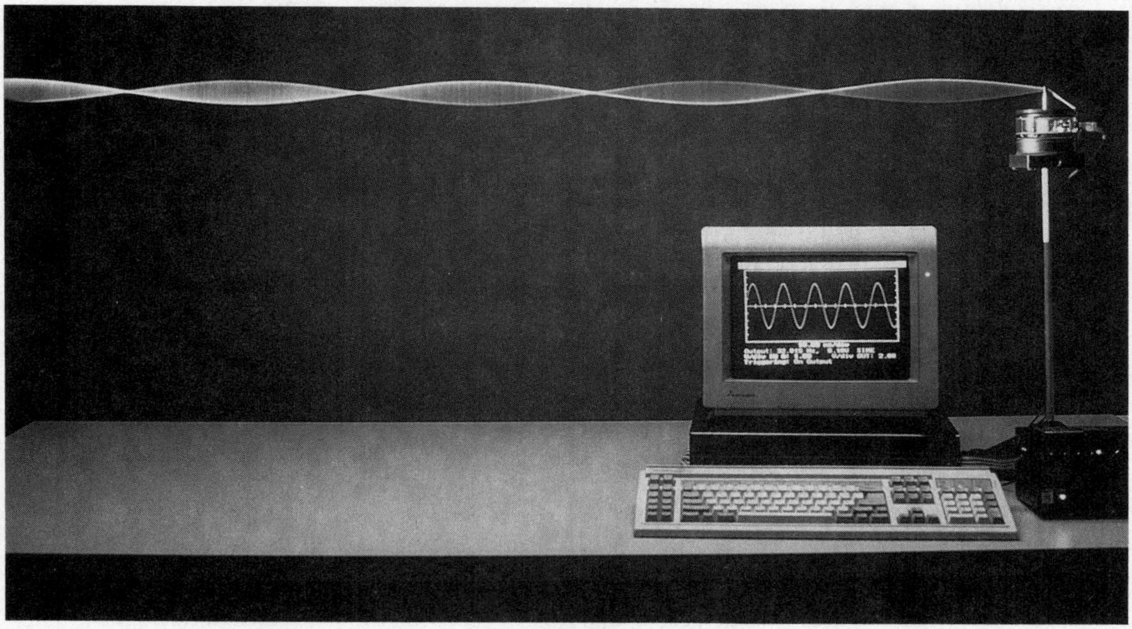

(b)

Figure 16.3 Standing wave apparatus. (a) A string vibrator that operates at a single frequency. Different standing waves are produced by varying the tension in the string. (b) A function generator may be used to vary the driving frequency. (Photos courtesy of (a) Sargent-Welch Scientific Co.; and (b) PASCO Scientific.)

hanger so that a standing-wave pattern of two loops is formed in the string (nodal point at the center). Adjust the tension by adding or removing some small weights until the loops are of maximum amplitude. If sufficiently small weights are not available, a fine adjustment can be made by loosening the clamp holding the vibrator rod and sliding it slightly back and forth so as to find the optimum string length between the ends that gives the maximum loop width or amplitude for a given tension.

When this is accomplished, measure with a meterstick the distance from the point where the string contacts the pulley to the center nodal point. The meterstick can be held alongside the vibrating string, or you may find it more convenient to grasp the string at the nodal point with your fingers, shut off the vibrator, and measure the distance from the pulley contact to the nodal point along the nonvibrating string. Make certain not to pull the string toward the vibrator, for that would increase the length by raising the weight hanger. Apply a slight tension in the string *away* from the vibrator if necessary.

Record this length L_1 and the total suspended mass in the data table. Since the length of one loop is one-half of a wavelength, $L_1 = \lambda/2$.

4. Remove enough weights from the weight hanger and adjust so that a standing-wave pattern of maximum amplitude with three loops (two nodal points in the string) is formed. Measure the distance from the pulley contact to the nodal point nearest the vibrator. (The fixed-end nodal point *at* the vibrator is not used because in vibrating up and down, it is not a "true" nodal point.) Record this length L_2 and the total suspended mass in the data table. Since the length of two loops is equal to one wavelength, $L_2 = \lambda$.

5. Repeat procedure 4 for consecutive standing-wave patterns up to eight measured loops if possible. [The weight hanger by itself may supply too much tension for higher-order patterns, so it may have to be removed and smaller weight(s) suspended.] Compute the wavelength for each case.

It should become evident that in general $\lambda = 2L_N/N$ or $L_N = N\lambda/2$, where N is the number of loops in a given L_N. Notice the similarity of the latter form of this equation with Eq. 16.2, wherein the length L is the total vibrating length of the string.

6. Notice that Eq. 16.5 can be rewritten as

$$\lambda = \frac{1}{f}\sqrt{\frac{F}{\mu}} = \left(\frac{1}{f\sqrt{\mu}}\right)\sqrt{F} \qquad \textbf{(16.6)}$$

where f and μ are constants. It has the form of an equation of a straight line, $y = mx + b$, with $x = \sqrt{F}$.

Plot the experimental data on a graph of λ versus $\sqrt{F}$. Draw the straight line that best fits the data, and determine the slope of the line. From this value and the previously determined value of μ, compute the average frequency f of the oscillations.*

[*Hint*: With the tension forces written with the symbolic form of g as suggested in the data table, it is convenient to plot $\sqrt{F}$ in the form $\sqrt{F} = \sqrt{mg} = \sqrt{m}\sqrt{g}$ (e.g., if $F = (0.050 \text{ kg})g$ N, then $\sqrt{F} = \sqrt{(0.050)g} = 0.22\sqrt{g}\ \text{N}^{\frac{1}{2}}$). The abscissa scale may be labeled in this form—a numerical prefix times the constant $\sqrt{g}$.]

The string vibrator operates on 60-cycle ac current. The vibrating action is accomplished by means of an electromagnet operated by the input current. The vibrator arm is attracted toward an electromagnet during each half-cycle, or twice each cycle, so the vibrating frequency is $2 \times 60 = 120$ Hz (cycles per second). Using this as the accepted value of the vibrational frequency, compute the percent error of the experimentally determined value.

* Should you have some scattered data points far from the straight line, see Question 2.

Name ______________________ Section ______________ Date ______________

Lab Partner(s) ____

EXPERIMENT 16

Standing Waves in a String

Laboratory Report

Mass of string ______________

Total length of string, L_o ______________

Linear mass density, μ ______________

Length of string between vibrator and pulley, L ______________

DATA TABLE

Purpose: To determine the frequency of oscillation from normal modes.

Number of loops measured N	Suspended mass ( )	Tension force, F* ( )	Measured length L_N for N loops ( )	Wavelength, λ ( )	$\sqrt{F}$ ( )
1		F_1	L_1		
2		F_2	L_2		
3		F_3	L_3		
4		F_4	L_4		
5		F_5	L_5		
6		F_6	L_6		
7		F_7	L_7		
8		F_8	L_8		

* For convenience, express the tension weight force in terms of g (e.g., if $m = 0.10$ kg, then $F = mg = 0.10\,g$ N).

Calculations
(show work)

Slope of graph ______________

Computed frequency, f ______________

Accepted frequency ______________

Percent error ______________

Don't forget units

(continued)

Calculations
(show work)

QUESTIONS

1. The wavelength associated with F_1 and L_1 in the experiment does not correspond to the wavelength of the fundamental frequency of the string.
   (a) To which natural frequency does the wavelength associated with F_1 and L_1 correspond?

   (b) What would be the tension in the string required to produce a standing wave with a wavelength corresponding to the fundamental frequency of the string? (*Hint*: Use Eq. 16.5.)

2. Theoretically, the vibrator frequency is 120 Hz. However, sometimes the vibrator resonates with the string at a "subharmonic" of 60 Hz.
   (a) If this were the case in all instances, how would it affect the slope of the graph?

(b) If you have some scattered data points far from the straight line on your graph, analyze the data for these points using Eq. 16.5 to determine the frequency.

3. How many normal modes of oscillation or natural frequencies does each of the following have: (a) a simple pendulum; and (b) a mass oscillating on a spring?

4. Stringed musical instruments, such as violins and guitars, use stretched strings. Explain (a) how tightening and loosening the strings tunes them to their designated tone pitch or frequency; (b) why the strings of lower tones are thicker or heavier; (c) why notes of higher pitch or frequency are produced when the fingers are placed on the strings.

(continued)

5. (*Optional*) Consider a long whip antenna of the type used on automobiles for CB radios. Show that the natural frequencies of oscillation for the antenna are $f_m = mv/4L$, where $m = 1, 3, 5, \ldots$, where v is the wave speed, and L is the length of the antenna. (*Hint*: The boundary conditions are a node and an antinode.)

Name ________________ Section ________________ Date ________________

Lab Partner(s) ________________

EXPERIMENT 17

Air Column Resonance: The Speed of Sound in Air

Advance Study Assignment

Read the experiment and answer the following questions.

1. What is resonance?

2. What variable is used in studying resonance in an air column in (a) a closed organ pipe of fixed length; (b) the resonance tube apparatus used in the experiment?

3. How does the speed of sound vary with temperature?

4. Should a tuning fork be set into oscillation by striking it with or on a hard object? Explain.

(continued)

5. For a resonance tube apparatus with a total tube length of 1 m, how many resonance positions would be observed when the water level is lowered through the total length of the tube for a tuning fork with a frequency of (a) 500 Hz; (b) 1000 Hz? (Show your calculations.)

Air Column Resonance: The Speed of Sound in Air

I. Introduction and Objectives

Systems generally have one or more natural vibrating frequencies. When a system is driven at a natural frequency, there is a maximum energy transfer and the vibrational amplitude increases to a maximum. For example, when you push a person on a swing, if you apply the pushes at the proper frequency, there will be maximum energy transfer and the person will swing higher (greater amplitude). When a system is driven at a natural frequency, we say that the system is in **resonance** (with the driving source) and refer to the particular frequency at which this occurs as a **resonance frequency**.

A swing or pendulum has only one natural frequency. However, a stretched string (see Experiment 16) and an air column can have several natural frequencies, depending on the number of wavelength segments that can be "fitted" into the system length. From the relationship between the frequency f, the wavelength λ, and the wave speed v, which is $\lambda f = v$, it can be seen that if the frequency and wavelength are known, the wave speed can be determined. And, if the wavelength and wave speed are known, the frequency can be determined.

As an application of resonance, in this experiment the speed of sound in air will be determined by driving an air column in resonance. Also, knowing the speed of sound, the unknown frequency of a tuning fork will be found from resonance conditions.

After performing this experiment and analyzing the data, you should be able to:

1. Explain why a closed organ pipe has particular resonant frequencies.
2. Tell how the speed of sound in air is affected by temperature and what effect this has on air column resonance.
3. Describe how a resonance tube can be used to measure the speed of sound in air or to determine the unknown frequency of a tuning fork.

II. Equipment Needed

- Resonance tube apparatus
- Three tuning forks (500- to 1000-Hz range), with stamped frequency of one fork covered or masked so as to serve as an unknown. It is helpful to have known-frequency tuning forks with frequencies different from those being used by neighboring groups or to have nearby groups use alternate frequencies so that the resonances coming from a particular tube can be distinguished.
- Rubber mallet or block
- Meterstick (if measurement scale not on resonance tube)
- Thermometer (to determine air temperature—one per class is sufficient)
- Vernier calipers
- Rubber bands (3 or 4)

III. Theory

Air columns in pipes or tubes of fixed lengths have particular resonant frequencies. For example, in a closed organ pipe (closed at one end*) of length L, when the air column is driven at particular frequencies, it vibrates in resonance. The interference of the waves traveling down the tube and the reflected waves traveling up the tube produces (longitudinal) standing waves (see Experiment 16), which must have a node at the closed end of the tube and an antinode at the open end Fig. 17.1. This corresponds to transverse standing waves in a metal strip or rod fixed at one end. (Keep in mind that the waves in the air column are longitudinal—particle displacement is parallel to the direction of wave propagation. The maximum *longitudinal* displacements of the air molecules are plotted (transversely) in the drawings and show the close relationship between standing waves in a column of air and standing waves in a string (Experiment 16).

The resonance frequencies of a pipe or tube (air column) depend on its length L. As illustrated in Fig. 17.1, only a certain number of wavelengths or "loops" can be "fitted" into the tube length with the node-antinode requirements (only the two lowest-frequency waves are shown in the figure). Since each loop corresponds to one half wavelength, resonance occurs when the length of the tube is nearly equal to

* A closed tube or organ pipe is open at one end. An open pipe is open at both ends.

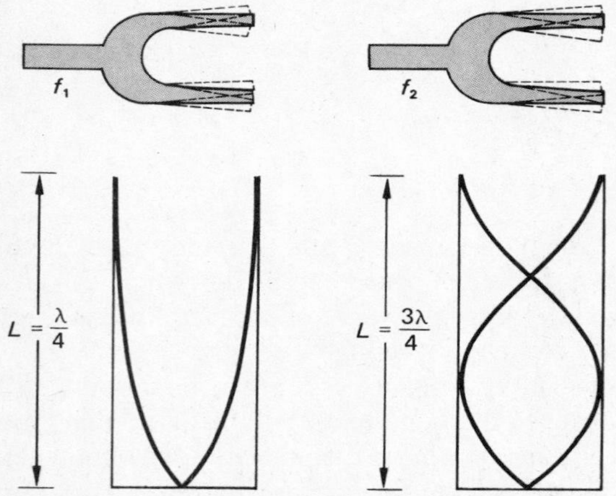

Figure 17.1 Standing waves. Illustrations of longitudinal standing waves of different frequencies in a tube of fixed length. There must be a node at the closed end and an antinode near the open end.

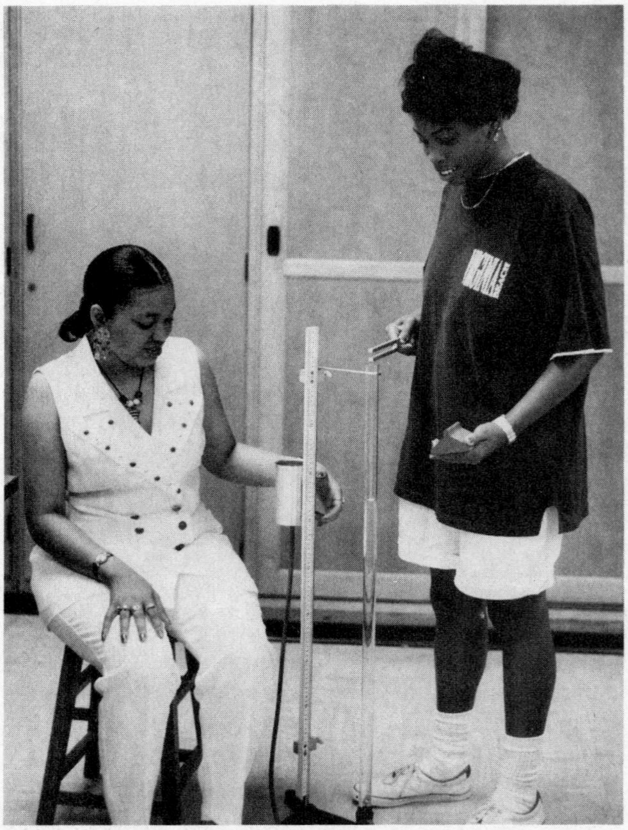

Figure 17.2 A resonance tube apparatus. The "length" of the tube is varied by raising and lowering the reservoir can to adjust the water level in the tube.

an odd number of quarter wavelengths* (i.e., $L = \lambda/4$, $L = 3\lambda/4$, $L = 5\lambda/4$, etc.) or in general $L = n\lambda/4$, where $n = 1, 3, 5, \ldots$, and $\lambda = 4L/n$. Incorporating the frequency f and speed v_s through the general relationship $\lambda f = v$, or $f = v/\lambda$, we have

$$f_n = \frac{nv}{4L} \qquad n = 1, 3, 5, \ldots \qquad \textbf{(17.1)}$$

Hence, an air column (tube) of length L has particular resonance frequencies and will be in resonance with the corresponding odd-harmonic driving frequencies.

As in the case of standing waves in a string (Experiment 16), the lowest natural or resonant frequency f_1 is called the fundamental frequency or first harmonic. Successively higher frequencies are higher harmonics and are sometimes called overtones (f_2, the second harmonic, is the first overtone, etc.).

As can be seen from Eq. 17.1, the three experimental parameters involved in the resonance condition of an air column are f, v, and L. To study resonance in this experiment, the length L of an air column will be varied for a given driving frequency, instead of varying f for a fixed L as in the case of the closed organ pipe described above. (The wave speed in air is relatively constant in either case.) The length of an air column will be varied by raising and lowering the water level in a tube (Fig. 17.2).

As the length of the air column is increased, more wavelength segments will fit into the tube, consistent with the node-antinode requirements at the ends (Fig. 17.3). The difference in the tube (air column) lengths when successive antinodes are at the open end of the tube and resonance occurs is equal to a half wavelength; for example,

$$\Delta L = L_2 - L_1 = \frac{3\lambda}{4} - \frac{\lambda}{4} = \frac{\lambda}{2}$$

(for the case illustrated in Fig. 17.3), and

$$\Delta L = L_3 - L_2 = \frac{5\lambda}{4} - \frac{3\lambda}{4} = \frac{\lambda}{2}$$

for the next resonance.

When an antinode is at the open end of the tube, a loud resonance tone is heard. Hence, the tube lengths for antinodes to be at the open end of the tube can be determined by lowering the water level in the tube and "listening" for successive resonances. No end correction is needed for the antinode occurring slightly above the end of the tube in this case, since the differences in tube lengths for successive antinodes is equal to $\lambda/2$.

If the frequency f of the driving tuning fork is known and the wavelength is determined by measuring the difference in tube length between successive antinodes, $\Delta L = \lambda/2$ or $\lambda = 2\Delta L$, the speed of sound

* The antinode does not occur exactly at the open end of the tube but at a slight distance above it, a distance which depends on the diameter of the tube.

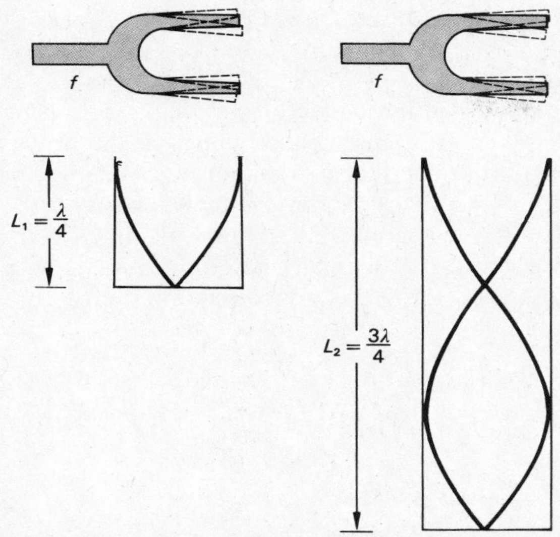

Figure 17.3 Standing waves. Illustrations of longitudinal standing waves of the same frequency in tubes of different lengths.

in air v_s can be determined from

$$v_s = \lambda f \quad \textbf{(17.2)}$$

Once v_s is determined (for a given ambient temperature), the unknown frequency of a tuning fork can be computed from Eq. 17.1 using the experimentally determined resonance wavelength in an air column for the unknown tuning fork frequency.

The speed of sound in air is temperature-dependent and is given to a good approximation over the normal temperature range by

$$v_s = 331.5 + 0.6T_c \text{ m/s} \quad \textbf{(17.3)}$$

where T_c is the air temperature in degrees Celsius. The equation shows that the speed of sound at 0 °C is 331.5 m/s and increases by 0.6 m/s for each degree of temperature increase. For example, if the air temperature is T_c = 20 °C (room temperature, 68 °F), then

$$v_s = 331.5 + (0.6)(20) = 343.5 \text{ m/s}$$

IV. Experimental Procedure

1. A resonance tube apparatus is shown in Fig. 17.2. Measure the inside diameter (I.D.) of the tube with a vernier caliper, and record in the data table, along with the room temperature.

   Place several rubber bands around the tube at various heights. (You will use the rubber bands later to mark resonance positions.) Then, raise the water level to near the top of the tube by raising the reservoir can. This can be done by depressing the can clamp and sliding it on the support rod. However, it may be more convenient to remove the reservoir can from the support rod so that it can be raised and lowered freely.

   With the water level near the top of the tube, there should be little water in the reservoir can. If this is not the case, remove some water from the can to prevent overflow and spilling when the can becomes filled on lowering. Practice lowering and raising the water level in the tube to get the ''feel'' of the apparatus.

2. With the water level in the tube near the top, take one of the tuning forks of known frequency (usually stamped on the fork) and set it into oscillation by striking it with a rubber mallet or on a rubber block, whichever is available. *Never strike the tuning fork on a hard object* (e.g., a table). This may damage the fork and cause a change in its characteristic frequency.*

   Hold the vibrating fork slightly above the top of the tube so that the sound is directed down the tube. (A fork has directional sound-propagation characteristics. Experiment with a vibrating fork and your ear to determine these directional characteristics.) *If the tube is glass, be careful not to let the vibrating fork strike the top of the tube.* This may chip the tube. Some resonance tubes are made of plastic.

3. With the vibrating tuning fork above the tube, *quickly* lower the reservoir can. The water level in the tube will fall slowly, and successive resonances will be heard as the level passes through the resonance-length positions. It may be necessary to strike the tuning fork several times to keep it vibrating sufficiently.

   As the water level passes through successive resonance positions, mark the approximate position of each by sliding a rubber band down to that position. Repeat, moving the water both up and down and adjusting the rubber-band heights as needed, until you are satisfied that the rubber bands are at the heights for the water levels where resonances are obtained.

   It is convenient to have one lab partner raise and lower the can and determine the resonance positions while another lab partner handles the tuning fork.

4. Determine the length from the top of the tube for the first resonance condition and record this

* It may be helpful to touch the vibrating tuning fork briefly about one-third of the way up from the base of the fork to dampen out the tinny sounds caused by the fork's overtones (resonant frequencies $> f_1$).

length in the data table. Repeat this procedure for the other observed resonance positions. (The number of observed lengths may be less than provided for in the data table.)

5. Repeat procedures 3 and 4 for the other tuning fork of known frequency.

6. (a) Compute the average wavelength for each fork from the average of the differences in the tube lengths between successive antinodes.
   (b) Using the known frequency of each fork, compute the speed of sound for each case.
   (c) Compare the average of these two experimental values with the value of the speed of sound given by Eq. 17.3 by computing the percent error.*

7. Repeat procedures 3 and 4 for the tuning fork of unknown frequency.

8. Compute the frequency of the tuning fork using the average experimental value of the wavelength and the speed of sound as given by Eq. 17.3. Your instructor may supply you with the known frequency of the tuning fork. If so, compare your experimentally determined value with the known frequency by computing the percent error.

* If there is a large percent error and the average experimental value is a multiple of the accepted value, it may be that you have observed the resonances of the tuning forks' overtone frequencies. Consult your instructor in this case.

Name ______________________ Section ______________ Date ______________

Lab Partner(s) ____

E X P E R I M E N T 1 7

Air Column Resonance: The Speed of Sound in Air

Laboratory Report

DATA TABLE

Purpose: To determine the speed of sound and the unknown frequency of a tuning fork.

Temperature ______________

Inside diameter of tube, I.D. ______________

	Tuning fork 1 Frequency, f ________		Tuning fork 2 Frequency, f ________		Tuning fork 3 Unknown frequency	
	Position of resonance ( )	ΔL ( )	Position of resonance	ΔL ( )	Position of resonance	ΔL ( )
L_1		X		X		X
L_2						
L_3						
L_4						
	Average ΔL					
	Average λ					

Calculations
(show work)

1. Speed of sound, v_s

v_s (from fork 1 data) ______________

v_s (from fork 2 data) ______________

Average v_s ______________

v_s (from Eq. 17.3) ______________

Percent error ______________

Don't forget units

(continued)

2. Frequency of tuning fork

Experimental value of f ______________

Known value ______________

Percent error ______________

QUESTIONS

1. Suppose that the laboratory temperature were 5 °C higher than the temperature at which you performed the experiment. Explain what effect(s) this would have on the experimental results.

2. With the water in the tube at the level for the tube length L_1 of the first resonance of the first tuning fork,
   (a) Would another tuning fork with a frequency lower than that of the first tuning fork produce a resonance?

   (b) Would another tuning fork of some higher frequency produce a resonance?

   (c) If your answer is yes in either case, what would be the frequency of the other fork?

Name ______ Section ______ Date ______

Lab Partner(s) ______

3. What are the resonant frequencies for an open organ pipe of fixed length L? (Show your sketches and calculations.)

4. (*Optional*) The uppermost antinode (Fig. 17.1) is slightly above the open end of the tube by an amount E (called the *end correction*).
   (a) Compute E from the data for each tuning fork.

   (b) Compare the computed E's with the theoretical values given by the equation $E = 0.4 \times \text{I.D.}$, where I.D. is the inner diameter of the tube.

Name ______________________ Section ______________ Date ______________

Lab Partner(s) ____

EXPERIMENT 18

The Thermal Coefficient of Linear Expansion

Advance Study Assignment

Read the experiment and answer the following questions.

1. What is isotropic expansion?

2. Explain how the thermal coefficient of linear expansion is determined experimentally.

3. What are the units of the thermal coefficient of linear expansion?

(continued)

4. Would taking L_o to be the length of the rod at 100 °C and measuring L at some other temperature change the experimental value of α significantly? Explain.

The Thermal Coefficient of Linear Expansion

I. Introduction and Objectives

With few exceptions, solids increase in size or dimensions as the temperature is increased. Although this effect is relatively small, it is very important in applications involving materials that undergo heating and cooling. Unless these changes are taken into account, material and structural damage can result: for example, a piston may become too tight in its cylinder, a rivet could loosen, or a bridge girder could produce damaging stress.

The expansion properties of a material depend on its internal makeup and structure. Macroscopically, we express the thermal expansion in terms of temperature coefficients of expansion, which are experimental quantities that represent the change in the dimensions of a material per degree of temperature change. In this experiment, the thermal expansion of some metals will be investigated and their temperature coefficients of linear expansion determined.

After performing this experiment and analyzing the data, you should be able to:

1. Tell how the thermal coefficient of linear expansion describes such expansion.
2. Explain how the thermal coefficient of linear expansion is measured and give an order of magnitude of its values for metals.
3. Describe and give examples of how thermal expansion considerations are important in applications of materials.

II. Equipment Needed

- Linear expansion apparatus and accessories
- Steam generator and stand
- Bunsen burner and striker or electric hot plate
- Rubber tubing
- Beaker
- Meterstick
- Thermometer (0 to 110 °C)
- Two or three kinds of metal rods (e.g., iron and aluminum)*

III. Theory

For solids, a temperature change leads to the expansion of a body as a whole. (A contraction resulting from a temperature decrease is a negative expansion.) The change in one dimension of the solid, length, width, or thickness, is called **linear expansion**. This may be different for different directions; however, if the expansion is the same in all directions, it is referred to as **isotropic expansion**.

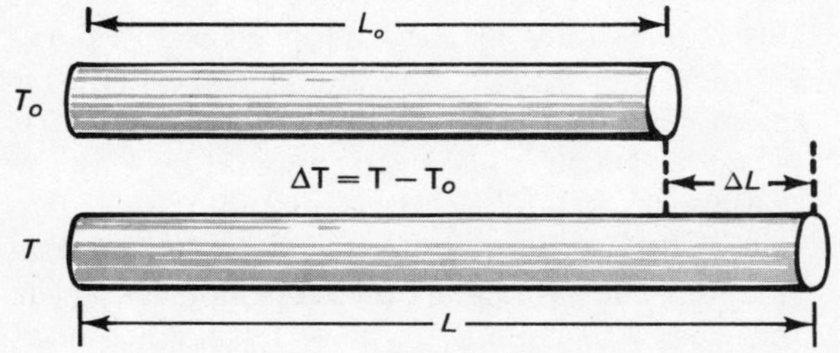

Figure 18.1 Linear thermal expansion. At the initial temperature T_o, the length of the rod is L_o. At some higher temperature T, the rod has expanded to length L, and the change in length is $\Delta L = L - L_o$ for the temperature change ΔT.

The fractional change in length $\Delta L/L_o$, where L_o is the length of the object at the initial temperature T_o (Fig. 18.1), is related to the change in temperature ΔT to a good approximation by

$$\frac{\Delta L}{L_o} = \alpha \Delta T \text{ or } \Delta L = \alpha L_o \Delta T \qquad \textbf{(18.1)}$$

where $\Delta L = L - L_o$ and $\Delta T = T - T_o$ and α is the **thermal coefficient of linear expansion**, with units of inverse temperature, that is, 1/C°. [It is convenient to write the unit of a ΔT as C° (Celsius degree) so as to distinguish from a particular temperature T (°C, degree Celsius).]

Note that α is the fractional change in length per degree temperature change.† This thermal coefficient of expansion may vary slightly for different temperature ranges, but this variation is usually negligible for

* To minimize the number of metal rods needed for convenience, lab groups can exchange jacketed rods after making measurements so that each group can obtain different rods.

† To help understand what is meant by *fractional change*, consider a money analogy. If you have \$1.00 in the bank and get 5¢ interest, then the fractional change (increase) in your money is $\Delta\$/\$_o$ = 5 cents/100 cents = 1/20 = 0.050 (or 5.0%).

common applications, and α is considered to be constant.

By Eq. 18.1, α is defined in terms of experimentally measurable quantities:

$$\alpha = \frac{\Delta L}{L_o \Delta T} \qquad \textbf{(18.2)}$$

Hence, by measuring the initial length L_o of an object (e.g., a metal rod) at an initial temperature T_o and the change in its length ΔL for a corresponding temperature change ΔT, α can be computed.

This development may be extended to two dimensions. The linear expansion expression (Eq. 18.1) may be written

$$L = L_o(1 + \alpha\Delta T) \qquad \textbf{(18.3)}$$

and for an isotropic material, its area is $A = L \times L$ or

$$\begin{aligned} A &= L^2 \\ &= L_o^2(1 + \alpha\Delta T)^2 \\ &= A_o(1 + 2\alpha\Delta T + \alpha^2\,\Delta T^2) \end{aligned}$$

where $A_o = L_o^2$. Since typical α's are of the order of $10^{-6}/\mathrm{C}^\circ$, the α^2 term may be dropped with negligible error, and to a good approximation

$$A = A_o(1 + 2\alpha\Delta T) \qquad \textbf{(18.4)}$$

Comparing this expression with Eq. 18.3, the thermal coefficient of area expansion is seen to be approximately twice the coefficient of linear expansion (i.e., 2α).

A similar development can be carried out for the coefficient of volume expansion, which is approximately equal to 3α.

Figure 18.2 Linear thermal expansion apparatus. Steam admitted to the steam jacket causes the metal rod to expand, and the expansion is measured by the micrometer attachment at the end of the rod. Notice the electrical contact indicator (lamp) near the hot plate. (Photo courtesy Central Scientific Co., Inc.)

IV. Experimental Procedure

1. A typical arrangement for determining thermal coefficients of linear expansion is shown in Fig. 18.2. The apparatus consists of a steam jacket with a micrometer attachment for measuring ΔL of a metal rod. A thermometer in the steam jacket measures the temperature of the rod. Steam is supplied to the jacket by a steam generator, and a beaker is used to catch the condensate.

2. Before assembling the apparatus, measure the lengths L_o of the metal rods with a meterstick to the nearest 0.1 mm and record these lengths in the data table. Avoid handling the rods with your bare hands in order not to raise their tempeature. Use a paper towel or cloth.

3. Assemble the apparatus, placing one of the rods in the steam jacket. Initially, have one end of the rod placed *firmly* against the fixed end screw and the other end not touching the micrometer screw.

   Carefully turn the micrometer screw until it just makes contact with the rod. Avoid mechanical backlash (and electrical spark-gap ionization, see below) by always turning the screw *toward* the rod just before reading. Do not force the screw. Record the micrometer setting. Do this three times and take the average as the initial setting. As soon as the initial micrometer is taken, read and record the initial temperature T_o.

   (The linear expansion apparatus may be equipped with an electrical circuit that uses a bell, light, or voltmeter to indicate when contact is made. The averaging process is unnecessary in this case. Also, another type of arrangement uses an optical lever mounted on a vertically standing expansion apparatus to measure ΔL. See Experiment 14 for instructions for the use of an optical lever.)

4. Turn the micrometer screw back from the end of the rod several millimeters to allow for the thermal expansion of the rod with increasing temperature. With the steam generator about one-half full, turn on the hot plate (or light the Bunsen burner) and boil the water so that steam passes through the jacket. The thermometer in the steam jacket should just touch the metal rod.

   Allow steam to pass through the jacket until the thermometer reading stabilizes (several minutes). When equilibrium has been reached, record the thermometer reading. Then carefully advance the micrometer screw until it touches the end of the rod and record the micrometer setting. Do this three times, and take the average of the micrometer readings unless contact is indicated by electrical circuit. Turn off the heat source.

5. Repeat procedures 3 and 4 for the other metal rods.

   Caution: *Be careful not to burn yourself with the condensed hot water in the steam jacket or the hot rod when you remove it. If jacketed rods are exchanged with other lab groups, again, be careful not to burn yourself. Take proper precautions.*

6. Compute ΔL and ΔT, and find the coefficient of linear expansion for each metal. Compare these α's with the accepted values given in Appendix A, Table A3, by computing the percent errors.

Name ____________________ Section ____________ Date ____________

Lab Partner(s) ______________________________

E X P E R I M E N T 1 8

The Thermal Coefficient of Linear Expansion

Laboratory Report

DATA TABLE

Purpose: To determine the thermal coefficients of expansion of metal samples.

	Initial length L_o ( )	Initial micrometer setting	Final micrometer setting	ΔL ( )	Init. temp. T_o ( )	Final temp. T ( )	ΔT ( )	α meas. ( )	α accepted ( )
1. Type of rod ________									
2. Type of rod ________									
3. Type of rod ________									

Calculations
(show work)

Metal	Percent Error
________	________
________	________
________	________

Don't forget units

(continued)

QUESTIONS

1. What are the probable sources of error in this experiment? Which will cause the biggest error?

2. Would the numerical values of the thermal coefficients of linear expansion be the same if the temperatures had been measured in degrees Fahrenheit? Explain, and give an example.

3. When a mercury-in-glass thermometer is placed in hot water, the thermometer reading first drops slightly and then rises. Explain why.

Name ______________________ Section ______________ Date ______________

Lab Partner(s) ____

4. If flat strips of iron and brass were bonded together and this bimetallic strip were heated, what would be observed? Justify your answer, and draw a sketch of the situation. (*Hint*: See Appendix A, Table A3 for α's.)

5. A Pyrex graduated cylinder has a volume of exactly 200 ml at 0 °C. If its temperature is increased to 100 °C, will its volume increase or decrease? Compute the change in volume.

6. Assume a metal rod with an intial length L_o is heated through a temperature increase of ΔT to a length L_1 then cooled to its initial temperature or through a temperature decrease of $-\Delta T$ (same ΔT increase and decrease). Calling the final length of the rod L_2 after this thermal cycle, (a) show that Eq. 18.3 implies that $L_2 = L_o[1 - (\alpha \Delta T)^2]$, i.e., $L_2 \neq L_o$.

(continued)

(b) What is the implication if the rod were taken through a number of such thermal cycles?

(c) Obviously something is wrong. Can you explain what it is? (*Hint*: think of *basis*, or reference. For example, if you had an investment that appreciated 100% in value one day, and you lost 100% of your investment the next, would you still have any money left?)

Name ______________________ Section ______________ Date ______________

Lab Partner(s) ____

EXPERIMENT 19

Specific Heats of Metals

Advance Study Assignment

Read the experiment and answer the following questions.

1. Distinguish between heat capacity and specific heat.

2. Why is the specific heat of water equal to unity, i.e., 1.0 cal/g-C° or 1.0 kcal/kg-C°?

3. Given that the specific heat of one material is twice that of another, compare the amounts of heat required to raise the temperatures of equal masses of each material by 1 C°. If the same amount of heat were added to samples of both materials and each sample had the same increase in temperature, compare the masses of each sample.

4. How is the method of mixtures used to determine specific heat?

Specific Heats of Metals

I. Introduction and Objectives

Different substances require different quantities of heat to produce a given temperature change. For example, about three and one-half times as much heat is needed to raise the temperature of 1 kg of iron through a given temperature interval ΔT as is needed to raise the temperature of 1 kg of lead by the same amount. This material behavior is characterized quantitatively by **specific heat**, which is the amount of heat necessary to raise the temperature of a unit mass of a substance by one unit temperature interval, e.g., 1 gram or 1 kilogram of a substance 1 Celsius degree. Thus, in the previous example iron has a greater specific heat than lead.

The specific heat of a material is specific or characteristic for that material. As can be seen from the definition, the specific heat of a given material can be determined by adding a known amount of heat to a known mass of material and noting the corresponding temperature change. It is the purpose of this experiment to determine the specific heats of some common metals by calorimetry methods.

After performing this experiment and analyzing the data, you should be able to:

1. Tell what is meant by the specific heat of a substance and compare the effects of different specific heats.
2. Calculate the heat necessary to raise the temperature of a given mass of a substance a particular number of degrees.
3. Describe and explain calorimetry and the method of mixtures.

II. Equipment Needed

- Calorimeter
- Boiler and stand
- Hot plate or Bunsen burner and striker
- Two thermometers (0 to 110 °C)
- Two kinds of metal (shot form or slugs with attached strings)
- Laboratory balance
- Ice
- Safety glasses

III. Theory

The change in temperature ΔT of a substance is proportional to the amount of heat ΔQ added (or removed) from it:

$$\Delta Q \propto \Delta T$$

In equation form, we may write

$$\Delta Q = C\,\Delta T \qquad \textbf{(19.1)}$$

where the constant of proportionality C is called the **heat capacity** of the substance.

However, the amount of heat required to change the temperature of an object is also proportional to the mass of the object. Hence, it is convenient to define a specific heat capacity (or simply specific heat) c:

$$c = \frac{C}{m} \qquad \textbf{(19.2)}$$

which is the heat capacity per unit mass of a substance. Thus, Eq. 19.1 becomes

$$\Delta Q = mc\,\Delta T \text{ or } c = \frac{\Delta Q}{m\Delta T} \qquad \textbf{(19.3)}$$

In common units the specific heat is then the amount of heat (in calories) required to change the temperature of 1 g of a substance 1 C°.*

The calorie unit of heat is defined as the amount of heat required to raise the temperature of 1 g of water 1 C°. By definition, then, water has a specific heat of 1 cal/g-C°.

$$c = \frac{\Delta Q}{m\Delta T} = \frac{1\text{ cal}}{(1\text{ g})(1\text{ °C})} = 1\text{ cal/g-C°}$$

[A kilocalorie (kcal) is the unit of heat defined as the amount of heat required to raise the temperature of 1 kg of water by 1 C°. In these units, water has a specific heat of 1 kcal/kg-C° or 4.18×10^3 J/kg-C°. Your instructor may recommend that you use one of these units.]

The specific heat of a material can be determined experimentally by measuring the temperature change of a given mass of material produced by a quantity of

* It is convenient to write the unit of a ΔT as C° (Celsius degree) so as to distinguish from a particular temperature T (°C, degrees Celsius).

heat. This is done indirectly by a calorimetry procedure known as the **method of mixtures**. If several substances at various temperatures are brought together, the hotter substances lose heat and the colder substances gain heat until all the substances reach a common equilibrium temperature. If the system is insulated so that no heat is lost to or gained from the surroundings, then by the conservation of energy, the heat lost is equal to the heat gained.

In this experiment, hot metal is added to water in a calorimeter cup and the mixture is stirred until the system is in thermal equilibrium. The calorimeter insulates the system from losing heat (Fig. 19.1). In equation form, we may write

$$\text{heat lost} = \text{heat gained}$$

or

$$\Delta Q_{\text{metal}} = \Delta Q_{\text{water}} + \Delta Q_{\text{cup and stirrer}}$$

and

$$\begin{aligned} m_m c_m (T_m - T_f) &= m_w c_w (T_f - T_w) + m_{cs} c_{cs} (T_f - T_w) \\ &= (m_w c_w + m_{cs} c_{cs})(T_f - T_w) \end{aligned} \qquad \textbf{(19.4)}$$

where T_f is the final intermediate equilibrium temperature of the system. The other subscripts indicate the masses, specific heats, and initial temperatures of the respective components. Hence, Eq. 19.4 may be used to determine the specific heat c_m of the metal if all the other quantities are known.

IV. Experimental Procedure

1. Weigh out 400 to 500 g (0.4 to 0.5 kg) of one kind of dry metal shot. [Do this by first determining the mass of the empty boiler cup (in which the metal shot is heated) and then adding an appro-

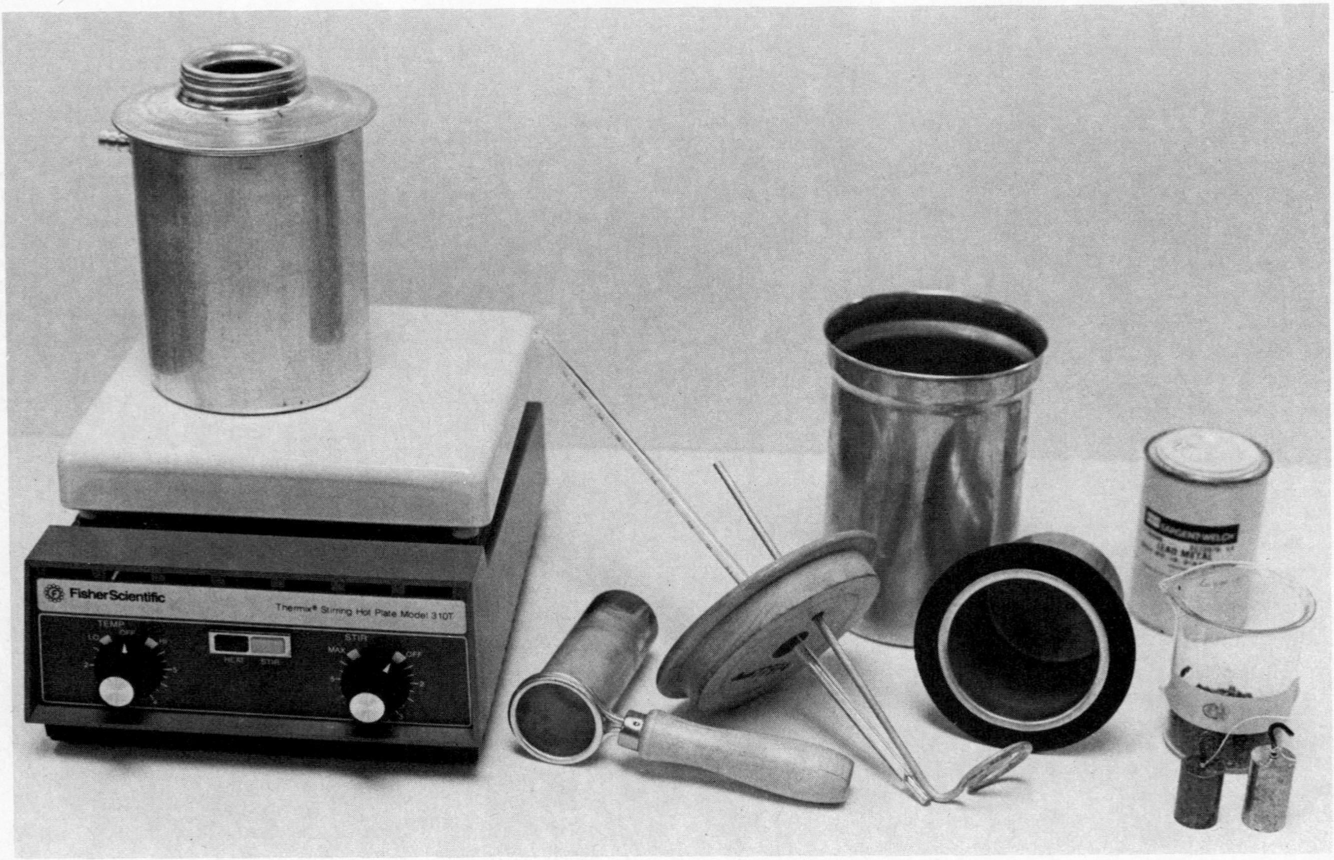

Figure 19.1 Apparatus for specific heat measurements. Metal shot or a solid piece of metal (right) is heated and then placed in a known amount of water in the calorimeter, which insulates the system from losing heat. The inner calorimeter cup is shown with its dark insulating ring laying in front of the outer cup.

priate amount of metal shot to the cup and reweighing.]

Record the mass of the metal m_m and the room temperature T_r in the data table. Your instructor may prefer to use a solid piece of metal with a string attached instead of metal shot. In this case it is necessary to weigh only the piece of metal.

2. Insert a thermometer well into the metal shot, (or into cup with piece of metal if used), place the cup and shot into the boiler, and start heating the boiler water.

   Caution: *If a mercury thermometer is used, special care must be taken. If the thermometer breaks and mercury spills into the hot metal, the mixture should be removed from the room immediately (to an exhaust hood or outdoors). Mercury fumes are* ***highly*** *toxic.*

   The boiler should be about half full of water. Keep steam or water from dampening the dry metal by shielding the cup with a cardboard lid (with a hole for the thermometer).

3. While the boiler is heating, determine and record the mass of the inner calorimeter cup (without the ring) and the stirrer. Record the total mass m_{cs}. Also, note and record the type of metal and specific heat of the cup and stirrer, which is usually stamped on the cup.* (The specific heat may be found in Appendix A, Table A4, if it is not stamped on the cup.)

4. Fill the calorimeter cup about one-half to two-thirds full of cold tap water and weigh the cup, stirrer, and water to determine the mass of the water m_w. (If a solid piece of metal is used, which usually has less mass than the recommended amount of shot, less water should be used so as to obtain an appreciable ΔT temperature change. This may also be the case at high elevations, where the temperature of boiling water is substantially less than 100 °C).

   Place the calorimeter cup with the water and stirrer in the calorimeter jacket and put on the lid, with a thermometer extending into the water.

5. After the water in the boiler boils and the thermometer in the metal has stabilized (allow several minutes), read and record the temperature of the metal T_m.

   Start with the water and stirrer in the cup at a temperature T_w several degrees below room temperature T_r. Adjust the temperature of the inner calorimeter cup and its contents by placing it in a beaker of ice water. Measure and record the temperature T_w.

6. Remove the thermometer from the metal. Then, remove the lid from the calorimeter and quickly, but carefully, lift the cup with the hot metal from the boiler and pour the metal shot into the calorimeter cup with as little splashing as possible so as not to splash out and lose any water. (If a solid piece of metal is used, carefully lower the metal piece into the calorimeter cup by means of the attached string.)

   Replace the lid with the thermometer, and stir the mixture gently. The thermometer should not touch the metal. While stirring, watch the thermometer and record the temperature when a maximum equilibrium temperature is reached (T_f).

   For the best results, the final temperature T_f should be above room temperature T_r by about as many degrees as T_w was below it. If this is not approximately the case, repeat procedures 4 through 6, adjusting T_w until the relationship $T_f - T_r \approx T_r - T_w$ is satisfied.

7. Repeat procedures 1 through 6 for another kind of metal sample. Make certain that you use fresh water in the calorimeter cup. (Dump the previous metal shot and water into a strainer in a sink so that it may be dried and used by others doing the experiment later.)

8. Compute the specific heat of each metal using Eq. 19.4. Look up the accepted values in Appendix A, Table A4, and compute the percent errors.

* If the cup and stirrer are not of the same material, they must be treated separately, and the last term in Eq. 19.4 becomes $(m_w c_w + m_c c_c + m_s c_s)(T_f - T_w)$.

Name ______________________ Section ____________ Date ____________
Lab Partner(s) ____

EXPERIMENT 19

Specific Heats of Metals

Laboratory Report

DATA TABLE

Purpose: To determine the specific heats of metal samples. Room temperature, T_r ____________

Type of metal	Mass of metal, m_m ( )	Mass of calorimeter and stirrer, m_{cs}	Specific heat of calorimeter and stirrer, c_{cs} ( )	Mass of water, m_w ( )	T_m ( )	T_w ( )	T_f ( )

Calculations (show work)	Type of metal	c_m (experimental)	c_m (accepted)	Percent error
	________	________	________	________
	________	________	________	________

Don't forget units

(continued)

QUESTIONS

1. (a) The percent errors of your experimental values of the specific heats may be quite large. Identify several sources of experimental error.

   (b) Why does it improve the accuracy of the experiment if $T_f - T_r \approx T_r - T_w$?

2. The specific heat of aluminum is 0.22 cal/g-C°. What is the value of the specific heat in (a) kcal/kg-C°; (b) Btu/lb-F°? (Show your calculations.)

3. If wet shot had been poured into the calorimeter cup, how would the experimental value of the specific heat have been affected?

Name ______________________ Section ______________ Date ______________
Lab Partner(s) ____

EXPERIMENT 19 | *Laboratory Report*

4. Explain how the unknown temperature of a hot piece of metal may be determined by the method of mixtures. (Assume c_m to be known.)

5. In solar heating applications, heat energy is stored in some medium until it is needed (e.g., to heat a home at night). Should the medium have a high or a low specific heat? Suggest a substance that would be appropriate for use as a heat-storage medium, and explain its advantages.

6. Explain why specific heat is *specific* and how it gives a relative indication of molecular configuration and bonding.

Name ______________________ Section ______________ Date ______________
Lab Partner(s) ____

EXPERIMENT 20

Heats of Fusion and Vaporization

Advance Study Assignment

Read the experiment and answer the following questions.

1. What is latent heat?

2. The heat of vaporization of water is almost seven times its heat of fusion. What does this imply?

3. Why is the water used in the experimental procedures for the heat of fusion and heat of vaporization initially heated and cooled, respectively?

(continued)

4. Why are the pieces of ice in the heat of fusion procedure dried and handled with a paper towel? Explain the effect on the experimental result if this were not done.

5. What is the purpose of the water trap in the steam line in the heat of vaporization procedure? Explain the effect on the experimental result if it were not used.

6. Explain how latent heat is computed from the experimental data.

Heats of Fusion and Vaporization

I. Introduction and Objectives

When heat is added to a substance, its temperature normally rises. However, when a substance undergoes a change of phase or state, e.g., solid to liquid or liquid to gas, the heat energy goes into doing work against the intermolecular forces and is not reflected in a change in the temperature of the substance. This heat energy is called the **heat of fusion** and the **heat of vaporization** for the phase changes that occur at the melting- (or freezing-) point temperature and boiling- (or condensation-) point temperature, respectively. The energy involved in a phase change is commonly referred to as **latent heat**, because the heat energy is seemingly hidden or concealed in that it is not evidenced by a temperature change. For the inverse processes, when a vapor or gas condenses or a liquid freezes, by the conservation of energy the (latent) heat of vaporization is given up or the (latent) heat of fusion must be extracted.

In this experiment, the heats of fusion and vaporization of water will be determined through the calorimetry method of mixtures.

After performing this experiment and analyzing the data, you should be able to:

1. Clearly distinguish between latent heat and specific heat (see Experiment 19).
2. Explain the role of latent heat in a phase change.
3. Describe how latent heat can be determined experimentally.

II. Equipment Needed

- Calorimeter
- Steam generator and stand
- Hot plate or Bunsen burner and striker
- Thermometer (0 to 110 °C)
- Rubber hose
- Water trap
- Ice
- Paper towels
- Laboratory balance
- Beaker
- Safety glasses

III. Theory

A general graph of heat energy versus temperature for a given mass m of water is shown in Fig. 20.1. The sloping phase lines follow the relationship

$$\Delta Q = mc\,\Delta T \qquad \textbf{(20.1)}$$

The slopes of the lines are mc, where c is the specific heat of the particular phase ($c_{water} = 1.0$ kcal/kg-C°, or 1.0 cal/g-C° and $c_{ice} \approx c_{steam} = 0.5$ kcal/kg-C°, or 0.5 cal/g-C°). (Actually, $c_{ice} = 0.50$ kcal/kg-C° and $c_{steam} = 0.48$ kcal/kg-C°.)

At the freezing and boiling points, the addition of certain amounts of heat has no effect on the temperature, as indicated by the vertical lines. At these points, the heat energy goes into the work of effecting the phase changes and not into increasing the molecular activity, which would be reflected as a temperature increase.

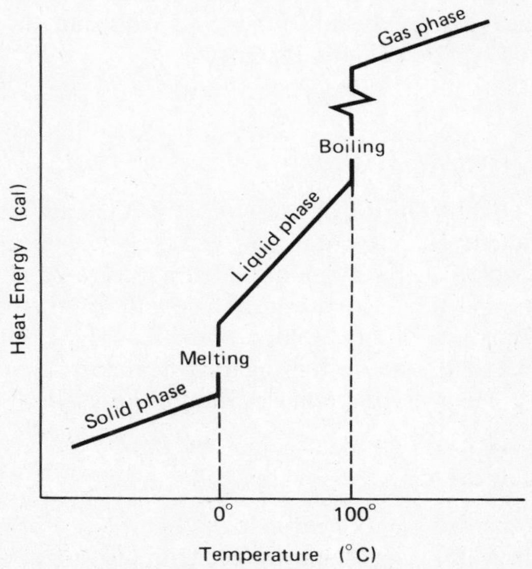

Figure 20.1 Energy versus temperature. For a given mass of water, a graph of heat energy versus temperature would generally be as shown, with the vertical lines of constant temperature indicating phase changes.

The **latent heat** L is defined as the amount of heat required to change the phase of a unit mass of a substance (without a change of temperature) and has the common units of kcal/kg or cal/g. Hence, the amount of heat absorbed or given up by a quantity of a substance when it undergoes a change of phase is

$$\Delta Q = mL_i \qquad \textbf{(20.2)}$$

where m is the mass of the substance and L_i the latent heat for the particular phase change.

The latent heats are, of course, characteristic of the substance. For example, the **(latent) heat of fusion** L_f of water is 80 kcal/kg (or 80 cal/g) and its **(latent) heat of vaporization** L_v is 540 kcal/kg (or 540 cal/g). This means that 80 kcal is required to melt 1 kg of ice at 0 °C (or 80 kcal must be removed from 1 kg of water at 0 °C to freeze it) and that 540 kcal is required to convert 1 kg of water at 100 °C to steam (or 540 kcal is released when 1 kg of steam at 100 °C condenses to water). Other substances have different latent heats.

In this experiment, the heats of fusion and vaporization of water will be measured by a calorimetry procedure called the methods of mixtures (see Experiment 19). If several substances at various temperatures are brought together, the hotter substances lose heat and the colder substances gain heat until all the substances reach a common equilibrium temperature. This is generally true even if one or more of the substances undergoes a phase change in the process. If the system is insulated and no heat is lost to the surroundings, then by the conservation of energy, the heat lost by the hot substances will equal the heat gained by the colder substances.

A. Heat of Fusion

If a quantity of ice of mass m_i at 0 °C is added to a sufficient quantity of warm water in a calorimeter cup with a stirrer at an initial temperature T_h, the ice melts and the system comes to equilibrium at some intermediate or final temperature T_f. (The calorimeter insulates the system against heat loss. See Fig. 19.1.) Then, by the conservation of energy,

$$\begin{array}{l}\text{heat of fusion} \\ \text{to melt the ice}\end{array} + \begin{array}{l}\text{heat gained by the} \\ \text{ice water}\end{array} = \begin{array}{l}\text{heat lost by the} \\ \text{warm water}\end{array} + \begin{array}{l}\text{heat lost by the} \\ \text{calorimeter cup and stirrer}\end{array}$$

or

$$\Delta Q_{\text{fusion}} + \Delta Q_{\text{ice water}} = \Delta Q_{\substack{\text{warm}\\\text{water}}} + \Delta Q_{\substack{\text{calorimeter cup}\\\text{and stirrer}}}$$

and

$$\begin{aligned} m_i L_f + m_i c_w(T_f - 0) &= m_w c_w (T_h - T_f) + m_{cs} c_{cs} (T_h - T_f) \\ &= (m_w c_w + m_{cs} c_{cs})(T_h - T_f) \end{aligned} \qquad \textbf{(20.3)}$$

where the m's and c's are the masses and specific heats, respectively, of the various components as indicated by the subscripts (i = ice, w = water, cs = calorimeter-stirrer). Hence, Eq. 20.3 may be used to determine the heat of fusion L_f of water if all the other quantities are known.

B. Heat of Vaporization

If a quantity of steam of mass m_s at 100 °C is added to cool water in a calorimeter cup with a stirrer at an initial temperature T_c, the steam condenses and the system comes to equilibrium at some intermediate or final temperature T_f. Assuming no heat loss to the surroundings, by the conservation of energy,

$$\begin{array}{l}\text{heat of vaporization lost} \\ \text{by steam in condensing}\end{array} + \begin{array}{l}\text{heat lost by hot} \\ \text{condensed water}\end{array} = \begin{array}{l}\text{heat gained by the} \\ \text{cool water}\end{array} + \begin{array}{l}\text{heat gained by the} \\ \text{calorimeter cup and stirrer}\end{array}$$

or

$$\Delta Q_{\text{vaporization}} + \Delta Q_{\substack{\text{hot}\\\text{water}}} = \Delta Q_{\substack{\text{cool}\\\text{water}}} + \Delta Q_{\substack{\text{calorimeter cup}\\\text{and stirrer}}}$$

and

$$\begin{aligned} m_s L_v + m_s c_w(100 - T_f) &= m_w c_w (T_f - T_c) + m_{cs} c_{cs} (T_f - T_c) \\ &= (m_w c_w + m_{cs} c_{cs})(T_f - T_c) \end{aligned} \qquad \textbf{(20.4)}$$

where the m's and c's are the masses and specific heats, respectively, of the various components, as indicated by the subscripts. Hence, Eq. 20.4 may be used to determine the heat of vaporization L_v of water if all the other quantities are known.

IV. Experimental Procedure

A. Heat of Fusion

1. Heat some water in the beaker (enough to fill the inner calorimeter cup about half full) to about 10 to 15 °C above room temperature. While the water is heating, determine the mass of the inner calorimeter cup (without ring) and stirrer (total mass m_{cs}) on a laboratory balance. Also, note

and record the type of metal and specific heat of the cup and stirrer, usually stamped on the cup.*

2. Fill the inner calorimeter cup about half-full of the warm water and weigh it (with the stirrer) to determine the mass of the water m_w. Place the calorimeter cup with the water and stirrer in the calorimeter jacket and put on the lid with a thermometer extending into the water. Stir the water gently and record its temperature T_h.

3. Select several small pieces of ice about the size of the end of your thumb and dry them with a paper towel. (It is important that the ice be dry.) Without touching the ice with your bare fingers (use the paper towel), carefully add the pieces of ice to the calorimeter cup one at a time without splashing. (It is good procedure to stir the water and check its temperature again just before adding the ice. If it has changed, take the later reading as T_h.)

4. Gently stir the water-ice mixture while adding the ice. Enough ice is to be added until the temperature of the mixture is about 10 to 15 °C below room temperature after the ice has melted. Add the ice more slowly toward the end so that you can better control the final temperature. Continue to stir gently, and read and record the equilibrium temperature T_f when the ice has melted completely.

   Then, weigh and record the mass of the inner calorimeter cup with its contents (water and stirrer) so as to determine the mass of the melted ice water or mass of the ice m_i.

5. Compute the heat of fusion L_f using Eq. 20.3, and compare it with the accepted value, L_f = 80 kcal/kg = 80 cal/g = 3.35×10^5 J/kg, by finding the percent error.

B. *Heat of Vaporization*

6. Set up the steam generator as shown in Fig. 20.2 with the boiler about two-thirds full of water, and begin heating the boiler. A water trap is used in the steam line (which should be as short as practically possible) to prevent hot water condensed in the tube from entering the calorimeter. (It is important that the hot water condensed in the tube be prevented from entering the calorimeter —note the hose arrangement in Fig. 20.2.)

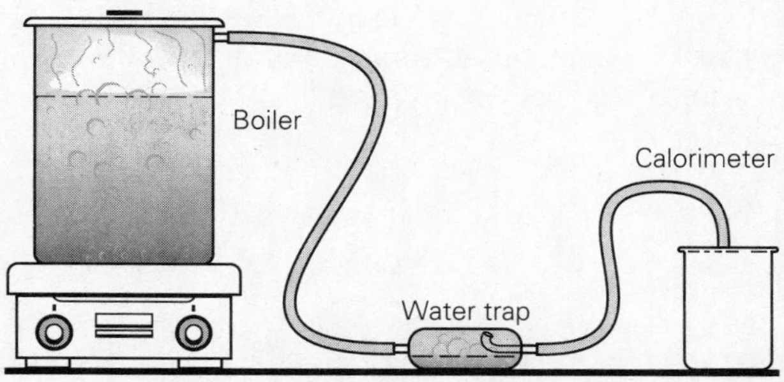

Figure 20.2 Steam generator arrangement. For the heat-of-vaporization measurement, steam from boiling water is transferred to the calorimeter through a water trap. The trap prevents hot water condensed in the tube from entering the calorimeter, which would introduce error.

7. Fill the inner calorimeter cup about two-thirds full of cool water at about 15 °C below room temperature. Either the cool water from the heat-of-fusion experiment or fresh tap water may be used with some ice added to obtain the desired temperature. (Make sure that all the ice has melted, however.)

   Weigh and record the mass of the calorimeter cup with the water and stirrer. Then place the cup in the calorimeter jacket and replace the lid. Gently stir the water and read and record the equilibrium temperature T_c.

8. With the water in the steam generator boiling gently and steam flowing freely from the steam tube as evidenced by water vapor coming from the tube (recall that steam is invisible), introduce steam into the calorimeter water and stir.

   Caution: *Be careful not to get a steam burn when placing the steam line into or removing it from the cup.*

   It is good procedure to stir the water and check its temperature again just before introducing the steam. If it has changed, take the later reading as T_c.

   When the temperature of the water is about 15 °C above room temperature, turn off the heat source and carefully remove the steam line from the calorimeter. Stir gently, and read and record the equilibrium temperature T_f.

* If the cup and stirrer are not of the same material, they must be treated separately, and the mass term in Eqs. 20.3 and 20.4 becomes $(m_w c_w + m_c c_c + m_s c_s)$.

Finally, reweigh the inner calorimeter cup and its contents so as to determine the mass of the condensed steam m_s.

9. Compute the heat of vaporization L_v using Eq. 20.4 and compare it with the accepted value L_v = 540 kcal/kg = 540 cal/g = 2.26×10^6 J/kg by finding the percent error.

Name ______________________ Section ______________ Date ______________

Lab Partner(s) ____

EXPERIMENT 20

Heats of Fusion and Vaporization

Laboratory Report

Mass of calorimeter cup and stirrer, m_{cs} ______________

Type of metal and specific heat of calorimeter cup and stirrer, c_{cs} ______________

A. Heat of Fusion

Mass of calorimeter plus water ______________

Initial temperature of water, T_h ______________

Mass of water, m_w ______________

Final equilibrium temperature, T_f ______________

Mass of calorimeter, water, and melted ice ______________

Mass of ice, m_i ______________

Calculations (show work)

Experimental L_f ______________

Accepted L_f ______________

Percent error ______________

Don't forget units

(continued)

B. Heat of Vaporization

Mass of calorimeter plus water ________________

Mass of water, m_w ________________

Mass of calorimeter, water, and condensed steam ________________

Mass of steam, m_s ________________

Initial temperature of water, T_c ________________

Final equilibrium temperature, T_f ________________

Calculations
(show work)

Experimental L_v ________________

Accepted L_v ________________

Percent error ________________

Name ______________________ Section ______________ Date ______________

Lab Partner(s) ______________________

EXPERIMENT 20 *Laboratory Report*

QUESTIONS

1. Discuss the most important sources of error in the experimental procedures. If the temperature of the ice added to the calorimeter in the heat-of-fusion experiment were less than 0 °C, how would this affect the results? Why should you use small pieces of ice rather than large ones?

2. Explain why burns caused by steam at 100 °C are more serious than those caused by an equal mass of boiling water at the same temperature.

3. How is the latent heat of water used in the cooling mechanism of our bodies?

4. What is the heat of sublimation? [*Hint*: Dry ice (solid CO_2) sublimes.]

(continued)

5. A piece of ice with a mass of 30 g at 0 °C is added to 100 mL of water at 20 °C. Assuming that no heat is lost to the surroundings, what is the situation when thermal equilibrium is reached? (Ignore the calorimeter or container.)

Calibration of a Thermometer

I. Introduction

The latent heat experiment is relatively short, and with ice and a means to boil water available, you can also quickly calibrate a thermometer, which is quite interesting and instructive.

II. Equipment Needed

- Uncalibrated thermometer (glass)
- Beaker (500 mL)
- Tripod stand and wire gauze pad (if Bunsen burner is used)
- Felt-tip pen or wax pencil
- Ruler
- Classroom Celsius thermometer

III. Theory

A thermometer may be calibrated by using two fixed-point temperatures and then making a graduated scale between these points.* For example, the ice point and steam point of water are convenient fixed points (0 °C or 32 °F and 100 °C or 212 °F, respectively). If the length between these two points is divided linearly into 100 intervals or degrees, the result corresponds with the Celsius temperature scale. Similarly, if the length between the fixed points is divided into 180 intervals or degrees, the result corresponds to the Fahrenheit temperature scale.

By analogy, the meter standard was originally referenced to two marks on a metal bar. The length between the marks may be divided into 100 intervals or centimeters. It could be divided into 180 intervals, but that would not produce a decimal scale.

* On the SI Kelvin (absolute) scale, the kelvin or interval is defined as 1/273.16 of the temperature of the triple point of water (point where water coexists in three phases, 0.01 °C and 4.58 mm Hg). Here the temperature scale fixed points are the triple point and absolute zero.

IV. Experimental Procedure

1. Start heating a *small* amount of water in the beaker. The water depth in the beaker should be several centimeters, enough to cover the thermometer bulb. (More water may be used, but it is unnecessary and will take longer to boil.)

   While the water is heating, draw an outline of the thermometer on a sheet of paper. The temperature scale will be marked off on the paper, and the outline will allow the thermometer to be replaced on the paper in the proper position. (The scales on many thermometers are not engraved on the glass tube of the thermometer, but on an attached frame.)

2. Place the uncalibrated thermometer into the heating water and heat until the water boils vigorously. With the supplied pen or pencil, mark the height of the thermometer's liquid column on the stem. Turn off the burner. Remove the thermometer and place it on the outline, making a mark on the paper at the mark of the fixed steam point on the thermometer.

3. Pour the hot water from the beaker into a sink.

   Caution: *Use paper towels or tongs to transport the hot beaker and pour carefully so as not to burn yourself. Recall that steam has a large latent heat.*

   Add a small amount of cold water to the beaker (1–2 cm in depth) and enough ice so the beaker is one-third to one-half full.

4. Insert the uncalibrated thermometer into the ice-water mixture and stir. The liquid column of the thermometer should reach a low stationary point after a few minutes. Make a mark on the thermometer stem at this lowest point. (Leave the thermometer in the ice water for another minute or so to make sure the column goes no lower. Adjust the mark accordingly if it does.) In thermal equilibrium, ice and water coexist at the ice point.

5. Remove the thermometer, place it on the outline, and mark the ice point on the paper. Lay the

thermometer aside and with a ruler divide the length between the two fixed points into 10 equal intervals (deka-degree or 10-degree intervals). Using the Celsius values for the fixed points, label these marks on one side of the thermometer outline.

Then, divide the interval between the 20 and 30 degree marks into 10 equal intervals or degrees. (The same could be done for the other 10-degree intervals, giving a centigrade or 100-degree scale, but this is unnecessary for the purpose of the experiment.)

6. Read the room temperature from the classroom thermometer and mark and record the value on the paper scale. Then, place the uncalibrated thermometer (which should now be at room temperature) on the outline and mark and read the temperature. Compare the temperature reading on your scale with the classroom (accepted) thermometer reading by finding the percent error. Show this calculation on the outline paper.

7. On the other side of the thermometer outline, make a graduated Fahrenheit scale with a fine scale in the vicinity of the room temperature reading. Note the value of your thermometer's room temperature reading on the Fahrenheit scale and record on the paper.

Compare the experimental Fahrenheit reading with the experimental Celsius reading by computing T_F from $T_F = (9/5)T_C + 32$ using the experimental value of T_C in the equation. How close did you come?

8. Attach the outline paper to the Laboratory Report for the latent heat portion of the experiment.

Name ______________________ Section ______________ Date ______________

Lab Partner(s) ______________________

EXPERIMENT 21

Newton's Law of Cooling: The Time Constant of a Thermometer

Advance Study Assignment

Read the experiment and answer the following questions.

1. According to Newton's law of cooling, would a body cool faster in the temperature range 100 to 150 °C or 50 to 100 °C? Explain.

2. What is meant by exponential decay function? An exponential growth function?

3. What is a "time constant," and on what does it depend for a cooling process?

(continued)

4. Is the temperature of a cooling object a linear function of time? Explain in terms of the slope of the function.

5. How is the time constant of a cooling process determined graphically?

Newton's Law of Cooling: The Time Constant of a Thermometer

I. Introduction and Objectives

All dynamic instruments used to make physical measurements require a time period to respond to the change in conditions which they measure. Some instruments respond very quickly, and their response times go unnoticed. However, the times required for some instruments to give "correct" readings are readily observed and measurable. For example, a thermometer requires a finite time to come to thermal equilibrium with its surroundings. This is evidenced by having to allow 2 to 3 min to get a correct reading when measuring one's body temperature with a thermometer. Similarly, a finite time interval is required for a thermometer to cool off from a high temperature reading to room temperature. (A clinical thermometer is prevented from returning to a lower reading by a constriction in its capillary.)

Newton's law of cooling is an empirical observation made by him which states that the cooling rate, or rate change of temperature of a body is directly proportional to the difference in temperature between the body and its surroundings, provided that the temperature difference is small.

In this experiment, Newton's law of cooling will be investigated and the time constant of a thermometer will be determined.

After performing this experiment and analyzing the data, you should be able to:

1. Describe exponential "decay" as a function of time.
2. Explain what is meant by a time constant and how it affects exponential decay.
3. State Newton's law of cooling and comment on its validity.

II. Equipment Needed

- One metal-stem dial thermometer (0 to 150 °C)
- One liquid-in-glass thermometer (0 to 110 °C)
- Metal cylinder of thermometer length
- Two stands and clamps
- Bunsen burner and striker
- Laboratory timer or stopwatch
- 1 sheet of Cartesian graph paper
- Safety glasses

III. Theory

Newton's law of cooling states that the cooling rate of a body is directly proportional to the difference in temperature ΔT between the body and its surroundings, provided the temperature difference is small. In terms of the time rate of heat loss, this may be expressed mathematically as

$$\frac{dQ}{dt} = -K\Delta T = -K(T - T_r) \qquad \textbf{(21.1)}$$

where dQ/dt is the time rate of cooling heat loss, $\Delta T = T - T_r$ the difference between the temperature T and the lower final temperature T_r (in this experiment, room temperature), and K a constant of proportionality. The minus sign indicates that the temperature decreases with time.*

* The heat loss includes contributions from all methods of heat transfer—conduction, convection, and radiation.

A small amount of heat dQ lost by an object over a small temperature interval dT can be expressed in terms of the object's specific heat c:

$$dQ = mc\, dT$$

where m is the mass of the object. Dividing both sides of the equation by a small time interval dt, we have

$$\frac{dQ}{dt} = mc\frac{dT}{dt} \qquad \textbf{(21.2)}$$

Equating Eqs. 21.1 and 21.2 yields

$$\frac{dT}{dt} = \frac{-K}{mc}(T - T_r)$$

By the methods of integral calculus, it can be shown that the temperature T of an object at any time t predicted by this equation is given by

$$T - T_r = (T_o - T_r)e^{-Kt/mc} \qquad \textbf{(21.3)}$$

where the e term is an exponential function (e = 2.71) and T_o is the original or initial termperature of the body at $t = 0$. The quantity $T_o - T_r$ is therefore a constant for a particular situation.

Eq. 21.3 is often written

$$T - T_r = (T_o - T_r)e^{-t/\tau} \qquad \textbf{(21.4)}$$

where $\tau = mc/K$ is called the **time constant** of the process. It depends on the mass and specific heat of the object and on the heat transfer parameters contained in the constant K.

The time constant τ has the units of time, so in a time $t = \tau$ (one time constant), $e^{-t/\tau} = e^{-\tau/\tau} = e^{-1} = 0.368$. Thus, the temperature of the object will have fallen to 0.368 (or 36.8 percent) of its original value; $(T - T_r)/(T_o - T_r) = 0.368$, where $(T_o - T_r)$ is the total temperature drop and $(T - T_r)$ is the remaining temperature interval. For $t = 2\tau$ then $e^{-2} = 0.135$, and so on. A plot of how the temperature of the cooling object varies with time according to Eq. 21.4 is shown in Fig. 21.1.

The T versus t plot in Fig. 21.1 is referred to as an **exponential decay curve**. The temperature of the object *decays* or decreases exponentially with time as a result of the negative exponent. (An exponential function with a positive exponent would increase or grow with time.) As will be noted, the smaller the time constant or the greater the negative exponent, the faster the decay or cooling. It is possible to determine the time constant graphically by using different coordinates. By taking the logarithm (to the base e) of Eq. 21.4, the equation becomes

$$\ln (T - T_r) = -\lambda t + \ln (T_o - T_r)$$

where $\lambda = 1/\tau$. The equation now has the slope-intercept form of a straight line,

$$y = mx + b$$

By plotting $\ln (T - T_r)$ versus time, the slope m can be determined. Then, $\lambda = -m$, and $\tau = 1/\lambda$.

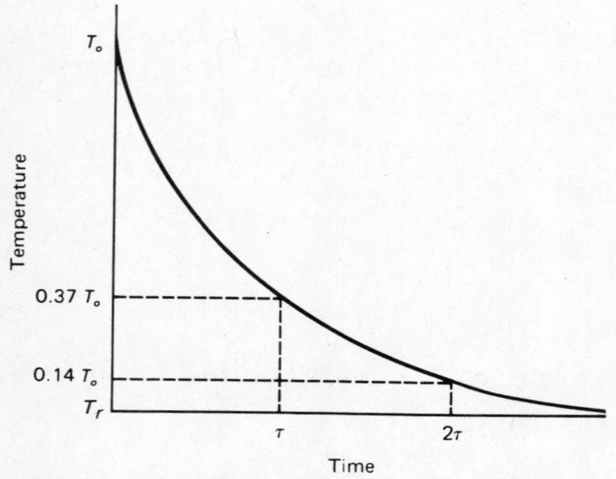

Figure 21.1 Exponential temperature decay. A graph of the theoretical temperature of a cooling object versus time.

IV. Experimental Procedure

1. Read the room temperature T_r of the dial thermometer and record in Data Table 1. Then clamp the thermometer on the stand and insert the stem into the metal cylinder as shown in Fig. 21.2. Make certain that the stem does not touch the cylinder walls and that the tip of the stem does not extend beyond the end of the cylinder.

2. *Slowly* heat the cylinder by wafting the flame of the Bunsen burner over the length of the cylinder. Do not let the flame touch the thermometer. Heat the cylinder until the thermometer reads nearly 150 °C. Maintain this temperature as

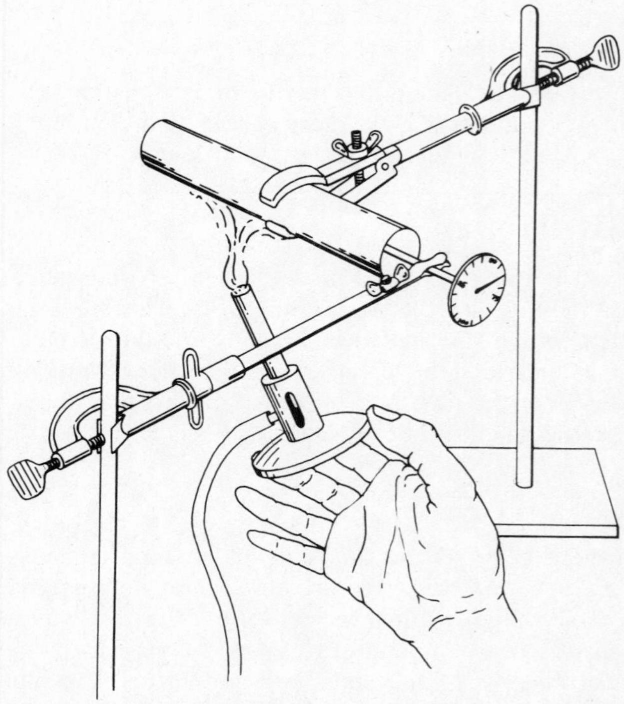

Figure 21.2 Experimental setup for Newton's law of cooling. See text for description.

closely as possible for a couple of minutes to ensure uniform heating of the thermometer stem. Record this high-temperature T_o in Data Table 1.

3. Turn off the Bunsen burner and carefully move the stand with the cylinder away, starting the timer at the same time. Read the thermometer temperature every 30 s for 4 min as it cools in the air and record the readings in Data Table 1.

   During this procedure, make certain that the cylinder is far away from the thermometer so that it will not affect the thermometer's cooling rate. Also, do not disturb the thermometer during the cooling process and avoid any drafts or stirring of air in its vicinity.

4. Repeat procedures 1 through 3 for the liquid-in-glass thermometer with a maximum temperature of about 100 °C. Be careful in clamping the thermometer so as not to break it, and be careful not to overheat the thermometer and to avoid hot spots.

***Caution:** Should you break the thermometer, be careful of the shattered glass. If a mercury thermometer is used and some mercury spills, notify your instructor immediately for proper cleanup. Mercury is **very** poisonous.*

5. **(a)** Compute $(T - T_r)$ and find $\ln (T - T_r)$ as indicated in the data tables (use a calculator or see Appendix B, Table B7).
   (b) Plot $\ln (T - T_r)$ versus t for each thermometer on the same Cartesian graph. Draw the best straight line that fits the first few data points near $t = 0$ for each set of data and determine the slope and intercept value for each line.

6. From the slope λ of each line, determine the time constant for each thermometer. Also, from the intercepts, compute the initial temperature T_o of each thermometer. Compare these initial temperature values with the recorded experimental values by computing the percent differences.

Name ______________________ Section ______________ Date ______________

Lab Partner(s) ____

EXPERIMENT 21

Newton's Law of Cooling: The Time Constant of a Thermometer

Laboratory Report

DATA TABLE 1

Purpose: To determine the time cooling constant using a dial thermometer.

Room temperature, T_r ______________

Time, t ( )	Temperature, T ( )	$T - T_r$	$\ln(T - T_r)$
0	(T_o)	X	X

Calculations
(show work)

Don't forget units

(continued)

Calculations
(show work)

DATA TABLE 2
Purpose: To determine the time cooling constant using a liquid-in-glass thermometer.

Room temperature, T_r ______________

Time, t ( )	Temperature, T ( )	$T - T_r$	$\ln (T - T_r)$
0	(T_o)		

Calculations
(show work)

	Metal	Glass
Slope	______________	______________
Time constant	______________	______________
T_o (from intercept)	______________	______________
Percent difference	______________	______________

Name ________________ Section ________________ Date ________________

Lab Partner(s) ________________________________

QUESTIONS

1. On what experimental parameter(s) do you think the constant K in the exponent of the exponential function depends? Why must you avoid air drafts in procedure 3?

2. Suppose that the cooling of another metal-stem dial thermometer of the same material, but having a larger-diameter stem, is investigated. How would this affect the time constant? Sketch the general form of the cooling curve of such a thermometer on the ln $(T - T_r)$ versus t graph (use a dashed line), and label it accordingly.

(continued)

3. How would the cooling rate of the metal-stem thermometer be affected if the thermometer were made of a different metal, but still had the same mass?

4. Explain why in general the liquid-in-glass thermometer does not follow a linear relationship for ln $(T - T_r)$ versus t as well as a metal dial thermometer does. (Check your graph.) What do different time constants for the different thermometers mean?

5. (a) Theoretically, does the T versus t curve (Fig. 21.1) ever reach the horizontal axis? Explain (mathematically) at what time $t = T_r$. (The curve is said to approach the horizontal axis *asymptotically*.)

(b) Practically, after how many time constants would a thermometer be "recovered" or have reached room temperature and be ready to take another reading? (Assume that the difference between the temperature of the thermometer and the temperature of its surroundings has to decrease to less than 1 percent of the initial temperature difference.) How many minutes would this be for the metal thermometer used in the experiment?

Name ______________________ Section ______________ Date ______________

Lab Partner(s) ____

EXPERIMENT 22

Archimedes' Principle: Buoyancy and Specific Gravity

Advance Study Assignment

Read the experiment and answer the following questions.

1. Describe the physical reason for the buoyant force in terms of pressure.

2. Give the conditions on densities that determine whether an object will sink or float in a fluid.

3. Distinguish between specific gravity and density.

(continued)

4. Describe how the specific gravity of an object less dense than water can be determined using Archimedes' principle. How about the specific gravity of a liquid?

5. Why is it important to make certain that no air bubbles adhere to objects during the submerged weighing procedures? How would the experimental results be affected if bubbles were present?

Archimedes' Principle: Buoyancy and Specific Gravity

I. Introduction and Objectives

Some objects will float and others will sink in a given fluid—a liquid or a gas. The fact that an object floats means it is "buoyed up" by a force greater than or equal to its weight. Archimedes (287–212 B.C.), a Greek scientist, deduced that the upward buoyant force acting on a floating object is equal to the weight of the fluid it displaces. Thus, a body will sink if its weight exceeds that of the fluid it displaces.

In this experiment, Archimedes' principle will be studied in one application: determining the densities and specific gravities of solid and liquid samples.

After performing this experiment and analyzing the data, you should be able to:

1. Tell whether or not an object will sink or float in a fluid, knowing the density of each.
2. Distinguish between density and specific gravity.
3. Describe how the specific gravities or densities of objects that sink or float may be determined experimentally.

II. Equipment Needed

- Triple-beam pan balance with swing platform (or single-beam double-pan balance with swing platform and set of weights); see Fig. 22.1.
- Overflow can (or graduated cylinder and eye dropper)
- Two beakers
- Metal cylinder, irregularly shaped metal object, or metal sinker
- Waxed block of wood
- Saltwater solution or alcohol
- String
- Hydrometer and cylinder

III. Theory

When a body is immersed in a fluid, it experiences an upward buoyant force that may cause it to float. The reason for the buoyant force can be understood by considering the pressure-depth relationship, $p = \rho g h$, where p is the pressure, ρ the mass density, g the acceleration due to gravity, and h the depth below the surface of the fluid. In a fluid, the pressure on the lower surface of an object is greater than that on the upper surface, so there is a pressure difference, or an upward force. (Consider a block or a cube for simplicity.)

The buoyant force is described by **Archimedes' principle**:

> *When a body is placed in a fluid, it is buoyed up by a force equal to the weight of the volume of fluid it displaces.*

Archimedes' principle applies to a body wholly or partially immersed in a fluid. The magnitude of the buoyant force depends only on the weight of the fluid displaced by the object and *does not* depend on the weight of the object.

Archimedes' principle shows that an object

1. will float in a fluid if the density of the object ρ_o is less than the density of the fluid ρ_f,
2. will sink if the object's density is greater than that of the fluid, and

Figure 22.1 Specific gravity measurement. An arrangement to determine the specific gravity of a solid less dense than water. The weight of the system with only the sinker submerged is measured, then the weight is measured with both the sinker and the light object submerged.

3. will float in equilibrium at any submerged depth where it is placed if its density is equal to that of the fluid.

This can be shown mathematically as follows. The weight of an object is $w_o = m_o g = \rho_o g V_o$, where V_o is the volume of the object and $\rho_o = m_o/V_o$. Similarly, the weight of the fluid displaced by the object, or the buoyant force, is $F_b = w_f = m_f g = \rho_f g V_f$. If the object is completely submersed in the fluid, then $V_o = V_f$, and dividing one equation by the other,

$$\frac{F_b}{w_o} = \frac{\rho_f}{\rho_o} \quad \text{or} \quad F_b = \left(\frac{\rho_f}{\rho_o}\right) w_o \qquad (22.1)$$

Hence

1. If $\rho_o < \rho_f$, then $F_b > w_o$ and the object will be buoyed up to the surface and float.
2. If $\rho_o > \rho_f$, then $F_b < w_o$, and the object will sink.
3. If $\rho_o = \rho_f$, the $F_b = w_o$, and the object is in equilibrium.

Specific Gravity

The **specific gravity** of a solid or liquid is defined as the ratio of the weight of a given volume of the substance to an equal volume of water

specific gravity (sp. gr.) =

$$\frac{w_s}{w_w} = \frac{\text{weight of a substance (of given volume)}}{\text{weight of an equal volume of water}} \qquad (22.2)$$

where the subscripts s and w refer to the substance and water, respectively.

Specific gravity is a density-type designation that uses water as a comparison standard. Since it is a weight ratio, specific gravity has no units. Conveniently, the numerical value of a substance's specific gravity is the same as the magnitude of its density *in cgs units*. This can be seen as follows:

$$\text{sp. gr.} = \frac{w_s}{w_w} = \frac{w_s/V_s}{w_w/V_w} = \frac{m_s g/V_s}{m_w g/V_w}$$

$$= \frac{m_s/V_s}{m_w/V_w} = \frac{\rho_s}{\rho_w} \qquad (22.3)$$

By definition the volumes are equal; $V_s = V_w$. Since, for practical purposes, the density of water is 1 g/cm³ over the temperature range in which water is liquid,

$$\text{sp. gr.} = \frac{\rho_s}{\rho_w} = \frac{\rho_s(\text{g/cm}^3)}{1\ (\text{g/cm}^3)} = \rho_s \qquad (22.4)$$

where ρ_s is the numerical value of the density of a substance in g/cm³. For example, the density of mercury is 13.6 g/cm³, and mercury has a specific gravity of 13.6. A specific gravity of 13.6 indicates that mercury is 13.6 times more dense than water, $\rho_s = (\text{sp. gr.})\rho_w$, or that a sample of mercury will weigh 13.6 times as much as an equal volume of water.

Archimedes' principle can be used to determine the specific gravity (and density) of a *submerged* object:

$$\text{sp. gr.} = \frac{w_o}{w_w} = \frac{w_o}{F_b} \qquad (22.5)$$

where w_o is the weight of the object and w_w is the weight of the water it displaces, and by Archimedes' principle, $w_w = F_b$.

For a heavy object that sinks, the net force as it does so is equal to $w_o - F_b$. (Why?) If attached to a scale while submerged, it would have a measured *apparent* weight w'_o and $w'_o = w_o - F_b$. Thus, $F_b = w_o - w'_o$, and Eq. 22.5 may be written

$$\text{sp. gr.} = \frac{w_o}{w_w} = \frac{w_o}{w_o - w'_o}$$

or in terms of mass measured on a balance ($w = mg$),

$$\text{sp. gr.} = \frac{m_o}{m_o - m'_o} \ (= \rho_o) \qquad (22.6)$$

(of a heavy object that sinks)

where ρ_o is the magnitude of the density of the object in g/cm³. This provides us with an experimental method to determine the specific gravity (and density) of an object that sinks.

To measure the specific gravity and density of an object that floats or is less dense than water, using Archimedes' principle, it is necessary to use another object of sufficient weight and density to submerge the light object completely.

Using an arrangement as illustrated in Fig. 22.1, $w_1 = w_o + w'_s$ is the measured weight (mass) of the object and the sinker, with only the sinker submerged, and $w_2 = w'_o + w'_s$ is the measured weight when both are submerged. Then

$$w_1 - w_2 = (w_o + w'_s) - (w'_o + w'_s) = w_o - w'_o$$

or, put in terms of mass,

$$m_1 - m_2 = m_o - m'_o$$

and the specific gravity can be found from Eq. 22.6. That is,

$$\text{sp. gr.} = \frac{m_o}{m_1 - m_2} \ (= \rho_o) \qquad (22.7)$$

(of a light object that floats)

The specific gravity of a liquid can also be found using Archimedes' principle. A heavy object is weighed first in air (w_o) and then when submerged in liquid (w'_o). Then $(w_o - w'_o)_\ell$ is the weight of the volume of liquid the object displaces, by Archimedes' principle. Carrying out a similar procedure for the object in water, $(w_o - w'_o)_w$ is the volume of water the object displaces. Then, by the definition of specific gravity (Eq. 22.2),

$$\text{sp. gr.} = \frac{(w_o - w'_o)_\ell}{(w_o - w'_o)_w} \; (= \rho_\ell) \qquad \textbf{(22.8)}$$

(of a liquid)

where ρ_ℓ is the density of the liquid in g/cm³.

You may have been thinking that there are easier ways to determine the density or specific gravity of a solid or liquid. This is true, but the purpose of the experiment is to familiarize you with Archimedes' principle. You may wish to check your experimental results by determining the densities and specific gravities of the solid samples by some other method. The specific gravity of the liquid sample will also be determined using a hydrometer.

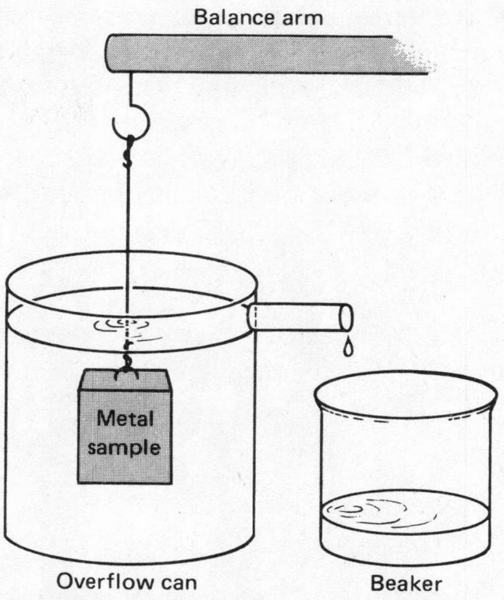

Figure 22.2 Archimedes' principle. Arrangement for proving Archimedes' principle. The weight of the displaced liquid in the beaker is equal to the reduction in the weight of the metal sample when it is submerged, or to the buoyant force.

IV. Experimental Procedure

A. *Direct Proof of Archimedes' Principle*

1. Weigh the metal sample and record its mass m_o and the type of metal in the Laboratory Report. Also, determine the mass of an empty beaker m_b and record. Fill the overflow can with water, and place it on the balance platform. Attach a string to the sample and suspend it from the balance arm as illustrated in Fig. 22.2.*

2. The overflow from the can when the sample is immersed is caught in the beaker. Take a mass reading m'_o of the submerged object. Make certain that no bubbles adhere to the object. (It is instructive to place the overflow can on a second balance, if available, and note that the "weight" of the overflow can does not change as the sample is submerged.)

   Then, weigh the beaker and water so as to determine the mass of the displaced water m_w. (If the can does not fit on the balance platform, first suspend and immerse the object in the full overflow can and catch the overflow in the beaker and find m_w. Then attach the sample to the balance arm and suspend it in a beaker of water that will fit on the balance platform to find m'_o.)

3. According to Archimedes' principle, the buoyant force $F_b = m_o g - m'_o g$ should equal the weight of the displaced water

$$w_w = m_w g$$

or

$$(m_o - m'_o)g = m_w g$$

Compute the buoyant force and compare it with the weight of the displaced water by finding the percent difference.

B. *Density of a Heavy Solid* ($\rho_o > \rho_w$)

4. Determine the specific gravity and density of the metal sample. This can be computed using the data from part A.

C. *Density of a Light Solid* ($\rho_o < \rho_w$)

5. Determine the specific gravity and density of the wooden block by the procedure described in Section III and illustrated in Fig. 22.1. First, measure the mass of the wooden block alone (in air). Then set up as in Fig. 22.1.

* You may use an alternative method if no overflow can is available. Attach a string to the sample and place it in a graduated cylinder. Fill the cylinder with water until the sample is completely submerged. Add water (with an eyedropper) until the water level is at a specific reference mark on the cylinder (e.g., 35 mL). Remove the sample, shaking any drops of water back into the cylinder, and weigh the cylinder and water (m_b). Refill the cylinder to the reference mark and weigh it again ($m_w + m_b$). The mass of the "overflow" water is then the difference between these measurements.

Make certain that no air bubbles adhere to the objects during the submerged weighing procedures. [The first weighing procedure may have to be modified to fit the apparatus (i.e., weighing the block and submerged sinker separately).] The block is waxed so that it does not become waterlogged.

D. Density of a Liquid (ρ_l)

6. Determine the specific gravity and density of the liquid provided, by the procedure described in Section III. Again, make certain that no air bubbles adhere to the object during the submerged weighing procedures.

7. Determine the specific gravity of the liquid using the hydrometer and cylinder. Compare this value with that found in procedure 6 by computing the percent difference.

Name ______________________ Section ______________ Date ______________

Lab Partner(s) ____

EXPERIMENT 22

Archimedes' Principle: Buoyancy and Specific Gravity

Laboratory Report

A. Direct Proof of Archimedes' Principle

Type of metal ______________

Mass of metal, m_o, in air ______________

Mass of beaker, m_b ______________

Mass of metal, m'_o, submerged in water ______________

Mass of beaker and displaced water, $m_w + m_b$ ______________

Mass of displaced water, m_w ______________

Buoyant force (in newtons) ______________

Weight of displaced water (in newtons) ______________

Percent difference ______________

Calculations (show work)

Don't forget units

(continued)

B. Density of a Heavy Solid ($\rho_o > \rho_w$)

Calculations (show work)

Specific gravity ________________

Density ________________

C. Density of a Light Solid ($\rho_o < \rho_w$)

Mass of block in air ________________

Mass of block and sinker with only sinker submerged ________________

Mass of block and sinker with both submerged ________________

Specific gravity ________________

Density ________________

Calculations (show work)

Name ______________________ Section ______________ Date ______________

Lab Partner(s) ____

D. Density of a Liquid (ρ_l)

Mass of object in air ______________

Mass of object submerged in liquid ______________

Mass of object submerged in water ______________

Computed sp. gr. ______________

Sp. gr. from hydrometer measurement ______________

Percent difference ______________

Calculations (show work)

Questions

1. Look up the density of the metal of the object used in parts A and B of the procedure, and compare it with the experimental value. Comment on the purity of the metal of the object. (Archimedes developed his principle while working on a similar inquiry. His problem was to determine whether an apparent gold crown had been made with some content of cheaper metal.)

(continued)

2. In part B, the string will cause error. When does it lead to an experimental density that is too high? Too low?

3. What would be the situation of an object immersed in a fluid if the object and the fluid had the same density?

4. (a) Explain how a submarine is caused to submerge and surface without the use of its propulsion propeller.

   (b) Which is heavier, equal volumes of milk or cream? Justify your answer.

5. A block of wood floats in a beaker of water. According to Archimedes' principle, the block experiences an upward buoyant force. If the beaker with the water and floating block is weighed, would the measured weight be less than the sum of the weights of the individual components? Explain.

Name ______________________ Section ______________ Date ______________

Lab Partner(s) ____

EXPERIMENT 22 — *Laboratory Report*

6. A person can lift 45 kg ($\approx$ 100 lb). Using the experimental value of the specific gravity for the metal object in part B, how many cubic meters of the metal could the person lift (a) in air; (b) in water? How many actual kg of metal is this (a) in air; (b) in water?

7. Explain the principle and construction of a hydrometer. What is the purpose of the common measurements of the specific gravities of an automobile's radiator coolant and battery electrolyte?

8. (*Optional*) Use the pressure-depth relationship, $p = \rho g h$, to show mathematically that the buoyant force on a wooden cube being held submerged in a liquid is equal to the weight of the volume of liquid it displaces.

Name ______________________ Section ______________ Date ______________

Lab Partner(s) ____

E X P E R I M E N T 2 3

Fields and Equipotentials

Advance Study Assignment

Read the experiment and answer the following questions.

A. Electric Field

1. What is an electric field, and what does it tell you?

2. What are "lines of force"?

(continued)

3. What are equipotentials, and how are they experimentally determined? What is their relationship to the electric field lines?

B. Magnetic Field

4. What is a magnetic field, and what does it tell you?

Name ______________________ Section ______________ Date ______________

Lab Partner(s) ____

EXPERIMENT 23 *Advance Study Assignment*

5. Does the magnetic **B** field have the same relationship to electric charge as the electric **E** field? Explain.

6. How may a magnetic pole be moved in a magnetic field without doing work?

(continued)

Fields and Equipotentials

I. Introduction and Objectives

When buying groceries, we are often interested in the price per pound. Knowing this, we can determine the price for a given amount of an item. Analogously, it is convenient to know the electric force per unit charge at points in space due to an electric charge configuration or the magnetic force per unit pole or "moving charge." Knowing these, we can easily calculate the electric force or magnetic force an interacting object would experience at different locations.

The electric force per unit charge is called the electric field intensity, or simply the **electric field**. By determining the electric force on a test charge at various points in the vicinity of a charge configuration, the electric field may be "mapped" or represented graphically by lines of force. The English scientist Michael Faraday (1791–1867) introduced the concept of lines of force as an aid in visualizing the magnitude and direction of an electric field.

Similarly, the magnetic force per unit pole is called the magnetic field intensity, or **magnetic field**. In this case, the field is mapped out by using the pole of a magnetic compass.

In this experiment, the concept of fields will be investigated and some electric and magnetic field configurations will be determined experimentally.

After performing this experiment and analyzing the data, you should be able to:

1. Describe clearly the concept of a force field.
2. Explain lines of force and the associated physical interpretations.
3. Distinguish between lines of force and equipotentials, and describe their relationships to work.

II. Equipment Needed

A. *Electric Field*

- Field mapping board and probes
- Conducting sheets with grids
- Conducting paint
- Connecting wires
- 1.5-V battery (or 10-V dc source)
- Galvanometer [or high resistance voltmeter or multimeter, or vacuum-tube voltmeter (VTVM) with two-point contact field probe*]
- Single-throw switch
- 3 sheets of Cartesian graph paper

B. *Magnetic Field*

- 2 bar magnets and one horseshoe magnet
- Iron filings
- 3 sheets of paper or a glass plate
- Small compass
- 3 sheets of Cartesian graph paper or regular paper

III. Theory

A. *Electric Field*

The magnitude of the electrostatic force between two point charges q_1 and q_2 is given by Coulomb's law:

$$F = \frac{kq_1q_2}{r^2} \qquad \textbf{(23.1)}$$

where r is the distance between the charges and the constant $k = 9.0 \times 10^9$ N-m²/C². The direction of the force on a charge may be determined by the law of charges: Like charges repel, and unlike charges attract.

The magnitude E of the **electric field** is defined as the electrical force per unit charge, or $E = F/q_o$ (N/C). By convention, the electric field is determined by using a *positive* test charge q_o. In the case of the electric field associated with a single-source charge q, the magnitude of the electric field a distance r away from the charge is

$$E = \frac{F}{q_o} = \frac{kq_oq}{q_or^2} = \frac{kq}{r^2} \qquad \textbf{(23.2)}$$

The direction of the electric field may be determined by the law of charges; that is, in the direction of the force experienced by the positive test charge.

The electric field vectors for several series of radial points from a positive source charge are illustrated in Fig. 23.1a. Notice that the lengths (magnitudes) of the vectors are smaller the greater the distance from the charge. (Why?)

By drawing lines through the points in the direction of the field vectors, we form lines of force (Fig. 23.1b), which give a graphical representation of the electric field. The direction of the electric field at a particular location is tangent to the line of force through that point (Fig. 23.1c). The magnitudes of the

* Leads from the dc input of an oscilloscope work nicely.

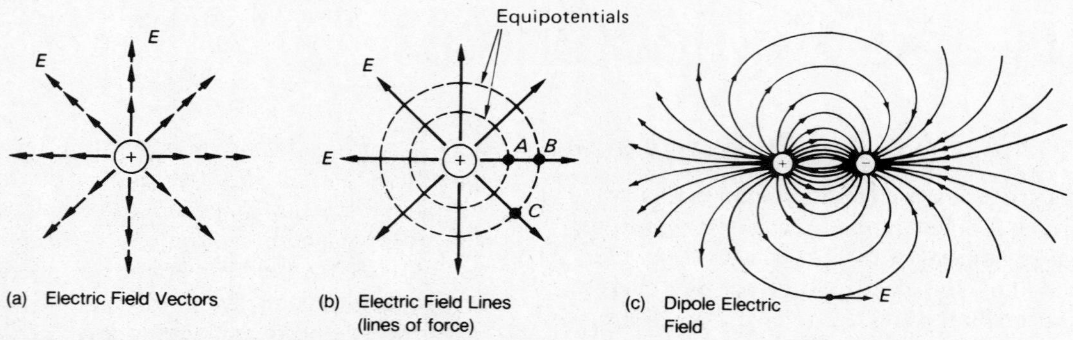

Figure 23.1 Electric field. (a) Electric field vectors near a positive charge. (b) Lines of force with equipotentials for a positive charge. (c) Electric dipole and its electric field. The direction of the electric field at a particular location is tangent to the line of force through that point, as illustrated on the bottom line of force.

electric field are not customarily listed, only the direction of the field lines. However, the closer together the lines of force, the stronger the field.

If a positive charge were released in the vicinity of a stationary positive source charge, it would move along a line of force in the direction indicated (away from the source charge). A negative charge would move along the line of force in the opposite direction. Once the electric field for a particular charge configuration is known, we tend to neglect the charge configuration itself, since the effect of the configuration is given by the field.

Since a free charge moves in an electric field by the action of the electric force, we say that work ($W = Fd$) is done by the field in moving charges from one point to another (e.g., from A to B in Fig. 23.1b). To move a positive charge from B to A would require work supplied by an external force to move the charge against the electric field (force). The work W per charge q_o in moving the charge between two points in an electric field is called the **potential difference** ΔV between the points:

$$\Delta V_{BA} = V_B - V_A = \frac{W}{q_o} \qquad \textbf{(23.3)}$$

(It can be shown that the potential at a particular point a distance r from the source charge q is $V = -kq/r$. See your textbook.)

If a charge is moved along a path at right angles or perpendicular to the field lines, no work is done ($W = 0$), since there is no force component along the path. Then along such a path (dashed-line paths in Fig. 23.1), $\Delta V = V_B - V_C = W/q_o = 0$, and $V_C = V_B$. Hence, the potential is constant along paths perpendicular to the field lines. Such paths are called **equipotentials**. (In three dimensions, the path is along an equipotential surface.)

An electric field may be mapped experimentally by determining either the field lines (of force) or the equipotential lines. Static electric fields are difficult to measure, and field lines are more easily determined by measuring small electric currents (flow of charges) maintained in a conducting medium between charge configurations in the form of metal electrodes.

The steady-state electric field lines closely resemble the static field that a like configuration of static charges would produce. The current is measured in terms of the voltage (potential) difference by a high-resistance voltmeter or multimeter (or VTVM).

In other instances, equipotentials are determined, and hence the field lines, using a simple galvanometer as a detector. When no current flows between two probe points, as indicated by a zero deflection on the galvanometer, there is no potential difference between the points ($\Delta V = 0$), and the points are on an equipotential.

B. Magnetic Field

As in the electric case, a **magnetic field** was originally defined as the magnetic force per unit pole. The direction of the force at a particular location is that of the force experienced by a north magnetic pole.

Just as we may map the electric field around an electric charge, we may draw magnetic lines of force around a magnet. A single magnetic pole, or magnetic monopole, has never been observed, so the magnetic field is mapped using the north pole (by convention) of a magnetic dipole, for example, the magnetic needle of a compass. The torque on the compass needle resulting from the magnetic force causes the needle to line up with the field, and the north pole of the compass points in the direction of the field (Fig. 23.2). If the compass is moved in the direction indicated by the north pole, the path of the compass traces out a field line.

Another observation is that an electric charge moving nonparallel to a magnetic field experiences a force. Since the magnetic field is defined at points of space in terms of a magnetic force exerted on a test object, this fact is now used to define a **magnetic field** vector **B** (sometimes called the magnetic induction).* The magnetic field **B** may be thought of as the magnetic force "per unit of moving charge." The **B** field has the same form as that mapped out using compass-needle poles.

It is instructive for comparative purposes to draw equipotential lines perpendicular to the field lines, as in the electric field case. No work would be done on a magnetic pole (or electric charge) when moved along these equipotential lines. (Why?)

A common method of demonstrating a magnetic field is to sprinkle iron filings over a paper or glass plate covering a magnet (Fig. 23.3). The iron filings become induced magnets and line up with the field as would a compass needle. This method allows one quickly to visualize the magnetic field configuration.

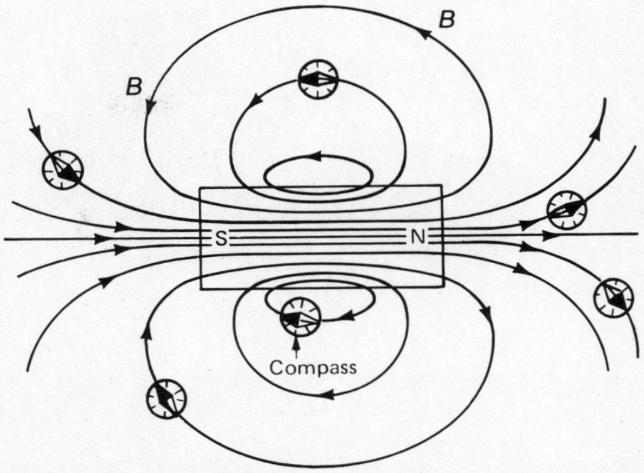

Figure 23.2 Magnetic field. The magnetic force causes the compass needle to line up with the field, and the north pole of the compass points in the direction of the field. If the compass is moved in the direction indicated by the north pole, the path of the compass needle traces out a field line.

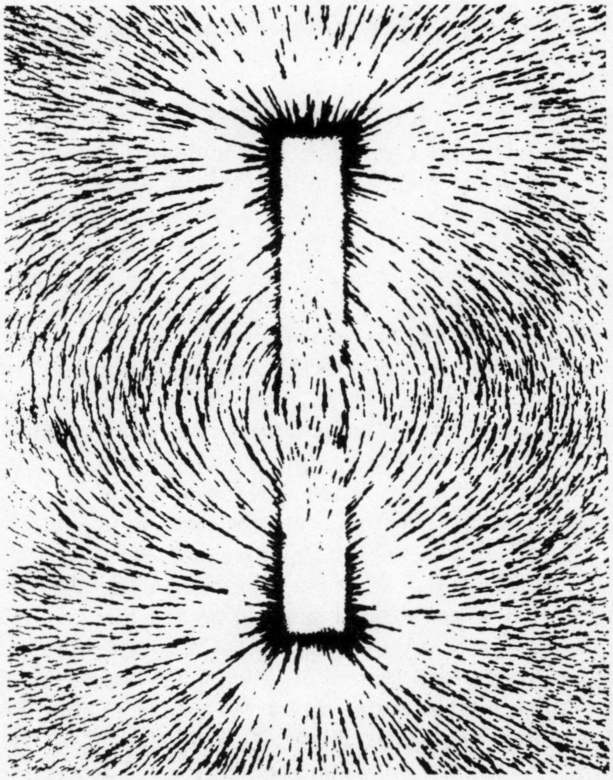

Figure 23.3 Iron filing pattern for a bar magnet. The iron filings become induced magnets and line up with the field as would a compass needle. (Courtesy *PSSC Physics;* D. C. Heath and Company with Educational Development Center, Inc., Newton, MA.)

IV. Experimental Procedure

A. Electric Field

1. An electric field mapping setup with a galvanometer is shown in Fig. 23.4a. The apparatus consists of a flat board on which is placed a sheet of carbonized conducting paper imprinted with a grid. The sheet has an electrode configuration of conducting silver paint, which provides an electric field when connected to a voltage source (e.g., a battery).

   The common electrode configurations ordinarily provided are two dots representing point charges of an electric dipole configuration (Fig. 23.1c) and two parallel linear electrodes representing a two-dimensional cross section of a parallel-plate capacitor (on the board in the photo in Fig. 23.4a).

2. Draw the electric dipole configuration on a sheet of graph paper to the same scale and coordinates as those of the painted dipole on the imprinted grid on the conducting sheet. Then place the

* The SI unit for the magnetic induction **B** is the tesla (T). Other units are the weber/m² (W/m²) and gauss (G). The units are named after early investigators of magnetic phenomena.

(a)

(b)

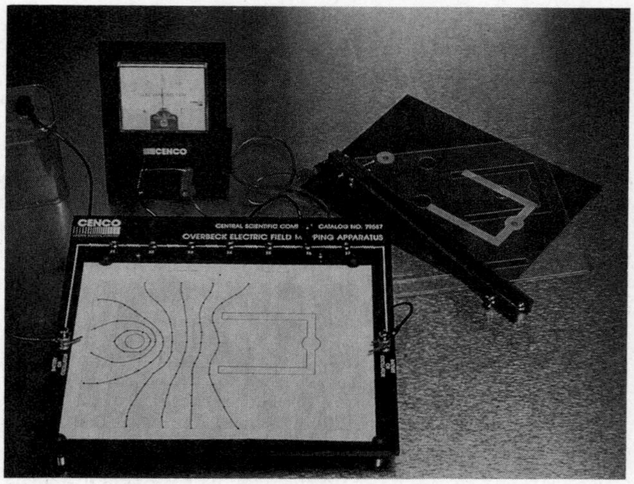

(c)

Figure 23.4 Electric field mapping apparatus. (a) A parallel plate capacitor configuration on the board and an electric dipole configuration to the right. (b) A variety of electrode configurations can be drawn with conductive ink on conductive paper. (c) This apparatus uses conductive plates and mapping is done on graph paper. (Photos courtesy of (a) Sargent-Welch Scientific Co.; (b) PASCO Scientific; (c) Central Scientific Co., Inc.)

dipole conducting sheet on the board, and set the contact terminals firmly on the painted electrode connections. If you are using a galvanometer, do procedures 3 through 7. If you are using a voltmeter, do procedures 8 through 12.

Galvanometer Measurements

3. Connect the probes to the galvanometer as shown in Fig. 23.4a. The probes are used to locate points in the field that are at equipotential. Connect the voltage source (1.5-V battery) to the board terminals. Place a switch in the circuit (not shown in figure) and leave it open until you are ready to take measurements.

   Place the stationary probe on the electric dipole sheet at some general point near the edge of the grid area in the region between the electrodes. The potential at this point will serve as a reference potential. Mark the probe position on your graph-paper map.

   The movable probe is then used to determine the location of a series of other points having the same potential. When the movable probe is at a point with the same potential as that of the stationary reference probe, no deflection will be observed on the galvanometer.

   The galvanometer is a delicate current-measuring instrument and should be limited to small current values to avoid damage. As a result, the electrodes should not be allowed to make contact with each other.

4. Close the switch and place the movable probe on the conducting paper at some location an appreciable distance away from the stationary probe. Move the probe until the galvanometer shows zero deflection (indicating a point of equipotential) and record this point on the graph-paper map. Locate a series of 8 or 10 points of the same potential across the general field region, and draw a dashed-line curve through these points on the graph-paper map.

5. Choose a new location for the reference probe 2 to 3 cm from the previous reference position and locate another series of equipotential points. Continue this procedure until you have mapped the field region. Open the switch. Draw curves perpendicular to the equipotential lines on the graph-paper map to represent the electric field lines. Do not forget to indicate the field direction on the field lines.

6. Repeat the procedure for the parallel linear (plate) electrode configuration. Be sure to investigate the regions around the ends of the plate electrodes.

7. (*Optional*) Your instructor may wish to have you map the electric field for a nonsymmetrical electrode configuration or a configuration of your own choosing. These can be prepared by painting the desired electrode configuration on a conducting sheet with silver paint.

Voltmeter Measurements

8. For the high resistance voltmeter (or VTVM), the field probe should have two contacts mounted about 2 cm apart. Connect the voltage source (10-V dc) to the board terminals. Place a switch in the circuit (not shown in Fig. 23.4a) and leave it open until you are ready to take measurements.

   Close the switch, and with the zeroed voltmeter set on the 10-V scale, position the negative (−) contact of the field probe near the negative electrode. Using the negative probe point as a pivot, rotate the positive (+) contact around the fixed negative contact until the position with the maximum meter reading is found.

   Record the positions of the probe contacts on the graph-paper map. (The sensitivity of the voltmeter may be increased by switching to a lower scale. A midscale reading is desirable. Check the zero on the voltmeter frequently, particularly when changing scales.)

9. Using the second probe point as a new negative probe point, repeat the procedure to determine another point of maximum meter reading, and record. Continue this procedure until the positive electrode is approached. Draw a smooth curve through these points on the graph-paper map.

   Then starting again at a new position near the negative electrode, repeat these procedures for another field line. Trace out four to six field lines in this manner. Do not forget to indicate the field direction on the lines.

10. Place the negative probe near the center of the field region, and rotate the positive contact until a position is found that gives a *zero* meter reading. Record several of these points on the graph paper with a symbol different from that used for the field lines.

    Use the second point as a new pivot point as before, and determine a series of null (zero) points. Draw a dashed-line curve through these equipotential points. Determine three to five equipotential lines in this manner.

11. Repeat this procedure for the parallel linear (plate) electrode configuration. Be sure to investigate the regions around the ends of the plate electrodes.

12. (*Optional*) Your instructor may wish to have you map the electric field for a nonsymmetrical electrode configuration or a configuration of your own choosing. These can be prepared by painting the desired electrode configuration on a conducting sheet with silver paint.

B. Magnetic Field

13. Covering the magnets with sheets of paper (or a glass plate), sprinkle iron filings to obtain an iron filing pattern for each of the arrangements shown in Fig. 23.5. For the bar magnet arrangements, the magnets should be separated by several centimeters, depending on the pole strengths of the magnets. Experiment with this distance so there is enough space between the ends of the magnets to get a good pattern.

14. Sketch the observed magnetic field patterns on Fig. 23.5 in the Laboratory Report. After the patterns have been sketched, collect the iron filings on a piece of paper and return them to the filing container (recycling them for someone else's later use). Economy in the laboratory is important.

15. Place the magnets for each arrangement on a piece of graph paper or regular paper. Draw an outline of the magnets for each arrangement on the paper. Using a small compass, trace out (marking on the paper) the magnetic field lines as smooth curves. Draw enough field lines so that the pattern of the magnetic field can be clearly seen. Do not forget to indicate the field direction on the lines.

16. Draw dashed-line curves perpendicular to the field lines.

Name ______________________ Section ______________ Date ______________

Lab Partner(s) ______________________

EXPERIMENT 23

Fields and Equipotentials

Laboratory Report

Attach graphs to Laboratory Report.

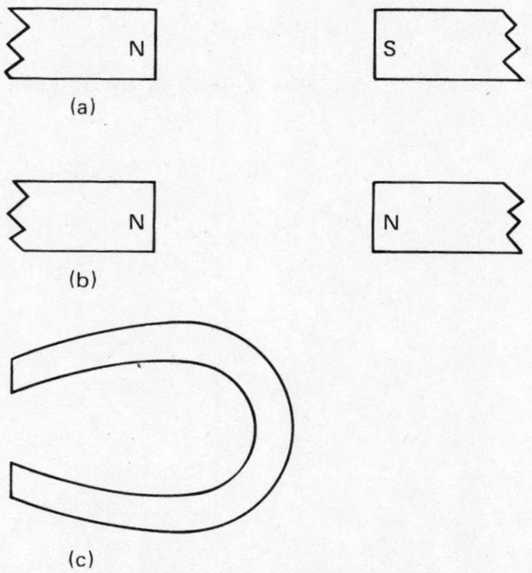

Figure 23.5 See Procedure Section B.

QUESTIONS

1. Directions of the fields are indicated on field lines. Why are no directions indicated on equipotential lines?

2. For the dipole configuration, in what region(s) does the electric field have the greatest intensity? Explain how you know from your map, and justify.

(continued)

3. Comment on the electric field of the parallel plates (a) between the plates, and (b) near the edges of the plates.

4. Sketch the electric field for (a) a negative point charge near a positively charged plate, and (b) two positive point charges.

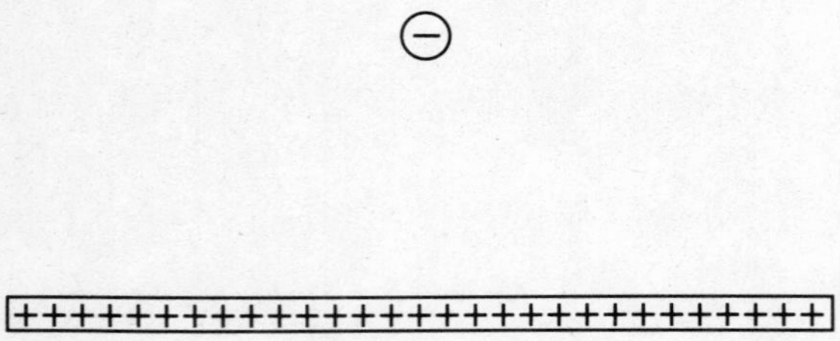

(a)

(b)

5. Compare the electric fields and magnetic fields of the experimental arrangements. Comment on any field similarities and differences.

Name ______________________ Section ______________ Date ______________

Lab Partner(s) ____

6. Explain how a gravitational field might be mapped. Sketch the gravitational field for two point masses.

Name ______________________ Section ______________ Date ______________

Lab Partner(s) ____

EXPERIMENT 24

Ohm's Law

Advance Study Assignment

Read the experiment and answer the following questions.

1. According to Ohm's law, how does (a) the current vary with voltage?

   (b) The voltage vary with resistance?

   (c) The current vary with resistance?

2. What is an "ohmic" resistance? Are all resistances ohmic in nature?

3. What are some analogs between liquid and electrical circuits?

(continued)

4. For a series circuit, what is the terminal voltage of a battery or power supply equal to in terms of the potential differences or voltage drops across circuit components?

Ohm's Law

I. Introduction and Objectives

One of the most frequently applied relationships in current electricity is that known as **Ohm's law**. This relationship, discovered by the German physicist Georg Ohm (1787–1854), is basic in the analysis of electrical circuits. Ohm's law applies to many, but not all, conductors. For an "ohmic" conductor, the potential difference or voltage drop V across the conductor is proportional to the current I through the conductor. All other conditions remaining unchanged, for a particular voltage and current, Ohm's law is expressed mathematically as

$$\frac{V}{I} = R$$

The constant R is called the **resistance** of the conductor and measured in units of ohms (Ω).

In this experiment, Ohm's law will be investigated as applied to components in a simple circuit.

After performing this experiment and analyzing the data, you should be able to:

1. Distinguish between ohmic and nonohmic resistances.
2. Explain current-voltage relationships by Ohm's law.
3. Apply Ohm's law to obtain values of current or voltage in investigating a circuit resistance.

II. Equipment Needed*

- Ammeter (0 to 0.5 A)
- Voltmeter (0 to 10 V dc)
- Decade resistance box (0.1 to 99.9 Ω)
- Rheostat ($\approx$ 200 Ω)
- Battery or power supply (6 V)
- Switch
- Connecting wires
- 2 sheets of Cartesian graph paper

III. Theory

For a wide range of materials used in electrical circuits (e.g., metallic conductors), the relationship of the potential difference or voltage drop V across a circuit component, the current I through the component, and the resistance R of the component are given by **Ohm's law**:

$$V = IR \tag{24.1}$$

That is, for a given circuit component which has an "ohmic" resistance (obeys Ohm's law), the voltage is linearly proportional to the current.

To understand the relationships of the quantities in Ohm's law, it is often helpful to consider a liquid analogy (Fig. 24.1).† In a liquid circuit, the force to move the liquid is supplied by a pump. The rate of liquid flow depends on the resistance to the flow (e.g., due to some partial obstruction in the circuit pipe)—the greater the resistance, the less liquid flow.

Analogously, in an electrical circuit, a voltage source (e.g., a battery or power supply) supplies the voltage (potential difference) for charge flow, and the magnitude of the current is determined by the resistance R in the circuit. For a given voltage, the greater the resistance, the less current through the resistance, as may be seen from Ohm's law,

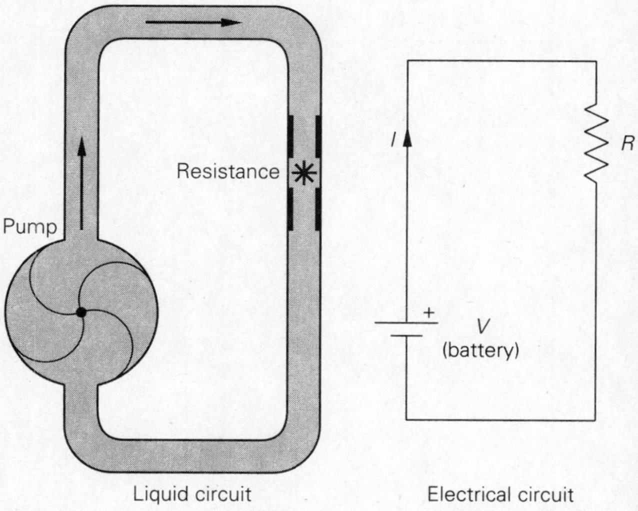

Figure 24.1 Liquid circuit analogy. In the liquid circuit analogy of an electric circuit, a pump corresponds to a voltage source, liquid flow correlates to electric current, and a hindrance to the current relates to a resistor.

* The ranges of the equipment are given as examples. These may be varied to apply to available equipment.

† Keep in mind that an analogy only illustrates a resemblance. Liquid and electrical circuits are quite different physically.

$I = V/R$. Notice that the voltage source supplies a voltage "rise" that is equal to the voltage "drop" across the resistance and is given by $V = IR$ (Ohm's law).

In an electrical circuit with two or more resistances and a single voltage source, Ohm's law may be applied to the entire circuit or to any portion of the circuit. When applied to the entire circuit, the voltage is the terminal input voltage supplied by the voltage source, and the resistance is the total resistance of the circuit. In the case of applying Ohm's law to a particular portion of the circuit, the individual voltage drops, currents, and resistances are used for that part of the circuit.

Consider the circuit diagram shown in Fig. 24.2. This is a series circuit. The applied voltage is supplied by a power supply or battery. R_h is a rheostat, a variable resistor that allows the voltage across the resistance R_s to be varied. (It is sometimes called a voltage divider because it divides the applied voltage across itself and R_s.) An ammeter Ⓐ measures the current through the resistor R_s, and a voltmeter Ⓥ registers the voltage drop across both R_s and the ammeter Ⓐ. S is a switch for closing and opening (activating and deactivating) the circuit.

Any component in a circuit that does not generate or supply a voltage acts as a resistance in the circuit. This is true for the connecting wires, the ammeter, and the voltmeter. However, the metallic connecting wires and the ammeter have negligibly small resistances, so they do not greatly affect the current. Also, a voltmeter has a high resistance, so there is little current through the voltmeter. Hence, to good approximations the ammeter registers the current in the circuit and the voltmeter reads the voltage drop across the resistance. These approximations are adequate for most practical applications.

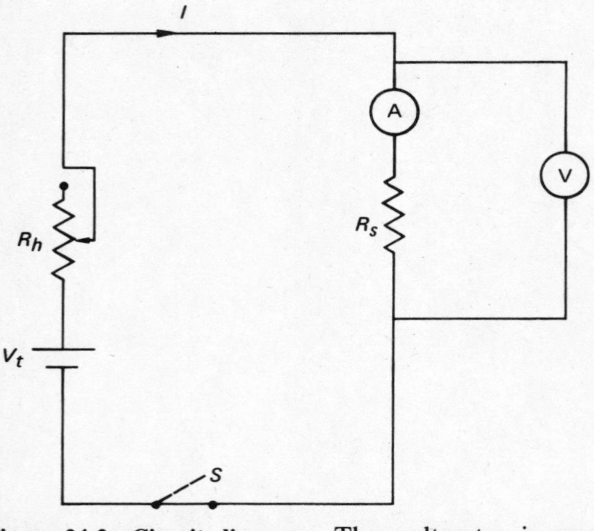

Figure 24.2 Circuit diagram. The voltmeter is connected in parallel across the ammeter and the resistance R_s. The other resistance, R_h, is that of the rheostat (a continuously variable resistor).

Applying Ohm's law to the portion of the circuit with R_s only, we have

$$V_s = IR_s \qquad \textbf{(24.2)}$$

where V_s and I are the voltmeter and ammeter readings, respectively. Notice that the same current I flows through the rheostat R_h and the resistance R_s. The voltage drop across R_h is then

$$V_h = IR_h \qquad \textbf{(24.3)}$$

To apply Ohm's law to the entire circuit, we use the fact that the applied voltage "rise" or the terminal voltage V_t of the voltage source must equal the voltage "drops" of the components around the circuit. Then

$$V_t = V_h + V_s$$

or

$$V_t = IR_h + IR_s = I(R_h + R_s) \qquad \textbf{(24.4)}$$

From Eq. 24.4, we see that for a constant R_s, the current through this resistance, and hence its voltage drop V_s, can be varied by varying the rheostat resistance R_h (V_t is constant). Similarly, the voltage V_s can be maintained constant when R_s is varied by adjusting R_h.

IV. Experimental Procedure

1. With the voltmeter, measure the terminal voltage of the power supply or battery and record in the Laboratory Report. Start with the voltmeter connection to the largest scale and increase the sensitivity by changing to a smaller scale if necessary. Most common laboratory voltmeters and ammeters have three scale connections and one binding post common to all three scales.

   It is good practice to take measurements initially with the meters connected to the largest scales. This prevents the instruments from being "pegged" (the needle forced off scale in galvanometer-type meters) and possibly damaged, should the magnitude of the voltage or current exceed the smaller scale limits. A scale setting may be changed for greater sensitivity by moving the connection to a lower scale after the general magnitude and measurement are known.

Also, attention should be given to the proper polarity (+ and −); otherwise, the meter will be "pegged" in the opposite direction. Connect + to + and − to −.

2. Set up the circuit shown in the circuit diagram (Fig. 24.2) with the switch open. A standard decade resistance box is used for R_s. Set the rheostat resistance R_h for maximum resistance and the value of the R_s to about 50 Ω. *Have the instructor check the circuit before closing the switch.*

A. Variation of Current with Voltage (R_s constant)

3. After the instructor has checked the circuit, close the switch and read the voltage and current on the meters. Open the switch after the readings are taken, and record them in Data Table 1. Repeat this procedure for a series of four successively lower rheostat settings along the length of the rheostat.

   It is convenient for data analysis to adjust the rheostat (after closing the switch) so that evenly spaced and convenient ammeter readings are obtained. The switch should be closed only long enough to obtain the necessary readings. This prevents unnecessary heating in the circuit.

4. Repeat procedure 3 for another value of R_s (about 30 Ω).

5. Plot the results for both resistances on a single V_s versus I_s graph and draw straight lines that best fit the sets of data. Determine the slopes of the lines and compare them with the constant values of R_s of the decade box by computing the percent errors. According to Ohm's law, the corresponding values should be equal.

B. Variation of Current and Resistance (V_s constant)

6. This portion of the experiment uses the same circuit arrangement as before. In this case, the voltage V_s is maintained constant by adjusting the rheostat resistance R_h when the R_s is varied.

   Initially, set the rheostat near maximum resistance and the resistance R_s of the decade box to about 100 Ω. Record the value of R_s in Data Table 2.

   Close the circuit and adjust the rheostat for a convenient voltmeter reading (about 4 volts). Record the voltmeter reading as the constant voltage V_s in Data Table 2. Record the current and resistance in the table. Open the circuit after making the readings.

7. Repeat this procedure for four more successive steps of current by reducing the value of R_s of the decade box. Keep the voltage across R_s constant for each setting by adjusting the rheostat resistance R_h. Do not reduce R_s below 30 Ω.

8. Plot the results on an I_s versus $1/R_s$ graph and draw a straight line that best fits the data. (Reciprocal ohms, $1/R$, is commonly given the unit name "mhos.") Determine the slope of the line and compare it with the constant value of V_s by computing the percent error. According to Ohm's law, these values should be equal.

Name ______________________ Section ______________ Date ______________

Lab Partner(s) ____

EXPERIMENT 24

Ohm's Law

Laboratory Report

A. Variation of Current with Voltage (R_s constant)

DATA TABLE 1

Terminal voltage, V_t ______________

Reading	Constant R_s ______		Constant R_s ______	
	Voltage, V_s ( )	Current, I_s ( )	Voltage, V_s ( )	Current, I_s ( )
1				
2				
3				
4				
5				

Calculations
(show work)

Slope of lines	Percent error from R_s
______	______
______	______

Don't forget units

(continued)

B. Variation of Current with Resistance (V_s constant)

DATA TABLE 2

Constant voltage, V_s ________________

Reading	Current, I_s ( )	Resistance, R_s ( )	$1/R_s$ ( )
1			
2			
3			
4			
5			

Calculations
(show work)

Slope of line ________________

Percent error from V_s ________________

QUESTIONS

1. If the switch were kept closed during the procedures and the circuit components heated up, how would this affect the measurements? (*Hint*: See Experiment 29.)

Name ______________________ Section ______________ Date ______________

Lab Partner(s) ______________________

EXPERIMENT 24 ***Laboratory Report***

2. Devise and draw a circuit using a long, straight wire resistor instead of a decade box that would allow the study of the variation of voltage with resistance (I_s constant). According to Ohm's law, what would a graph of the data from this circuit show?

3. Compute the values of R_h and the voltage drops across this resistance for the two situations in Data Table 1, reading #1.

Name ______________________ Section ______________ Date ______________

Lab Partner(s) ____

E X P E R I M E N T 2 5

The Potentiometer: emf and Terminal Voltage

Advance Study Assignment

Read the experiment and answer the following questions.

1. What is an electromotive force? Is it actually a force?

2. Are the emf and the terminal voltage of a battery the same? Are they constant? Explain.

3. Why is a potentiometer more accurate than a voltmeter in measuring emf?

(continued)

4. What is meant when we say that a potentiometer is "balanced"?

5. Show mathematically that a graph of terminal voltage versus the current drawn from a battery should have the form of a straight line.

The Potentiometer: emf and Terminal Voltage

I. Introduction and Objectives

The **potentiometer** is an instrument for the accurate measurement of the potential differences or voltages of electrical sources such as batteries. Unlike the common voltmeter, which measures approximate source potential differences because it draws some current from the source, the potentiometer does not disturb or affect the potential difference of the source. This is accomplished by *balancing* the source to be measured against another "working" source in the circuit. Therefore, the potentiometer is a valuable instrument for calibrating voltmeters and ammeters as well as for measuring the electromotive force or source potential differences of cells and batteries.

In this experiment, the principle of the potentiometer will be investigated and used in measuring the electromotive forces of battery cells. Also, the internal resistances of the cells will be determined.

After performing this experiment and analyzing the data, you should be able to:

1. Clearly distinguish between the emf and terminal voltage of a battery.
2. Describe the operation of a potentiometer and its usefulness.
3. Explain how the internal resistance of a battery may be measured.

II. Equipment Needed

- Slide-wire potentiometer
- Portable galvanometer
- Rheostat (20 to 40 Ω)
- 12-V dc power supply or battery
- Resistor (5 kΩ)
- Two switches: one key switch, and one single-pole, single-throw (SPST) switch
- Connecting wires
- Ammeter (0 to 3 A)
- Voltmeter (3 to 30 V)
- Two dry cells, 1.5 or 3 V (preferably one old and one fresh cell)
- Standard cell
- 1 sheet of Cartesian graph paper

III. Theory

An electrical source supplies a potential difference to the circuit to which it is connected. For example, a dry-cell battery transforms chemical energy into electrical energy. (Technically, a battery is a combination of single cells.) When no current is flowing in the source, the "open circuit" potential difference $\mathcal{E}$ between the terminals is called the **electromotive force (emf)**. Electromotive "force" is an unfortunate name because the quantity is not a force but a potential difference or voltage.

Every source of emf has some internal resistance r, which gives rise to an internal voltage drop when a current flows through it. For example, when the terminal voltage of a cell is measured with a voltmeter as in Fig. 25.1, a current I flows in the circuit. The terminal potential difference or voltage V as measured by the voltmeter is less than the open-circuit emf potential difference of the battery by an *internal* voltage drop Ir (Ohm's law) due to the internal resistance of the battery, or

$$V = \mathcal{E} - Ir. \quad \textbf{(25.1)}$$

(terminal voltage = emf − internal voltage drop)

Cell symbol

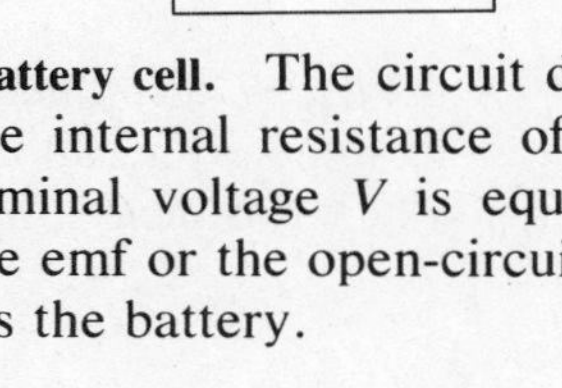

Figure 25.1 Battery cell. The circuit diagram explicitly shows the internal resistance of the cell. The measured terminal voltage V is equal to $\mathcal{E} - Ir$, where $\mathcal{E}$ is the emf or the open-circuit potential difference across the battery.

As mentioned previously, with an open circuit ($I = 0$), the potential difference across the battery terminals is the emf ($V = \mathscr{E}$).

As can be seen from Eq. 25.1, when measuring the terminal voltage of a battery with a voltmeter (a completed circuit), the meter does not read the emf of the cell. However, for many practical situations, the terminal voltage is taken as the emf, since for a high-resistance voltmeter the current I is quite small and the Ir term is negligible for common low-resistance cells.

Also, as expressed in Eq. 25.1, for a battery cell or other source of constant emf, the terminal voltage decreases linearly as the current drawn from the sources increases. However, a cell of low internal resistance can supply a relatively large current without a great decrease in its terminal voltage.

A simple slide-wire potentiometer circuit is illustrated in Fig. 25.2a. This circuit may be used to measure the emf of a cell or battery, which requires the condition of zero current through the battery ("open-circuit" condition). The so-called "working source" with an emf of $\mathscr{E}_w$ maintains a constant current I through the resistor.

The resistor is in the form of a wire with a sliding contact key C which allows R_x or L_x to be varied. (The resistance R_x is proportional to the length of the wire L_x). The key is adjusted until the galvanometer G (a sensitive current-detecting instrument) has a zero or "null" reading, indicating that no current is flowing through the test cell $\mathscr{E}_x$. Therefore, $\mathscr{E}_x$ is "balanced" against $\mathscr{E}_w$, and the emf of the test cell is equal to the voltage drop across R_x, since they are connected in parallel:

$$\mathscr{E}_x = IR_x \tag{25.2}$$

If the resistance R_x is greater than that for the null condition, some of the current I from the working source flows through R_x and some through the test battery, charging it if it is of a rechargeable type. If the resistance R_x is less than that for a null condition, currents from both batteries go through R_x.

The adjustable resistance also in effect acts as a "voltage divider." A portion of the input emf or voltage V_i is tapped off as an output voltage V_o by dividing the resistor (Fig. 25.2b). Since $V_o = IR_o$ and $V_i = IR_i$, then $V_o = (R_o/R_i)V_i$. Obviously, should $R_o = R_i$, then $V_o = V_i$.

If the test cell is then replaced by a standard cell of known emf $\mathscr{E}_s$ and the potentiometer is again balanced, then by the same reasoning,

$$\mathscr{E}_s = IR_s \tag{25.3}$$

The current is the same in both cases, since $\mathscr{E}_w$ and the total resistance R of the wire are constant, i.e., $I = \mathscr{E}_w/R$. Then, taking the ratio of the two equations,

$$\frac{\mathscr{E}_x}{\mathscr{E}_s} = \frac{R_x}{R_s}$$

or

$$\mathscr{E}_x = \left(\frac{R_x}{R_s}\right)\mathscr{E}_s \tag{25.4}$$

For a uniform slide wire, the length of a segment of the wire is proportional to the resistance of the segment, and in terms of the lengths L of the two balanced conditions, which are easily measured,

$$\mathscr{E}_x = \left(\frac{L_x}{L_s}\right)\mathscr{E}_s$$

Hence, knowing the emf of the standard cell, $\mathscr{E}_s$, and measuring the lengths of the segments of the wire for each balanced condition, the emf of the test cell can be computed.

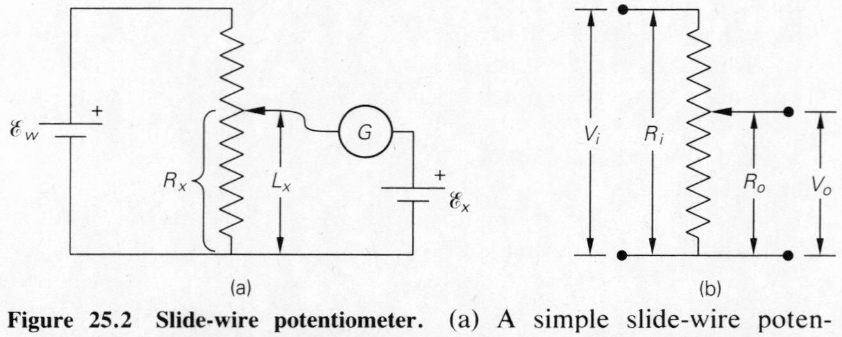

Figure 25.2 Slide-wire potentiometer. (a) A simple slide-wire potentiometer circuit diagram. (b) The principle of a "voltage divider." See text for description.

IV. Experimental Procedure

A. *Measurement of* emf

1. Set up the potentiometer circuit as shown in Fig. 25.3 with one of the dry cells as $\mathscr{E}_x$. Keep switches S (SPST) and K (key) open while connections are being made. The resistance R_1 (5 kΩ) protects the galvanometer from large initial currents in an unbalanced circuit, which could damage the instrument. This protective resistance will be short-circuited during the experiment by closing K. Set the rheostat R_h at its maximum resistance.

Caution: *Do not plug in the power supply (or connect a battery source) until the instructor has checked the circuit.**

2. After the circuit has been approved, plug in the power supply and close switch S. Depress the wire contact key C and note the galvanometer deflection. The circuit is balanced when the galvanometer deflection is zero. This is accomplished by sliding the contact key along the wire. *Do not slide the contact key when it is depressed.* This could scrape the wire and make it nonuniform. Balance the circuit.

Then, adjust the rheostat resistance R_h and the contact key C so that when the circuit is balanced again, the length of segment L is about two-thirds to three-fourths of the length of the wire. Note and record the current reading of the ammeter.

3. Close switch K and rebalance the circuit. Closing K short-circuits R_1 and greatly increases the sensitivity of the galvanometer. Only a fine adjustment will be needed to balance the circuit. Record the current I in the Laboratory Report.

Upon completion, open K and deactivate the circuit (unplug the power supply). Measure and record the length of segment L of the slide wire.

4. Place the other dry cell in the circuit as $\mathscr{E}_x$ (keeping the same polarity). Activate the circuit and repeat procedure 3.

* If your galvanometer is equipped with several scale settings, resistor R_1 and switch K may be omitted from the circuit. The galvanometer should be set initially to its least sensitive scale, then changed to a more sensitive scale if applicable. (This is equivalent to closing K.) Your instructor will advise you if this should be done and which scales are more and less sensitive in this case.

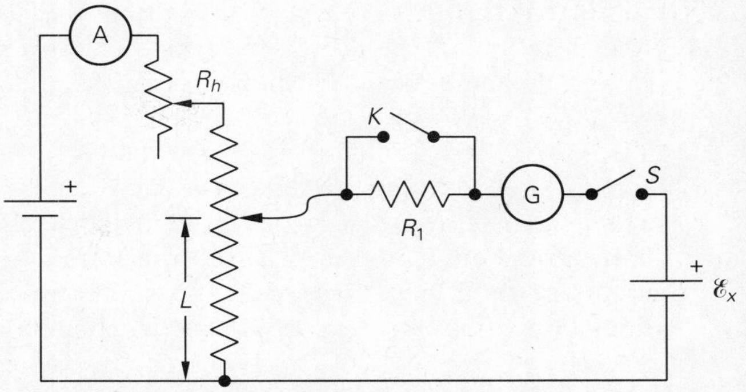

Figure 25.3 Potentiometer circuit for experimental procedure. See text for description.

5. Place the standard cell in the circuit in place of the test dry cell. Record the emf $\mathscr{E}_s$ of the standard cell (on the cell or provided by the instructor). Activate the circuit and repeat procedure 3. Then, from the experimental data, compute the emf's of the dry cells. (*Note*: The current I should be the same in all determinations. If not, repeat the measurements or consult with your instructor.)

B. *Measurement of Internal Resistance*

6. Set up the circuit as shown in Fig. 25.4 with one of the dry cells. Do not connect one terminal of the cell and leave switch S open. Set the rheostat at its maximum resistance. *Have the instructor check the circuit.*

7. After the circuit has been approved, connect the cell terminal and read the terminal voltage registered on the voltmeter (switch S still open), and record in the data table.

Then close the switch and record the voltmeter and ammeter readings. The ammeter registers

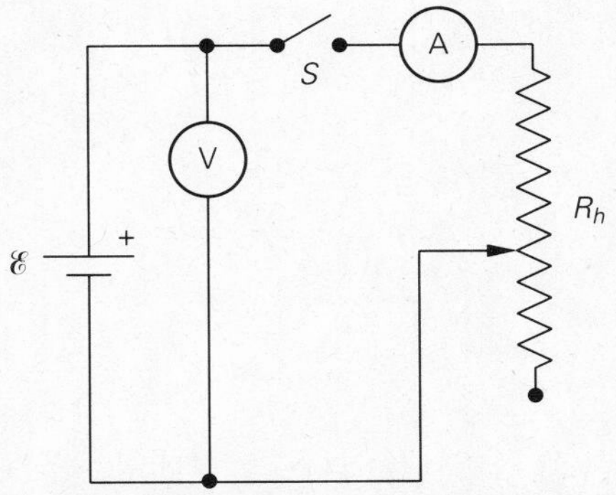

Figure 25.4 Circuit diagram for measuring a cell's internal resistance. See text for description.

the current through the external resistance R_h. Note that the voltage drop across R_h (i.e., $V = IR_h$) is the same as the terminal voltage of the cell.

8. Starting at R_{max}, adjust (reduce) the rheostat resistance in a series of steps that produce current changes of about 0.50 A until the current reaches a value of about 3 A. Record the voltmeter and ammeter readings for each step. Then disconnect the cell.

9. Repeat procedures 7 and 8 for the other dry cell.

10. Plot on a single graph the terminal voltage V versus I (the current delivered to the external resistance) for each cell. Draw straight lines that best fit the data, with the lines extrapolated to intercept both axes. Determine the (negative) slopes and intercepts of the lines.

As can be seen from Eq. 25.1, which has the form of a straight line, the slope of the line is equal to the internal resistance of the cell.

Name ______________________ Section ______________ Date ______________

Lab Partner(s) ____

EXPERIMENT 25

The Potentiometer: emf and Terminal Voltage

Laboratory Report

A. Measurement of emf

	Current I ( )	Slide-wire segment: L ( )	emf ( )
Cell 1	________	________	________
Cell 2	________	________	________
Standard cell	________	________	________

Calculations
(show work)

Don't forget units

(continued)

B. Measurement of Internal Resistance

DATA TABLE

Voltage with switch open: ____________________

Cell 1 ____________________

Cell 2 ____________________

Rheostat step	Cell 1		Cell 2	
	Voltage, V ( )	Current, I ( )	Voltage, V ( )	Current, I ( )
1 $R_{h_{max}}$				
2				
3				
4				
5				
6				
7				
8				

Calculations
(show work)

	Cell 1	Cell 2
Slope r	____________	____________
y intercept	____________	____________
x intercept	____________	____________

Name ______________________ Section ______________ Date ______________

Lab Partner(s) ____

EXPERIMENT 25 *Laboratory Report*

QUESTIONS

1. Compare the terminal voltages of the cells to their emf's by computing what percent the rated terminal voltage is of the emf. Give an explanation for the difference in these quantities, if any.

2. Were the current capabilities of the dry cells the same? If not, explain why.

3. Interpret the *Y*- and *X*-axis intercepts of a graph of *V* versus *I* for a cell, and explain why the *Y* intercept corresponds to an ''open-circuit'' condition and the *X* intercept to a ''short-circuit'' condition.

(continued)

4. Compare the emf's of the cells found in part A with their emf's as determined from the graphical analysis of the data in part B by computing the percent differences.

5. Using known and measured experimental quantities, find the total resistance of the slide-wire of the potentiometer.

Name ______________________ Section ______________ Date ______________

Lab Partner(s) ____

EXPERIMENT 26

The Voltmeter and Ammeter

Advance Study Assignment

Read the experiment and answer the following questions.

1. What is the function of the galvanometer in a voltmeter or ammeter?

2. What is the purpose of the "multiplier" resistor in a voltmeter? Is the voltmeter a high- or low-resistance instrument?

3. How is the voltmeter connected in the circuit? Explain why.

(continued)

4. What is the purpose of the "shunt" resistance in an ammeter? Is the ammeter a high- or low-resistance instrument?

5. How is the ammeter connected in a circuit? Explain why.

6. What would happen if the ammeter were connected in parallel with a circuit element?

The Voltmeter and Ammeter*

I. Introduction and Objectives

Voltmeters and ammeters are widely used instruments for detecting and measuring voltages and currents. Electrical quantities cannot be seen directly by looking at a wire. Like a weather vane, these instruments are used to help us observe that which cannot be seen directly. This experiment is intended to provide a behind-the-scenes look at the construction of these meters and insight into their proper use. The design of a meter and the calculation of the appropriate series or parallel resistance not only illustrates the inner workings of the voltmeter and ammeter but provides experience analyzing a circuit using Ohm's law.

An understanding of these instruments will be useful in future experiments to avoid the damage resulting from misuse and to recognize the conditions under which the meters introduce errors as their internal resistance becomes a part of the circuit.

In this experiment you will measure the characteristics of a galvanometer and use resistances to convert it into several voltmeters and a three-range ammeter. After performing the experiment, you should be able to:

1. Explain the principle of the galvanometer and how voltmeters and ammeters are made by combining a galvanometer with resistors.
2. Understand why voltmeters are high-resistance instruments and ammeters are low-resistance instruments.
3. Describe how ammeters and voltmeters are correctly connected in circuits, and what would happen if they were incorrectly connected.

II. Equipment Needed

- Galvanometer†
- Decade resistance box (1 to 999999 Ω)
- Voltmeter (≈ 10 V, triple-range preferred)
- Millivoltmeter (≈ 100 mV)
- Power supply or battery (≈ 1.5 V and 6 V)
- Wheatstone-bridge slide-wire
- Triple-range milliammeter
- Single-pole switch
- Miscellaneous wires including at least 6 clip leads

III. Theory

The **galvanometer** is the chameleon of scientific instruments. With the addition of a resistor and a new face it can become a voltmeter or ammeter of whatever scale you want. The galvanometer is the basic indicating component of all deflection-type meters. The galvanometer is an electromagnetic device capable of detecting very small currents. (How small depends on how much you want to pay.) The basic design of a moving-coil galvanometer is shown in Fig. 26.1 (sometimes called a *D'Arsonval galvanometer*, after the French physicist who invented it around 1882). It consists of a coil of wire mounted on bearings between two poles of a permanent magnet. When a current passes through the coil, it experiences a torque and rotates the pointer along the scale until balanced by the torque supplied by two small springs. The deflection is proportional to the current in the coil.

Some galvanometers have a scale marked with zero at the center. These are used in circuits like the potentiometer and Wheatstone bridge to detect a balance point. The galvanometer used in most voltmeters and ammeters has the zero at the left.

The galvanometers used for meter construction are characterized by their coil resistance, r, and the coil current required to give a full-scale deflection of the pointer, I_c. Once these are known, the resistances necessary to convert the galvanometer to the desired voltmeter or ammeter can be calculated.

A. The dc Voltmeter

The goal here is to design a circuit that can be connected across a resistance, R, that will allow a small current that is proportional to the voltage difference to flow through the galvanometer, and that will divert as little current as possible from the resistance, R. The circuit in Fig. 26.2a accomplishes both these goals. The series resistor, R_m, is called a *multiplier* resistor because it multiplies the voltage range of the

* This experiment was written and designed by Professor Fred B. Otto, Maine Maritime Academy, Castine, ME.

† A left-zero galvanometer like those used in meters is preferred. The galvanometer from an open bench-type voltmeter can be used by clipping directly to the galvanometer terminals on the back, or a microammeter can be used as a galvanometer.

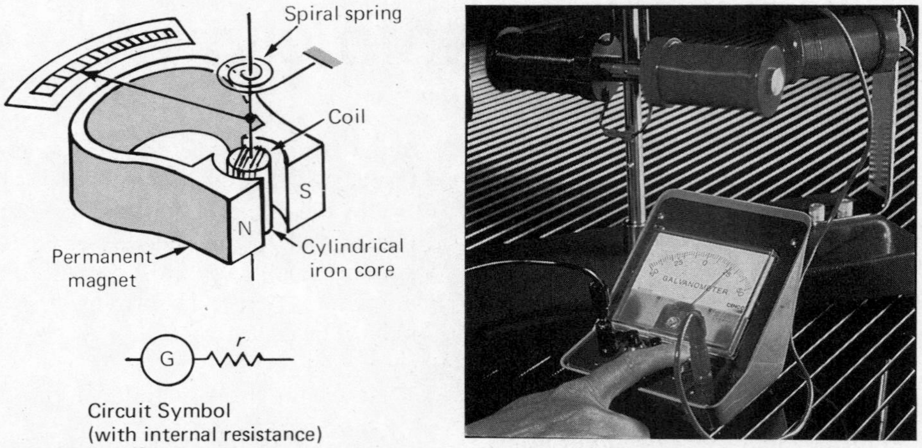

Figure 26.1 Galvanometer. The drawing shows the basic design of a moving-coil (D'Arsonval) galvanometer. An actual galvanometer is shown in the photo. (Photo courtesy of Central Scientific Co., Inc.)

galvanometer. The combination of the multiplier resistance and the galvanometer is the voltmeter. These are usually combined in a single box.

The resistance of the voltmeter can be calculated using Ohm's law. If V_{max} is to be the maximum scale reading on the meter, the total resistance of the meter equals V_{max}/I_c. Since the galvanometer resistance, r, represents part of the total resistance of the voltmeter, it must be subtracted to give the value of the multiplier resistance, R_m, to be added in series to make a voltmeter.

$$R_m = \frac{V_{max}}{I_c} - r \qquad \textbf{(26.1)}$$

Example 26.1 Suppose that we wish to calculate the multiplier resistor to convert a galvanometer with a full scale current (I_c) of 2.0×10^{-3} A and a coil resistance of 100 Ω into a 3-V voltmeter. That is a voltmeter with a $V_{max} = 3.0$ V.

Solution

$$R_m = \frac{V_{max}}{I_c} - r$$

$$= \frac{(3.0 \text{ V})}{(2.0 \times 10^{-3} \text{ A})} - 100 \ \Omega = 1400 \ \Omega$$

The deflection is proportional to the voltage, and a scale is provided showing the value of V_{max} at the right end. The scale is subdivided and graduated so that the voltage can be read directly from the scale.

A voltmeter is always connected "across" or in parallel with a circuit component to measure the potential difference or voltage drop across the component.

If a voltmeter were connected in series with a circuit component, its high resistance would reduce the current in the circuit and the voltage drop across that component.

B. The dc Ammeter

The challenge here is to design a circuit that will divert a small amount of current through the galvanometer that is proportional to the much larger current flowing through the resistor, R. This diversion is accomplished by placing a small "shunt" resistance, R_s, in series with R as shown in Fig. 26.2b. The small resistance connected in parallel with the galvanometer is called a "shunt" because it directs or "shunts" most of the current away from the galvanometer. As the current flows through the shunt resistance, a small voltage is developed that diverts a small amount of the current through the galvanometer, causing it to have a controlled deflection proportional to the current through the circuit. The galvanometer and shunt resistance combination is the ammeter.

As with the voltmeter, the value of the shunt resistance required to give a full-scale deflection for a desired maximum current can be calculated using Ohm's law. With the pointer reading full scale, the current through the galvanometer is I_c and the voltage drop across the galvanometer is $I_c r$. Because the galvanometer and the shunt resistor are in parallel, there must be the same voltage drop across the shunt; therefore

$$I_c r = I_s R_s \qquad \textbf{(26.2)}$$

R_s is much smaller than r; therefore, the current through the shunt must be much larger than the current through the galvanometer. With the pointer de-

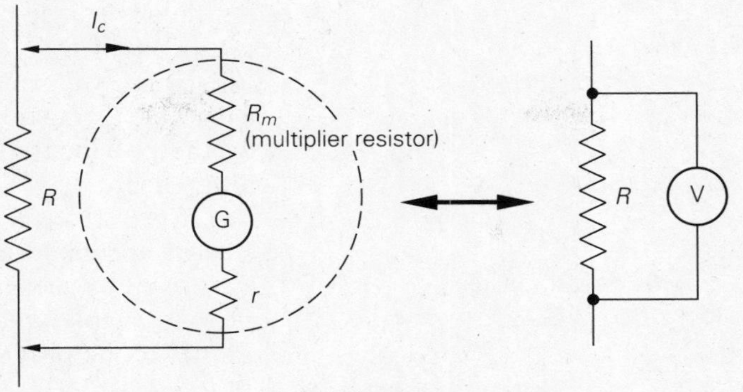

(a) Voltmeter

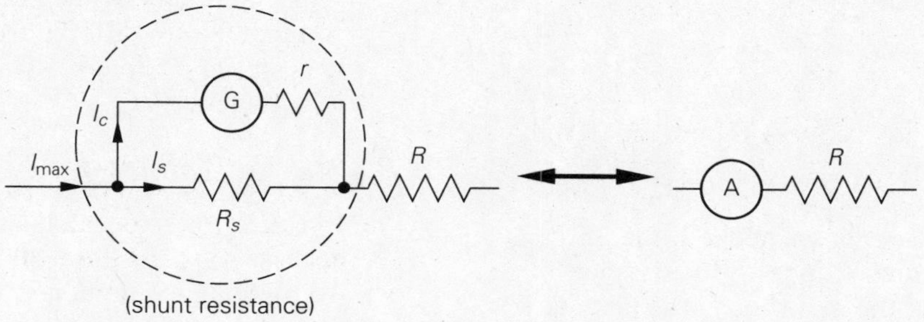

(b) Ammeter

Figure 26.2 Circuit diagrams for voltmeter and ammeter. (a) A voltmeter has a large "multiplier" resistor, R_m, in series with the galvanometer. (b) An ammeter has a "shunt" resistance, R_s, in parallel with the galvanometer.

flecting to maximum, the current flowing in the resistor, R, is that of the maximum scale reading of the ammeter. Since $I_s = I_{max} - I_c$, Eq. 26.2 can be solved for R_s to give

$$R_s = \frac{I_c r}{I_{max} - I_c} \tag{26.3}$$

Example 26.2 Suppose that we wish to calculate the shunt resistor to convert a galvanometer with a full-scale current, I_c, of 2.0×10^{-3} A and a coil resistance of 100 Ω to a 3-A ammeter. That is, an ammeter with an $I_{max} = 3.0$ A.

Solution

$$R_s = \frac{I_c r}{I_{max} - I_c} = \frac{(2.0 \times 10^{-3}\ \text{A})(100\ \Omega)}{3.000\ \text{A} - 0.0020\ \text{A}}$$

$$= \frac{0.20\ \text{V}}{2.998\ \text{A}} = 0.067\ \Omega$$

(where any number of significant figures is assumed for I_{max}).

A scale is designed for the ammeter with the value of the maximum current marked at the right-hand end. The scale is subdivided to read the current directly.

The low shunt resistance in parallel with the galvanometer makes the resistance of the ammeter small enough that it can usually be considered negligible relative to R in calculating circuit currents.

An ammeter is always connected in line (in series) with a circuit component to measure the current flowing through that component.

Since an ammeter is a low-resistance instrument, if an ammeter were connected in parallel with a circuit component, the meter would carry a large current and could burn out. Some meters have fuses to save the meter. Some others have diodes across the galvanometer that protect it from voltages above about 0.5 V.

IV. Experimental Procedure

1. Determine the full-scale current of the galvanometer by setting up the circuit as shown in Fig. 26.3. Set the resistance box to maximum. If you are using the galvanometer from a voltmeter, use clip leads to connect directly to the terminals

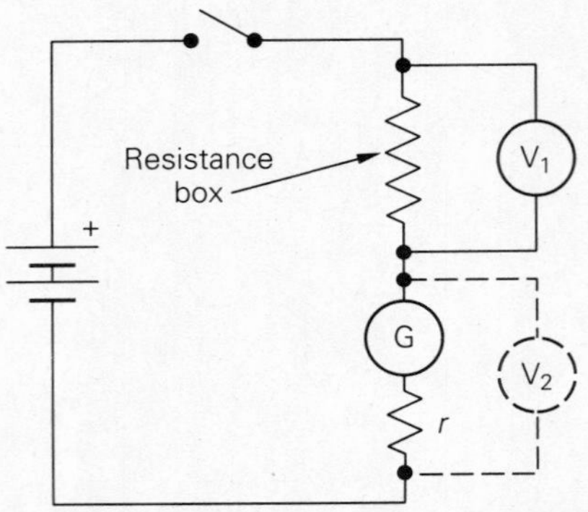

Figure 26.3 The circuit for measuring the full-scale current and the resistance of the galvanometer. See text for description.

on the back. Do not connect the meter to measure V_2 yet.

2. After the instructor has checked the circuit, close the switch and reduce the resistance box until the pointer of the meter is on the last mark. The full-scale current, I_c, is now flowing through both the resistance box and the galvanometer. Record the resistance box setting and the voltmeter reading, V_1. Open the switch after the reading is taken. Use Ohm's law to calculate the current I_c:

$$I_c = \frac{V_1}{R_{box}}$$

and record it in the Laboratory Report.

3. Connect the millivoltmeter or a low-range digital voltmeter to measure the voltage V_2. Millivoltmeters tend to have somewhat low resistance and may draw some current away from the galvanometer. If the galvanometer reading falls below the maximum, adjust the resistance box until the galvanometer needle indicates that the full maximum coil current is again flowing through the galvanometer. Record the voltage across the galvanometer, V_2. Open the switch after the reading is taken. Use Ohm's law to calculate the resistance of the galvanometer coil:

$$r = \frac{V_2}{I_c}$$

and record it in the Laboratory Report.

A. The dc Voltmeter

4. Use Eq. 26.1 to calculate the multiplier resistance for a 1.5-V voltmeter (a voltmeter with a maximum reading of 1.5 V).

5. Set the resistance box as a multiplier resistor by setting it to the calculated value and use this "home-grown" meter to measure the voltage of a dry cell. Compare this reading to the value read by the provided voltmeter and find the percent difference.

6. Design and build a 6-V and a 15-V voltmeter. Test each by using it to measure the voltage of the 6-V supply and compare your measurement to that of the provided voltmeter.

7. Devise and draw a circuit for building a triple-scale voltmeter where the scale is changed by connecting to different terminals. If possible, look inside a triple-scale voltmeter and compare its circuit to yours.

B. The dc Ammeter

8. Use Eq. 26.3 to calculate the shunt resistance necessary to make a 300-mA (0.3-A) ammeter from your galvanometer. This can be recorded in Data Table 3 as the first scale of the three-scale meter you will be making later.

9. Small resistances like those used for ammeter shunts are hard to obtain from resistance boxes. The slide wire that is used for the Wheatstone bridge or the potentiometer experiments can be used for this purpose. We will measure the resistance of one meter long wire and then calculate the length required to provide the required shunt resistance. To measure the resistance of the wire, connect the voltmeter and ammeter as shown in Fig. 26.4a. Initially set the resistance box to 20 Ω. Use the 500-mA (0.5-A) scale of the ammeter.

10. After the instructor has checked your circuit, close the switch and carefully reduce the resistance until the ammeter reads about 500 mA (0.5 A). Record the current and voltage under slide-wire data. Open the switch and calculate the resistance of the wire using Ohm's law.

11. Compute the length of wire that will have a resistance equal to the required shunt resistance.

$$\text{Length} = \frac{\text{Shunt } R}{R \text{ of one meter}}$$

12. Near the "zero" end of the wire, construct a shunt by attaching two clip leads as shown in Fig. 26.4b. Make the distance between the leads equal to the length computed above. Attach the

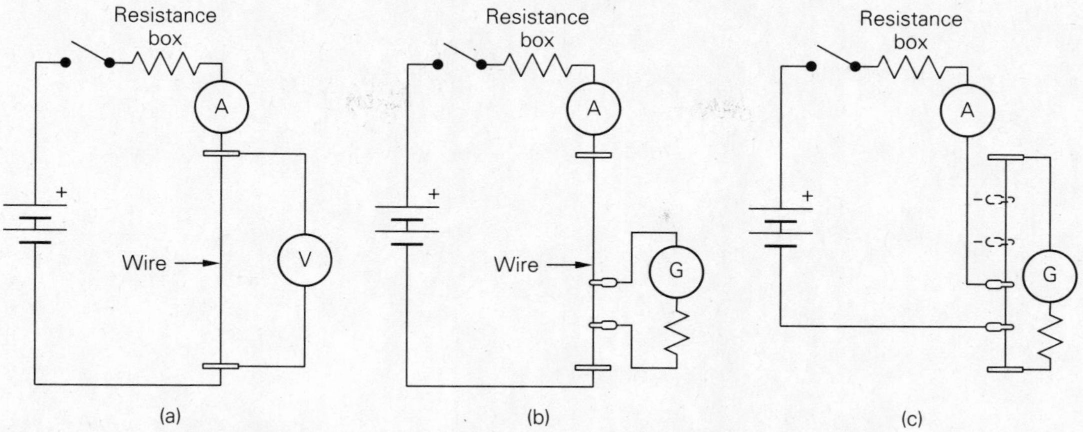

Figure 26.4 Experiment circuits. (a) Circuit to measure the resistance of the wire. (b) Single-range ammeter. (c) Multi-range ammeter. See text for descriptions.

other ends of these leads to your galvanometer. Your ammeter is complete.

13. Test your ammeter. Set the resistance box to 100 Ω. As you reduce the resistance, compare the readings of your meter with that of the ammeter at about 100, 200, and 300 mA and record the results in Data Table 2.

Note: Whenever a connection is made there is an unpredictable amount of contact resistance. Contact resistance can give large errors when dealing with small resistances. The better high-current shunts are four-terminal resistors, providing separate terminals for the current-carrying wires and the wires to the galvanometer. This way the extra voltage drop at the current-carrying connections is not included in the shunt voltage drop seen by the galvanometer. Our slide-wire shunt has provided us with these separate connections.

14. Making a three-range ammeter is a little more complex than making a three-range voltmeter. The first step toward expanding your ammeter into a three-range ammeter will be to reverse the connections as shown in Fig. 26.4c. Connect the galvanometer to the ends of the wire and connect the circuit so that the current flows in and out through the clip leads. It may be less obvious, but the contact resistance at the current connections is still not a part of the shunt resistance seen by the galvanometer.

15. Test your ammeter again against the laboratory meter. It will probably read a little lower this time. The extra wire of the slide-wire in effect increases the r of the galvanometer. Adjust the length of the shunt by sliding the clip up the wire until both meters read the same. Record this as the experimental length and compute the percent difference.

16. To add a second scale to your meter, first calculate the shunt resistance and wire length for a 150-mA meter. Leave the first two clip leads in place. Attach a third lead at the calculated distance from the zero-end lead. You now have a two-scale meter with the zero-end lead acting as the common terminal. Test your meter against the laboratory meter and adjust the length until the meters agree. Record the computed and experimental lengths.

17. Repeat the process and add a third scale with a full-scale reading of 60 mA.

18. If possible, look inside a laboratory triple-scale ammeter and compare its circuit with yours. Draw the circuit for the triple-scale ammeter.

Name ______________________ Section ______________ Date ______________
Lab Partner(s) ____

EXPERIMENT 26

The Voltmeter and Ammeter

Laboratory Report

Galvanometer characteristics:

Resistance box setting ______________

V_1 ______________

Full-scale coil current, I_c ______________

Full-scale voltage drop, V_2 ______________

Galvanometer resistance, r ______________

A. The dc Voltmeter

DATA TABLE 1

Scale	R_m ( )	Your meter ( )	Lab voltmeter ( )	Percent difference

Circuit diagram for a triple-scale voltmeter:

Don't forget units

(continued)

B. The dc Ammeter

Slide-wire data:

Current ____________ Voltage ____________

Computed resistance for one meter ____________

DATA TABLE 2

Your meter ( )	Lab voltmeter ( )	Percent difference

DATA TABLE 3

Scale	Shunt resistance ( )	Computed length ( )	Experimental length ( )	Percent difference

Circuit diagram for a triple-scale ammeter:

Name ______________________ Section ______________ Date ______________

Lab Partner(s) ____

EXPERIMENT 26 ***Laboratory Report***

QUESTIONS

1. Indicate how the dial for the triple-scale voltmeter having 1.5-V, 6-V, and 15-V scales might be labeled.

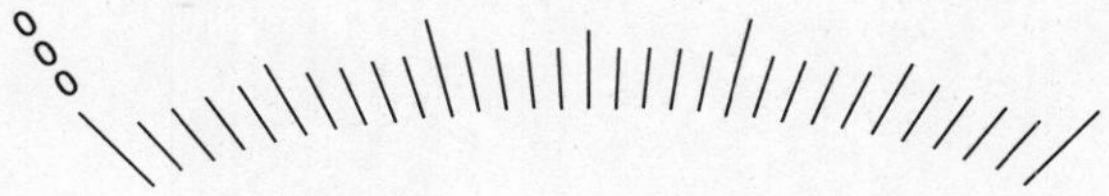

2. What would be the lowest voltage scale that could be made using your galvanometer?

3. The sensitivity of a voltmeter is commonly expressed in *ohms per volt* (Ω/V), which is the total resistance of the meter ($r + R_m$) divided by the full-scale reading. Calculate the *ohms per volt* sensitivity for each of the three voltage scales that you designed for your galvanometer. Are they the same? Are they equal to $1/I_c$?

4. Indicate how the dial for the triple-scale ammeter you designed might be labeled.

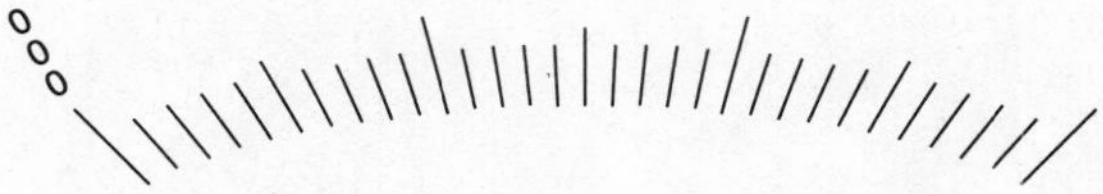

5. Ammeter shunts are rated in terms of the voltage drop when the rated full-scale current is flowing. For example, it might be 200 A, 50 mV. What would be the millivolt rating on shunts designed for use with your galvanometer?

(continued)

6. **Challenge question**: If ρ is the linear resistivity of the slide-wire used for the ammeter shunts, the shunt resistance in Eq. 26.3 is $\rho\ell$, and the resistance of the rest of the wire, $\rho(1 - \ell)$, is added to the galvanometer resistance, r. Make these changes to Eq. 26.3 and solve for ℓ to obtain an equation that compensates for the extra wire length when calculating the lengths for shunts.

Name ______________________ Section ______________ Date ______________

Lab Partner(s) ____

EXPERIMENT 27

The Measurement of Resistance: Ammeter-Voltmeter Methods and Wheatstone Bridge Method

Advance Study Assignment

Read the experiment and answer the following questions.

A. Ammeter-Voltmeter Method

1. When measuring a resistance with an ammeter and voltmeter, is the resistance given exactly by $R = V/I$? Explain.

2. Comment on the relative magnitudes of the resistances of an ammeter and a voltmeter.

3. Are (a) an ammeter and (b) a voltmeter connected in a series or parallel with a circuit component (a resistance)? Explain.

(continued)

B. Wheatstone Bridge Method

4. Why is the Wheatstone bridge called a ''null'' instrument?

5. When the galvanometer in a Wheatstone bridge circuit shows no deflection, why are the voltages across opposite branches on each side of the galvanometer necessarily equal?

6. For a slide-wire Wheatstone bridge, why should the sliding key not be moved with the key depressed?

The Measurement of Resistance: Ammeter-Voltmeter Methods and Wheatstone Bridge Method

I. Introduction and Objectives

The magnitude of a resistance can be measured by several methods. One common method is to measure the voltage drop V across a resistance in circuit with a voltmeter and the current I through the resistance with an ammeter. By Ohm's law, then, $R = V/I$. However, the ratio of the measured voltage and current does not give the exact value of the resistance because of the resistances of the meters.

This problem is eliminated when one measures a resistance, or, more properly, compares a resistance with a standard resistance in a Wheatstone bridge circuit [named after Sir Charles Wheatstone (1802–1875)]. In this experiment, the ammeter-voltmeter and the Wheatstone bridge methods of measuring resistances will be investigated.

After performing this experiment and analyzing the data, you should be able to:

1. Explain the two ways to measure resistance with an ammeter and voltmeter, and how they differ.
2. Describe the basic principle and operation of the Wheatstone bridge.
3. Discuss the relative accuracy of the ammeter-voltmeter methods and the Wheatstone bridge method of measuring resistance.

II. Equipment Needed*

A. Ammeter-Voltmeter Methods

- Ammeter (0 to 0.5 A)
- Voltmeter (0 to 3 V)
- Rheostat (10 Ω)
- Resistors (e.g., 10 Ω and 25 Ω)
- Battery or power supply (3 V)
- Connecting wires

B. Wheatstone Bridge Method

- Slide-wire Wheatstone bridge
- Galvanometer
- Standard decade resistance box (0.1 to 99.9 Ω)
- Single-pole, single-throw switch

III. Theory

A. Ammeter-Voltmeter Methods

There are two basic arrangements by which resistance is measured with an ammeter and a voltmeter. One circuit is shown in Fig. 27.1. The current I through the resistance R is measured with an ammeter, and the potential difference or voltage drop V across the resistance is measured with a voltmeter. Then, by Ohm's law, $R = V/I$.

Strictly, however, this value of the resistance is not altogether correct, since the current registered on the ammeter divides between the resistance R and the voltmeter in parallel. A voltmeter is a high-resis-

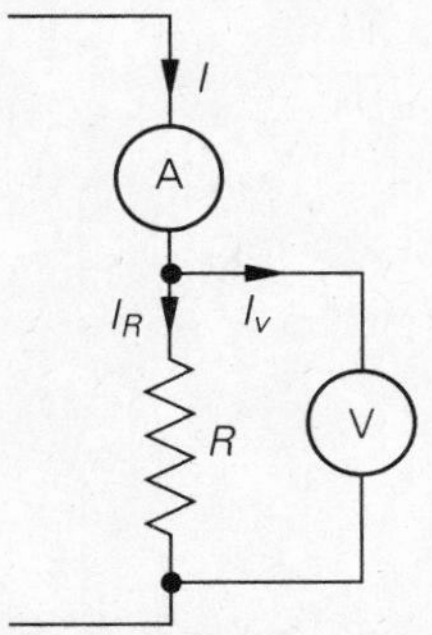

Figure 27.1 Resistance measurement. One of the basic arrangements for measuring resistance with an ammeter and a voltmeter. The ammeter measures the sum of the currents through the resistance and the voltmeter. Therefore, the true value of R is *greater* than the measured value, if the measured value is taken to be V/I.

* The ranges of the equipment are given as examples. These may be varied to apply to available equipment.

tance instrument and draws relatively little current provided that voltmeter resistance R_v is much greater than R (see Experiment 26). Hence, it is more appropriate to write

$$R \simeq \frac{V}{I} \quad \text{if} \quad R_v \gg R \qquad (27.1)$$

For more accurate resistance measurement, one must take the resistance of the voltmeter into account. The current drawn by the voltmeter is $I_v = V/R_v$. Since the total current I divides between the resistance and the voltmeter in the parallel branch, we have

$$I = I_R + I_v$$

or

$$I_R = I - I_v \qquad (27.2)$$

where I_R is the true current through the resistance. Then, by Ohm's law,

$$R = \frac{V}{I_R} = \frac{V}{I - I_v} = \frac{V}{I - V/R_v} \qquad (27.3)$$

Another possible arrangement for measuring R is shown in the circuit diagram in Fig. 27.2. In this case, the ammeter measures the current through R alone, but now the voltmeter reads the voltage drop across *both* the ammeter *and* the resistance. Since the ammeter is a low-resistance instrument (Experiment 26), to a good approximation

$$R \simeq \frac{V}{I} \quad \text{if} \quad R_a \ll R \qquad (27.4)$$

where R_a is the resistance of the ammeter. When $R_a \ll R$, the voltage drop across R_a, that is, $V_a = IR_a$, is small compared to that across R, which is $V_R = IR$.

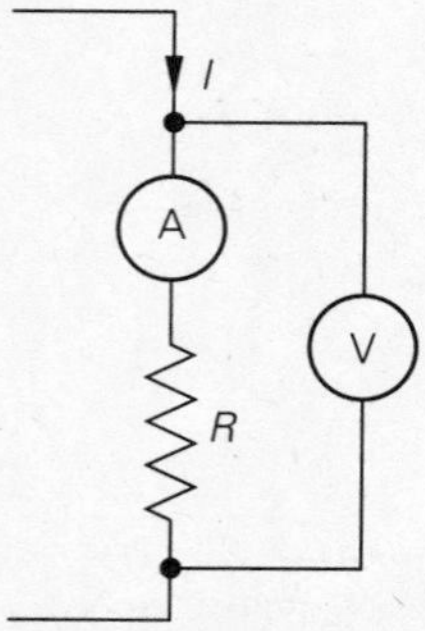

Figure 27.2 Resistance measurement. Another basic arrangement for measuring resistance with an ammeter and a voltmeter. The ammeter measures the current through R, but the voltmeter measures the voltage across R *and* the ammeter. Therefore, the true value of R is *less* than the measured value, if the measured value is taken to be V/I.

Taking the voltage drop or the resistance of the ammeter into account, we have

$$V = V_R + V_a = IR + IR_a$$
$$= I(R + R_a) = IR'$$

and $\quad R' = R + R_a. \qquad (27.5)$

Or, from Eq. 27.5, we may write

$$R = \frac{V}{I} - R_a$$

B. Wheatstone Bridge Method

The basic diagram of a Wheatstone bridge circuit is shown in Fig. 27.3. In its simplest form, the bridge circuit consists of four resistors, a battery or voltage source, and a sensitive galvanometer. The values of R_1, R_2, and R_s are all known, and R_x is the unknown resistance.

Switch S is closed and the bridge is balanced by adjusting the standard resistance R_s until the galvanometer shows no deflection (indicating no current flow through the galvanometer branch). As a result, the Wheatstone bridge is called a "null" instrument. This is analogous to an ordinary double-pan beam balance, which shows a null or zero reading when there are equal masses on its pans.

Assume that the Wheatstone bridge is balanced so that the galvanometer registers no current. Then points b and c in the circuit are at the same potential; current I_1 flows through both R_s and R_x, and current I_2 flows through both R_1 and R_2. Also, the voltage drop V_{ab} across R_s is equal to the voltage drop across R_1, V_{ac}, for a zero galvanometer deflection:

$$V_{ab} = V_{ac}$$

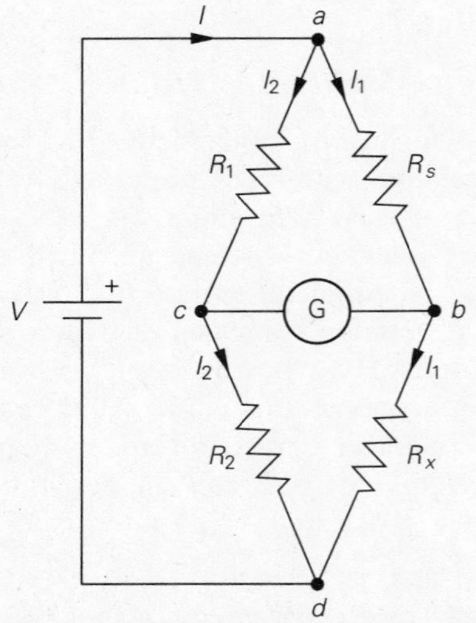

Figure 27.3 Wheatstone bridge circuit diagram. See text for description.

Similarly,

$$V_{bd} = V_{cd} \tag{27.6}$$

(Why?)

Writing these equations in terms of currents and resistances, by Ohm's law,

$$I_1R_x = I_2R_2$$
$$I_1R_s = I_2R_1 \tag{27.7}$$

Then, dividing one equation by the other and solving for R_x yields

$$R_x = \left(\frac{R_2}{R_1}\right)R_s \tag{27.8}$$

Hence, when the bridge is balanced, the unknown resistance R_x can be found in terms of the standard resistance R_s and the ratio R_2/R_1.

Notice that the difficulties of the preceding method are eliminated. The Wheatstone bridge in effect compares the unknown resistance R with a standard resistance R_s. Should $R_1 = R_2$, then $R_x = R_s$.

The circuit diagram for a slide-wire form of the Wheatstone bridge is shown in Fig. 27.4 along with a photo of an actual bridge. The line from a to d represents a wire, and C is a contact key that slides along the wire so as to divide the wire into different-length segments. The resistances of the segments are proportional to their lengths, so the resistance ratio may be expressed in terms of a length ratio

$$\frac{R_2}{R_1} = \frac{L_2}{L_1} \tag{27.9}$$

Eq. 27.8 can then be written in terms of the length ratio:

$$R_x = \left(\frac{L_2}{L_1}\right)R_s \tag{27.10}$$

This type of bridge is convenient since the length segments can easily be measured. The resistances R_1 and R_2 of the length segments may be quite small relative to R_x and R_s because the bridge formula depends only on the ratio of R_2/R_1 or L_2/L_1. This fact allows a wire to be used as one side of the bridge.

IV. Experimental Procedure

A. Ammeter-Voltmeter Methods

1. Set up a circuit as shown in Fig. 27.5a where R is a small known resistance and R_h is the rheostat. Record the value of R in the first of the spaces provided for this purpose in part A of the Laboratory Report.

   Most common meters have three scale connections, with a binding post common to all three scales. It is good practice initially to make connections to the largest scales. This prevents the instruments from being "pegged" and possibly damaged should the magnitudes of the current

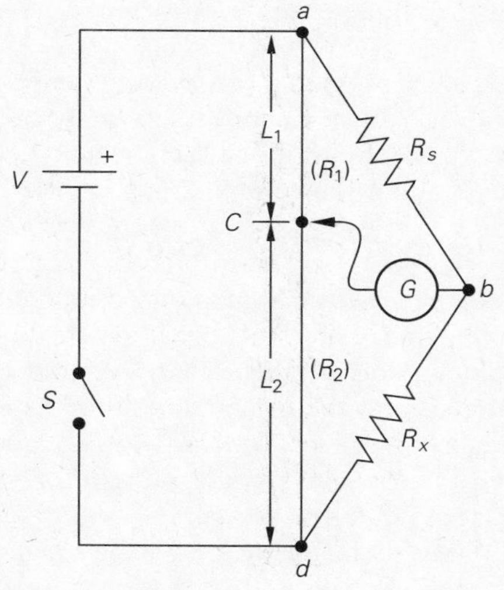

(a)

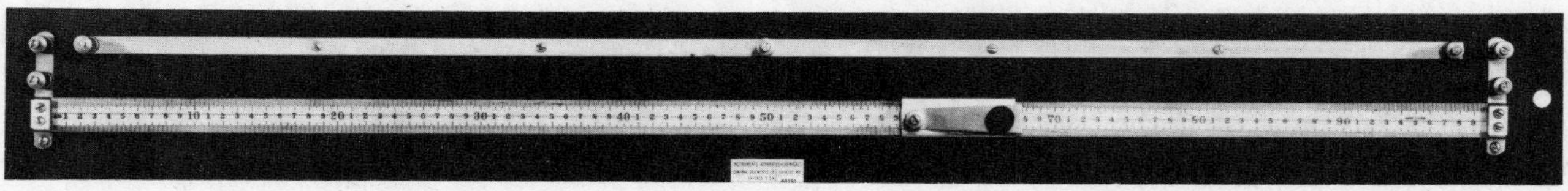

(b)

Figure 27.4 Slide-wire Wheatstone bridge. (a) Circuit diagram for resistance measurements. The resistances R_1 and R_2 are varied by sliding the contact C along the wire. The galvanometer G is used to indicate when the bridge is "balanced." (b) The contact slides over wire on the meterstick. When contact is made, the lengths L_1 and L_2 on either side of C are easily read.

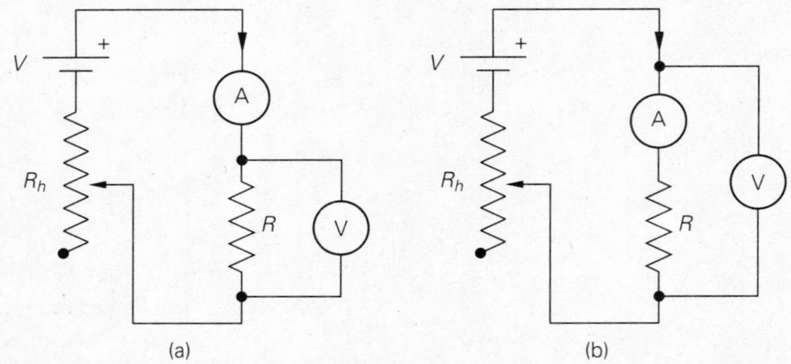

Figure 27.5 Resistance measurement. Circuit diagrams for experimental procedures for ammeter-voltmeter method of measuring resistance.

and voltage exceed the smaller scale limits. The scale setting may be changed for greater sensitivity by moving the connection to a lower scale after the general magnitude of a measurement is known.

Also, attention should be given to the proper polarity (+ and −). Otherwise, the meter will be "pegged" in the opposite direction. Connect + to + and − to −. However, *do not activate the circuit until your laboratory instructor has checked it.*

2. The current in the circuit is varied by varying the rheostat resistance R_h. Activate the circuit and take three different readings of the ammeter and voltmeter for three different currents. Adjust R_h so that the three currents differ as much as possible. Record the data in Data Table 1 and deactivate the circuit after each of the three readings until the rheostat is set for the next reading.

Also, record the resistance of the voltmeter. The resistance of the meter will be found on the meter face or will be supplied by the instructor. The voltmeter resistance is commonly given as so many ohms per volt, which is the total resistance of the meter divided by the full-scale reading.

For example, if the meter has a resistance of 1000 Ω/V and the full-scale reading of a particular range is 3 V, then $R_v = 3\text{ V}(1000\ \Omega/\text{V}) = 3000\ \Omega$. The resistance in ohms/volt applies to any range setting of the meter. (*Note:* if voltmeter scales are changed during readings, R_v will be different for different sets of V and I measurements. Be sure to record this if it occurs.)

3. Using Eq. 27.3, compute the value of R for each current setting and find the average value. Compare this with the accepted value by finding the percent error.

4. Set up a circuit as shown in Fig. 27.5b. This is accomplished by changing only one wire in the previous circuit. Repeat the measurements as in procedure 2 for this circuit, recording your findings in Data Table 2.

5. (a) Compute the resistance $R' = V/I$ directly from each set of current and voltage measurements, and find the average value.

(b) When not taking into account the ammeter resistance, R' would be taken to be the value of the resistance R. Compare the average experimental value of R' with the accepted value of R by finding the percent error.

(c) Using the values of R and R', compute R_a (Eq. 27.5). Mentally compare the magnitudes of the ammeter and voltmeter resistances.

6. Repeat the previous procedures with a large known resistance. Record its value in the second space in the Laboratory Report and use Data Tables 3 and 4 for your findings.

B. *Wheatstone Bridge Method*

7. Set up a slide-wire Wheatstone bridge circuit as in Fig. 27.4a using the previous small known resistance R as R_x. The wires connecting the resistances and the bridge should be as short as practically possible. The decade resistance box is used for R_s. This should be initially set for a value about equal to R_x.

Contact is made to the wire by sliding contact key C. *Do not slide the key along the wire while it is pressed down.* This will scrape the wire, causing it to be nonuniform. Have the instructor check your setup before activating the circuit.

8. Activate the circuit by closing the switch S, and balance the bridge by moving the slide-wire contact. Open the switch and record R_s, L_1, and L_2 in Data Table 5. Leave the switch open unless actually making measurements.

9. Repeat procedures 7 and 8 for R_s settings of (a) $R_s \approx 3R_x$, and (b) $R_s \approx 0.3R_x$.

10. Compute the value of R_x for each case and find the average value. Compare this value to the accepted value of R by finding the percent error.

11. Repeat the previous procedures with a large known resistance. Record your findings in Data Table 6.

Name ______________________ Section ____________ Date ____________

Lab Partner(s) ____

EXPERIMENT 27

The Measurement of Resistance: Ammeter-Voltmeter Methods and Wheatstone Bridge Method

Laboratory Report

A. Ammeter-Voltmeter Methods

DATA TABLE 1

Purpose: To measure resistance values.

Voltmeter resistance, R_v ____________

Rheostat setting, R_h	Current, I ( )	Voltage, V ( )	Resistance, R ( )
1			
2			
3			
		Average R	

Percent error of R ____________

Accepted value of R ____________

DATA TABLE 2

Purpose: To measure resistance values.

Rheostat setting, R_h	Current, I ( )	Voltage, V ( )	$R' = V/I$ ( )
1			
2			
3			
		Average R'	

Percent error of R' ____________

Ammeter resistance, R_a ____________

Calculations
(show work)

Don't forget units

(continued)

DATA TABLE 3
Purpose: To measure resistance values.

Voltmeter resistance, R_v ________________

Rheostat setting, R_h	Current, I ( )	Voltage, V ( )	Resistance, R ( )
1			
2			
3			
		Average R	

Percent error of R ________________

Accepted value of R ________________

DATA TABLE 4
Purpose: To measure resistance values.

Rheostat setting, R_h	Current, I ( )	Voltage, V ( )	$R' = V/I$ ( )
1			
2			
3			
		Average R'	

Percent error of R' ________________

Ammeter resistance, R_a ________________

Calculations
(show work)

Name ______________________ Section ______________ Date ______________
Lab Partner(s) ____

EXPERIMENT 27 **Laboratory Report**

B. Wheatstone Bridge Method

DATA TABLE 5
Purpose: To measure resistance values.

Accepted value of R ______________

R_s ( )	L_1 ( )	L_2 ( )	R ( )
		Average R	

Percent error ______________

DATA TABLE 6
Purpose: To measure resistance values.

Accepted value of R ______________

R_s ( )	L_1 ( )	L_2 ( )	R ( )
		Average R	

Percent error ______________

Calculations
(show work)

Questions

A. Ammeter-Voltmeter Methods

1. An ideal ammeter would have zero resistance and an ideal voltmeter an infinite resistance. Explain why we would want these ideal cases when using the meters.

(continued)

2. If in general R were calculated as $R = V/I$, which circuit arrangement in part A of the experiment would have the smallest error? Explain.

3. (a) Prove that the true resistance R is given by

$$R = R'\left(1 - \frac{R_a}{R'}\right)$$

where $R' = V/I$ is the measured resistance as given by the voltmeter and ammeter readings for measurements done by the arrangement in Figs. 27.2 or 27.5b. Is the true resistance larger or smaller than the apparent resistance?

(b) Prove that the true resistance R is given approximately by

$$R = R'\left(1 + \frac{R'}{R_v}\right)$$

where $R' = V/I$ is the measured resistance as given by the voltmeter and ammeter readings for measurements done by the arrangement in Figs. 27.1 or 27.5a. *Hint:* Use the binomial theorem,

$$\frac{1}{1 - \dfrac{R'}{R_v}} \simeq 1 + \frac{R'}{R_v}$$

Name ______________________ Section ______________ Date ______________
Lab Partner(s) ____

Is the true resistance larger or smaller than the apparent resistance?

B. Wheatstone Bridge Method

4. Why should the wires connecting the resistances and the bridge be as short as possible?

5. Suppose that the slide-wire on the bridge did not have a uniform cross-section. How would this affect your measurements? Was there any experimental evidence of this?

Name ______________________ Section ______________ Date ______________
Lab Partner(s) ____

EXPERIMENT 28

Resistivity

Advance Study Assignment

Read the experiment and answer the following questions.

1. What are the factors affecting the resistance of an electrical conductor?

2. If the length and diameter of a wire conductor were both doubled, would the resistance be the same? Explain.

3. Why is resistivity called a material property?

4. In the experiment, why is it important to close the circuit switch only long enough to obtain meter readings?

Resistivity

I. Introduction and Objectives

The resistance of an electrical conductor depends on several factors. Its physical shape is one factor. The type of conductor material is another, as might be expected. That is, two conductors with the same physical shape, but of different materials, have different resistances. This important material characteristic of resistance is expressed in terms of a quantity called **resistivity**.

Temperature is another factor affecting resistance. However, the temperature dependence of resistance will be investigated in another experiment (Experiment 29). In the present experiment, the factors of shape or dimensions and resistivity will be considered.

After performing this experiment and analyzing the data, you should be able to:

1. Explain on what factors the resistance of a wire depends and why.
2. Distinguish between resistance and resistivity.
3. Describe how the resistivity of a material may be measured.

II. Equipment Needed*

- Ammeter (0 to 0.5 A)
- Voltmeter (0 to 3 V)
- Rheostat (20 Ω)
- Single-pole, single-throw switch
- Battery or power supply (3 V)
- Meterstick
- Micrometer calipers
- Conductor board with wires of various types, lengths, and diameters.† For example, two wires of the same material (No. 24 and 30) and two wires of different material.

III. Theory

The resistance of an electrical conductor depends on several factors. Consider a wire conductor. The resistance, of course, depends on the *type* of conductor material, and also on (a) the length, (b) the cross-sectional area, and (c) the temperature of the wire. As might be expected the resistance of a wire conductor is directly proportional to its length ℓ and inversely proportional to its cross-sectional area A:

$$R \propto \frac{\ell}{A}$$

For example, a 4-m length of wire has twice as much resistance as a 2-m length of the same wire. Also, the larger the cross-sectional area, the greater the current flow (less resistance) for a given voltage. These geometrical conditions are analogous to those for liquid flow in a pipe. The longer the pipe, the more resistance to flow. But, the larger the cross-sectional area of the pipe, the greater the flow rate or the smaller the resistance to flow.

The material property of resistance is characterized by the **resistivity** ρ, and for a given temperature,

$$R = \frac{\rho \ell}{A} \qquad \textbf{(28.1)}$$

The resistivity is independent of the shape of the conductor, and rearranging Eq. 28.1,

$$\rho = \frac{RA}{\ell} \qquad \textbf{(28.2)}$$

From this equation, resistivity can be seen to have the units Ω-m or Ω-cm. Common metal conductors have resistivities on the order of 10^{-6} Ω-cm. Another name sometimes used for resistivity is *specific resistance,* indicating that it is specific for a given material.

To determine the resistivities of some materials, a circuit arrangement as illustrated in Fig. 28.1 will be used. The ammeter Ⓐ measures the current I in a wire conductor on the conductor board and the voltmeter Ⓥ registers the voltage drop V across the conductor. Then, the resistance of the wire, by Ohm's law, is $R = V/I$.

Measuring the length ℓ of the wire and its cross-sectional area A (from diameter d measurement, $d/2 = r$ and $A = \pi r^2$), the resistivity of the conductor can be calculated from Eq. 28.2. The rheostat R_h is used to limit the current in the circuit initially so as to protect the meters.

* The ranges of the equipment are given as examples. These may be varied to apply to available equipment.

† If resistance spools or coils are used, either the coils should be provided with taps, or coils of different lengths should be provided.

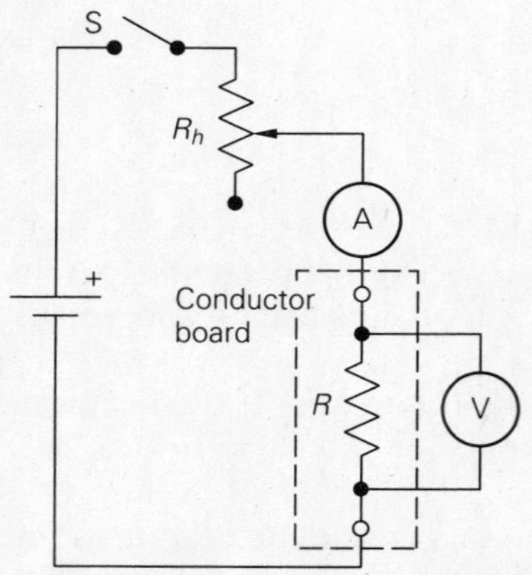

Figure 28.1 Resistivity measurement. The circuit diagram for experimental procedure to measure resistivity. See text for description.

IV. Experimental Procedure

1. Set up the circuit shown in Fig. 28.1 with one of the wires on the conductor board in the circuit. Leave the switch S open and set the rheostat at maximum resistance. *Have the instructor check the circuit before activating.**

2. After the circuit has been checked, close the switch and adjust the rheostat until the current in the circuit as indicated on the ammeter is 0.5 A. Read and record the meter values and open the switch as soon as possible to prevent heating and temperature change.

3. Measure (a) the length of the wire between the voltmeter connections and (b) the diameter of the wire. Record these in the data table.

4. Test the effect of length. Change the length of the wire being tested to about 0.50 m by moving one of the voltmeter contact points and repeat the measurements.

5. Return the rheostat to its maximum resistance and repeat the procedure for the other wires on the board.

6. **(a)** Compute the resistances and cross-sectional areas of the wires, and use these values to determine the resistivities of the materials.
(b) Find the average resistivity for each material with more than one experimental value.

7. Compare the experimental values of the resistivities with the accepted values listed in Appendix A, Table A6, by computing the percent error.

* For best results, the voltmeter should make contact with the resistance wire (R) about 5 cm *in* from the terminals, not *at* the terminals. Also, the copper wire on the conductor board should be a single piece zig-zagging back and forth across the board so that readings can be taken with various lengths of this wire (e.g., 1, 2, 3, etc., meters).

Name ______________________ Section ______________ Date ______________

Lab Partner(s) ____

EXPERIMENT 28

Resistivity

Laboratory Report

DATA TABLE

Purpose: To determine the resistivities of various metals.

Wire	Type of material	Voltage, V ( )	Current, I ( )	Resistance, $R = V/I$ ( )	Length ( )	Diameter ( )	Cross-sectional area ( )	Resistivity ( )
1								
2								
3								
4								

Type of material	Accepted value	Experimental value	Percent error

Calculations
(show work)

Don't forget units

(continued)

QUESTIONS

1. Do the experimental data confirm that the resistance of a conductor is (a) directly proportional to its length and (b) inversely proportional to its cross-sectional area? Support your answers either graphically or mathematically with experimental results.

2. How does the resistance of a wire vary with resistivity?

3. An annealed copper wire (No. 15 AWG gauge) is to be replaced with an aluminum wire with approximately the same length and resistance. What gauge of aluminum wire would be required? (See Appendix A, Table A7, for wire gauges.)

Name ______________________ Section ______________ Date ______________

Lab Partner(s) ____

EXPERIMENT 29

The Temperature Dependence of Resistance

Advance Study Assignment

Read the experiment and answer the following questions.

1. Does the resistance of all substances increase with temperature? Explain.

2. What is the temperature coefficient of resistance, and what are its units?

3. Distinguish between a positive and a negative temperature coefficient of resistance.

4. Are the α of a metal conductor and the β of a thermistor the same? Explain.

(continued)

5. What are the circuit conditions when a Wheatstone bridge is ‘‘balanced’’?

The Temperature Dependence of Resistance

I. Introduction and Objectives

The electrical resistance of all substances varies somewhat with temperature. For pure metals and most alloys, the resistance increases with increasing temperature. However, for some substances, such as carbon and many electrolytes (conducting solutions), the resistance decreases with increasing temperature. Then, too, for some special alloys [e.g., constantan (55% Cu–45% Ni)] the resistance is virtually independent of temperature over a limited range.

The temperature dependence of resistance for a substance is commonly expressed in terms of its **temperature coefficient of resistance,** the fractional change in the resistance per degree change in temperature. For many electrical applications, it is important to know the temperature coefficient and to take into account the temperature dependence of resistance. In this experiment, this dependence will be investigated and the temperature coefficients of some materials will be determined.

After performing this experiment and analyzing the data, you should be able to:

1. Explain how the resistances of common metallic conductors vary with temperature.
2. Discuss the temperature coefficient of resistance for various materials and the differences among them.
3. Describe what is meant by the exponential temperature coefficient of a thermistor.

II. Equipment Needed

- Slide-wire Wheatstone bridge assembly (with a 3-V battery and a single-pole, single-throw switch)
- Standard decade resistance box
- Copper coil (and optional constantan or manganese coil)
- Thermistor
- Immersion vessel and stirrer
- Thermometer
- Immersion heater and power source (or Bunsen burner and stand or hot plate)
- 2 sheets of Cartesian graph paper

III. Theory

The change in resistance ΔR of a substance is proportional to the change in temperature ΔT. This change in resistance is commonly expressed in terms of the fractional change $\Delta R/R_o$, where R_o is the initial resistance. For many substances (e.g., metals) the change in resistance is to a good approximation a linear function of temperature,

$$\frac{\Delta R}{R_o} = \alpha \Delta T \qquad \textbf{(29.1)}$$

where the constant of proportionality α is called the **temperature coefficient of resistance** and has the units of inverse temperature (1/C° or C°$^{-1}$, that is, per Celsius degree).

For the change in temperature $\Delta T = T - T_o$, it is convenient to take the initial temperature T_o as 0 °C and with $\Delta R = R - R_o$, Eq. 29.1 can be written

$$\frac{R - R_o}{R_o} = \alpha T$$

or

$$R = R_o + R_o \alpha T = R_o(1 + \alpha T) \qquad \textbf{(29.2)}$$

where R is then the resistance of the conductor at some temperature T (°C), and R_o is the resistance at T_o = 0 °C. The linearity of the temperature dependence is only approximate, but Eq. 29.2 can be used over moderate temperature ranges for all but the most accurate work.

In contrast to pure metals, which have positive temperature coefficients of resistance (increase in resistance with increase in temperature), some materials have negative temperature coefficients (decrease in resistance with an increase in temperature). Carbon is an example, and negative temperature coefficients of resistance generally occur in materials of intermediate conductivity, or semiconducting materials. Carbon has a relatively small negative temperature coefficient of resistance compared to other semiconducting materials. Such materials with large negative temperature coefficients are used in commercial components called **thermistors.** A thermistor is a thermally sensitive resistor made of semiconducting materials such as oxides of manganese, nickel, and cobalt.

Because of relatively large (negative) temperature coefficients, thermistors are very sensitive to small temperature changes and are used for temperature measurement and in a variety of temperature-sensing applications such as voltage regulation and time-delay switches.

Unlike common metal conductors, the change of resistance with a change of temperature for a thermistor is nonlinear, and the α in Eq. 29.1 is not constant. The temperature dependence of a thermistor is given by an exponential function,

$$R = R_a e^{\beta(1/T - 1/T_a)} \qquad \textbf{(29.3)}$$

where R = resistance at a temperature T (in kelvins, K)
R_a = resistance at temperature T_a (K)
T_a = initial temperature (K), near ambient room temperature in the experiment
e = 2.718, the base of natural logarithms
β = *exponential* temperature coefficient of resistance, which has temperature units (K)

In this case, as T increases, the exponential function and hence the resistance R becomes smaller. This expression can be written in terms of the natural logarithm (to the base e) as

$$\ln\left(\frac{R}{R_a}\right) = \beta\left(\frac{1}{T} - \frac{1}{T_a}\right) \qquad \textbf{(29.4)}$$

Hence, by plotting $y = \ln(R/R_a)$ versus $x = (1/T - 1/T_a)$ on a Cartesian graph, β is the slope of the line. This, too, is an approximation, but β is reasonably constant for moderate temperature ranges.

The temperature coefficient of resistance of a material can be determined by using an experimental arrangement with a slide-wire Wheatstone bridge circuit, as illustrated in Fig. 29.1. The resistance R_c of a material (coil of wire) when the bridge circuit is balanced is given by

$$R_c = \left(\frac{R_2}{R_1}\right)R_s$$

or

$$R_c = \left(\frac{L_2}{L_1}\right)R_s \qquad \textbf{(29.5)}$$

where R_s is a standard resistance and R_2/R_1 and L_2/L_1 are the ratios of the resistances and lengths of the slide-wire segments, respectively. (See Experiment 27 for the theory of the Wheatstone bridge.) By measuring the resistance of a material at various temperatures, the temperature coefficient can be determined.

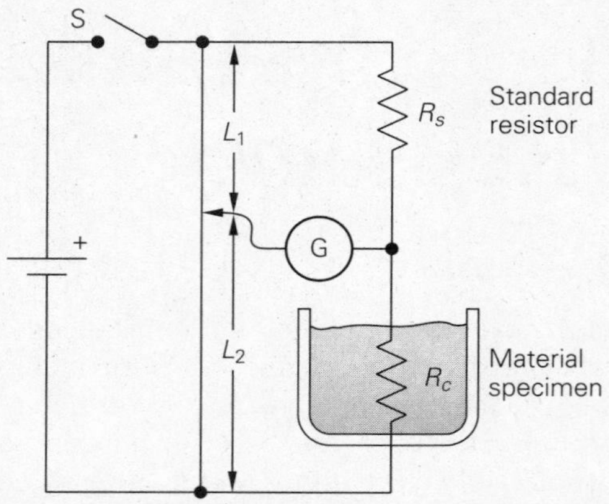

Figure 29.1 Temperature dependence of resistance measurement. The circuit diagram for experimental procedure to measure the temperature dependence of resistance. See text for description.

IV. Experimental Procedure

A. *Metal Conductor(s)*

1. Set up the circuit as in Fig. 29.1 with the copper coil in the container of water (near room temperature) and the heating arrangement for the water (immersion heater or other heat source). Place the thermometer in the water. *Have the instructor check your setup.*

2. After your setup has been checked, close the switch and balance the bridge circuit to measure the resistance R_c of the coil at the initial water temperature. The value of the standard resistance R_s should be selected so that the bridge is balanced with the contact key C near the center of the slide-wire. Then with $L_1 \simeq L_2$, we have $R_c \simeq R_s$ (Eq. 29.5).

Record in Data Table 1 the initial temperature of the water, the magnitude of R_s, and the lengths of the wire segments of the bridge.

3. *Slowly*, raise the temperature of the water by about 10 C°. Stir the water while heating, and discontinue heating when the temperature is about 2 C° below the desired temperature. Continue stirring until a maximum steady temperature is reached. Balance the bridge and record the measurements. Adjust R_s if necessary. Record the temperature and bridge length measurements in the data table.

4. Repeat procedure 3, taking a series of measurements at approximately 10 C° temperature intervals until a final temperature of about 90 °C is reached.

5. (*Optional*) Repeat the foregoing procedures using the constantan wire coil starting near room temperature. (Data Table 1A.)

6. Compute R_c of the coil(s) at the various temperatures and plot a graph of R_c versus T with a temperature range of 0 to 100 °C. Draw the straight line(s) that best fits the data and extrapolate the line(s) to the y axis. Determine the slope and y intercept of the line(s).

   From the slope, find the temperature coefficient of resistance for the specimen(s) and compare with the accepted value found in Appendix A, Table A6, by computing the percent error.

B. *Thermistor*

7. Replace the coil with the thermistor in the bridge circuit and repeat the previous measurement procedures 1–4 starting at a temperature near room temperature. In this portion of the experiment, exercise great care in order to have temperatures as constant as possible when making resistance measurements, since a thermistor shows considerable variation in resistance with temperature.

8. (a) Find the quantities listed in the second part of Data Table 2. Logarithm values may be found in Appendix B, Table B7, if your calculator does not have this function.
   (b) Plot a graph of $y = \ln (R/R_a)$ versus $x = (1/T - 1/T_a)\ \mathrm{K}^{-1}$, and draw the straight line that best fits the data.
   (c) Determine the slope of the line, which is the value of β. Compare this to the accepted value provided by the instructor by computing the percent error.

Name ______________________ Section ______________ Date ______________

Lab Partner(s) ____

EXPERIMENT 29

The Temperature Dependence of Resistance

Laboratory Report

A. Metal Conductor(s)

DATA TABLE 1

Purpose: To determine the temperature coefficient of resistance.

Material ______________

Temperature ( )	Decade box resistance, R_s ( )	L_1 ( )	L_2 ( )	Coil resistance, $R = (L_2/L_1)R_s$ ( )

Calculations
(show work)

Slope, $R_o\alpha$ ______________

Intercept, R_o ______________

Experimental α ______________

Accepted α ______________

Percent error ______________

Don't forget units

(continued)

DATA TABLE 1A (optional)
Purpose: To determine the temperature coefficient of resistance.

Material ________________

Temperature ( )	Decade box resistance, R_s ( )	L_1 ( )	L_2 ( )	Coil resistance, R_c ( )

Calculations
(show work)

Slope, $R_o\alpha$ ________________

Intercept, R_o ________________

Experimental α ________________

Accepted α ________________

Percent error ________________

Name ________________ Section ________________ Date ________________

Lab Partner(s) ________________

EXPERIMENT 29 *Laboratory Report*

B. Thermistor

DATA TABLE 2

Purpose: To determine the exponential temperature coefficient of resistance.

Calculations (show work)

Temperature, T ( )	Decade box resistance, R_s ( )	L_1 ( )	L_2 ( )	Thermistor resistance, $R = (L_2/L_1)R_s$ ( )
(T_a)				(R_a)

Temperature ( ) $T_K = T_C + 273$	$1/T$	$1/T - 1/T_a$	R/R_a	$\ln(R/R_a)$

Slope, β ________________

Accepted β ________________

Percent error ________________

(continued)

QUESTIONS

A. *Metal Conductor*

1. What is the value of α for copper in terms of Fahrenheit degrees (1/F°)? If the resistance is a linear function on the Celsius scale, would it be a linear function on the Fahrenheit scale? Explain.

2. Replot the copper data R_c versus T with smaller temperature scale extending to −300 °C, and extrapolate the line to the temperature axis. At what temperature would the resistance go to zero? What are the practical electrical implications for a conductor with zero resistance?

   [It is interesting to note that the value for many pure metals is roughly the same, approximately $\frac{1}{273}$ or 0.004 $C^{\circ -1}$. This is the same as the value of the coefficient of expansion of an ideal gas. Also, some metals and alloys do become ''superconductors,'' or have zero resistance at low temperatures. Recently discovered ''high temperature'' ceramic materials show superconductivity at liquid nitrogen temperatures (77 K or −196 °C or −321 °F).]

3. A coil of copper wire has a resistance of 10.0 Ω, and a coil of silver wire has a resistance of 10.1 Ω, both at 0 °C. At what temperature would the resistance of the coils be equal?

Name ______________________ Section ______________ Date ______________

Lab Partner(s) ____

EXPERIMENT 29 — *Laboratory Report*

B. Thermistor

4. Explain why the ambient temperature for T_a for the thermistor cannot be taken as T_a = 0 °C, and the expression for the resistance is written $R = R_o e^{\beta/T}$, where T is in degrees Celsius.

5. Assuming that β remained constant, what would be the resistance of the thermistor in the experiment as the temperature approached absolute zero?

6. Assume the temperature coefficient of resistance α to be defined over the temperature range $\Delta T = T - T_a$, where $T_a > 273\text{K}$ (0 °C), by $R - R_a = R_a\alpha(T - T_a)$. Show that for a thermistor, α is a function of temperature given by

$$\alpha = \frac{1 - e^{\beta(1/T - 1/T_a)}}{T - T_a}$$

Name ______________________ Section ______________ Date ______________
Lab Partner(s) ____

EXPERIMENT 30

Resistances in Series and Parallel

Advance Study Assignment

Read the experiment and answer the following questions.

1. Explain the difference between series and parallel connections.

2. When resistors are connected in series in a circuit, what are the relationships between the voltage drops across the resistors and the currents through the resistors?

3. When resistors are connected in parallel in a circuit, what are the relationships between the voltage drops across the resistors and the currents through the resistors?

(continued)

4. Give (draw and explain) a liquid analogy of the series–parallel circuit in part C of the experiment.

5. How would the current divide in a parallel branch of a circuit containing two resistors R_1 and R_2 if (a) $R_1 = R_2$, and (b) $R_1 = 4R_2$?

Resistances in Series and Parallel

I. Introduction and Objectives

The components of simple circuits are connected in series and/or parallel arrangements. Each component may be represented as a resistance to the flow of current in the circuit. In computing the voltage and current requirements of the circuit (or part of the circuit), it is necessary to know the equivalent resistances of the series and parallel arrangements.

In this experiment, the circuit characteristics of resistors in series and parallel will be investigated. A particular circuit will first be analyzed theoretically, and then those predictions will be checked experimentally.

After performing this experiment and analyzing the data, you should be able to:

1. Describe the current-voltage relationships for resistances in series.
2. Describe the current-voltage relationships for resistances in parallel.
3. Reduce a simple series–parallel resistance circuit to a single equivalent resistance and compute the voltage drops across and the currents through each resistance in the circuit.

II. Equipment Needed*

- Battery or power supply (3 V)
- Ammeter (0 to 500 mA)
- Voltmeter (0 to 3 V)
- Single-pole, single-throw switch
- Four resistors (10 Ω, 20 Ω, 100 Ω, and 10 kΩ, composition type, 1 W)
- Connecting wires

III. Theory

A. *Resistances in Series*

Resistors are said to be connected in **series** when they are connected as in Fig. 30.1. (The resistors are connected in line or "head to tail," so to speak, although there is no distinction between the connecting ends of a resistor.) When they are connected to a voltage source V and the switch is closed, the source supplies a current I to the circuit.

By the conservation of charge, this current I flows through each resistor. However, the voltage drop across each resistor is not equal to V, but the *sum* of the voltage drops is:

$$V = V_1 + V_2 + V_3 \qquad \textbf{(30.1)}$$

In an analogous liquid-gravity circuit (Fig. 30.1), a pump, corresponding to the voltage source, raises the liquid a distance h.† The liquid then falls or "drops" through three paddle-wheel "resistors" and the distances h_1, h_2, and h_3. The liquid "rise" supplied by the pump is equal to the sum of the liquid "drops," $h = h_1 + h_2 + h_3$. Analogously, the voltage "rise" supplied by the source is equal to the sum of the voltage drops across the resistors (Eq. 30.1).

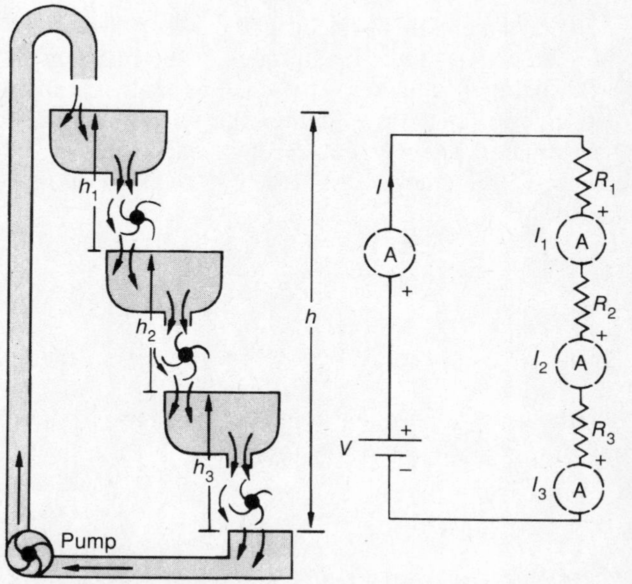

Figure 30.1 Series connection. Liquid analogy and circuit diagram for resistors in series. See text for description.

* The ranges of the equipment are given as examples. These may be varied to apply to available equipment.

† Keep in mind that an analogy represents only a resemblance. Liquid and electrical circuits are quite different physically.

The voltage drop across each resistor is given by Ohm's law (e.g., $V_1 = IR_1$). Eq. 30.1 may be written

$$\begin{aligned} V &= V_1 + V_2 + V_3 \\ &= IR_1 + IR_2 + IR_3 \\ &= I(R_1 + R_2 + R_3) \qquad \textbf{(30.2)} \end{aligned}$$

For a voltage across a single resistance R_s in a circuit, $V = IR_s$, and by comparison,

$$R_s = R_1 + R_2 + R_3 \qquad \textbf{(30.3)}$$

where R_s *is the equivalent resistance of the resistors in series*. That is, the three resistors in series could be replaced by a single resistor with a value of R_s, and the same current I would flow from the battery.

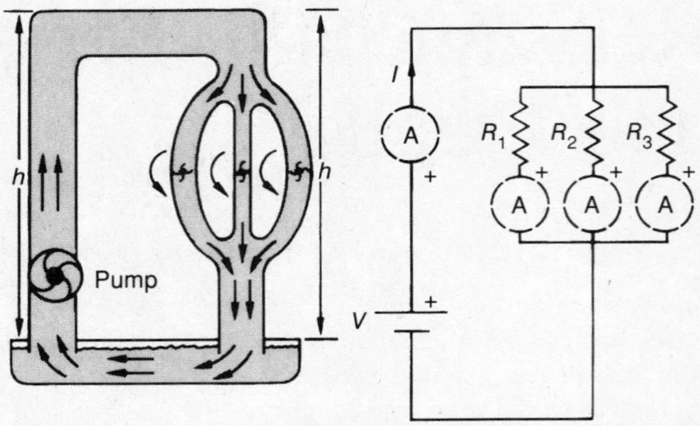

Figure 30.2 Parallel connections. Liquid analogy and circuit diagram for resistors in parallel. See text for description.

B. Resistances in Parallel

Resistors are said to be connected in **parallel** when connected as in Fig. 30.2. (In this arrangement, all the "heads" are connected together, as are all of the "tails.") The voltage drops across all the resistors are the same and equal to the voltage V of the source. However, the current I from the source divides among the resistors such that

$$I = I_1 + I_2 + I_3 \qquad \textbf{(30.4)}$$

In the liquid circuit analogy (Fig. 30.2), the height h the pump raises the liquid is equal to the distance the liquid "drops" through each paddle-wheel "resistor." The liquid flow coming into the junction of the parallel arrangement divides among the three pipe paths, analogously to the current dividing in the electrical circuit.

The current in an electrical parallel circuit divides according to the magnitudes of the resistances in the parallel branches—the smaller the resistance of a given branch, the greater the current through that branch. The current through each resistor is given by Ohm's law (e.g., $I_1 = V/R_1$), and Eq. 30.4 may be written

$$\begin{aligned} I = I_1 + I_2 + I_3 &= \frac{V}{R_1} + \frac{V}{R_2} + \frac{V}{R_3} \\ &= V\left(\frac{1}{R_1} + \frac{1}{R_2} + \frac{1}{R_3}\right) \qquad \textbf{(30.5)} \end{aligned}$$

For the current through a single resistance R_p in a circuit, $I = V/R_p$, and by comparison

$$\frac{1}{R_p} = \frac{1}{R_1} + \frac{1}{R_2} + \frac{1}{R_3} \qquad \textbf{(30.6)}$$

where R_p *is the equivalent resistance of the resistors in parallel*. That is, the three resistors in parallel could be replaced by a single resistor with a value of R_p, and the same current I would flow from the battery.

The previous developments for equivalent resistances may be extended to any number of resistors (i.e., $R_s = R_1 + R_2 + R_3 + R_4 + \cdots$ and $1/R_p = 1/R_1 + 1/R_2 + 1/R_3 + 1/R_4 + \cdots$).

In many instances, two resistors are connected in parallel in a circuit, and

$$\frac{1}{R_p} = \frac{1}{R_1} + \frac{1}{R_2}$$

or

$$R_p = \frac{R_1R_2}{R_1 + R_2} \qquad \textbf{(30.7)}$$

This particular form of R_p for two resistors may be more convenient for calculations than the reciprocal form.

Also, in a circuit with three resistors in parallel, the equivalent resistance of two of the resistors can be found by Eq. 30.7, and then the equation may be applied again to the equivalent resistance and the other resistance in parallel to find the total equivalent resistance of the three parallel resistors. However, if your calculator has a $1/x$ function, the reciprocal form may be easier to use.

Note that the voltage drops across R_1 and R_2 in parallel are the same, and by Ohm's law,

$$I_1R_1 = I_2R_2$$

or

$$\frac{I_1}{I_2} = \frac{R_2}{R_1} \qquad \textbf{(30.8)}$$

Thus, the ratio of the resistances gives the relative magnitudes of the currents in the resistors.

Example 30.1 Given two resistors R_1 and R_2, with $R_2 = 2R_1$, in parallel in a circuit, what fraction of the current I from the voltage source goes through each resistor?

Solution With $R_2 = 2R_1$, or $R_2/R_1 = 2$, by Eq. 30.8

$$I_1 = \left(\frac{R_2}{R_1}\right) I_2 = 2I_2$$

Since $I = I_1 + I_2$, we have

$$I = I_1 + I_2 = 2I_2 + I_2 = 3I_2$$

or

$$I_2 = \frac{I}{3}$$

Hence, the current divides with one-third going through R_2 and two-thirds going through R_1.

Consider the circuit in Fig. 30.3. To find the equivalent resistance of this series–parallel circuit, one first "collapses" the parallel branch into a single equivalent resistance, which is given by Eq. 30.7. This equivalent resistance is in series with R_1, and the total equivalent resistance R of the circuit is $R = R_1 + R_p$.

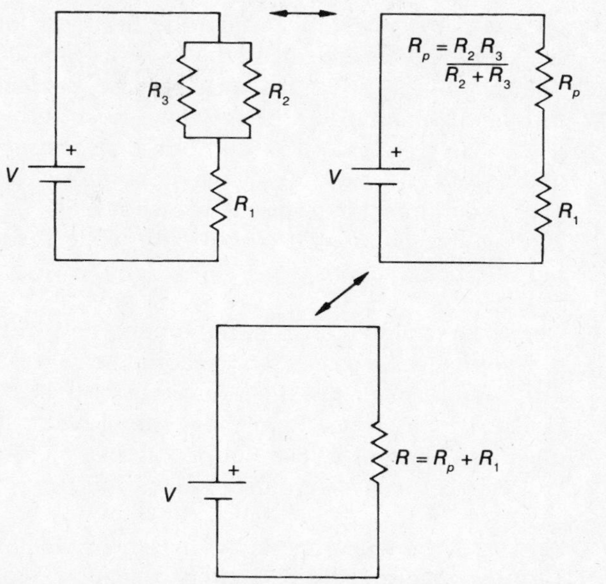

Figure 30.3 Circuit reduction. Series and parallel resistances are combined to find the equivalent resistance of a series-parallel circuit.

IV. Experimental Procedure

1. Examine the resistors. The colored bands conform to a color code that gives the value of a resistor. Look up the color code in Appendix A, Table A5, read the value of each resistor, and record in the Laboratory Report. Designate the smallest resistance as R_1 and consecutively larger values as R_2, R_3, and R_4.

2. In the following procedures, you will be asked to compute theoretically various quantities for a given circuit arrangement. The quantities are then determined by actual circuit measurements and the calculated and experimental results compared. Before initially activating each circuit arrangement, *have the circuit checked by the instructor, unless otherwise instructed.*

A. Resistors in Series

3. Set up a series circuit with R_1, R_2, and R_3, as in Fig. 30.1, with a switch and only one ammeter in the circuit next to the voltage source. A convenient way to check a circuit to see if it is properly connected is to trace the path of the current (with your finger) through the circuit. Do this for the circuit under consideration to make sure that the current goes through each circuit component in series. Remember, an ammeter is *always* connected in series, and for proper polarity, + is connected to +.

   Connect the voltmeter across (in parallel with) the voltage source. After having the circuit checked by the instructor, close the switch. If using a variable power supply, adjust the voltage, if necessary, to the suggested value (3.0 V). Read and record the voltmeter value (V). This is the voltage "rise" of the source. (*Note:* If the needle of the ammeter goes in the wrong direction, reverse the polarity, i.e., reverse the hookup of the leads of the ammeter.)

   Open the circuit after completing the reading.

4. Using the resistor values and the measured voltage, *compute* (a) the equivalent resistance R_s of the circuit, (b) the current in the circuit, and (c) the voltage drop across each resistor. Show your calculations in the Laboratory Report.

5. Returning to the experimental circuit, close the switch and read the current I. Compare this with the computed value by finding the % difference. Open the switch and move the ammeter in the

circuit to the position "after" the first resistor (i.e., on the opposite side of the resistor from the voltage source so as to measure the current through [coming from] the resistor.) Record this as I_1. Carry out this procedure for each resistor and record the currents in the Laboratory Report. The ammeter positions are shown in Fig. 30.1. Leave the switch closed only while readings are being taken.

6. Remove the ammeter from the circuit, and with the voltmeter, measure and record the voltage drop across each resistor and across all three resistors as a group. Remember, a voltmeter is *always* connected in parallel or "across" a circuit element to measure its voltage drop.

7. Compare the experimentally measured values with the theoretically computed values by finding the percent error. (Use the theoretical values as the accepted values.)

B. *Resistors in Parallel*

8. Set up a parallel circuit with R_1, R_2, and R_3, as in Fig. 30.2, with the ammeter and voltmeter connected as before in procedure 3. Check the circuit arrangement by tracing the current from the source through the circuit to see that it divides into three parallel branches at the junction of the resistors and comes together again at the opposite junction. Close the circuit (after it's been checked) and record the voltage and current readings in the Laboratory Report. (If using a variable power supply, adjust voltage if necessary.)

   Open the circuit after reading the voltage.

9. Using the resistor values and the measured voltage, *compute* the equivalent resistance R_p of the circuit, (b) the current supplied by the source, and (c) the current through each resistor. Show your calculations in the Laboratory Report.

10. Returning to the experimental circuit, measure and record the voltage drops across each resistor and across all three resistors as a group.

    Remove the voltmeter and connect the ammeter so as to measure the current I supplied by the source. Then, move the ammeter to measure the current through each resistor by connecting the meter between a given resistor and one of the common junctions. The ammeter positions are shown in Fig. 30.2. Leave the switch closed only while readings are being taken.

11. Compare the theoretical and experimental values by computing the percent errors.

12. (*Optional*) Repeat procedures 8 through 11 with R_2 replaced by R_4.

C. *Resistors in Series–Parallel*

13. If R_1 were connected in series with R_2 and R_3 in parallel (Fig. 30.3):
    (a) What would be the equivalent resistance R_{sp}?
    (b) How much current would be supplied by the source?
    (c) What would be the voltage drop across R_1?
    (d) What would be the voltage drop across R_2 and R_3?
    (e) What would the voltage drop across all three resistors?
    (f) What would be the currents through R_2 and R_3?

14. Set up the actual circuit and trace the current flow to check the circuit. With the voltmeter and ammeter, measure and record the calculated quantities.

    You need not compute the percent errors in this case. However, make a mental comparison to satisfy yourself that the measured quantities agree with the computed values within experimental error.

Name ______________________ Section ______________ Date ______________

Lab Partner(s) ____

E X P E R I M E N T 3 0

Resistances in Series and Parallel

Laboratory Report

Resistor values R_1 ______________ R_3 ______________

R_2 ______________ R_4 ______________

A. Resistors in Series

Calculations
(show work)

Source voltage V ______________

Equivalent resistance R_s ______________

Current I ______________

Voltage drops across resistors V_1 ______________

V_2 ______________

V_3 ______________

Don't forget units

(continued)

Experimental measurements

				Percent error
I	________			________
I_1	________	V_1	________	________
I_2	________	V_2	________	________
I_3	________	V_3	________	________
		$V_1 + V_2 + V_3$	________	

B. Resistors in Parallel

Calculations
(show work)

Source voltage V ________

Equivalent resistance R_p ________

Current I ________

Current through resistors I_1 ________

I_2 ________

I_3 ________

Experimental measurements

				Percent error
		I	________	________
V_1	________	I_1	________	________
V_2	________	I_2	________	________
V_3	________	I_3	________	________
		$I_1 + I_2 + I_3$	________	

Name ______________________ Section ______________ Date ______________

Lab Partner(s) ____

EXPERIMENT 30 **_Laboratory Report_**

(Optional Procedure)

Calculations
(show work)

Source voltage V ______________

Equivalent resistance R_p ______________

Current I ______________

Current through resistors I_1 ______________

I_3 ______________

I_4 ______________

Experimental measurements

				Percent error
		I	______________	______________
V_1	______________	I_1	______________	______________
V_3	______________	I_3	______________	______________
V_4	______________	I_4	______________	______________

(continued)

C. Resistors in Series-Parallel

Calculations
(show work)

Source voltage V ________________

Equivalent resistance R_{sp} ________________

Current I ________________

Voltage drops

V_1 ________________

$V_2 = V_3$ ________________

Currents

I_2 ________________

I_3 ________________

Experimental measurements

I ________________

V_1 ________________

$V_2 = V_3$ ________________

I_2 ________________

I_3 ________________

QUESTIONS

1. Discuss the sources of error in the experiment.

Name ______________________ Section ______________ Date ______________

Lab Partner(s) ____

EXPERIMENT 30 *Laboratory Report*

2. Suppose that the resistors in the various circuit diagrams represented the resistances of light bulbs. When a light bulb "burns out," the circuit is open through that particular component, i.e., R is infinite. Would the remaining bulbs continue to burn for the following conditions? If so, would the bulbs burn more brightly (draw more current) or burn more dimly (draw less current), if:

   (a) R_2 burned out in the circuit in part A?

   (b) R_1 burned out in the circuit in part B?

   (c) Then R_3 also burned out in the circuit in part B?

   (d) R_3 burned out in the circuit in part C?

(continued)

(e) Then R_1 also burned out in the circuit in part C?

3. Explain the effect of replacing R_2 with R_4 in procedure 12. (Explain theoretically even if procedure 12 of the experiment was not done.)

4. Given the four resistors in the experiment, how many possible different resistance values could be obtained by using one or more of the resistors? [List the specific combinations (e.g., R_1 and R_2 in series).]

Name ______________________ Section ______________ Date ______________

Lab Partner(s) ____

EXPERIMENT 31

Multiloop Circuits: Kirchhoff's Rules

Advance Study Assignment

Read the experiment and answer the following questions.

1. Do Kirchhoff's rules represent any new physical principles in the sense that Ohm's law does? Explain.

2. (a) What is a junction?

   (b) Distinguish between a branch and a loop.

3. A household wiring circuit consists of a voltage source (ac power from the electric company) connected across many loads (resistances) in parallel.
   (a) Draw a circuit diagram showing the voltage source and three loads, e.g., a light bulb, a clock, and a TV set.

(continued)

(b) The diagram has several loops. Are Kirchhoff's rules needed to analyze the current through each load? Explain.

4. (a) The direction one goes around a circuit loop makes no difference in the loop theorem equation obtained for the loop. Show this explicitly by going around the loops for the circuit in Example 31.1 in the opposite directions.

(b) Apply the loop theorem to loop 3 in Fig. 31.1 and show that it is redundant or unnecessary with the inside loop equations (Example 31.1).

Multiloop Circuits: Kirchhoff's Rules

I. Introduction and Objectives

The analysis of electrical circuits is the first step toward understanding their operation. By "analysis" is meant the process of calculating how the electrical currents in a circuit depend on the values of the voltage sources (or vice versa). For our discussion, we will refer to any voltage source as a battery with a terminal or "operating" voltage V.

Many electrical circuits can be analyzed by using nothing more than Ohm's law (Experiment 24). The simplest situation consists of one battery (V) and one resistor (R) connected in a single closed loop (Fig. 24.1). In this case, $I = V/R$. Several batteries may appear in series, or several resistors (Experiment 30) may appear in series. In these cases, a combination can be represented by a single equivalent element, and then Ohm's law can be used. Situations that look more complicated include the potentiometer (Fig. 25.3) and the Wheatstone bridge (Fig. 27.3). These circuits contain more than one loop. However, the loops are independent; that is, there is no current flow between the loops when the bridge is balanced. So even these circuits can be analyzed with Ohm's law in this condition.

The more general electrical circuit contains several loops, with batteries and currents shared among the loops. Such a general circuit cannot be analyzed directly by using Ohm's law; however, it can be analyzed using Kirchhoff's rules, or laws as they are sometimes called, named after Gustav Kirchhoff (1824–1887), the German physicist who developed them. In this experiment,* we will investigate, use, and verify Kirchhoff's rules in analyzing multiloop circuits.

After performing this experiment and analyzing the data, you should be able to:

1. Clearly distinguish between circuit branches and junctions.
2. Apply Kirchhoff's rules to multiloop circuits.
3. Explain how Kirchhoff's rules are related to the conservation of charge and energy.

II. Equipment Needed

- Ammeter (0 to 10/100/1000 mA)
- Voltmeter (0 to 5/25 V)
- Two batteries or voltage supplies (6 V and 12 V)
- Two single-pole, single-throw switches
- Composition resistors, 2-W rating (100 Ω, 150 Ω, 220 Ω, 330 Ω, 470 Ω, 680 Ω, 1000 Ω)
- Connecting wires

Note: Items may be varied to apply to available equipment.

III. Theory

The simple multiloop circuit shown in Fig. 31.1 will be used to illustrate the principles of Kirchhoff's rules and the terminology involved. Terminology definitions vary among textbooks, even though the principles remain the same. Therefore, it is important to define terms carefully as they will be used here.

A **junction** is a point in a circuit at which three or more connecting wires are joined together, or a point where the current divides or comes together in a circuit. For example, in Fig. 31.1a points B and D are junctions.

A **branch** is a path connecting two junctions, and it may contain one element or two or more elements. In Fig. 31.1a there are three branches connecting junctions B and D. These are the left branch BAD, the center branch BCD, and the right branch BD with R_3.

A **loop** is a closed path of two or more branches. There are three loops in the circuit in Fig. 31.1, as shown in Fig. 31.1b—two inside loops (loops 1 and 2) and one outside loop (loop 3). Notice that each loop in this case is a closed path of two branches.

Kirchhoff's Rules

These rules do not represent any new physical principles. They embody two fundamental conservation

* Contributed in part by Professor I. L. Fischer, Bergen Community College, New Jersey.

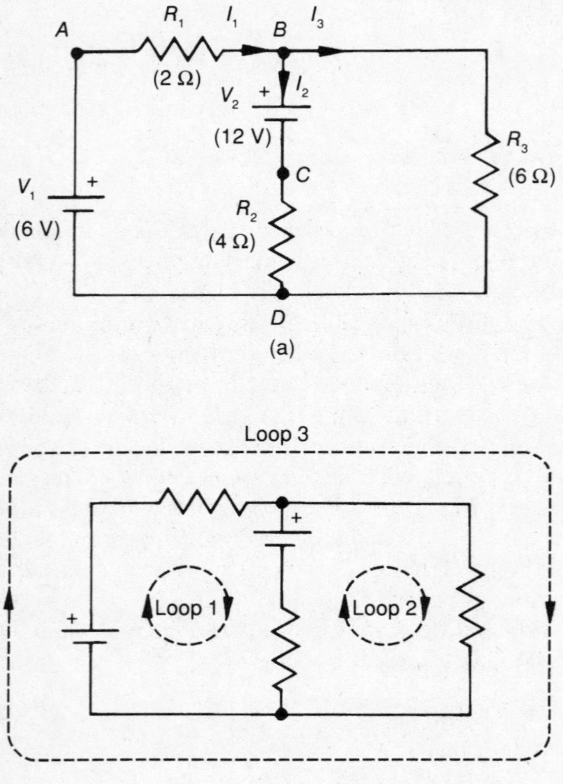

Figure 31.1 Multiloop circuit. (a) By Kirchhoff's junction theorem, the sum of the currents at a junction is zero, that is, the current in equals the current out of the junction, or $I_1 = I_2 + I_3$, at junction B. (b) The circuit has three loops, about which the sum of the voltage changes is zero (Kirchhoff's loop theorem).

laws: conservation of electrical charge and conservation of (electrical) energy.

A current flows in each branch of a circuit. In Fig. 31.1a these are labeled I_1, I_2, and I_3. At a junction, *by the conservation of electrical charge,* the current (or currents) into a junction equal the current(s) leaving the junction. For example, in Fig. 31.1a,

$$I_1 = I_2 + I_3$$
$$\text{(current in = current out)}$$

By the conservation of electrical charge, this means that charge cannot "pile up" or "vanish" at a junction. This current equation may be written

$$I_1 - I_2 - I_3 = 0 \qquad \textbf{(31.1)}$$

Of course, we do not generally know whether a particular current flows into or out of a junction by looking at a multiloop circuit diagram. We simply assign labels and assume the directions the branch currents flow at a particular junction.

If these assumptions are wrong, we will soon find out from the mathematics, as will be shown in a following example. Notice that once the branch current directions are assigned at one junction, the currents at a common branch junction are fixed; for example in Fig. 31.1a, at junction D, $I_2 + I_3 = I_1$ [current(s) in = current out].

Eq. 31.1 may be written in mathematical notation as

$$\sum_i I_i = 0 \qquad \textbf{(31.2)}$$

which is a mathematical statement of **Kirchhoff's first rule** or **junction theorem:**

The algebraic sum of the currents at any junction is zero.

In a simple single-loop circuit as in Fig. 24.1, it is easy to see that *by the conservation of energy* the voltage "drop" across the resistor must be equal to the voltage "rise" of the battery,* i.e.,

$$V_{\text{battery}} = V_{\text{resistor}}$$

where the voltage drop across the resistor is by Ohm's law equal to IR, i.e., $V_{\text{resistor}} = IR$. By the conservation of energy, this means that the energy (per charge) delivered by the battery to the circuit is the same as that expended in the resistances. The conservation law holds for any loop in a multiloop circuit, although there may sometimes be more than one battery and more than one resistor in a particular loop.

Similar to the summation of the currents in the first rule, we may write for the voltages **Kirchhoff's second rule** or **loop theorem:**

$$\sum_i V_i = 0 \qquad \textbf{(31.3)}$$

or

The algebraic sum of the voltage changes around a closed loop is zero.

Since one may go around a circuit loop in either a clockwise or a counterclockwise direction, it is important to establish a sign convention for voltage changes. For example, if we went around a loop in one direction and crossed a resistor, this might be a

* Here we take the terminal or "operating" voltage of the battery instead of the emf ($\mathscr{E}$). The terminal or "operating" voltage of the battery is $V = \mathscr{E} - Ir$, where r is the internal resistance of the battery (not usually known) and Ir is the internal voltage "drop" of the battery (see Experiment 25).

voltage drop (depending on the current flow). However, if we went around the loop in the opposite direction, we would have a voltage "rise" in terms of potential.

We will use the sign convention illustrated in Fig. 31.2. The voltage change of a battery is taken as positive when the battery is traversed in the direction of the "positive" terminal (a voltage "rise"), and negative if the battery is traversed in the direction of the "negative" terminal. Note that the assigned branch currents have nothing to do with determining the voltage change of a battery, only the direction one goes around a loop or through a battery.

The voltage change across a resistor, on the other hand, involves the direction of the assigned current through the resistor. The voltage change is taken to be negative if the resistor is traversed in the direction of the assigned branch current (a voltage "drop") and positive if traversed in the opposite direction.

The sign convention allows you to go around a loop either clockwise or counterclockwise at your choice. Going in opposite directions merely makes all the signs opposite, and Eq. 31.2. is the same.

Kirchhoff's rules may be used in circuit analysis in several ways. We will consider two methods.

Branch (Current) Method

First, label a current for *each branch* in the circuit. This is done by a current arrowhead, which also indicates the current direction, and is most conveniently done at a junction as in Fig. 31.1 at junction B. Kirchhoff's first rule applies at any junction. Remember, the current directions are arbitrary, but

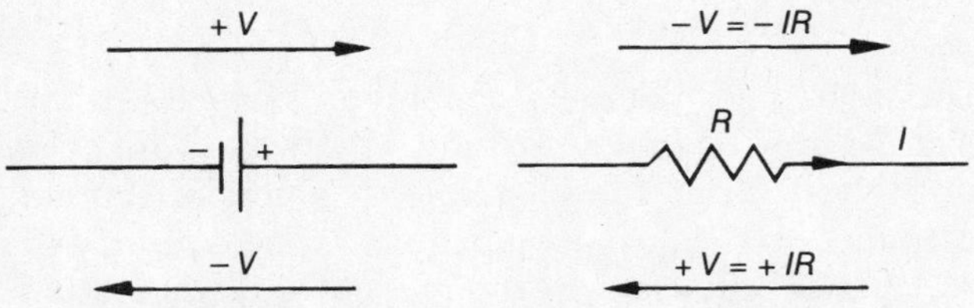

(a) Traversing a battery (b) Traversing a resistor

Figure 31.2 Sign convention for Kirchhoff's rules. (a) When one goes around a loop and passes through a battery, the voltage change is taken to be positive when the battery is traversed toward the positive terminal and negative when traversed toward the negative terminal. (b) When one passes through a resistor, the voltage change across the resistor is taken to be negative ("voltage drop") if it is traversed in the direction of the assigned branch current and positive if traversed in the opposite direction.

there must be at least one current in and one current out. (Why?) Then, draw loops so that every branch is in at least one loop. This is shown for the circuit in Fig. 31.1, which has three loops. Again, the direction of a loop is arbitrary because of our sign convention.

With this done, current equations are written for each junction according to Kirchhoff's junction theorem (rule 1) that gives different equations. In general, this gives a set of equations that includes all branch currents. For the simple circuit in Fig. 31.1, this is one equation, since the sum of the currents at junction D is the same as that at junction B.

Then, Kirchhoff's loop theorem (rule 2) is applied to the circuit loops. This gives additional equations that form a set of N equations with N unknowns, which can be solved for the unknowns. There may be more loops than necessary. Only the number of loops that include all branches is needed.

To illustrate this method, the circuit in Fig. 31.1 is analyzed in the following example. (Assume the component values in the circuit to be exact, that is, ignore significant figures.)

Example 31.1 Apply Kirchhoff's rules and the above sign convention to the circuit shown in Fig. 31.1 and find the value of the current in each branch.

Solution By rule 1 (junction theorem),

$$I_1 = I_2 + I_3 \qquad \textbf{(31.4)}$$

with directions as assigned in the figure.

Going around loop 1 as indicated in the figure, with Kirchhoff's second rule (loop theorem) and our sign convention, we have, starting at battery 1,

$$V_1 - I_1R_1 - V_2 - I_2R_2 = 0$$

or with known values

$$6 - I_1(2) - 12 - I_2(4) = 0$$

and

$$I_1 + 2I_2 = -3 \qquad \textbf{(31.5)}$$

Similarly, around loop 2, starting at battery 2,

$$V_2 - I_3R_3 + I_2R_2 = 0$$

or

$$12 - I_3(6) + I_2(4) = 0$$

and

$$3I_3 - 2I_2 = 6 \qquad \textbf{(31.6)}$$

Eqs. 31.3–31.5 constitute a set of three equations with three unknowns from which the values of I_1, I_2, and I_3 can be found. Solving these equations for the currents, one obtains

$$I_1 = -\tfrac{3}{11}\text{ A}$$
$$I_2 = -\tfrac{15}{11}\text{ A}$$
$$I_3 = \tfrac{12}{11}\text{ A}$$

The negative values of I_1 and I_2 indicate that the wrong directions were assumed for these currents. In the actual circuit, I_2 would flow into junction B, and I_1 would flow out of the junction as well as I_3 as assumed. Hence, if we had guessed correctly, we would have written for junction B,

$$I_2 = I_1 + I_3$$
$$\underset{\text{(current in)}}{\tfrac{15}{11}\text{ A}} = \underset{\text{(current out)}}{\tfrac{3}{11}\text{ A} + \tfrac{12}{11}\text{ A}}$$

and $\Sigma I_i = 0$ as required by rule 1.

In looking at Fig. 31.1 more carefully, one might have surmised this. Battery 2 (12 V) has twice the voltage of battery 1 (6 V) and it would have been a good guess that (conventional) current would flow out of battery 2 toward junction B. If battery 1 were a rechargeable battery, it would be recharging in the circuit. (Why?)

Notice that loop 3 was not used to solve the problem. This loop would have provided a redundant equation with the other two loop equations. However, loop 3 could have been used with one of the other loops to solve the problem.

Loop (Current) Method *(Optional)*
This method is similar to the previous branch method, but some consider it to be simpler mathematically. Loops are drawn as before so that every branch is in at least one loop. Then, each loop is labeled as if it were a current, as shown in Fig. 31.3

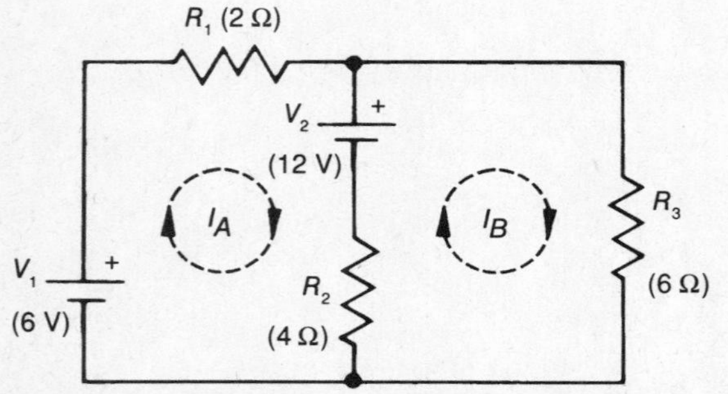

Figure 31.3 Loop method. In this method, the loops are taken as "current loops" with a particular current assigned to each loop.

for the circuit in Fig. 31.1. The "current loop" direction is arbitrary as in the previous method for loop directions.

Kirchhoff's loop theorem (rule 2) is then used to write an equation for each loop, applying the sign convention. For the circuit in Fig. 31.3, there are two loop equations for the "loop currents" I_A and I_B. These are, starting at V_1 and V_2, respectively,

$$\text{(loop A)}\quad V_1 - I_AR_1 - V_2 - I_AR_2 + I_BR_2 = 0$$
$$\text{(loop B)}\quad V_2 - I_BR_3 - I_BR_2 + I_AR_2 = 0$$

Note that you have to take into account all the "loop currents" that affect each loop. That is, when going around a loop and for a branch resistor through which two "loop currents" flow, the voltage changes for both currents must be considered for the resistor as for R_2 in this case.

Traversing the current loops produces two equations for this circuit with two unknowns, I_A and I_B. (Note that in the branch method analysis in Example 31.1, the loop equations had three unknowns.) Putting in the known values, the equations may be solved simultaneously to find the value of each unknown:

$$\text{(loop A)}\quad 6 - I_A(2) - 12 - I_A(4) + I_B(4) = 0$$
$$\text{(loop B)}\quad 12 - I_B(6) - I_B(4) + I_A(4) = 0$$

These reduce to

$$-3I_A + 2I_B = 3$$
$$2I_A - 5I_B = -6$$

Solving for I_A and I_B, we find

$$I_A = -\tfrac{3}{11}\text{ A}$$
$$I_B = \tfrac{12}{11}\text{ A}$$

The computed values of the "loop currents" may then be utilized in a straightforward way to find the actual branch currents. Kirchhoff's junction theorem is applied to the various junctions in the circuit, and the branch currents are compared with the "loop currents." For example, compare the branch currents at junction B in Fig. 31.1 and the "loop currents" in Fig. 31.3. (The branch currents may be drawn directly on the current-loop diagram.) It should be evident by comparison that:

$$I_1 = I_A = -\tfrac{3}{11}\text{ A}$$
$$I_2 = I_A - I_B = -\tfrac{3}{11}\text{ A} - \tfrac{12}{11}\text{ A} = -\tfrac{15}{11}\text{ A}$$
$$I_3 = I_B = \tfrac{12}{11}\text{ A}$$

the same values obtained for the circuit by the branch method.

IV. Experimental Procedure

1. Examine the resistors. The colored bands on composition resistors conform to a color code that gives the resistance value of the resistor. Look up the color code in Appendix A, Table A5, to identify each resistor. Note that the actual resistance value may vary according to the tolerance indicated by the last band (gold $\pm 5\%$, silver $\pm 10\%$, no band $\pm 20\%$).

2. Connect the two-loop circuit as illustrated in Fig. 31.4. If you are using variable power supplies, adjust each power supply as closely as possible to the values specified in the figure. Leave the switches open until the circuit has been checked by the instructor.

   Note: Lay out the circuit on your table exactly as shown in the diagram. This will help prevent errors and will facilitate your measurements.

3. After your circuit has been checked, close the switches and measure the "operating" value of each battery (V_1 and V_2) by temporarily connecting the voltmeter across it. Record these operating values in Data Table 1.

   Caution: To avoid damage to the voltmeter, always start with the meter on its least-sensitive scale. Increase the sensitivity of the meter only as needed for accurate measurement, and remember to return the meter to its least-sensitive scale before proceeding.

4. Temporarily open the switches. Insert the ammeter in series with one of the branches. Close the switches, measure and record the branch current, then open the switches.

   Caution: Observe the same precautions described under procedure 3 to avoid damage to the ammeter. Also, if the ammeter deflects downscale (below zero), open the switches before reversing the polarity of the meter.

5. Repeat procedure 4 for each of the branches.

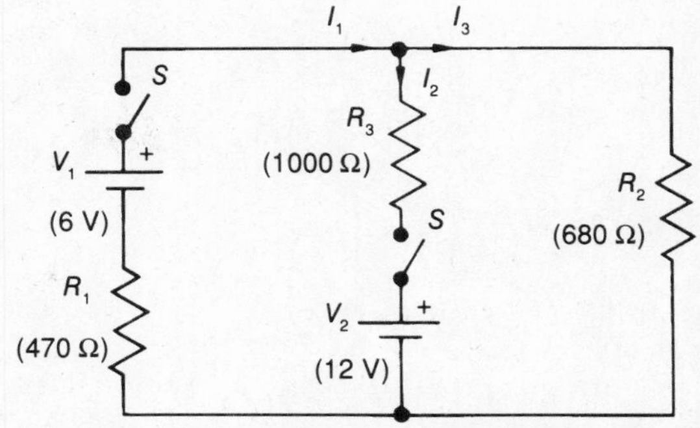

Figure 31.4 Multiloop circuit. Experimental two-loop circuit.

6. Compute the theoretical values of each branch current for this circuit. In the analysis, use the measured values of the batteries V_1 and V_2 and the labeled values of the resistors (procedure 1). Compare the measured values of the branch currents with the computed theoretical values by finding the percent error.

7. Connect the three-loop circuit as shown in Fig. 31.5. Repeat procedures 3 through 6 for this circuit. The instructor may wish to provide you with a different circuit to investigate. (In Fig. 31.5, why is there no current indicated between the two connection points on the bottom wire?)

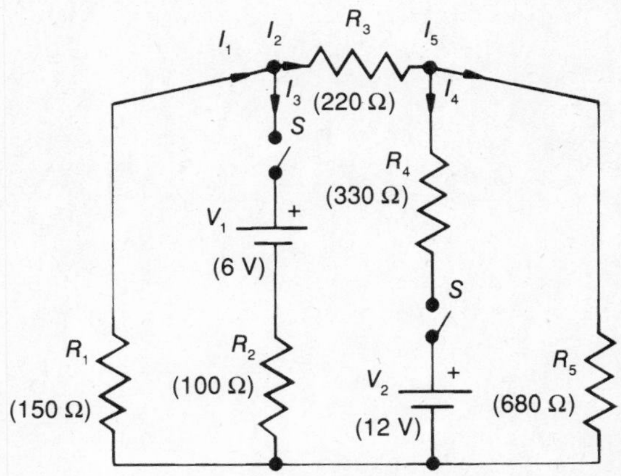

Figure 31.5 Multiloop circuit. Experimental three-loop circuit.

Name ______ Section ______ Date ______

Lab Partner(s) ______

EXPERIMENT 31

Multiloop Circuits: Kirchhoff's Rules

Laboratory Report

DATA TABLE 1

Purpose: To investigate Kirchhoff's rules by means of a two-loop circuit (Fig. 31.4).

R_1 ______

R_2 ______

R_3 ______

	Measured value ( )	Theoretical value ( )	Percent error
V_1		X	X
V_2		X	X
I_1			
I_2			
I_3			

Calculations (show work)

DATA TABLE 2

Purpose: To investigate Kirchhoff's rules by means of a three-loop circuit (Fig. 31.5).

R_1 ______ R_4 ______

R_2 ______ R_5 ______

R_3 ______

	Measured value ( )	Theoretical value ( )	Percent error
V_1		X	X
V_2		X	X
I_1			
I_2			
I_3			
I_4			
I_5			

Don't forget units

(continued)

QUESTIONS

1. A typical ammeter has a resistance of 22 Ω when it is set to its 10-mA scale, a resistance of 2.7 Ω on its 100-mA scale, and a resistance of 0.7 Ω on its 1000-mA (1-A) scale.
   (a) What percent error might the ammeter resistance cause in the circuit of Fig. 31.4 when reading the current through R_3? (*Hint:* The fractional error is approximately the ratio of the meter resistance to the circuit resistance.)

   (b) How does this error compare with the resistor tolerance noted in procedure 1 of the experiment?

   (c) If all the resistors were 1/100 times the values shown in the figure, the currents would be 100 times greater. What percent error would now be introduced by the ammeter?

Name ______________________ Section ______________ Date ______________
Lab Partner(s) ____

2. The potentiometer (see Fig. 25.3) and the Wheatstone bridge (see Fig. 27.3) each have several loops.
   (a) Assume the potentiometer or bridge is balanced, i.e., the galvanometer reads zero. Are Kirchhoff's rules needed to calculate the currents through the resistors? Explain. *Could* Kirchhoff's rules be used?

   (b) Assume the galvanometer does not read zero. Are Kirchhoff's rules now needed? Explain.

3. Draw a diagram showing the junctions and loops for the analysis of an unbalanced Wheatstone bridge (see Experiment 27). How many simultaneous equations would be needed for analysis?

(continued)

4. Two batteries with emf's of 1.5 V and 1.2 V and internal resistances of 0.50 Ω and 0.80 Ω, respectively, are connected in parallel.
   (a) Determine the current they would deliver to an external resistance of 2.0 Ω.

   (b) Would more current be delivered if only one battery were used? If so, which one? Explain.

Name ______________________ Section ______________ Date ______________

Lab Partner(s) ____

EXPERIMENT 32

Joule Heat

Advance Study Assignment

Read the experiment and answer the following questions.

1. Explain (a) joule heat; and (b) I^2R losses.

2. What is the difference between joule heat and power?

3. Given two different resistances, how does the joule heat of the resistances vary if they are connected to a battery of fixed voltage V_o (a) in series; and (b) in parallel?

4. In the experiment, why isn't the final temperature of the system read at the same time that the power supply is unplugged and the timer stopped?

(continued)

5. Suppose that oil were used in the experiment instead of water. Would (a) the joule heat and (b) the temperature rise be the same? Explain.

Joule Heat

I. Introduction and Objectives

Whenever there is an electrical current in a conductor, some electrical energy is converted into heat energy. For a given current I, the energy conversion is greater in a conductor of greater resistance. This is analogous to the conversion of mechanical energy into heat energy due to frictional resistance. The heat generated in an electrical circuit is commonly referred to as **joule heat**, after James Prescott Joule (1818–1889), the English scientist who investigated the conversion of electrical energy to heat (and also the mechanical equivalent of heat).

In many electrical applications, such as electrical motors, the joule heat is an undesirable loss of energy. However, in other applications, such as toasters and electrical heaters, electrical energy is purposefully converted to heat energy. In this experiment, the heating effect of an electrical current and the "electrical equivalent of heat" will be investigated.

After performing this experiment and analyzing the data, you should be able to:

1. Describe what is meant by joule heat.
2. Explain the factors on which joule heat depends.
3. Tell how joule heat may be measured experimentally.

II. Equipment Needed

- Electrocalorimeter (immersion heater and calorimeter)
- Power supply or battery (12 V)
- Ammeter (0 to 3 A)
- Voltmeter (30 V)
- Rheostat (40 Ω)
- Connecting wires
- Thermometer
- Stopwatch or laboratory timer
- Laboratory balance
- Ice

III. Theory

The work W done (or energy expended) per unit charge in moving a charge q from one point to another is the potential difference or voltage V

$$V = \frac{W}{q}$$

or

$$W = qV \qquad \textbf{(32.1)}$$

The time rate of flow of charge is described in terms of current I, and

$$I = \frac{q}{t} \qquad \textbf{(32.2)}$$

Hence, Eq. 32.1 may be written

$$W = qV = IVt \qquad \textbf{(32.3)}$$

which represents the work done or the energy expended in a circuit in a time t. This is often expressed as work or energy per time, or power P,

$$P = \frac{W}{t} = IV \qquad \textbf{(32.4)}$$

When this general expression is applied to a resistance R, for which $V = IR$ (Ohm's law), the expanded energy or work in Eq. 32.4 can be written

$$W = IVt = I^2Rt = \frac{V^2t}{R} \qquad \textbf{(32.5)}$$

The electrical energy expended is manifested as heat energy and is commonly called joule heat or I^2R losses, I^2R being the power or energy expended per time.

Eq. 32.5 shows how the joule heat varies with resistance:

1. For a constant current I, the joule heat is directly proportional to the resistance, I^2R.
2. For a constant voltage V, the joule heat is inversely proportional to the resistance, V^2/R.

The energy expended in an electrical circuit as given by Eq. 32.5 has the unit of joule. The relationship (conversion factor) between joules and heat units in calories was established by James Joule from mechanical considerations—the *mechanical equivalent of heat*. You may recall that in his mechanical experiment Joule had a descending weight turn a paddle wheel in a liquid. He then correlated the mechanical (gravitational) potential energy lost by the descending weight to the heat generated in the liquid. The result was 1 cal = 4.186 J or 1 kcal = 4186 J.

A similar electrical experiment may be done to determine the "electrical equivalent of heat." By the conservation of energy, the heat equivalents of mechanical and electrical energy are the same (i.e., 1 cal = 4.186 J).

Experimentally, the amount of electrical joule heat generated in a circuit element of resistance R is measured by calorimetry methods. If a current is passed through a resistance (immersion heater) in a calorimeter with water in an arrangement as illustrated in Fig. 32.1, by the conservation of energy the electrical energy expended in the resistance is equal to the heat energy (joule heat) Q gained by the system:

$$\text{energy expended electrical} = \text{heat gained}$$

$$W = Q$$

or

$$IVt = (m_w c_w + m_{\text{cal}} c_{\text{cal}} + m_{\text{coil}} c_{\text{coil}})(T_f - T_i) \quad \textbf{(32.6)}$$

where the m's and c's are the masses and specific heats of the water, calorimeter cup, and immersion coil, respectively, as indicated by the subscripts. T_f and T_i are the final and initial temperatures of the system, respectively. (See Experiment 19 for the detailed theory of calorimetry procedure.)

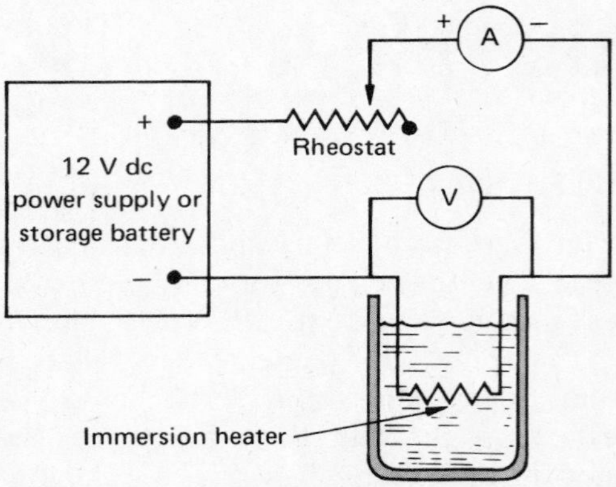

Figure 32.1 Joule heat determination. Circuit diagram for experimental procedure to measure joule heat. See text for description.

IV. Experimental Procedure

1. Determine and record in the Laboratory Report the masses of the inner calorimeter cup (without ring) and the coil of the immersion heater. (The latter may be supplied by the instructor if the coil is permanently mounted.)

Also, record the types of materials and their specific heats. (The type of material and specific heat of the calorimeter cup is usually stamped on the cup. For the coil, usually copper, a table of specific heats is given in Appendix A, Table A4.)

2. Fill the calorimeter cup about two-thirds full of cool tap water several degrees below room temperature. (The cup should be filled high enough that the immersion heater will be completely covered when immersed later.) Determine and record the mass of the calorimeter cup with the water.

3. Place the immersion heater in the calorimeter cup and set up the circuit as illustrated in Fig. 32.1 with the rheostat set at its maximum resistance. Make certain that the heating coil is completely immersed. If not, add more water and reweigh the cup and water as in procedure 2. *Do not plug in the power supply (or connect battery) until the circuit has been checked by the instructor.*

4. After the circuit has been checked, plug in the power supply set to 10 to 12 V. Adjust the rheostat until there is a constant current between 2 and 3 A in the circuit as indicated on the ammeter. (If a variable power supply is used, it may also be used to make fine current adjustments.) Then unplug the power supply. This procedure should be done as quickly as possible to avoid heating the water.

5. Add some ice to the water in the calorimeter cup with the immersion coil or thermometer. When the ice has melted, measure and record the equilibrium temperature T_i.

This should be 5 to 8 C° below room temperature. Then plug in the power supply and at the same time start the stopwatch or laboratory timer. Immediately read and record the initial ammeter and voltmeter readings.

As time goes on, keep the current as constant as possible by varying the rheostat (and/or the power supply). Record the voltage and the current every minute. Stir the water frequently.

6. When the temperature of the water (and calorimeter system) is 10 to 15 C° above the initial temperature, simultaneously unplug the power supply and stop the timer at the time of a particular minute interval reading. Continue stirring until a maximum temperature is reached, and record this temperature (T_f).

7. Compute the electrical energy expended in the coil (in joules) from the electrical and time readings. Use the average value of the voltage readings as the effective voltage across the coil.

8. **(a)** Compute the heat energy (in calories) gained by the calorimeter system.
(b) Then take the ratio of the electrical and heat energy results to find the "electrical equivalent of heat" (J/cal or J/kcal). Compare this to the value of the mechanical equivalent of heat by computing the percent error.

9. If time permits (ask instructor), repeat the experiment and use the average value of the experimental results in determining the percent error. Attach these results to the Laboratory Report.

Name ______________________ Section ______________ Date ______________

Lab Partner(s) ____

EXPERIMENT 32

Joule Heat

Laboratory Report

	Mass	Material	Specific heat
Calorimeter cup	________	________	________
Immersion coil	________	________	________
Calorimeter cup and water	________		
Water	________	________	________

DATA TABLE

Purpose: To determine the mechanical equivalent of heat.

Time ( )	Voltage, V ( )	Current, I ( )	Temperature ( )
0			
			T_i ________
			T_f ________

Calculations
(show work)

Average voltage ________

Average current ________

Electrical energy expended ________

Heat energy gained ________

Ratio of results ________

Percent error ________

Don't forget units

(continued)

QUESTIONS

1. What are the major sources of error in the experiment? Why should the initial temperature of the water be several degrees below room temperature?

2. Why was it necessary to make adjustments to maintain a constant current in the circuit?

3. If the cost of electricity is 12 cents per kWh, what was the cost of the electricity used in performing the experiment?

4. A piece of No. 24 gauge (AWG) copper wire is three times the length of a piece of No. 18 gauge copper wire. If the same voltage is applied to the wires, which wire would have more joule heat, and how many times more? (*Hint:* See Experiment 28 and Appendix A, Table A7.)

Name ______________________ Section ______________ Date ______________

Lab Partner(s) ____

EXPERIMENT 32 *Laboratory Report*

5. Do heating appliances such as electric blankets and toasters have high-resistance or low-resistance elements? Explain.

Name ______________________ Section ______________ Date ______________

Lab Partner(s) ____

EXPERIMENT 33

The *RC* Time Constant

Advance Study Assignment

Read the experiment and answer the following questions.

1. What is an *RC* time constant?

2. When a *RC* series circuit is connected to a dc source, what is the voltage on a capacitor after one time constant when (a) charging from zero voltage; and (b) discharging from a fully charged condition?

3. If the resistance in a capacitor circuit is increased, would the charging time of the capacitor increase or decrease? Explain.

(continued)

4. Can the voltage across a capacitor be measured with a common voltmeter? Explain.

EXPERIMENT 33

The *RC* Time Constant

I. Introduction and Objectives

When a capacitor is connected to a dc power supply or battery, charge builds up on the capacitor plates and the potential difference or voltage across the plates increases until it equals the voltage of the source. At any time, the charge Q of the capacitor is related to the voltage across the capacitor plates by $Q = CV$, where C is the capacitance of the capacitor in farads (F). The rate of voltage rise depends on the capacitance of the capacitor and the resistance in the circuit. Similarly, when a charged capacitor is discharged, the rate of voltage decay depends on the same parameters.

Both the charging and discharge times of a capacitor are characterized by a quantity called the **time constant** τ, which is the product of the capacitance C and the series resistance R, that is, $\tau = RC$. In this experiment, the time constants and the charging and discharging characteristics of capacitors will be investigated.

After performing this experiment and analyzing the data, you should be able to:

1. Explain the *RC* time constant and what its value means in terms of circuit characteristics.
2. Describe how a capacitor charges and discharges through a resistor as a function of time.
3. Tell how an *RC* time constant may be measured experimentally.

II. Equipment Needed

- Two capacitors (e.g., 1000 μF and 2200 μF electrolytic)
- Two resistors (e.g., 4.5 kΩ and 10 kΩ)
- Power supply or battery (12 V)
- High-resistance digital readout voltmeter
- Single-pole, double-throw switch
- Connecting wires
- Laboratory timer
- 2 sheets of Cartesian graph paper

III. Theory

When a capacitor is charged through a resistor by a dc voltage source (the single-pole, double-throw switch in position a in Fig. 33.1), the charge in the capacitor and the voltage across the capacitor increase with time. The voltage V as a function of time is given by

$$V = V_o\,(1 - e^{-t/RC}) = V_o(1 - e^{-t/\tau}) \quad \textbf{(33.1)}$$

where the exponential $e = 2.718$ is the base of natural logarithms and V_o is the voltage of the source. The quantity $\tau = RC$ is called the **time constant** of the circuit. The curve of the exponential rise of the voltage with time during the charging process is illustrated in Fig. 33.2.

At time $t = \tau = RC$ (one time constant), the voltage across the capacitor has grown to a value of $(1 - 1/e)$ of V_o; that is, $V = V_o(1 - e^{-RC/RC}) = V_o(1 - e^{-1}) = V_o(1 - 1/e) = 0.63\ V_o$.

When the fully charged capacitor is discharged through a resistor (switch in position b in Fig. 33.1), the voltage across (and the charge on) the capacitor "decays" or decreases with time according to the equation

$$V = V_o\,e^{-t/RC} \quad \textbf{(33.2)}$$

The exponential decay of the voltage with time is also illustrated in Fig. 33.2. After a time $t = \tau = RC$ (one time constant), the voltage across the capacitor has decreased to a value of $1/e$ of V_o; that is, $V = V_oe^{-t/RC} = V_oe^{-RC/RC} = V_oe^{-1} = V_o/e = 0.37\ V_o$. In order to analyze the voltage versus time, it is helpful to put Eqs. 33.1 and 33.2 in the form of a straight line. From Eq. 33.1, we obtain

$$(V_o - V) = V_o\,e^{-t/RC}$$

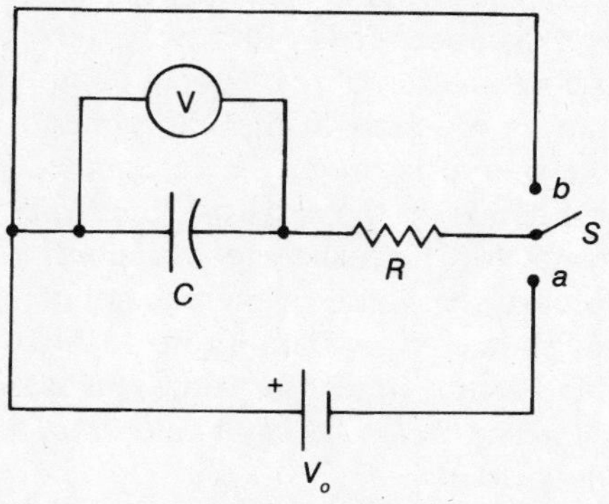

Figure 33.1 Capacitor charging and discharging. Circuit diagram for charging (switch S in position a) and discharging (switch S in position b) a capacitor through a resistor.

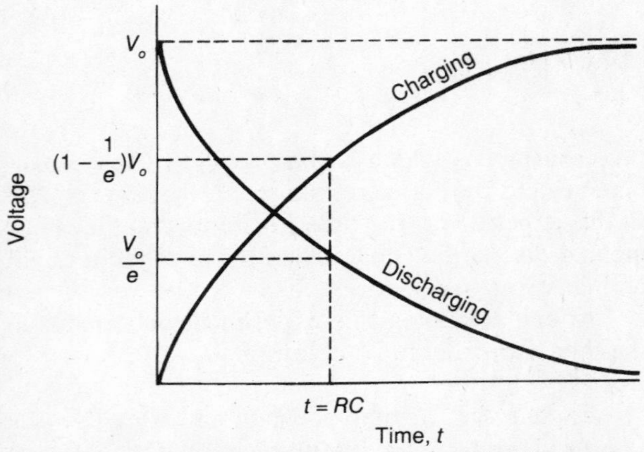

Figure 33.2 Voltage versus time. A graph illustrating voltage versus time for a charging and discharging capacitor. The "steepness" of the curves depends on the time constant *RC*.

and taking the natural logarithm of both sides of the equation gives

$$\ln (V_o - V) = -\frac{t}{RC} + \ln V_o \qquad (33.3)$$

Then from Eq. 33.2, taking the natural logarithm, we obtain

$$\ln V = -\frac{t}{RC} + \ln V_o \qquad (33.4)$$

Both of these equations have the form of the equation of a straight line, $y = mx + b$. (Can you identify the variables and constants?) Both have negative slopes of magnitude $1/RC$. Hence, the time constant can be found from the slopes of the graphs of $\ln (V_o - V)$ versus t and/or $\ln V$ versus t.

IV. Experimental Procedure

1. Set up the circuit as shown in Fig. 33.1 with the capacitor of smaller capacitance and resistor of larger resistance. It is often necessary to use a series combination of resistors to obtain the large resistances required in the experiment. The resistance of a resistor may be determined from the colored bands on the resistor. (See Appendix A, Table A5, for the resistor color code.)

   Record the value of the capacitance C_1 and the resistance R_1 in Data Table 1. Also prepare the laboratory timer for time measurements. *Have the instructor check the circuit before closing the switch.*

2. Close the switch to position *a* and note the voltage rise of the capacitor on the voltmeter. When the capacitor is fully charged, move the switch to position *b* and note the voltage decrease as the capacitor discharges. In the following procedures, the voltage is read as a function of time. You should try trial time runs to become familiar with the procedures.

3. Simultaneously close the switch to position *a* and start the timer. Read and record the capacitor voltage at small time intervals (e.g., 3–5 s) until the capacitor is fully charged (V_o). This should be done with two persons working together. However, if necessary, the switch may be opened (and the timer stopped) to stop the charging process after a given interval without appreciable error if a high-quality, low-leakage capacitor is used.

4. After the capacitor is fully charged, open the switch to the neutral position and reset the timer. Then, simultaneously close the switch to position *b* and start the timer. Read and record the decreasing voltage at small time intervals. Open the switch when the capacitor is discharged.

5. Replace R_1 and C_1 with R_2 and C_2 (smaller resistance and larger capacitance), and repeat procedures 3 and 4, using Data Table 2 to record your findings.

6. Compute the quantity $(V_o - V)$ for the charging and discharging processes, respectively. Then, using a calculator or Appendix B, Table B7, find the value of $\ln (V_o - V)$ and $\ln V$.

7. On a Cartesian graph, plot $\ln (V_o - V)$ versus t for both sets of data. On the other graph, plot $\ln V$ versus t for both sets of data. Draw the straight lines that best fit the data, and determine the slope of each line. Record the slopes in the data tables. Compute the time constants from the average slope values.

8. Compute $\tau_1 = R_1C_1$ and $\tau_2 = R_2C_2$ from the known resistance and capacitance values and compare with the experimental values by finding the percent errors.

Name ______________________ Section ______________ Date ______________

Lab Partner(s) ____

EXPERIMENT 33

The *RC* Time Constant

Laboratory Report

C_1 ______________

R_1 ______________

DATA TABLE 1

Purpose: To determine the *RC* time constant.

Charging				Discharging		
V ( )	t ( )	$V_o - V$	$\ln (V_o - V)$	V ( )	t ( )	$\ln V$
				V_o		
V_o						

Calculations
(show work)

Slope (charging) ______________

Slope (discharging) ______________

Average slope ______________

R_1C_1 (from slope) ______________

R_1C_1 (from known values) ______________

Percent error ______________

Don't forget units

(continued)

C_2 ____________

DATA TABLE 2
Purpose: To determine *RC* time constant.

R_2 ____________

Charging				Discharging		
V ( )	t ( )	$V_o - V$	$\ln (V_o - V)$	V ( )	t ( )	$\ln V$
				V_o		
V_o						

Calculations
(show work)

Slope (charging) ____________

Slope (discharging) ____________

Average slope ____________

R_2C_2 (from slope) ____________

R_2C_2 (from known values) ____________

Percent error ____________

Name ______________________ Section ______________ Date ______________

Lab Partner(s) ____

EXPERIMENT 33 **_Laboratory Report_**

QUESTIONS

1. Show that the magnitude of the charge on a capacitor is given by $Q = Q_o(1 - e^{-t/\tau})$ and $Q = Q_o e^{-t/\tau}$ for charging and discharging, respectively.

2. What is the voltage across a capacitor after a time of two constants when (a) charging from zero voltage, and (b) discharging from a fully charged condition?

3. With $V = V_o e^{-t/RC}$, it mathematically takes an infinite time for a capacitor in an *RC* circuit to discharge. Practically, how many time constants does it take for a capacitor to discharge to less than 1% of its initial voltage?

4. A 2.0-μF capacitor in a circuit in series with a resistance of 1.0 MΩ is charged with a 6.0-V battery. How long would it take to charge the capacitor to three-fourths of its maximum voltage?

Name ______________________ Section ______________ Date ______________

Lab Partner(s) ____

E X P E R I M E N T 3 4

Introduction to the Oscilloscope

Advance Study Assignment

Read the experiment and answer the following questions.

1. What is a CRT?

2. What is the purpose of the deflection plates in the oscilloscope CRT?

3. How is a graph of voltage versus time obtained on the oscilloscope screen?

4. Distinguish between peak voltage and rms voltage.

5. What is the condition for a stationary trace of an ac voltage input signal?

(continued)

6. What are Lissajous figures, and how are they produced? (*See exercise below*)

ADVANCE STUDY EXERCISE

To help you better understand the answer to Question 6, here is an exercise to show you how the *x-y* position of the oscilloscope beam varies with time and gives different patterns or figures.

In each of the three parts of the exercise, graphs of x and y versus time are given below and beside an *x-y* graph. For a particular time, find the respective x and y coordinates on the time graphs, and plot this point (x, y) on the *x-y* graph. For example, in (a) at $t = 0$, $(x, y) = (0 \text{ cm}, 0 \text{ cm})$. Select 8 to 10 increasing times over each complete cycle and plot the corresponding points. Number each point sequentially so you can see how they progress with time.

Finally, connect the points with a smooth curve so as to see what kind of figure or pattern is produced. The oscilloscope beam can trace out similar patterns in very short times. Continuous, cyclic tracings give rise to continuous patterns on the fluorescent screen of the oscilloscope.

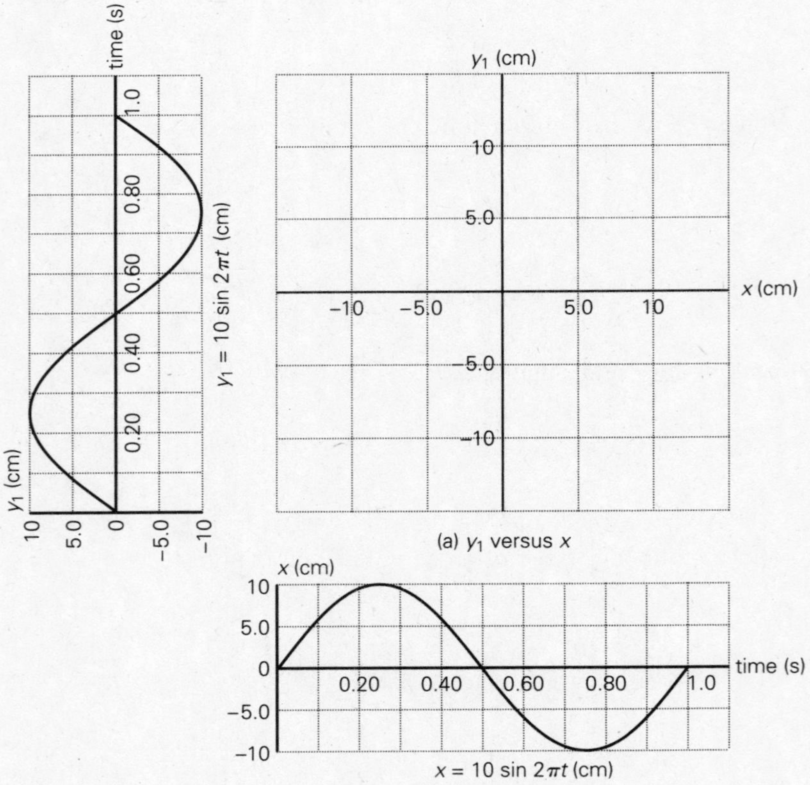

(a) y_1 versus x

Name ______________________ Section ______________ Date ______________

Lab Partner(s) ____

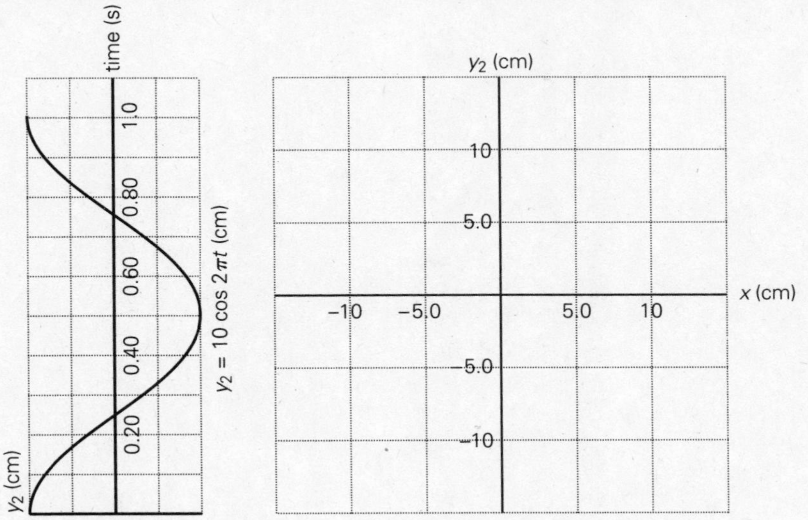

(b) y_2 versus x

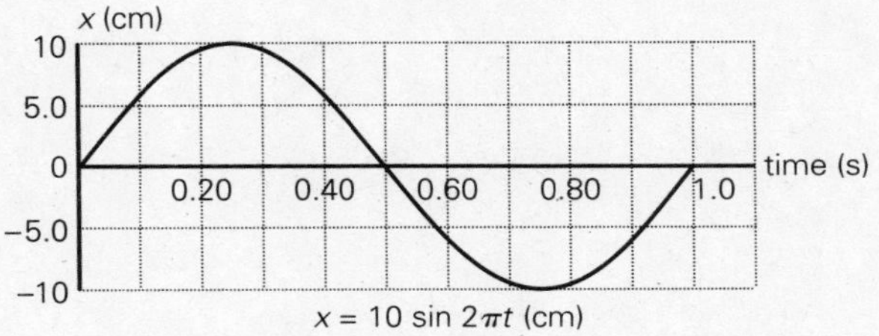

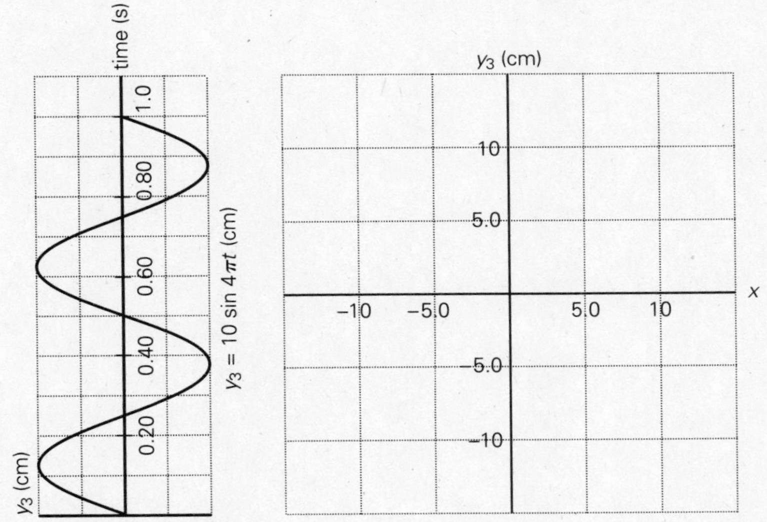

(c) y_3 versus x

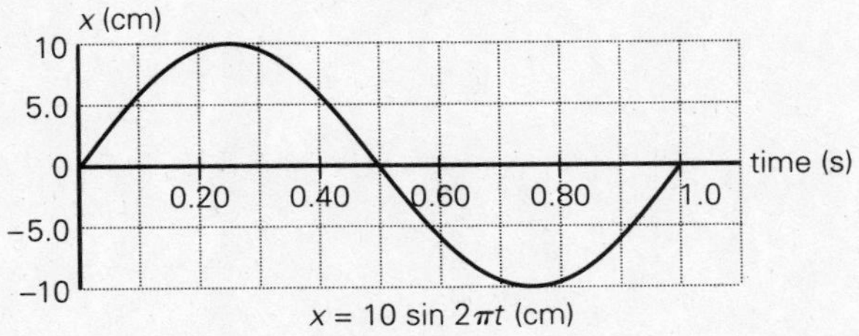

(continued)

Introduction to the Oscilloscope

I. Introduction and Objectives

The cathode-ray oscilloscope is one of the most versatile laboratory instruments for studying ac circuits. Having long been quite common in the physics laboratory, the oscilloscope is finding increasing uses and applications in biology and medicine. In its most basic application, the oscilloscope is used to display a graph of voltage versus time on its screen. The signal may be the voltage across a component in an electrical circuit or that generated by a nerve impulse or a heartbeat.

In this experiment, an introduction to the basic principles of the oscilloscope is presented, and you will operate an oscilloscope so as to become familiar with its controls and characteristics.

After performing this experiment and analyzing the data, you should be able to:

1. Describe the basic principle of the cathode-ray tube of an oscilloscope.
2. Explain how time and voltage measurements may be made with an oscilloscope.
3. Explain how Lissajous figures are formed.

II. Equipment Needed

- Cathode-ray oscilloscope (student model)
- Operating instruction manual for particular oscilloscope used
- Audio-signal function generator (sine and square waves)
- (60-Hz sine wave source, or second generator if oscilloscope does not have internal line input)
- Connecting wires

III. Theory

The basic component of an oscilloscope (or "scope") is a **cathode-ray tube** (CRT) or electron-beam tube (Fig. 34.1). The name "cathode-ray tube" comes from early experiments with gas discharge tubes in which "rays" coming from the cathode or negative electrode were observed. The beam of electrons (cathode rays) in a CRT is formed by an "electron gun," in which electrons thermally emitted from a cathode filament are accelerated through a potential difference of several thousand volts and focused into a beam. The electron beam strikes a fluorescent screen coated with a phosphor that emits visible light, and a spot of light is seen on the screen.

The CRT is also equipped with sets of vertical and horizontal deflection plates. If no voltage signals are applied to the deflection plates, the beam is undeflected and strikes the center of the screen. However, if a voltage signal is applied to the horizontal deflection plates, the electron beam experiences a force and is deflected horizontally.

A constant dc voltage deflects the beam spot on the screen a fixed distance. An ac voltage, on the other hand, deflects the beam back and forth, since the polarity is continually changing. If the frequency of the ac voltage signal is high enough, the beam spot traces out an observable continuous horizontal line.

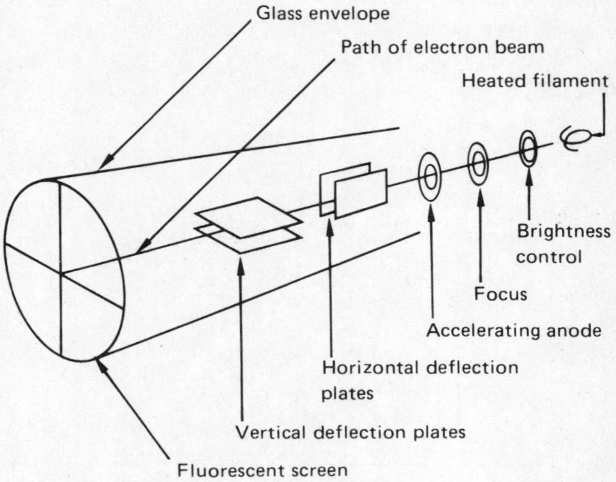

Figure 34.1 Cathode ray tube. The basic components of an oscilloscope cathode ray tube (CRT). See text for description.

This is due to the relatively slow decay of the brightness of the fluorescent screen after each excitation and the persistence of vision in the human eye.

Similarly, a voltage signal applied to the vertical deflection plates causes the beam to move vertically. In either case, the magnitude of the deflection of the beam spot from the center of the screen is proportional to the magnitude of the voltage applied to the deflection plates. The cathode-ray oscilloscope is an extremely fast X-Y plotter that is capable of plotting an input signal versus either time or another signal.

In ac voltage applications, it is usually desired to display the voltage on the screen as a function of time (i.e., a graph of voltage versus time). The signal to be studied is applied to the vertical deflection plates. The oscilloscope has an internal amplifier or gain to amplify weak vertical input signals. A horizontal linear time axis is obtained if the beam spot moves horizontally (left to right) with a constant speed.

The time axis is generated by applying a deflecting voltage to the horizontal plates, which increases linearly with time (e.g., a voltage signal with a "sawtooth" wave form, as illustrated in Fig. 34.2). As the voltage increases uniformly, the spot sweeps uniformly (with constant speed) across the screen from left to right. When the voltage suddenly drops to zero, the beam flies back to its initial position and begins another horizontal sweep with the "triggering" of the next sawtooth.

With a slow sweep rate, the spot can be observed moving periodically from left to right. However, with a fast sweep rate, a continuous trace is observed, as the eye cannot follow the motion. The oscilloscope is equipped with an internal variable sawtooth generator to supply such horizontal signals with no signal on the horizontal plates.

When a sinusoidal voltage having the form $V = V_o \sin 2\pi ft$ is applied to the vertical plates, the beam moves up and down, as well as side to side. If the sweep is triggered to start each sweep at the same point on the cycle of the signal applied to the vertical plates, the combined motions of the beam spot will trace out a graph of the applied voltage versus time as shown in Fig. 34.3.

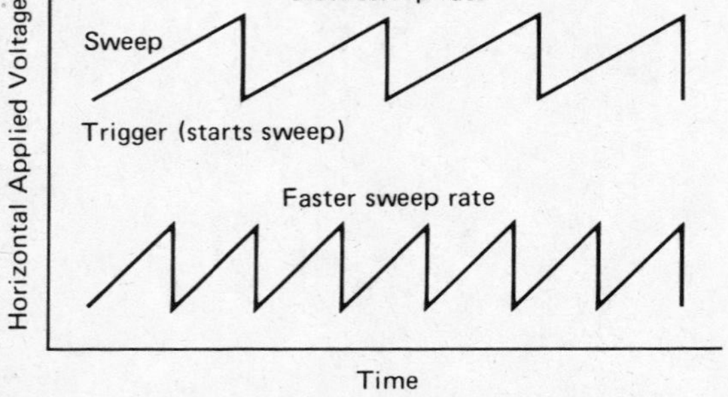

Figure 34.2 Voltage versus time. Sawtooth voltage functions that supply different oscilloscope sweep rates.

A. Time and Frequency Measurements

The sweep rate is given in time per division. This is major divisions of about 1 cm, not one of the small divisions. To make time measurements on the signal, count the number of divisions between two points and multiply the sweep time or rate (time per division, which is typically of the order of milliseconds/div (ms/div). For example, if there are 4 divisions between the points of interest and the sweep time is 2 ms/div, then

$$t = (4 \text{ div}) \times (2 \text{ ms/div}) = 8 \text{ ms}$$

and 4 divisions correspond to 8 ms on the horizontal time base. Care must be taken to see that the sweep controls are in a calibrated position.

To measure frequency (f), first measure the time for one full wave (one wavelength), which is the period T. Then use the relationship $f = 1/T$ to calculate the frequency. Another method of measuring frequency will be discussed in Section C on Lissajous figures.

B. Voltage Measurements

In addition to frequency measurements, the oscilloscope can be used as a voltmeter to read the peak-to-peak voltages of ac signals as well as dc voltages. The voltage readings are read directly from a plastic screen or grid attached to the face of the oscilloscope tube. Recall that the vertical deflection of the beam is proportional to the voltage of the signal applied to the vertical deflection plates.

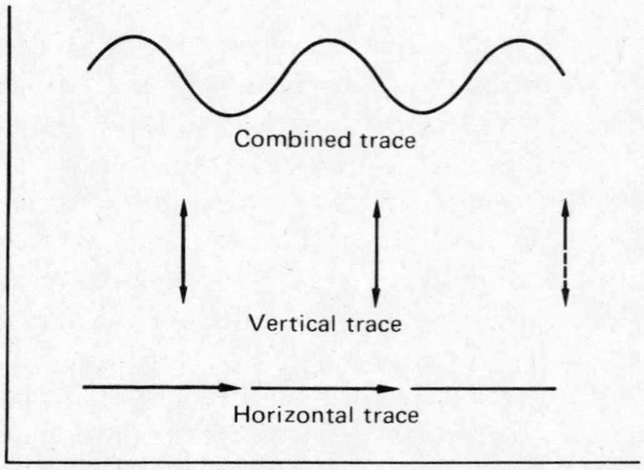

Figure 34.3 Sinusoidal wave form. The combination of a horizontal sweep signal and a vertical sinusoidal signal produces a sine-wave trace on an oscilloscope screen.

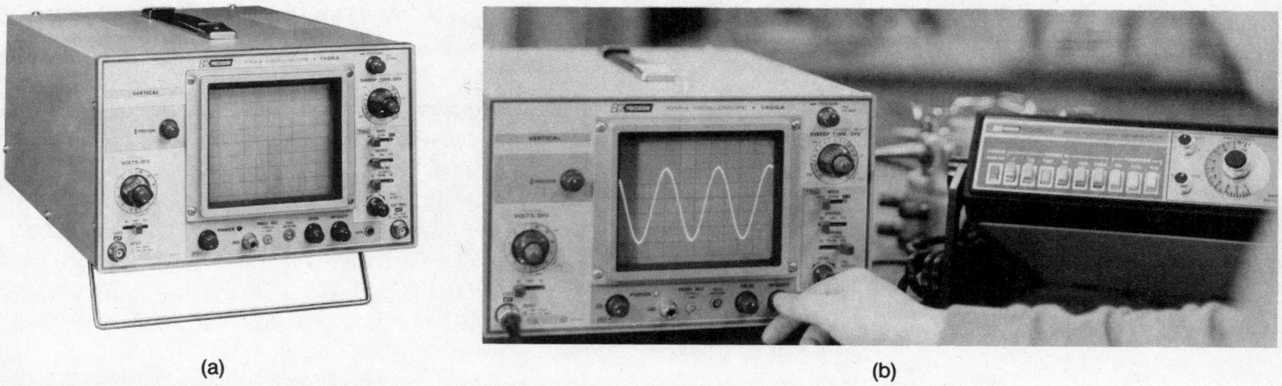

Figure 34.4 Oscilloscopes. (a) A typical student model oscilloscope. (Photo courtesy of B+K Precision, Dynascan Corporation.) (b) A sine-wave trace on an oscilloscope from a function generator input.

The peak-to-peak height of the trace of an ac input signal is then measured and the peak-to-peak voltage computed from the calibration. Dividing by two gives the peak voltage V_o and multiplying by $1/\sqrt{2} = 0.707$ gives the root-mean-square (rms) value of the voltage.*

There is a large variety of oscilloscopes, and the controls of each model and make cannot be discussed here. All oscilloscopes have some operating controls in common; however, some have controls that others lack, depending on the purpose and sophistication of the scope. Also, controls and connectors are not always found in the same location or in the same form on all oscilloscopes. A typical oscilloscope (B+K, Model 1466A) found in an introductory physics lab is shown in Fig. 34.4a.

C. Lissajous Figures

The frequency of a sinusoidal voltage can also be determined by comparing it with another calibrated sinusoidal signal. The simplest oscilloscope pattern results when the two sinusoidal signals have the same frequency and are in phase, for example,

$$x = A \sin 2\pi ft$$

and

$$y = A \sin 2\pi ft \qquad \textbf{(34.1)}$$

A diagonal line appears on the screen (Fig. 34.5). The pattern observed when the frequency of the y signal is three times that of the x signal is also shown in Fig. 34.5. Such patterns are called **Lissajous figures**. As before, a stationary pattern results when the frequency of the X-axis signal and the frequency of the Y-axis signal are integral or half-integral.

Suppose that two sinusoidal signals have the same frequency but different phases, for example,

$$x = A \sin 2\pi ft$$

and

$$y = A \sin(2\pi ft - \delta) \qquad \textbf{(34.2)}$$

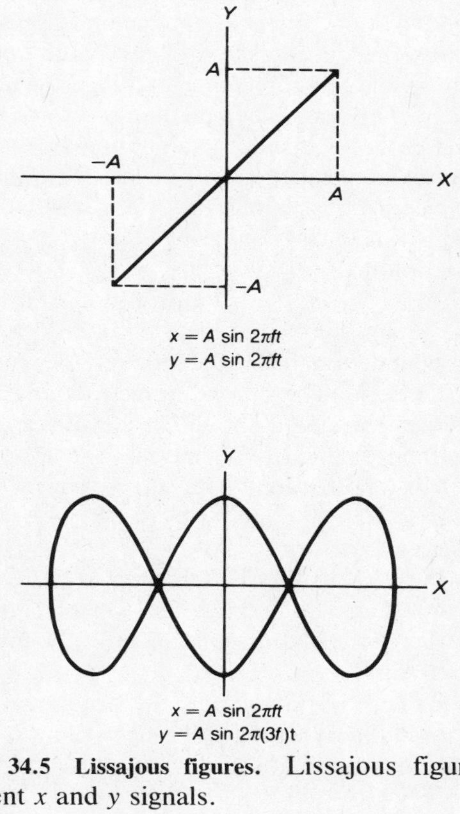

Figure 34.5 Lissajous figures. Lissajous figures for different x and y signals.

* For alternating current, Ohm's law is written $V_{rms} = I_{rms}R$, where $V_{rms} = V_o/\sqrt{2} = 0.0707\ V_o$, and $I_{rms} = 0.707 I_o$; here V_o and I_o are the peak voltage and peak current, respectively. It is customary to measure and specify rms values for ac quantities.

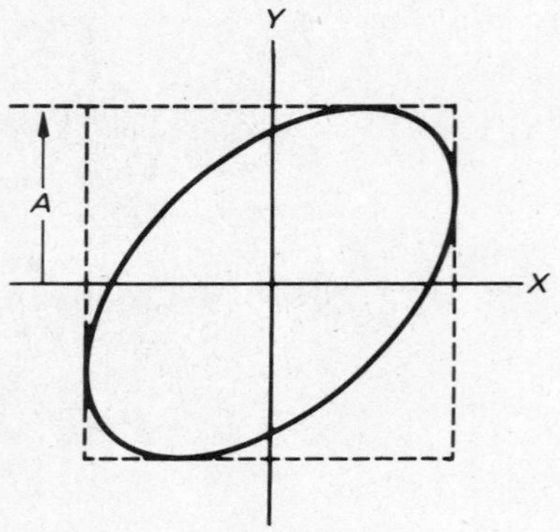

Figure 34.6 Lissajous figure. The Lissajous figure for signals having the same frequency but different phases is an ellipse.

where δ is the *phase angle* or *phase difference*. The phase angle of the x signal is equal to zero. Then an ellipse will be traced out on the screen (Fig 34.6). If the phase difference is 90°, the pattern is a circle. (Why?)

IV. Experimental Procedure

Note: Because different brands and models of oscilloscopes may have somewhat different control names and settings, the described procedures may need modification. Even so, the general operation of all oscilloscopes is the same. Consult the operating instructions manual for your particular instrument if there is a question. Keep in mind that this is an *introduction* to the oscilloscope. You may encounter a variety of oscilloscopes in your career, some very sophisticated, but a familiarity with the theory and functions of the basic controls will aid you greatly in their operation.

1. Locate and familiarize yourself with the following general controls and connections on your oscilloscope. The operating instructions manual of your instrument should be consulted for specific and detailed explanations of the operating controls and for initial control settings.

Display Controls

(a) POWER SWITCH (OFF-ON)—turns the oscilloscope on and off. This switch is often on the same shaft as one of the following controls.

(b) INTENSITY—adjusts the brightness of the spot (by adjusting the rate of electron emission from the cathode).

(c) FOCUS—adjusts the sharpness of the spot.

(d) ASTIG (astigmatism)—adjusts vertical and horizontal positions of trace to same position. If a well-defined trace cannot be obtained with focus control, it may be necessary to adjust the astigmatism control.

(e) SCALE LIGHT (*optional*)—adjusts a lamp that lights the edges of the screen scale.

Position Controls

(a) HORIZONTAL POSITION (H-POS)—adjusts the horizontal position of the spot or trace on the screen.

(b) VERTICAL POSITION (V-POS)—adjusts the vertical position of the spot or trace on the screen.

(c) HORIZONTAL GAIN—provides continuous adjustment of the gain of the horizontal amplifier (i.e., amplifies or "magnifies" the trace).

(d) VERTICAL GAIN—provides continuous adjustment of the gain of the vertical amplifier (i.e., amplifies or "magnifies" the trace).

(e) VOLTS/DIV or VERTICAL ATTENUATOR—provides step adjustment of vertical sensitivity in calibrations of volts per grid division or V/cm.

(f) VARIABLE VOLTS/DIV (VERTICAL GAIN)—provides fine control of vertical sensitivity. In CAL (calibrated) position, the VERTICAL ATTENUATOR is calibrated. May also serve as vertical gain in some operations. (On uncalibrated scopes, the VERTICAL GAIN provides fine control of vertical sensitivity between steps of VERTICAL ATTENUATOR settings, usually in steps of 10.)

Sweep Time and Triggering Mode

(a) SWEEP TIME/DIV or SWEEP (HOR) SELECTOR—selects calibrated horizontal sweep rates in terms of time per grid division.

(b) VARIABLE TIME/DIV (*X* or HORIZONTAL GAIN or SWEEP VERNIER)—provides fine sweep time adjustment. In CAL (calibrated) position, the sweep time is calibrted in time/div steps. (On uncalibrated scopes, horizontal gain adjustment is provided by a HORIZONTAL GAIN control.)

(c) TRIG MODE—three-position switch that selects triggering mode.

AUTO—triggers sweep operation when trigger signal is present and automatically generates sweep in absence of trigger signal.

NORM—normal triggered sweep operation. No trace unless proper trigger signal is applied.
X-Y —vertical input signal produces vertical (*Y*-axis) deflection; EXT input signal produces horizontal (*X*-axis) deflection.

(d) SYNC (HOR) SELECTOR or SOURCE—selects the triggering source (i.e., source that determines *when* spot is triggered or starts sweeping across screen).
INT —wave form being observed is used as sync trigger.
LINE—sweep is triggered by line voltage or in step with (60 Hz) line frequency.
EXT —sweep is triggered by signal applied to EXT jack.

EXTERNAL CONNECTIONS

(a) VERTICAL INPUT—applies an external signal to the vertical amplifier. The lower terminal is usually grounded (GND) to the instrument case. Sometimes there are two terminals above ground for balanced inputs. The lower terminal must be grounded for grounded-side input and is usually ganged to the ground terminal by a connector. See the operating instructions manual for the instrument.

(b) HORIZONTAL INPUT and/or EXT TRIG—applies an external signal to the horizontal amplifier. May also be input terminal for external trigger signal.

2. Consult the instrument's operating instructions manual for initial starting procedure and control settings. Make the appropriate control adjustments. Turn on oscilloscope. A trace should appear on the screen.

Adjust the INTENSITY and FOCUS. *Never advance the intensity control to the point where an excessively bright spot or trace appears on the screen. A bright spot can burn the screen and decrease its useful life.* Adjust the HORIZONTAL POSITION and VERTICAL POSITION controls so that the spot is in the center of the screen. If you have trouble obtaining a spot, ask the instructor for assistance.

3. With a low SWEEP TIME/DIV setting, adjust the VARIABLE TIME control and note the effect.

A. Time and Frequency Measurements

4. Set the TRIG MODE to NORM, the SOURCE SWITCH to INT, and the SWEEP TIME variable control to CAL. Connect the function generator sine-wave output to the VERTICAL (*X*) INPUT of the scope. Turn on the function generator and set the generator frequency at 90 Hz. Adjust the function generator amplitude control so that the sine-wave pattern is almost full-scale on the screen. (Switch the TRIG MODE momentarily to *X-Y*. What do you observe and why?)

5. Adjust the SWEEP TIME/DIV control so that a wave pattern with two peaks appears on the screen. Read the number of divisions for one full sine-wave cycle and record in the Laboratory Report.

6. **(a)** Compute the time period (T) of one cycle of the wave pattern using the calibrated SWEEP TIME/DIV setting and record.
(b) Compute the sine-wave frequency ($f = 1/T$) and compare with the function generator setting by computing the percent difference.

7. Repeat the preceding procedures for a function generator output of 300 Hz.

8. With the generator output still at 300 Hz, adjust the SWEEP TIME/DIV control in various steps and note the relationship of the number of wave cycles to the sweep time/div. (Can you explain? See Question 1 at the end of the experiment.)

9. Set the SYNC (HOR) SELECTOR to LINE. Adjust the function generator frequency to 60 Hz so a stationary pattern appears on the screen. This matches the generator frequency to the relatively stable 60-Hz line frequency, which is more accurate than the calibration markings on the function generator. Compare the generator frequency setting to the line frequency by finding the percent error.

10. Adjust the calibrated SWEEP TIME/DIV control until one or more full sine-wave cycles appear on the screen. Then, compute the frequency of the sine wave appearing on the scope as before.

B. Voltage Measurement

11. **(a)** With the full sine-wave cycle(s) on the screen (procedure 10), record the VOLTS/DIV control setting (with variable control at CAL).

(b) Read the number of peak-to-peak divisions for the height of the wave pattern on the screen.

(c) Compute the rms voltage of the wave.

C. Lissajous Figures

12. Set TRIG MODE to *X-Y* and apply a 60-Hz sine wave to the HORIZONTAL or *X* INPUT. A second function generator may be used.* (Do not exceed the voltage limitation of the oscilloscope in any case.)

With either the VERTICAL or HORIZONTAL INPUT set at 60 Hz, adjust the other input frequency to 30 Hz, making a fine adjustment of this generator frequency to obtain a stationary pattern. (If two generators are used, adjust the generator amplitude control(s) so the signals have equal amplitudes. This is done by alternately adjusting the signal amplitude with the other generator switched off.) Observe the pattern on the screen.

13. Adjust the generator frequency to 60 Hz and obtain a stationary wave pattern. Note that by slight adjustment you can vary the pattern between a straight line and a circle. (Can you explain why?)

14. Continue to increase the generator frequency and observe the various stationary and moving patterns. Record in the Laboratory Report.

D. General

15. You should now be getting a feeling for the oscilloscope controls and operations. Adjust the various control knobs so as to understand their functions better. Also, connect the square-wave output of the function generator to the VERTICAL INPUT and investigate this wave form.

* With two function generators, it is important to have a common ground for both generators and the oscilloscope.

Name ______________________ Section ______________ Date ______________

Lab Partner(s) ____

EXPERIMENT 34

Introduction to the Oscilloscope

Laboratory Report

A. Time and Frequency Measurements

Generator frequency 90 Hz

Calculations (show work)

No. of divisions ______________

Time sweep/div ______________

Period ______________

Frequency ______________

Percent difference ______________

Generator frequency 300 Hz

Calculations (show work)

No. of divisions ______________

Time sweep/div ______________

Period ______________

Frequency ______________

Percent difference ______________

Don't forget units

(continued)

Source—Line (60 Hz)

Generator frequency setting ____________________

Percent error ____________________

No. of divisions ____________________

Time sweep/div ____________________

Period ____________________

Frequency ____________________

Calculations (show work)

B. Voltage Measurement

Calculations (show work)

Volts/div ____________________

No. of divisions (peak to peak) ____________________

rms voltage ____________________

Name ____________________ Section ____________ Date ____________

Lab Partner(s) ____________________

EXPERIMENT 34 *Laboratory Report*

C. Lissajous Figures

X-input frequency	*Y*-input frequency	Sketches of patterns (attach separate sheet)
____	____	
____	____	
____	____	
____	____	
____	____	
____	____	
____	____	

QUESTIONS

1. How does the number of wave cycles seen on a screen for a fixed input frequency vary with the SWEEP TIME/DIV control setting? Why?

2. Explain why the 60-Hz Lissajous figure could be varied between a straight line and a circle.

Name ______________________ Section ______________ Date ______________

Lab Partner(s) ____

EXPERIMENT 35

The *RC* Circuit: Oscilloscope Study

Advance Study Assignment

Read the experiment and answer the following questions.

1. Compare the voltages across a capacitor in dc and ac *RC* circuits.

2. How is the time base of the horizontal oscilloscope trace determined?

3. What is the significance of the *RC* time constant for the circuit?

4. Explain how the time constant of an *RC* circuit is determined from a stationary oscilloscope pattern.

The *RC* Circuit: Oscilloscope Study

I. Introduction and Objectives

The oscilloscope can be used to study many ac circuit characteristics. The screen display of voltage versus time allows observation of a variety of measurements. In particular, in an ***RC* (resistance-capacitance) circuit,** the charging effect of the capacitor can be visually observed. And using the horizontal time scale, the time constant of the charging process can be readily determined.

In this experiment, the oscilloscope will be used to determine the time constant of an *RC* circuit as the capacitor is continually charged and discharged by an ac signal voltage.

After performing this experiment and analyzing the data, you should be able to:

1. Explain the charging characteristics of a capacitor with ac voltage.
2. Appreciate how the oscilloscope can be used to monitor electrical characteristics and to make electrical measurements.
3. Describe how an *RC* time constant may be measured from an oscilloscope trace.

II. Equipment Needed

- Function generator (square wave)
- Oscilloscope
- Three capacitors (0.05 μF, 0.1 μF, and 0.2 μF, or capacitor substitution box)
- Three resistors (5 kΩ, 10 kΩ, and 20 kΩ, or resistance box)
- Connecting wires
- 2 sheets of Cartesian graph paper
- (Optional) Unknown resistor wrapped in masking tape to conceal value

(Optional)

- Computer-assisted experiment as with PASCO's Series 6500 Interface System

III. Theory

When an *RC* circuit is connected to a dc voltage source, charge must flow into the capacitor before the voltage across the capacitor can change. This takes time. As the voltage across the capacitor becomes closer to that of the source, the flow of charge becomes slower and slower. The capacitor voltage approaches the supply voltage as an asymptote—coming ever closer, but never getting there. When the capacitor starts with no voltage across it, $V = 0$ at $t = 0$, the changing voltage is given by the formula

$$V = V_o(1 - e^{-t/RC}) = V_o(1 - e^{-t/\tau}) \qquad \textbf{(35.1)}$$

where e is the base of the natural logarithms ($e = 2.718\ldots$), V_o the voltage of the dc source, R the resistance in the circuit, and C the capacitance. The quantity $\tau = RC$ is the **time constant** of the circuit. (See the Theory section in Experiment 33.)

After a time of one time constant, $t = \tau = RC$, the voltage is

$$V = V_o(1 - e^{-RC/RC}) = V_o(1 - e^{-1}) = V_o(0.63)$$

or

$$\frac{V}{V_o} = 0.63 \qquad \textbf{(35.2)}$$

That is, the voltage across the capacitor is 0.63 (or 63%) of its maximum value (Fig. 35.1). For a dc voltage source, the capacitor voltage further in-

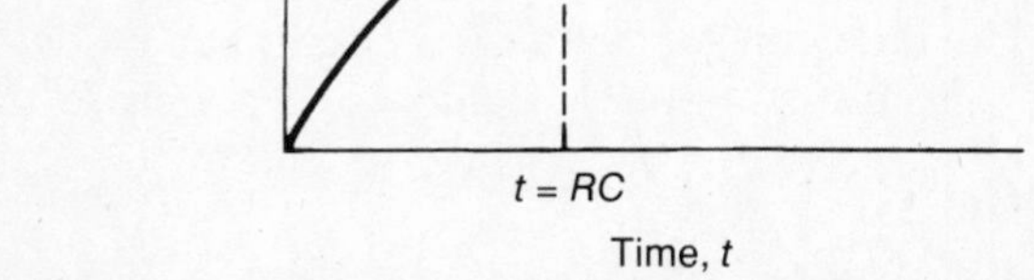

Figure 35.1 Voltage rise. A graph of voltage versus time for a capacitor charging in an *RC* circuit. In a time $t = RC$, the capacitor charges to 63% of its maximum value.

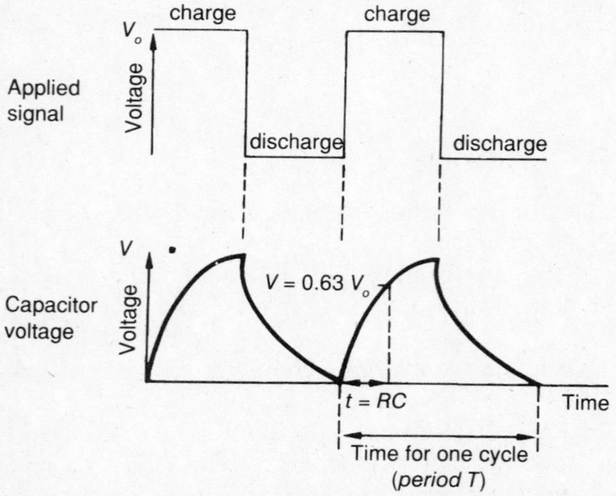

Figure 35.2 Charging and discharging. When a square-wave signal is applied to a capacitor in an *RC* circuit, the capacitor periodically charges and discharges.

creases to V_o and maintains this voltage unless discharged.

However, for an ac voltage source, the capacitor voltage increases and decreases as the voltage of the applied signal alternately increases and decreases. For example, suppose that a square-wave ac signal as illustrated in Fig. 35.2 is applied to the circuit. The voltage across the capacitor increases according to Eq. 35.1 and then decreases according to the relationship*

$$V = V_o e^{-t/RC} \qquad (35.3)$$

On an oscilloscope, the time base or the magnitude of the horizontal time axis is determined by the SWEEP TIME/DIV. From this control setting, you can determine time functions for traces on the screen. For example, suppose two complete wave cycles of a stationary sinusoidal pattern covers 6.66 horizontal divisions with a SWEEP TIME/DIV setting of 5 ms/div. Then, the time for these two cycles is time = ST/div × div = 5 ms/div × 6.66 div = 33.3 ms. So, the time for one cycle or the period of the wave is T = 33.3 ms/2 = 16.7 ms. (What is the frequency of the wave?)

The time constant of an *RC* circuit can be determined from a stationary oscilloscope pattern of the capacitor voltage versus time. This is done by finding the horizontal distance (time) needed for the trace to reach 0.63 V_o.

On an oscilloscope, time is measured as a horizontal distance. The scale is set by the knob marked SWEEP TIME/DIV.

Example 35.1 If the horizontal distance from the starting point to the point where the trace reaches 63% of the maximum voltage V_o, as shown in Fig. 35.1, is 6.5 divisions (1 division ≈ 1 cm), the time for 6.5 horizontal divisions is equal to one time constant (τ).

With the SWEEP TIME/DIV set at 5 ms/div, the value of the *RC* time constant would be (6.5 div) × (5 ms/div) = 32.5 ms.

IV. Experimental Procedure

1. Turn on the oscilloscope and function generator. Set the function generator frequency to 100 Hz and the wave amplitude near maximum. Connect the square-wave output of the function generator directly to the vertical input terminals of the oscilloscope.

   Obtain a stationary trace of one or two cycles of the square-wave pattern on the screen using the oscilloscope techniques learned in Experiment 34. Adjust the vertical VOLTS/DIV and the function generator amplitude until the pattern is exactly 8 divisions high. (This is about 8 cm high.) If V_o is 8 divisions, the 5-division horizontal line will be very close to the 0.63 V_o criterion for measuring the time constant (since 5/8 = 0.625, actually 0.625 V_o).

2. Then, set up the circuit as shown in Fig. 35.3, with $R = R_1$ = 10 kΩ and $C = C_1$ = 0.1 μF. *Have the instructor check the circuit before attaching the final lead to the oscilloscope.*

3. Close the oscilloscope circuit by connecting the wire to the circuit and note the pattern. Carefully

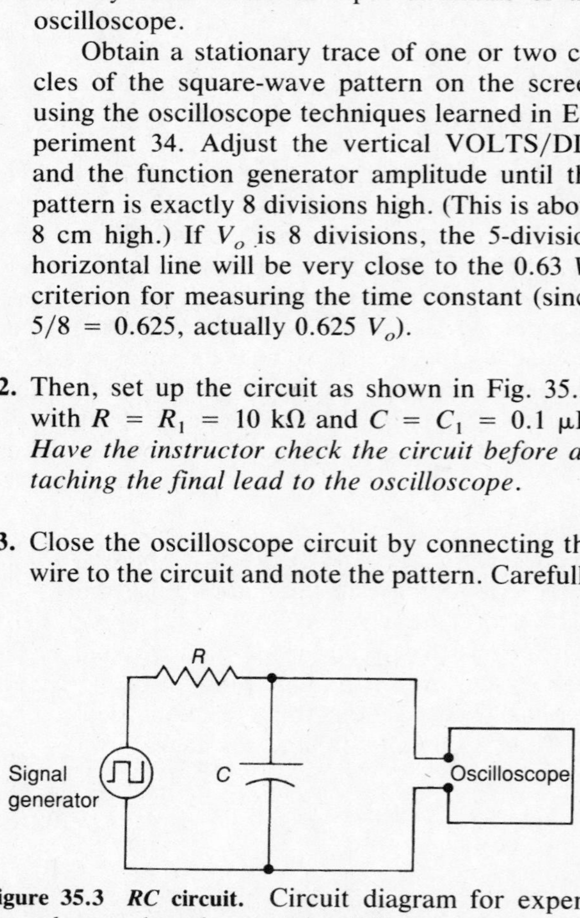

Figure 35.3 *RC* circuit. Circuit diagram for experimental procedure for studying *RC* circuits.

* It should be noted that the high point on the charging curve and the low point on the decay curve in Fig. 35.2 are not $V = V_o$ and $V = 0$, respectively, since it takes infinite times for the capacitor to charge and discharge to these values. However, if the time constant is several times smaller than one-half the period T of the square wave, $T = 1/f$, then to a good approximation the high and low points of the curve may be taken to correspond to $V = V_o$ and $V = 0$, respectively.

adjust the trigger controls so that the curve starts upward at the left end of the trace. The exponential rise time can be observed in greater detail by increasing the sweep rate (decreasing the TIME/DIV). Adjust the time (TIME/DIV) until the rising curve extends well across the screen. Be sure that the variable TIME/DIV remains in the calibrated position.

4. With the total pattern 8 divisions high, the time constant is represented by the horizontal distance from the point where the trace starts to move up to the point where it crosses the horizontal line 5 divisions up. The time is found by multiplying the horizontal distance by the TIME/DIV setting (see Example 35.1). Record in the data table.

5. Open the circuit and repeat procedures 3 and 4 with $R = R_2 = 5\ \text{k}\Omega$ and $R = R_3 = 20\ \text{k}\Omega$.

6. On a Cartesian graph, plot the experimental τ versus R. Determine the slope of the straight line that best fits the data. To what does the value of the slope correspond?

7. Relace R with $R_1 = 10\ \text{k}\Omega$, and repeat procedures 3 and 4 with $C = C_2 = 0.05\ \mu\text{F}$ and $C = C_3 = 0.2\ \mu\text{F}$.

8. On a Cartesian graph, plot the experimental τ versus C. (You should have three data points for τ with R_1. Why?) Determine the slope of the straight line that best fits the data. To what does the value of the slope correspond?

9. Compute the time constants for each of the *RC* combinations using the known R and C values and compare with the experimentally determined values by finding the percent errors.

10. *(Optional)* Use your knowledge gained in this experiment to experimentally determine the value of the unknown resistor. Remove the masking tape after doing so and compute the percent error.

Name ______________________ Section ______________ Date ______________

Lab Partner(s) ____

E X P E R I M E N T 3 5

The *RC* Circuit: Oscilloscope Study

Laboratory Report

DATA TABLE 1

Purpose: To determine the effect of R on the time constant.

	R ( )	C ( )	Divisions for 0.63 rise	Sweep time = div	Exp. time constant	Computed RC	Percent error
Case 1 R_1C_1							
Case 2 R_2C_1							
Case 3 R_3C_1							

Calculations (show work)

Slope of the τ versus R plot ______________

Percent difference between slope and C_1 ______________

Don't forget units

(continued)

DATA TABLE 2
Purpose: To determine the effect of C on the time constant.

	R ( )	C ( )	Divisions for 0.63 rise	Sweep time = div	Exp. time constant	Computed RC	Percent error
Case 4 R_1C_2							
Case 5 R_1C_3							

Slope of the τ versus C plot ________________

Percent difference between slope and R_1 ________________

Experimental RC time constant ________________

Capacitance, C ________________

Computed R ________________

Marked value of R ________________

Percent error ________________

QUESTIONS

1. Based on experimental results, under what conditions are the charging times of different RC circuits the same?

2. In the form $V = V_o\,(1 - e^{-t/\tau})$, the $\tau = RC$ in the exponential must have units of time. (Why?) Show that this is the case.

3. How could the value of an unknown capacitance be determined using the experimental procedures? Show explicitly by assuming a value for an experimentally determined time constant.

Name ______________________ Section ______________ Date ______________

Lab Partner(s) ____

EXPERIMENT 36

Phase Measurements and Resonance in ac Circuits

Advance Study Assignment

Read the experiment and answer the following questions.

1. What is meant by the phase difference between the voltage and current in an ac circuit?

2. What is the effect of (a) capacitive reactance and (b) inductive reactance, and how does each affect the phase?

3. What is impedance, and is a circuit with impedance capacitive or inductive?

(continued)

4. State the condition for resonance in a series *RLC* circuit, and describe the circuit effect of resonance.

5. Explain how the phase difference between voltage and current can be measured with a single-beam oscilloscope.

Phase Measurements and Resonance in ac Circuits

I. Introduction and Objectives

In **ac (alternating current) circuits**, the current in the circuit alternates in direction. For an applied sinusoidal voltage, the current varies sinusoidally with time. However, the current is not always exactly in phase with the voltage. The current may "lead" or "lag" the voltage, depending on the circuit elements.

In this experiment, the phase properties of particular circuit elements will be studied, together with the important condition of resonance. In this condition, the current and voltage are in phase and the current in the circuit is a maximum. This means that there is maximum power transfer from the voltage source to the circuit.

After performing this experiment and analyzing the data, you should be able to:

1. Describe phase differences in ac circuits.
2. Clearly distinguish between capacitive reactance, inductive reactance, and impedance.
3. Explain what is meant by *RLC* series circuit resonance and its circuit effects.

II. Equipment Needed

- Audio signal generator (sine wave)
- Oscilloscope (with horizontal and vertical amplifiers in phase or completely out of phase)
- Standard decade resistance box (10 to 9990 Ω)
- Two capacitors (0.10 μF and 0.50 μF, or capacitor substitution box)
- Air-core inductor (250 mH)
- Connecting wires

(*Optional*)

- Computer-assisted experiment, as with PASCO's Series 6500 Interface System

III. Theory

When a dc (direct current) voltage source, such as a battery, is applied to an electrical circuit, the resulting current flows only in one direction, as the polarity (+ and −) of the voltage remains constant. For an ac (alternating current) voltage source, however, the polarity of the voltage alternates with time, and the direction of the current flow in the circuit alternates with the same frequency as the voltage source.

One of the most commonly used ac voltages is one that varies sinusoidally with time. This may be generally described by the equation

$$V(t) = V_m \sin(2\pi ft - \phi_V) \qquad \textbf{(36.1)}$$

where V_m is the maximum voltage amplitude and f is the frequency of the source. The angle ϕ_V is called the **phase angle**. If $\phi_V = 0$, then

$$V(t) = V_m \sin 2\pi ft \qquad \textbf{(36.2)}$$

which means that the voltage is zero at $t = 0$.

The current in the ac circuit may or may not be in phase with the voltage, depending on the nature of the components in the circuit. In any case, if the applied voltage is sinusoidal, the current I is also sinusoidal, and as a function of time may be expressed as

$$I(t) = I_m \sin(2\pi ft - \phi) \qquad \textbf{(36.3)}$$

where I_m is the maximum amplitude of the current and ϕ a phase angle. In Eq. 36.2 the phase angle of the voltage has been assumed to be zero. In this case, ϕ is also the *phase difference* between the applied voltage and the resulting current. (More generally, $\phi = \phi_I - \phi_V$ and is the angle between I_m and V_m, as illustrated in Fig. 36.1.)

The phase angle ϕ in Eq. 36.3 can be either positive or negative. When it is positive, the maximum value of the current I_m is reached at a later time than the maximum value of the voltage V_m (Fig. 36.1). In this case, we say that the voltage *leads* the current or the current *lags* behind the voltage by a phase difference ϕ. Similarly, if ϕ is negative, the current leads and the voltage lags.

When there is a capacitive element in the circuit (an *RC* circuit, Fig. 36.2a), the alternate charging and discharging of the capacitor opposes the current flow. This opposition is expressed as **capacitive reactance** X_C, and

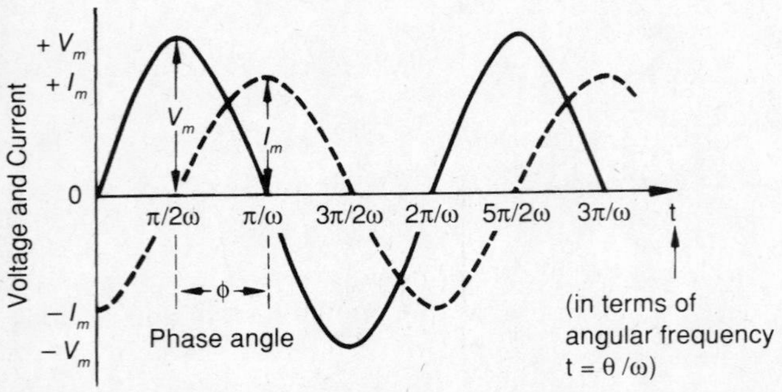

Figure 36.1 ac Voltage and current. The voltage and the current are out of phase, and in this case, the voltage leads the current by a constant phase difference or angle ϕ.

$$X_C = \frac{1}{2\pi fC} \tag{36.4}$$

where C is the value of capacitance (in farads, F). The unit of X_C is ohms (Ω).

Similarly, when there is an inductive element in an ac circuit (an *RL* circuit, Fig. 36.2b), the self-induced counter emf in the induction coil opposes the current. The **inductive reactance** X_L is given by

$$X_L = 2\pi fL \tag{36.5}$$

where L is the inductance of the coil (in henrys, H). The unit of X_L is ohms.

Many ac circuits have both capacitive and inductive reactance elements. The combined opposition to the current flow of resistive and reactive elements in a series circuit as shown in Fig. 36.2C, a series *RLC* circuit, is expressed in terms of the **impedance** Z of the circuit, which is given by

$$Z = [R^2 + (X_L - X_C)^2]^{1/2}$$

$$= \left[R^2 + \left(2\pi fL - \frac{1}{2\pi fC}\right)^2\right]^{1/2} \tag{36.6}$$

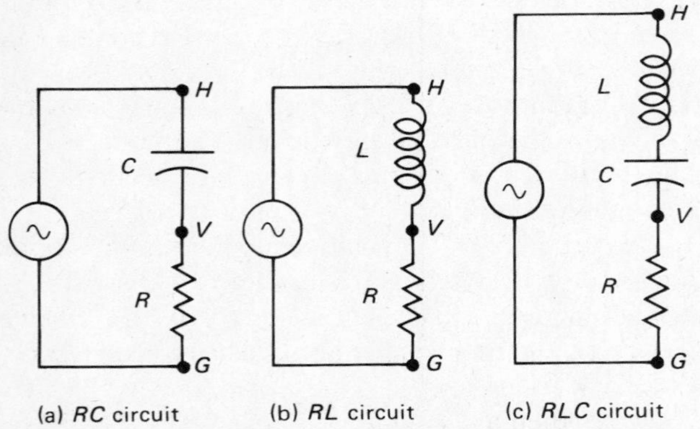

Figure 36.2 Basic circuits. Circuit diagrams for (a) *RC*, (b) *RL*, and (c) *RLC* series circuits.

The unit of Z is also ohms. (R is the total resistance of the circuit. In general, it is assumed that the resistance of the induction coil is negligible compared with the resistor element.)

For the *RLC* series circuit, the phase relation of the voltage and current is given by

$$\tan \phi = \frac{X_L - X_C}{R} \tag{36.7}$$

This relationship is often represented in a *phasor diagram,* in which the resistance and reactances are added like vectors (Fig. 36.3). Note that the angle ϕ is either positive or negative, depending on whether the inductive or capacitive reactance is greater. If X_L is greater than X_C, then ϕ is positive and the current lags behind the applied voltage. The circuit is then said to be *inductive*.

Similarly, if X_C is greater than X_L, ϕ is negative and the current leads the voltage. In this case, the circuit is said to be *capacitive*. (Eq. 36.7 can be applied to single-reactance circuits, as in Fig. 36.2a and b, by letting the appropriate reactance by zero.)

A common way to remember the phase relationship in inductive and capacitive circuits is by the phrase

ELI the *ICE* man

Here E represents the voltage (V). In an inductive circuit (L), the voltage leads the current as indicated by E "leading" I in *ELI* (see Fig. 36.1). Similarly, in a capacitive circuit (C), the current leads the voltage, *ICE*.

Since the voltage and current are continually changing in an ac circuit, it is convenient to consider effective or time-average values of the voltage and current. These root-mean-square (rms) values are given by $V = V_m/\sqrt{2}$ and $I = I_m/\sqrt{2}$, where V_m and I_m are the maximum or "peak" voltage and current, respectively. The rms values of V and I are the values read on most ac voltmeters and ammeters.

An Ohm's-law type relationship holds between these values and the impedance Z:

$$V = IZ \tag{36.8}$$

and it follows that

$$V_m = I_m Z$$

Thus, for a given applied voltage, the smaller the impedance of a circuit, the greater the current in the circuit ($I = V/Z$).

Notice in the reactance term in Eq. 36.6 that there is a minus sign and that the individual reactances are reciprocally frequency-dependent. As a result, for given L and C values, the total reactance can be zero for a particular frequency at which $X_L = X_C$. That is,

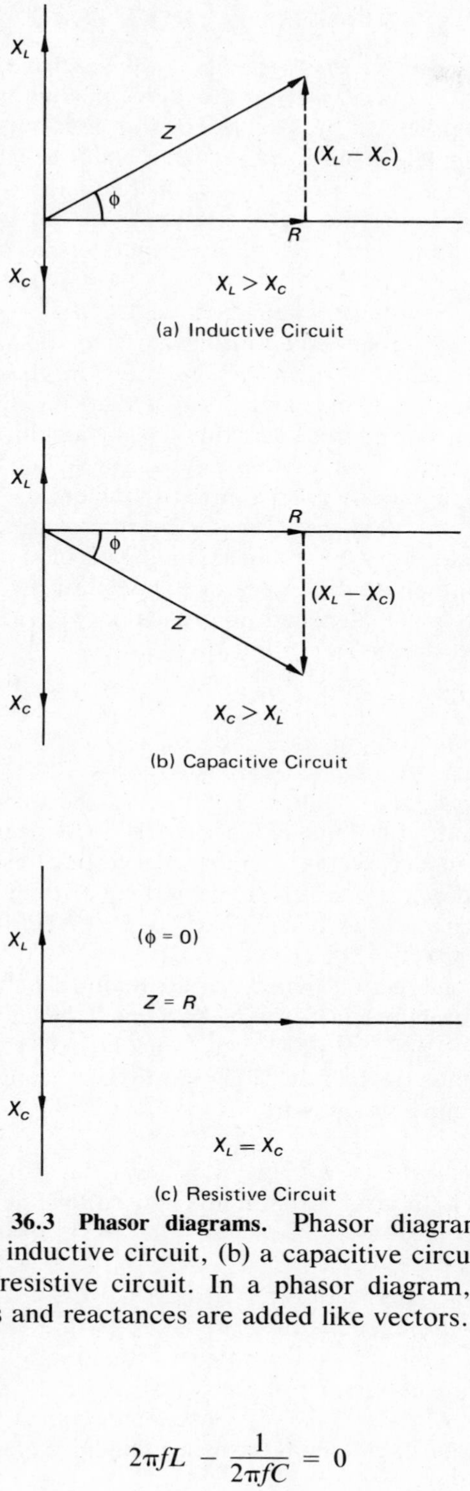

Figure 36.3 Phasor diagrams. Phasor diagrams for (a) an inductive circuit, (b) a capacitive circuit, and (c) a resistive circuit. In a phasor diagram, resistances and reactances are added like vectors.

$$2\pi fL - \frac{1}{2\pi fC} = 0 \quad \textbf{(36.9)}$$

and solving for f,

$$f_r = \frac{1}{2\pi\sqrt{LC}} \quad \textbf{(36.10)}$$

where f_r is called the **resonance frequency.** Driven at this frequency, the circuit is said to be **in resonance.** The impedance is then equal to the resistance in the circuit, $Z = R$, and the circuit is resistive (Fig. 36.3c).

Since the impedance is a minimum at the resonance condition, the maximum current flows in the circuit from the voltage source, and maximum power $P = I^2Z = I^2R$. For fixed values of L and C, resonance occurs at the particular resonance frequency f_r given by Eq. 36.10. However, notice from Eq. 36.9 that for a given source frequency, resonance can also be obtained by varying L and/or C in the circuit.

Example 36.1 A 10 (rms)-V, 1000-Hz voltage is applied to a series *RLC* circuit with $R = 1.0\ \text{k}\Omega$ and $L = 250$ mH. (a) What value of capacitance would put the circuit in resonance? (b) How much current would flow in the circuit in this condition?

Solution Given: $V = 10\text{(rms) V}$, $f = 10^3$ Hz, $R = 1.0\ \text{k}\Omega = 1000\ \Omega$ and $L = 250\ \text{mH} = 0.250$ H. (a) To have f_r be 10^3 Hz, the required capacitance is given by

$$f_r = \frac{1}{2\pi\sqrt{LC}}$$

or

$$C = \frac{1}{L4\pi^2 f_r^2} = \frac{1}{(0.250\ \text{H})(4\pi^2)(10^3\ \text{Hz})^2}$$
$$= 0.10 \times 10^{-6}\ \text{F} = 0.10\ \mu\text{F}$$

(b) Since $Z = R$, for resonance, and with $V = 10$ V and $R = 1000\ \Omega = 10^3\ \Omega$,

$$I = \frac{V}{Z} = \frac{V}{R} = \frac{10\ \text{V}}{10^3\ \Omega} = 0.010\ \text{A (rms)}$$

In this experiment, it is desired to measure the phase difference between the applied voltage and current in ac circuits, and to investigate resonance condition in a series (or parallel) *RLC* circuit using an oscilloscope. Notice from Eq. 36.7 that for the resonance condition, $X_L = X_C$, and the voltage and current are in phase ($\phi = 0$), since $\tan\phi = 0$ (and $\tan 0 = 0$).

To obtain a double-trace graph of V and I as in Fig. 36.1 requires a double-beam oscilloscope or special electronics, which are often not available. However, phase measurements can be made with an ordinary oscilloscope by the following method.

Suppose that different voltage signals are applied to the horizontal and vertical inputs of an oscilloscope. If the ratio of the horizontal and vertical input frequencies is an integral or half-integral (see Experiment 34), then a stationary elliptical pattern such as the one in Fig. 36.4 is observed. Assume that the applied voltages have the forms

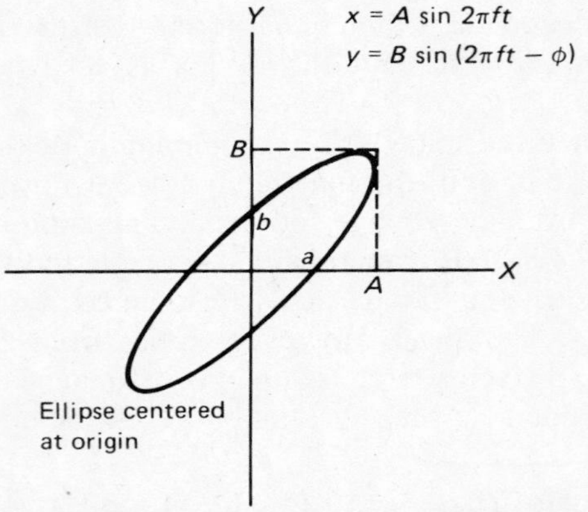

Figure 36.4 Phase measurements. An elliptical pattern is used to measure the phase angle difference. See text for description.

$$x = A \sin 2\pi ft$$
$$y = B \sin(2\pi ft - \phi) \quad \textbf{(36.11)}$$

where A and B are the amplitudes. [Compare with Eqs. 36.1 and 36.3 that give the voltage $V(t)$ and circuit current $I(t)$, respectively.] Note that the y intercepts, $+b$ and $-b$, occur when $x = 0$, or when $2\pi ft = 0$ (since $\sin 0 = 0$).

Then from the second equation, $b = B \sin(-\phi)$. Hence,

$$\sin \phi = \pm \frac{b}{B}$$

and similarly

$$\sin \phi = \pm \frac{a}{A} \quad \textbf{(36.12)}$$

You should be able to prove and understand that if $A = B$ and $\phi = 90°$, the trace would be a circle. Also, if $A = B$ and $\phi = 0°$, the trace is a straight line.

To measure the phase angle difference of the voltage and current in a circuit, the voltage signal from the signal generator is applied to the horizontal input. For example, for the circuits in Fig. 36.2, connections are made to points H and G, where G is to the horizontal ground terminal. The voltage input signal has the form of Eq. 36.1.

The current signal is applied to the vertical input with connections made to points V and G, where G is to ground. This is actually a voltage input from across the resistor in the circuit. However, it is proportional to and in phase with the current through the resistor (and therefore through the entire series circuit). Hence, the phase angle difference between the voltage and the current can be determined from the shape of the resulting elliptical oscilloscope pattern, as described above.

IV. Experimental Procedure

1. Turn on the oscilloscope and the signal generator. It is necessary for the horizontal and vertical amplifiers of the oscilloscope to be in phase (or completely out of phase, $\phi = 180°$) to measure the phase differences. See if this is the case by connecting the signal generator output to both the horizontal and vertical inputs of the oscilloscope.

Set the generator frequency at 1000 Hz with the wave amplitude near maximum. If the horizontal and vertical amplifiers are in phase, the resulting trace is a diagonal straight line through the first and third quadrants. If the amplifiers are completely out of phase, the diagonal line will be through the second and fourth quadrants.

In either case, phase measurements can be made. Vary the frequency of the generator to see if the phase difference of the amplifiers remains reasonably constant, in particular over the range 100 to 1000 Hz.

A. *Capacitive Circuit*

2. Set up a circuit as in Fig. 36.2a. Use the standard decade resistance box as R set at 500 Ω and a capacitance of about 0.50 μF. Set the signal generator at a frequency of 1000 Hz. Connect point G to one of the oscilloscope ground terminals and points V and H to the vertical and horizontal inputs, respectively. The SWEEP (HOR) SELECTOR should be on EXT.

Obtain on the screen an elliptical pattern of appropriate size for measurement by adjusting the HORIZONTAL and VERTICAL GAINS. Adjust the INTENSITY and FOCUS controls to obtain a sharp pattern.

3. Then vary (a) the generator frequency, (b) R, and (c) C (if a substitution box is used) one at a time and observe the effects.

4. Using the parameter values suggested in procedure 2, make measurements on the shape of the elliptical trace required to determine the phase difference angle ϕ. (Measure $2b$ and $2B$ or $2a$ and $2A$ for convenience; $\sin b/B = \sin 2b/2B$.) Record the measurements in the Laboratory Report.

5. Compute the phase-difference angle (Eq. 36.12) and the value of R (Eq. 36.7). Compare the experimental and known values of R by finding the percent error.

B. Inductive Circuit

6. Replace the capacitor with the inductor (Fig. 36.2b) and make $R = 2000\ \Omega$. Repeat part A for this arrangement. Alternatively, if the value of L is unknown, use the known values of R and f to compute L.

C. RLC *Circuit Resonance*

7. Set up a circuit as in Fig. 36.2c with $R = 500\ \Omega$ and $C = 0.50\ \mu F$. Vary the frequency of the signal generator, and observe what happens. Determine, as accurately as possible, the frequency at which the circuit is in resonance with the trace a diagonal straight line. Record the resonance frequency in the Laboratory Report. Using the known values of L and C, compute the resonance frequency and compare to the measured value by finding the percent difference.

8. Repeat procedure 7 with the 0.50-μF capacitance replaced by a 0.10-μF capacitance.

9. Change the scope SWEEP TIME SELECTOR from EXT to a suitable SWEEP rate. Observe the magnitude of the current $I(t)$ as the generator frequency is varied around the resonance frequency f_r, with the circuit as shown in Fig. 36.2c. (What happens to I at f_r? How sharp is the effect?) Calculate and record

$$\frac{I\ (\text{at } f_r)}{I\ (\text{at } 2f_r \text{ or } 0.5f_r)}$$

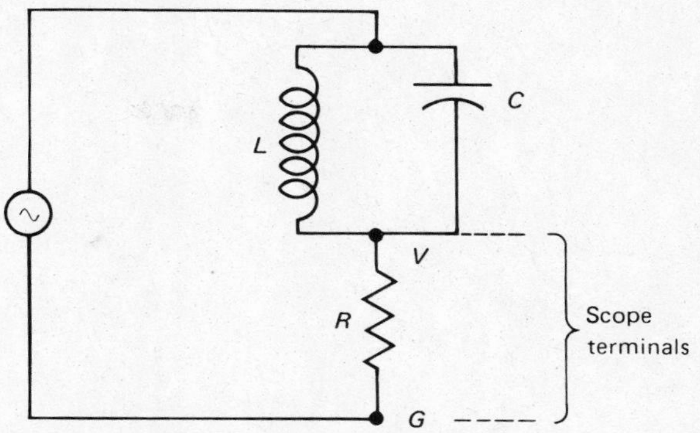

Figure 36.5 Anti-resonance. Circuit diagram for a parallel LC circuit.

(Use the number of scale divisions for I. This is proportional to the actual value.)

Occasionally check the voltage of the frequency generator by moving the vertical connection from point V to point H in the circuit in Fig. 36.2c to verify that the voltage of the frequency generator remains unchanged. Adjust if necessary.

10. Rearrange the circuit for the parallel LC arrangement, as shown in Fig. 36.5. (This is sometimes called an *anti-resonance* circuit.) Repeat procedure 9. (Now what happens to I at f_r? How sharp is the effect?) Calculate and record

$$\frac{I\ (\text{at } 2f_r \text{ or } 0.5f_r)}{I\ (\text{at } f_r)}$$

Name ______________________ Section ______________ Date ______________
Lab Partner(s) ____

EXPERIMENT 36

Phase Measurements and Resonance in ac Circuits

Laboratory Report

A. Capacitive Circuit

R ______________

C ______________

Calculations (show work)

Generator frequency ______________

$2a$ or $2b$ ______________

$2A$ or $2B$ ______________

Computed ϕ ______________

Computed R ______________

Percent error ______________

B. Inductive Circuit

R ______________

L ______________

Calculations (show work)

Generator frequency ______________

$2a$ or $2b$ ______________

$2A$ or $2B$ ______________

Computed ϕ ______________

Computed R ______________

Percent error ______________

Don't forget units

(continued)

C. RLC *Circuit Resonance*

1. R ______ Measured resonance frequency ______

   L ______ Computed resonance frequency ______

   C ______ Percent error ______

2. R ______ Measured resonance frequency ______

   L ______ Computed resonance frequency ______

   C ______ Percent error ______

   Describe current behavior at $f = f_r$.

   Divisions at $f = f_r$ ______ Sharpness ratio ______

   Divisions at $f = 2f_r$ or $0.5f_r$ ______

3. Parallel (anti-resonance) LC circuit

   R ______ Measured resonance frequency ______

   L ______ Computed resonance frequency ______

   C ______ Percent error ______

   Describe current behavior at $f = f_r$.

   Divisions at $f = f_r$ ______ Sharpness ratio ______

   Divisions at $f = 2f_r$, or $0.5f_r$ ______

Name ______________________ Section ____________ Date ____________

Lab Partner(s) ____

EXPERIMENT 36 *Laboratory Report*

QUESTIONS

1. Prove mathematically that the oscilloscope pattern for horizontal and vertical input signals of the same frequency and amplitude (a) is a circle when the phase difference of the signals is 90°; (b) is a straight line for the resonance condition.

2. In tracing out an elliptical pattern on the screen, the oscilloscope beam moves in either a clockwise or a counterclockwise sense.
   (a) Which way would the beam move in the series *RLC* circuit in terms of voltage and current lead or lag and the capacitive and inductive nature of the circuit.

   (b) Which way would the beam move in the *RLC* circuit in the experiment if the generator frequency were (1) greater than f_r, and (2) less than f_r?

(continued)

3. A series *RLC* circuit is driven by a voltage signal of a given frequency other than f_r. For a fixed *R*, how should *L* and *C* be varied so that the maximum current flows in the circuit?

4 Suppose that the resistance of the inductor coil were not negligible compared with the resistance in an *RL* or *RLC* circuit. How would this affect the impedence?

5. Why is a parallel *LC* circuit called an ''anti-resonance'' circuit?

Name ______________________ Section ______________ Date ______________

Lab Partner(s) ____

EXPERIMENT 37

Electromagnetic Induction

Advance Study Assignment

Read the experiment and answer the following questions.

1. If a straight wire in the plane of this paper and parallel to this printed line carries a conventional current from left to right, indicate the directions of the magnetic field on both sides of the wire. (Make a sketch.)

2. What does magnetic flux measure?

3. Explain Faraday's law of induction.

(continued)

Name ______________________ Section ______________ Date ______________

Lab Partner(s) ____

4. Explain how Lenz's law gives the direction of the induced current in a wire when the change of flux is known.

5. What is magnetic permeability?

Electromagnetic Induction

I. Introduction and Objectives

Electromagnetic induction is one of the most important and most importantly applied relationships between electricity and magnetism. A classic discovery was made by the Danish physicist Hans Oersted in 1820 when he noticed the deflection of the needle of a compass near a current-carrying wire. This led to the conclusion that a magnetic field is produced by an electrical current.

A reasonable question to ask is whether the reverse is possible. That is, can a magnetic field produce an electrical current or potential difference in a conductor? The English scientist Michael Faraday investigated this question and found that the answer was yes, under certain conditions. This phenomenon is expressed in Faraday's famous law of induction, which is the basis of generation of electrical power.

After performing this experiment and analyzing the data, you should be able to:

1. Apply the right-hand rule to a current to determine the direction of the associated magnetic field.
2. Explain Faraday's law of induction and how a voltage can be generated.
3. Describe Lenz's law and its implications.
4. Explain what is meant by magnetic permeability.

II. Equipment Needed

- Pair of insulated cylindrical coils (many turns on secondary relative to primary)*
- Iron and brass or aluminum-core rods
- Two bar magnets of different pole strengths
- Low-voltage dc power supply or dry cell
- Magnetic compass
- Knife switch
- Portable galvanometer
- Metric ruler or meterstick
- Connecting wires
- 1 sheet of Cartesian graph paper

III. Theory

Oersted discovered that a magnetic field is associated with an electrical current. He further established a relationship between the direction of the current and the direction of the magnetic field. The magnetic field lines are found to be closed circles around the current-carrying wire, as may be illustrated with a compass.

The **direction of the magnetic field** is given by a **right-hand rule** (Fig. 37.1):

> *If a current-carrying wire is grasped with the right hand with the thumb extended in the direction of the* conventional *current, the curled fingers indicate the circular sense of the magnetic field lines.*

The direction of the magnetic field at any point is then tangential to the circle. (Recall that the direction of the conventional current is the direction that *positive* charges would flow in a circuit.)

Faraday investigated the possible reverse effect, a current being produced by a magnetic field in the vicinity of a wire. No effect was found with a stationary magnet or magnetic field. However, it was discovered that a current is induced when there is relative *motion* or a *changing* magnetic field.

Thus, electromagnetic induction involves a time-varying magnetic field, for example, when a magnet

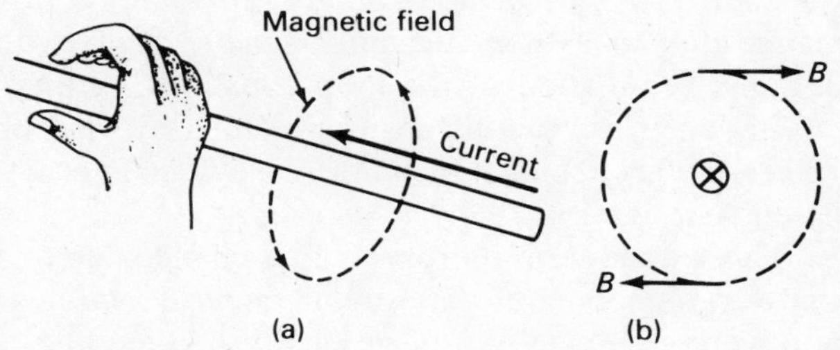

Figure 37.1 Right-hand rule for determining direction of magnetic field. (a) When the thumb of the right hand points in the direction of the conventional current, the fingers curl around the conductor in the circular sense of the magnetic field. (b) The magnetic field vector is tangent to the circle at any point on the circle. (The ⊗ symbol indicates that the current direction is into the page; that is, as viewed along the conductor in the direction of the current. A dot (●) would indicate a current coming out of the page.)

* The primary coil is to be inserted into the secondary coil.

is moved toward or away from a loop of wire. Since magnetic induction depends on *relative* motion, the same effect could be produced by moving the coil toward or away from a stationary magnet.

Investigation led Faraday to the conclusion that the important factor in electromagnetic induction was the time rate of change of the magnetic field **B** through a loop. The "total" magnetic field through a loop of wire can be characterized by what is called **magnetic flux** Φ:

$$\Phi = \mathbf{B} \cdot \mathbf{A} = BA \cos \theta \qquad (37.1)$$

where A is the cross-sectional area of the loop and θ is the angle between a normal to the plane of the loop and the magnetic field.*

The result of this work was **Faraday's law of induction**, which relates the induced voltage or emf in a wire to the time rate of change of flux:

$$V = -\frac{\Delta\Phi}{\Delta t} \qquad (37.2)$$

where V is the average value of the induced voltage over the time interval Δt. (By Ohm's law, the average induced current is $I = V/R$, where R is the resistance of the circuit.)

Substituting the magnetic flux (Eq. 37.1) into Eq. 37.2 shows that a change in flux can result from changes other than a change in magnetic field. In general,

$$\frac{\Delta\Phi}{\Delta t} = -\left[\left(\frac{\Delta B}{\Delta t}\right)(A \cos \theta) + B\left(\frac{\Delta A}{\Delta t}\right)(\cos \theta) + BA\left(\frac{\Delta(\cos \theta)}{\Delta t}\right)\right] \qquad (37.3)$$

The first term within the brackets represents a flux change due to a time-varying magnetic field (with area and orientation of the loop constant). A time-varying magnetic field is easily obtained by varying the current producing it, as in the case of an alternating current.

The second term represents flux change due to a time-varying loop area. This could occur if a circular loop were stretched in a place or if it had an adjustable circumference. The third term represents a change in the orientation of the loop with time. This occurs when a loop is rotated in a magnetic field.

In all cases, the number or density of field lines through a loop changes. In this experiment, we are concerned only with the effect of the first term in Eq. 37.3—a flux change due to a time-varying magnetic field.

* The SI unit for the magnetic field B is the tesla (T). Hence, the units of the magnetic flux Φ are tesla-m² (T-m²). An older unit of magnetic flux is weber/m² (Wb/m²), and the flux has the unit of weber (Wb) in this case.

The negative sign in Eq. 37.2 expresses another important law of electromagnetic induction, **Lenz's law,** which gives the direction of the induced current:

> *An induced current flows in such a direction that its effects oppose the change that produces it.*

Essentially, this means the induced current gives rise to a magnetic field that opposes the change in the original magnetic field. If this were not the case and the magnetic field arising from the induced current augmented the original field (i.e., was in the same direction as the original field), the induced field would increase the flux, which would increase the current, which would increase the flux, and so on. This would give rise to a something-for-nothing situation that would violate the conservation of energy.

To investigate this phenomenon, consider producing a time-varying magnetic field through a stationary loop, as illustrated in Fig. 37.2. When the switch in the battery circuit is closed, the current in the loop goes from zero to a constant value in a short time. During this time, however, the magnetic field associated with the current also increases or changes with time.

The magnetic flux through the adjacent loop then changes with time, and an induced current momentarily flows in the loop, as indicated by the galvanometer deflection. The induced current goes to zero when the current in the battery circuit has a constant value. (Why?) Similarly, when the switch is opened, the magnetic field decreases and a current flows momentarily in the detector loop in the direction opposite to that of the first induced current. (Why?)

If there are a number of loops N in the detector circuit, the flux change through each loop contributes to the induced current or voltage, and Faraday's law becomes

$$V = -N\frac{\Delta\Phi}{\Delta t} \qquad (37.4)$$

Similarly, the magnitude of the magnetic field (number of field lines) would be increased if there were a number of loops in the battery circuit. (Loops of wire wound in a tight helix so as to form a coil are called a **solenoid**.)

It can be shown that the magnetic field near and along the axis of a current-carrying solenoid is given by

$$B = \mu_o nI \qquad (37.5)$$

where n is the linear turn density of the coil (i.e., the number of turns per unit length N/L where L is the length of the coil).

The constant μ_o is called the **permeability of free space** (vacuum or, approximately, air), and indicates

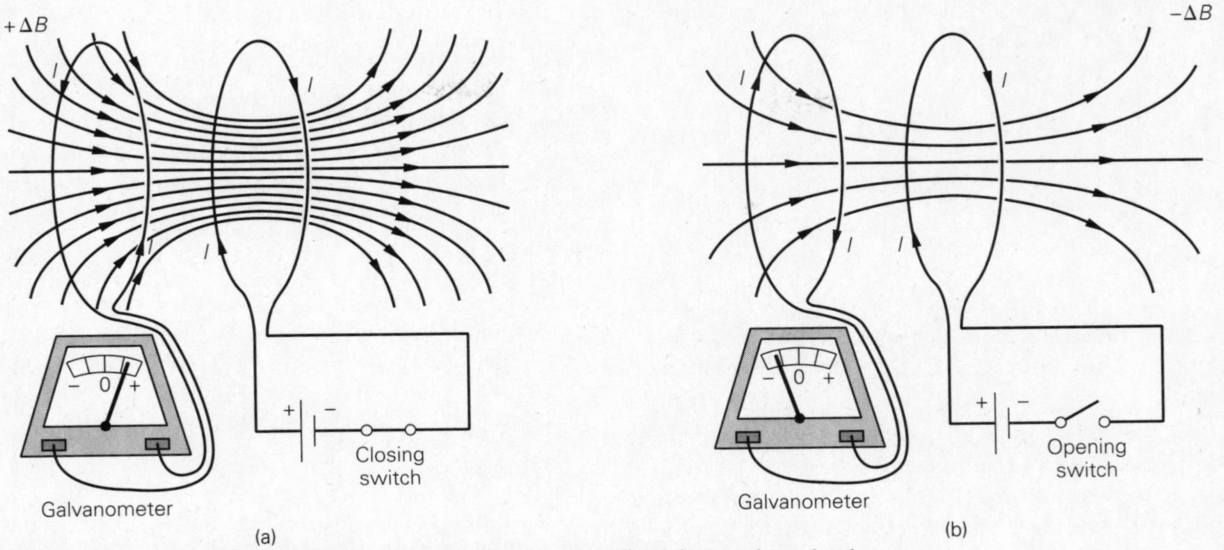

Figure 37.2 Electromagnetic induction. (a) A time-varying field is produced when the switch is closed and the current goes from zero to some steady value. As the current increases, the field builds up, and the number of field lines through a nearby loop changes, inducing a current in the loop as indicated by the galvanometer deflection. (b) When the switch is opened, the current decays to zero, the field lines decrease, and a current is induced in the opposite direction in the nearby loop. Both processes take place in a very short time.

that the solenoid has an air core. If a material with a magnetic permeability μ is used as a solenoid core, μ_o is replaced by μ in Eq. 37.5. The **permeability** expresses the magnetic characteristics of a material. Some materials with large permeabilities can be used to increase greatly the magnetic field in a current-carrying solenoid.

IV. Experimental Procedure

1. In this experiment, it is important to know the direction of the induced current in a circuit. This is related to the positive and negative deflections of the galvanometer. To establish the direction of the galvanometer deflection due to a known current direction, connect one terminal of the dry cell (or dc power supply at 1.5 to 3.0 V) to one terminal of the galvanometer and the other source terminal *through a large resistance* to the other galvanometer terminal (Fig. 37.3). Use yourself as the large resistance. (Really get into the circuit, so to speak.)

   From the known polarity of the source, relate the galvanometer deflection to the direction of current flow. For conventional current (assuming positive charge carriers), the current flows *from* the positive source terminal. Galvanometer deflections to the right are usually labeled as positive and deflections to the left as negative. It is convenient to have a conventional current entering the positive galvanometer terminal to give a positive deflection.

A. Induced Current

2. Connect the galvanometer to the terminals of the secondary coil (the larger coil with the greater number of turns) as shown in Fig. 37.4. Use the compass to determine the relative strengths of the bar magnets.

   Then, move the stronger magnet in and out of the coil, noting and recording the effects (relative magnitude and direction of the galvanometer

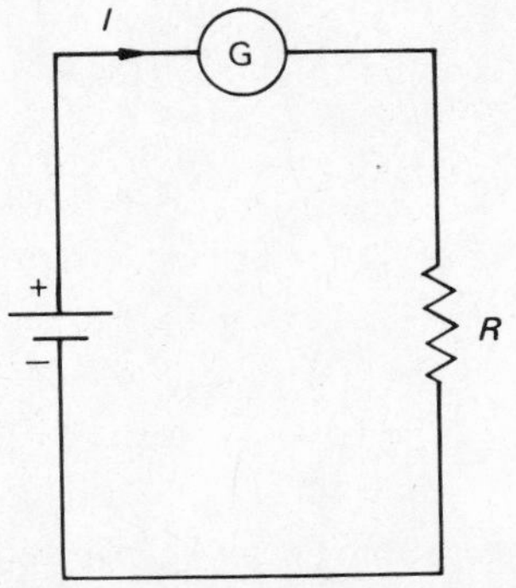

Figure 37.3 Galvanometer deflection. Circuit diagram for determining the direction of the galvanometer deflection with respect to the current direction.

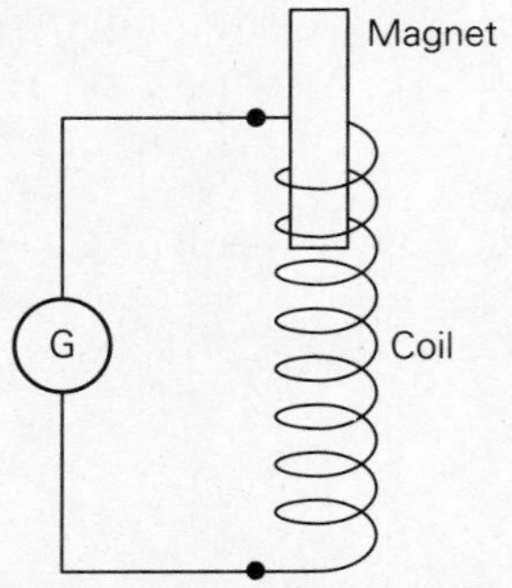

Figure 37.4 Induced current. Experimental setup for determining the induced current due to a moving magnet.

deflection) with (a) the speed at which the magnet is moved and (b) the change of the magnet's polarity. Also note the effect when the magnet is stationary in the coil. Record your results in the Laboratory Report.

3. Repeat procedure 2 with the other magnet, and draw conclusions based on the experimental data.

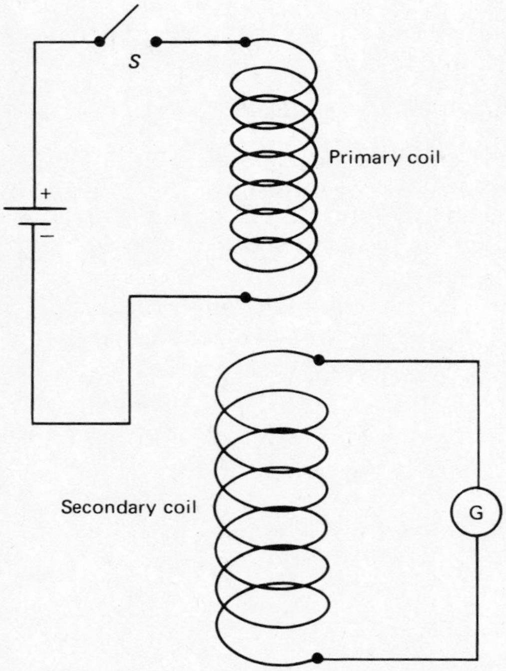

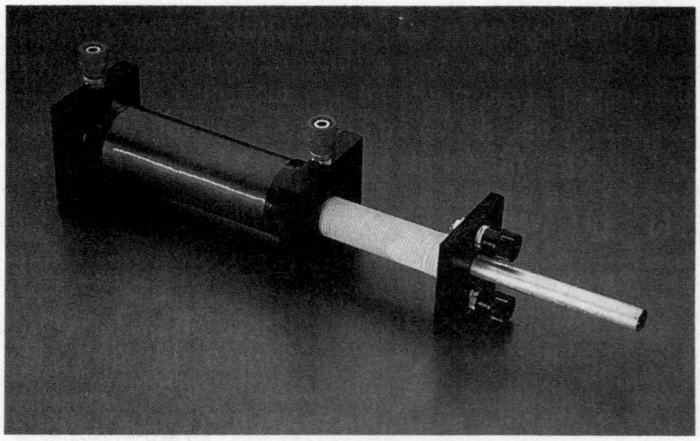

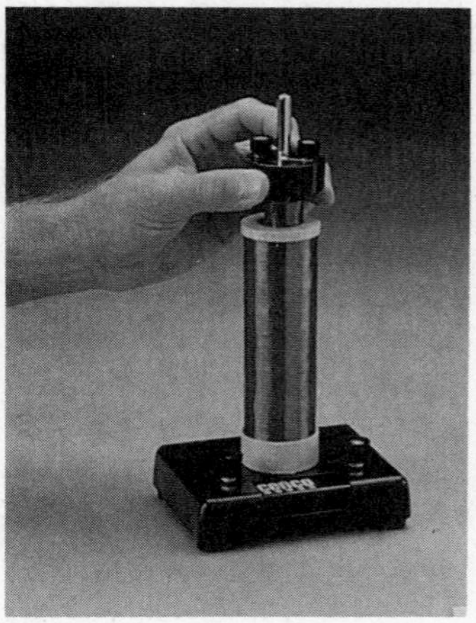

Figure 37.5 Coil effects. A diagram illustrating the experimental setup for investigating electromagnetic induction. The primary coil is inserted into the secondary coil as shown in the photos of actual coil apparatus. [Photos courtesy of (top) PASCO Scientific and (bottom) Central Scientific Co., Inc.]

B. Induced Magnetic Field

4. Set up the primary coil circuit as shown in Fig. 37.5, with the knife switch *S* open. (A secondary coil circuit is not needed in parts B and C.) Close the switch and with the compass, investigate the magnetic field around the coil. Make a sketch of the field pattern in the Laboratory Report.

C. Lenz's Law

5. Open the switch and insert the stronger bar magnet into the primary coil almost the full length of the magnet. Close the switch and slowly remove the magnet from the coil. Note, record, and explain any observed effects.

D. Permeability

6. Open the switch and insert the primary coil into the secondary coil, which is connected to the galvanometer (Fig. 37.5). Close and open the switch, noting and recording the magnitude and direction of the galvanometer deflection in each case.

7. Repeat procedure 6 with each of the two metal cores. Draw conclusions based on the experimental data.

E. *Length of Coil*

8. Measure and record the length of the primary coil. With the switch open, insert the primary coil with the iron core completely into the secondary coil. Make a series of observations of the magnitudes of the deflections as the switch is opened and closed, withdrawing the primary coil 1 cm between the observations. Record the length of the primary coil still inside the secondary coil in each case.

   Find the average magnitude of the plus and minus deflections for each observation, and plot a graph of the average deflection magnitude versus the length of the primary inside the secondary. Use an abcissa scale of decreasing length. Interpret the results of the data.

Name ______________________ Section ______________ Date ______________

Lab Partner(s) ____

EXPERIMENT 37

Electromagnetic Induction

Laboratory Report

A. Induced Current

	Maximum deflection (scale divisions)	Current direction (+ or −)
Magnet 1		
Motion toward coil		
v_1	______	______
$v_2 > v_1$	______	______
Motion away from coil		
v_1	______	______
$v_2 > v_1$	______	______
Magnet 2		
Motion toward coil		
v_1	______	______
$v_2 > v_1$	______	______
Motion away from coil		
v_1	______	______
$v_2 > v_1$	______	______

Conclusions

Don't forget units

(continued)

B. Induced Magnetic Field

(Sketch)

C. Lenz's Law

Observation and explanation

D. Permeability

	Galvanometer deflection (scale divisions)	Secondary current direction (+ or −)
Air core		
switch closed	________	________
switch opened	________	________
Iron core		
switch closed	________	________
switch opened	________	________
________ core		
switch closed	________	________
switch opened	________	________

Name ______________________ Section ______________ Date ______________

Lab Partner(s) ____

EXPERIMENT 37 ***Laboratory Report***

Conclusions

E. Length of Coil

DATA TABLE

Primary coil length L ______________

Length of primary in secondary	Switch-closed deflection	Switch-opened deflection	Average deflection

Interpretation of data

(continued)

QUESTIONS

1. Suppose that a bar magnet is dropped through a horizontal loop of wire connected to a galvanometer. Explain what would be observed on the galvanometer as the magnet enters, as it is in the middle, and as it leaves the loop. Why?

2. Describe the change of flux through and the induced current in a loop of wire rotated in a uniform magnetic field. (Rotational axis of loop perpendicular to field.)

Name ______________________ Section ______________ Date ______________

Lab Partner(s) ____

E X P E R I M E N T 3 8

Reflection and Refraction

Advance Study Assignment

Read the experiment and answer the following questions.

1. What is the law of reflection, and does it apply to all reflecting surfaces?

2. Distinguish between regular and irregular reflection. Give an example of each.

3. Why is light refracted when it passes from one medium into an optically different medium?

(continued)

4. Show by Snell's law that if the speed of light is less in a particular medium, then a light ray is bent toward the normal when entering that medium. What happens if the speed of light is greater in the medium?

5. What is the difference between the relative index of refraction and the absolute index of refraction? Explain why we can experimentally determine the absolute index of refraction fairly accurately using air as a medium.

Reflection and Refraction

I. Introduction and Objectives

Reflection and refraction are two commonly observed properties of light. The reflection of light from smooth and polished surfaces, such as ponds of water and mirrors, allows us to view the images of objects. Also, when light passes from one medium into another, it is bent or refracted. As a result, a stick in a pond or a spoon in a glass of water appears to be bent.

As part of geometrical optics, these phenomena are explained by the behavior of light rays. Through ray tracing, the physical laws of reflection and refraction can be conveniently investigated in the laboratory. In this experiment a plane mirror and a glass plate are used to study these laws and the parameters used in describing the reflection and refraction of light.

After performing this experiment and analyzing the data, you should be able to:

1. Describe the law of reflection and explain how it can be verified experimentally.
2. Explain Snell's law and its application to transparent materials.
3. Explain what the index of refraction tells you about a transparent material and how it can be measured experimentally.

II. Equipment Needed

- Pins
- Pin board (cardboard or poster board suffices)
- Sheets of white paper ($8\frac{1}{2} \times 11$ in.)
- Ruler and protractor
- Short candle (less than 5 cm) or some similar light source
- Rectangular mirror (and holder if available)
- Thick glass plate (approximately 8×10 cm)

Note: Ray boxes may be used if available.

III. Theory

A. *Reflection*

When light strikes the surface of a material, some light is usually reflected. The reflection of light rays from a plane surface like a glass plate or a plane mirror is described by the **law of reflection:**

> *The angle of incidence is equal to the angle of reflection (i.e., $\theta_i = \theta_r$).*

These angles are measured from a line perpendicular or *normal* to the reflecting surface at the point of incidence (Fig. 38.1). Also, the incident and reflected rays and the normal lie in the same plane.

The rays from an object reflected by a smooth plane surface appear to come from an image behind the surface, as shown in the figure. From congruent triangles it can be seen that the image distance d_i from the reflecting surface is the same as the object distance d_o. Such reflection is called **regular** or **specular reflection**.

The law of reflection applies to any reflecting surface. If the surface is relatively rough, like the paper of this page, the reflection becomes diffused or mixed, so that no image of the source or object will

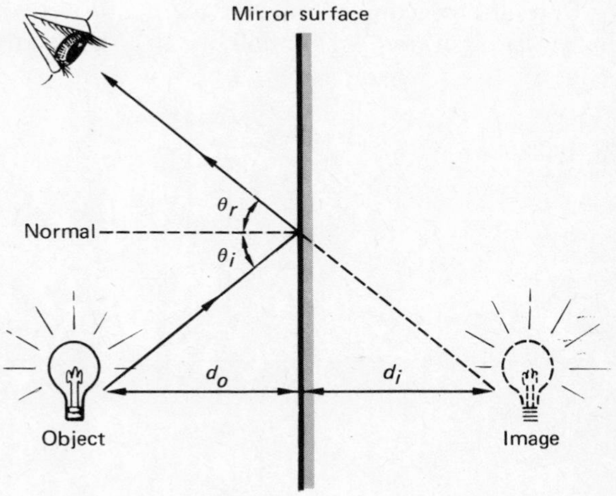

Figure 38.1 Law of reflection. The angle θ_i between the incident ray and the normal to the surface is equal to the angle θ_r between the reflected ray and the normal, that is, $\theta_i = \theta_r$. (Only a single ray is shown.) The object distance d_o is also equal to the image distance d_i for a plane mirror.

be produced. This type of reflection is called **irregular** or **diffuse reflection**.

B. Refraction

When light passes from one medium into an optically different medium at an angle other than normal to the surface, it is "bent" or undergoes a change in direction, as illustrated in Fig. 38.2 for two parallel rays in a beam of light. This is due to the different velocities of light in the two media. In the case of refraction, θ_1 is the angle of incidence and θ_2 is the angle of refraction.

From the geometry of Fig. 38.2, where d is the distance between the parallel rays at the boundary, we have

$$\sin\theta_1 = \frac{v_1 t}{d} \quad \text{and} \quad \sin\theta_2 = \frac{v_2 t}{d}$$

or

$$\frac{\sin\theta_1}{\sin\theta_2} = \frac{v_1}{v_2} = n_{12} \qquad \textbf{(38.1)}$$

where the ratio of the velocities n_{12} is called the **relative index of refraction.** Equation 38.1 is known as **Snell's law**. If $v_2 < v_1$ (as in Fig. 38.2), the rays are bent toward the normal in the second medium. And if $v_2 > v_1$, the rays are bent away from the normal (e.g., reversed rays in Fig. 38.2 with medium 2 taken as medium 1).

For light traveling initially in vacuum (or approximately for light traveling initially in air), the relative index of refraction is called the **absolute index of refraction** or simply the **index of refraction**, and

$$n = \frac{c}{v} \qquad \textbf{(38.2)}$$

where c is the speed of light in vacuum and v the speed of light in the medium. Hence, the index of refraction of vacuum is $n = c/c = 1$, and for air $n \simeq c/c = 1$. For water, $n = 1.33$.

Snell's law can then be written

$$\frac{\sin\theta_1}{\sin\theta_2} = \frac{v_1}{v_2} = \frac{c/n_1}{c/n_2} = \frac{n_2}{n_1}$$

or

$$n_1 \sin\theta_1 = n_2 \sin\theta_2 \qquad \textbf{(38.3)}$$

where n_1 and n_2 are in indices of refraction of the first and second medium, respectively.

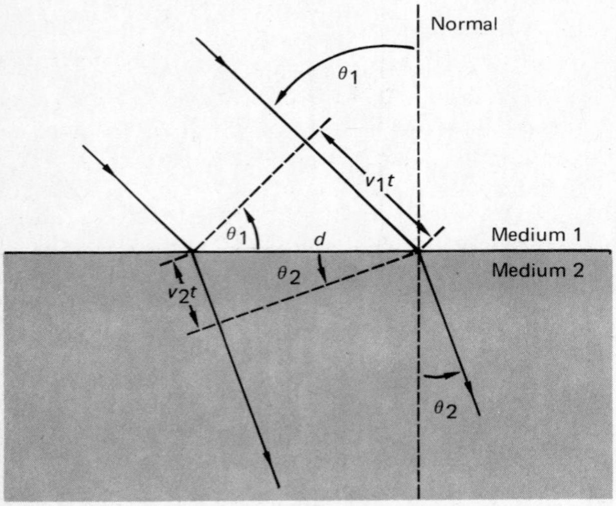

Figure 38.2 Refraction of two parallel rays. When medium 2 is more optically dense than medium 1, then $v_2 < v_1$, and the rays are bent toward the normal as shown here. If $v_2 > v_1$, the rays are bent away from the normal (as if the ray arrows were reversed in reverse ray tracing).

IV. Experimental Procedure

A. Reflection

Glass Plate as a Mirror

1. Place a sheet of white paper on the table. As illustrated in Fig. 38.3, draw a line where the candle (or object) will be placed. The line should be drawn parallel to the shorter edge of the page and about 3 to 4 cm from that edge. Make a mark near the center of the line, and place the candle on the mark.

   Put the glass plate near the center of the paper as shown in the figure. With the length of the plate parallel to the candle line, draw a line along the edge of the glass plate (side toward the candle). Light the candle.

   Caution: *Take care not to burn yourself during the experimental procedure.*

   Looking *directly over the candle* with your eye as in position 1 in Fig. 38.3, you will observe an image of the candle (image 1) in the glass

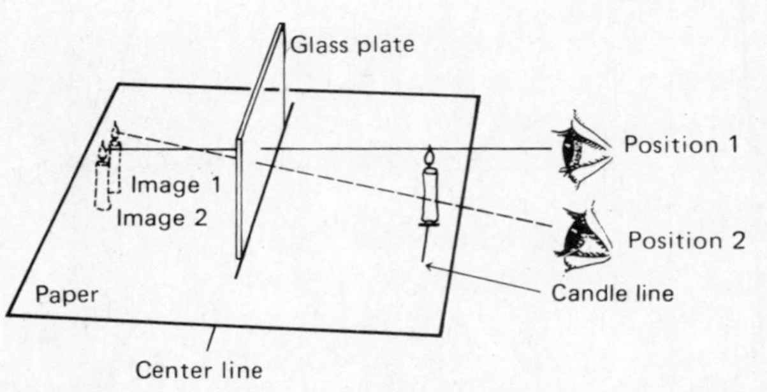

Figure 38.3 Experimental arrangement. Arrangement for experimental procedure for using a glass plate as a mirror. See text for description.

plate. The glass plate reflects light and serves as a mirror. (Observing should be done with only one eye open.)

2. Observing the top of the flame from a side position (2 in Fig. 38.3), you will see a double image, one nearer than the other. Can you explain why?

   Place a pin in the pin board near the glass plate so that it is aligned (in the line of sight) with the front or nearer image of the candle (image 2 in Fig. 38.3; double image not shown in figure). Place another pin closer to you or to the edge of the paper so that both pins and the candle image are aligned. Mark the locations of the pins.

   Repeat this procedure, viewing from a position on the other side of the candle.

3. Remove the equipment from the paper. Draw straight lines through the pair of pin points extending from the candle line through the glass plate line. (Extend the candle line if necessary.) The lines will intersect on the opposite side of the plate line at the location of the candle image.

   Draw lines from the actual candle position or mark to the points of intersection of the previously drawn lines *and* the plate line. These lines from the candle (mark) to the glass-plate line and back to the observation positions are ray tracings of reflected light rays.

4. Draw normal lines to the glass-plate line at the points of intersection of the ray lines. Label and measure the angles of incidence θ_i and reflection θ_r. Record the data in the Laboratory Report.

   Also, measure the perpendicular distances from the glass-plate line to the candle mark (the object distance d_o) and to the candle image position (the image distance d_i). Compute the percent differences of the quantities, as indicated in the Laboratory Report.

Plane Mirror

5. (a) Place the mirror near the center of a sheet of paper as with the glass plate used previously. (The mirror may be propped up by some means or a holder used if available.) Draw a line along the silvered side of the mirror. Then lay an object pin about 10 cm in front of the mirror and parallel to its length (Fig. 38.4). Mark the locations of the ends of the object pin on the paper with a pencil.
   (b) Stick a reference pin *R* in the board to one side of the object pin and near the edge of the paper, as illustrated in Fig. 38.4, and mark its location.
   (c) Placing another pin nearer the mirror, visually align this pin and the reference pin with the head of the object pin's image in the mirror. Mark the position of this pin, and label it with an "H." Then, move this pin over and align it and the reference pin with the "tail" of the image pin. Mark this location, and label it with a "T."
   (d) Repeat this procedure on the opposite side of the object pin with another reference pin.

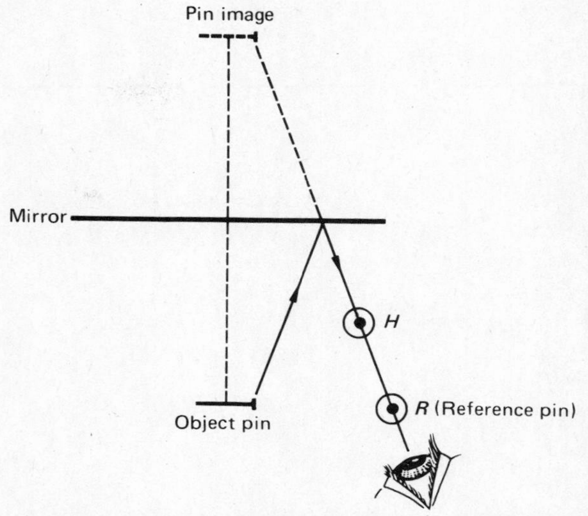

Figure 38.4 Experimental arrangement. Arrangement for experimental procedure for plane mirror. See text for description.

6. Remove the equipment from the paper and draw straight lines from the reference points through each of the H and T locations and the mirror line. The H lines and T lines will intersect and define the locations of the head and tail of the pin image, respectively.

   Draw a line between the line intersections (the length of the pin image). Measure the length of this line and the length of the object pin and record. Also, measure the object distance d_o and the image distance d_i from the mirror line and record.

   Compute the percent differences of the respective measured quantities.

Rotation of a Mirror

7. Place the mirror near the center of a sheet of paper (as described above) and draw a line along the length of the silvered side of the mirror. Measure so as to find the center of the line, and mark that location.

   Stick two pins (*A* and *B*) in the board to one side and in front of and in line with the center of the mirror, as in Fig. 38.5. Viewing the aligned images of these pins from the other side of the

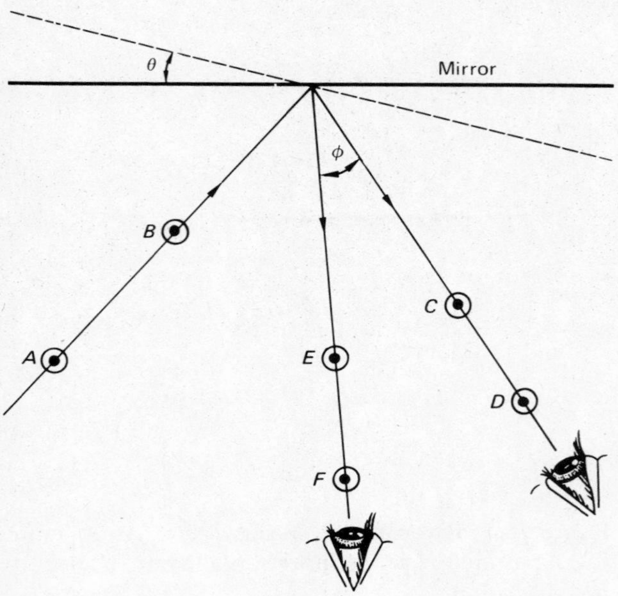

Figure 38.5 Experimental arrangement. An illustration of the experimental arrangement and procedure for the rotation of a mirror. See text for description.

page, place two more pins (*C* and *D*) in alignment. Label the locations of the pins.

8. Leaving pins *A* and *B* in place, rotate the mirror a small but measurable angle θ (approximately 10 to 15°) about its center point, and draw a line along the silvered side of the mirror. Align two pins (*E* and *F*) with the aligned images of *A* and *B*, and mark and label the locations of *E* and *F*.

9. Remove the equipment from the paper and draw the incident ray and the two reflected rays. Measure the angle of rotation θ of the mirror and the angle of deflection φ between the two reflected rays, and record in the Laboratory Report.

Double θ, and compute the percent difference between 2θ and φ. Make a conclusion about the relationship between the angle of rotation of a mirror and the angle of deflection of a ray.

B. Refraction

Index of Refraction of a Glass Plate

10. Lay the glass plate in the center of a sheet of paper, and outline its shape with a pencil (Fig. 38.6). Draw a line normal to one of the sides of the plate, and place a pin (*R*) at the intersection of this line and the face of the plate. Measure an angle of θ_1 of 15° relative to this line, and place a pin (*A*) about 6 to 8 cm from the plate at this angle.

Then sighting through the edge of the plate from the eye position shown in Fig. 38.6, place a pin (*A′*) adjacent to the face of the plate so that it is aligned with *R* and *A*. Mark and label the locations of the pins.

Repeat with pins *B* and *C* at angles of 30° and 45°, respectively. For the 45°-angle case, align an additional pin (*C″* Fig. 38.6).

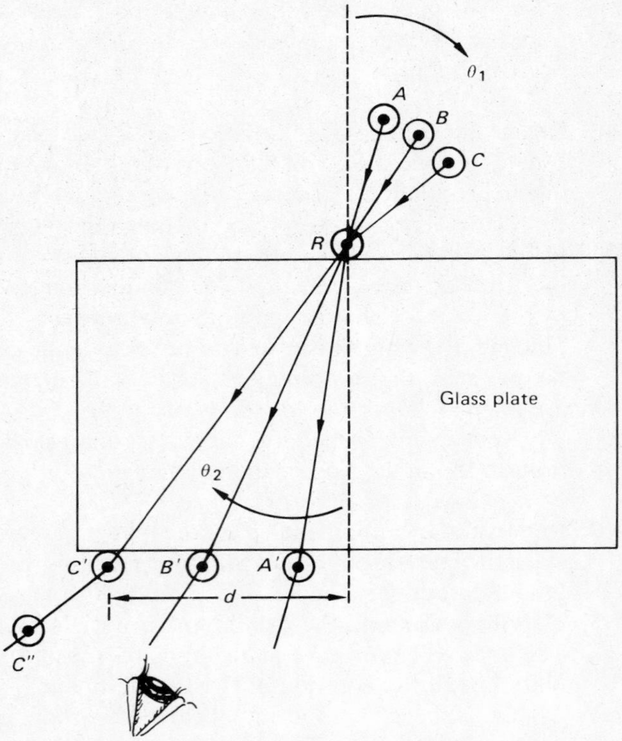

Figure 38.6 Experimental arrangement. An illustration (top view) of the experimental arrangement and procedure for determining the index of refraction of a glass plate. See text for description.

11. Trace the various rays, and measure and record θ_1 and θ_2 for each case. Also measure and record the displacement *d* of ray *C′C″* from the normal and the thickness of the plate. Using Eq. 38.3, compute the index of refraction of the glass.

Compare the average experimental value of the index of refraction with the general range of the index of refraction of glass (n = 1.5–1.7, depending on type).

Name ______________________ Section ______________ Date ______________

Lab Partner(s) ____

EXPERIMENT 38

Reflection and Refraction

Laboratory Report

A. Reflection

Glass Plate as a Mirror

	θ_i	θ_r			Percent differences between θ_i and θ_r
Ray 1	______	______	d_o	______	Ray 1 ______
Ray 2	______	______	d_i	______	Ray 1 ______

Percent difference between d_o and d_i ______

Plane Mirror

Length of pin ______ d_o ______

Length of image ______ d_i ______

Percent difference between pin length and image length ______

Percent difference between d_o and d_i ______

Rotation of a Mirror

Angle of rotation, θ ______ 2θ ______

Angle of deflection of ray, ϕ ______

Percent difference between ϕ and 2θ ______

Calculations
(show work)

Don't forget units

(continued)

B. Refraction

Index of Refraction of a Glass Plate

	θ_1	θ_2	Computed n
Ray *ARA′*			
Ray *BRB′*			
Ray *CRC′*			

Average n ____________

General range of the index of refraction of glass ____________

Displacement d of ray $C'C''$ ____________

Thickness of glass plate ____________

Calculations
(show work)

QUESTIONS

1. (a) Why are two images seen in the glass plate when it is viewed from position 2 in part A of the experiment? Why is only one image seen when it is viewed from position 1?

(b) Explain why reflection images are easily seen at night in a window pane from inside the house, whereas during the day they are not.

2. Based on your experimental data, draw conclusions (a) about the relationship of the distance of the object in front of a plane mirror and the distance of its image "behind" the mirror; and (b) the image magnification (i.e., how much bigger the image is than the object).

3. Explain the situation shown in Fig. 38.7. Is it dumb for someone to hold the palm of his or her hand over a burning candle? (*Hint:* The author's hand extends inside the sliding glass–windowed door of a laboratory cabinet.)

Figure 38.7 See Question 3.

(continued)

4. Prove mathematically that when a plane mirror is rotated an angle θ about an axis through its center (part A of the experiment), the angle of deflection ϕ of a light ray is equal to 2θ. Draw a diagram and show the work involved in your proof. Attach additional sheet if necessary.

5. Referring to the situation in Fig. 38.6, show theoretically that ray $C'C''$ is parallel to ray CR. Compute the displacement d of the ray passing through the glass plate. Compare this with the measured experimental displacement.

6. Using the experimentally determined n for the glass plate, compute the speed of light in the glass plate.

Name ______________________ Section ______________ Date ______________
Lab Partner(s) ____

EXPERIMENT 39

Spherical Mirrors and Lenses

Advance Study Assignment

Read the experiment and answer the following questions.

1. Distinguish between concave and convex spherical mirrors.

2. What is the difference between a real image and a virtual image?

3. Distinguish between diverging and converging lenses.

4. What does the word "focal" mean with regard to the focal point of spherical mirrors and lenses?

(continued)

5. If an object is placed 15 cm in front of a concave mirror with a radius of curvature of 20 cm, what are the image characteristics? (Show work.)

Spherical Mirrors and Lenses

I. Introduction and Objectives

Mirrors and lenses are familiar objects that are used daily. The most common mirror is a plane mirror, the type we look into every morning to see our image. However, spherical mirrors have many common applications. For example, convex spherical mirrors are used in stores to monitor aisles and merchandise, and concave spherical mirrors are used as flashlight reflectors.

Mirrors reflect light, whereas **lenses** transmit light. Spherical lenses are used to converge and focus light (convex spherical lenses) and to diverge light (concave spherical lenses). Many of us wear lenses in the form of eyeglasses. Cameras and projectors use lens systems to magnify and form images on screens.

In this experiment, the fundamental properties of spherical mirrors and lenses will be investigated so as to learn the parameters that govern their use.

After performing this experiment and analyzing the data, you should be able to:

1. Distinguish among converging and diverging spherical mirrors and lenses.
2. Determine the image characteristics for spherical mirrors graphically using ray diagrams and analytically using the mirror equation and magnification factor.
3. Determine the image characteristics for spherical lenses graphically using ray diagrams and analytically using the thin-lens equation and magnification factor.

II. Equipment Needed

- Concave and convex spherical mirrors
- Convex lens (focal length 10 to 20 cm)
- Concave lens (focal length longer than convex lens)
- Meterstick optical bench (or precision bench) with lens holder, screen, and screen holder (white cardboard can serve as the screen)
- Light source: candle and candle holder, or electric light source with object arrow

III. Theory

A. *Spherical Mirrors*

A **spherical mirror** is a section of a sphere and is characterized by a center of curvature C (Fig. 39.1). The distance from the center of curvature to the vertex of the mirror along the optic axis is called the **radius of curvature** R. The focal point F is midway between C and the vertex, and the **focal length** is one-half the radius of curvature:

$$f = \frac{R}{2} \tag{39.1}$$

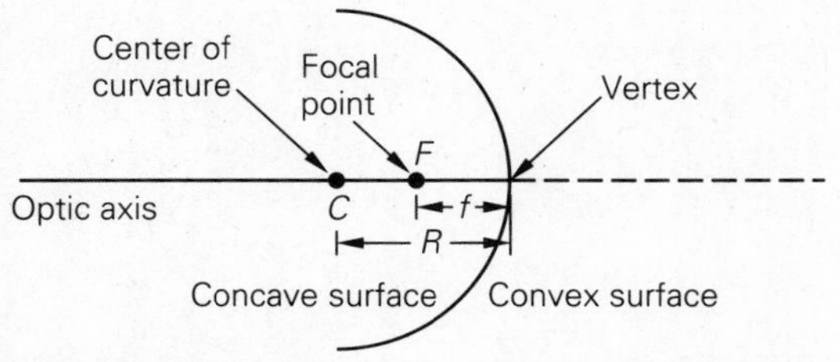

Figure 39.1 Spherical mirrors. The parameters used to describe spherical mirror surfaces. See text for description.

If the reflecting surface is on the inside of the spherical section, the mirror is said to be **concave**. For a **convex** mirror, the reflecting surface is on the outside of the spherical section.

The characteristics of the images formed by spherical mirrors can be determined either graphically or analytically. Examples of the graphical ray method are shown in the ray diagrams in Fig. 39.2. For a concave mirror (Fig. 39.2a), a ray from an object through the center of curvature C, called the **chief ray** (1), is reflected back through C. A ray parallel to the optic axis, called a **parallel ray** (2), is reflected through the focal point F. A ray through the focal point F, called the **focal ray** (3), is reflected parallel to the optic axis.

The intersection of these rays defines the location of the tip of the **image arrow**, which extends from the optic axis. The focal ray is a "mirror" image of the parallel ray and is not needed to locate the tip of the image. It is often omitted, but is helpful when the object is inside the center of curvature.

For a convex mirror, the chief and parallel rays appear to go through C and F, as illustrated in Fig. 39.2b.

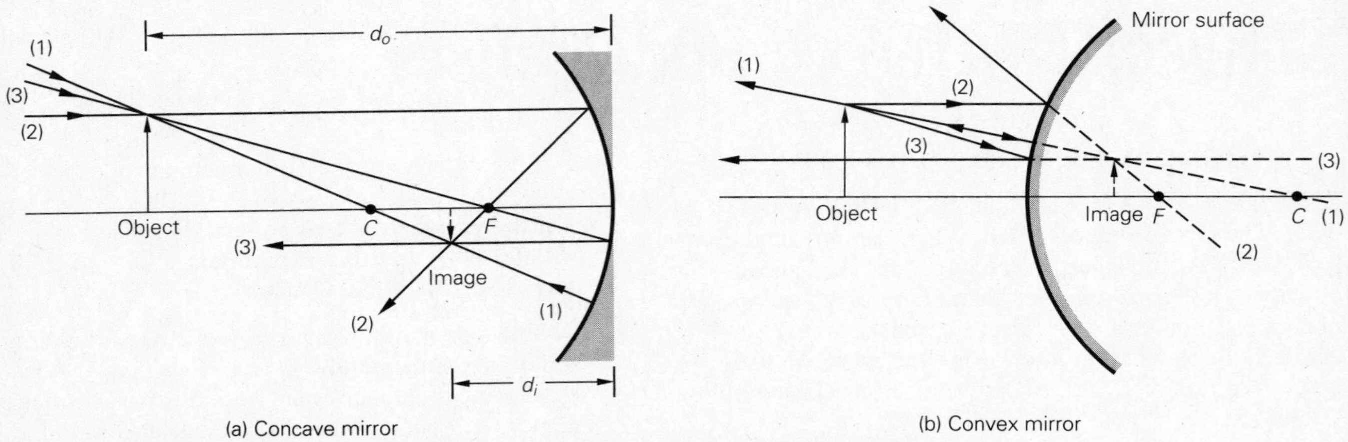

Figure 39.2 Ray diagrams. Examples of the ray method for determining the image characteristics for (a) a concave or converging spherical mirror, and (b) a convex or diverging spherical mirror.

A concave mirror is called a **converging mirror** because rays parallel to the optic axis converge at the focal point. Similarly, a convex mirror is called a **diverging mirror** because the rays parallel to the optic axis appear to diverge from the focal point.

If the image is formed on the same side of the mirror as the object, the image is said to be a **real image**. In this case, the light rays converge and are concentrated, and an image can be observed on a screen placed at the image distance. An image that is formed "behind" or "inside" the mirror is called a **virtual image**. Here, the rays appear to diverge from the image, and no image can be formed on a screen.

In general, an image is described by the following characteristics:

1. real or virtual,
2. upright (erect) or inverted (relative to the object orientation), and
3. magnified or reduced (or smaller).

In Fig. 39.2a the image is real, inverted, and reduced; in Fig. 39.2b the image is virtual, upright, and smaller.

The distance from the object to the vertex along the optic axis is called the **object distance** d_o, and the distance from the vertex to the image is the **image distance** d_i. Knowing the focal length f of the mirror, the position of the image d_i can be found from the **spherical mirror equation**,

$$\frac{1}{d_o} + \frac{1}{d_i} = \frac{1}{f} \tag{39.2a}$$

Another convenient form of this equation is

$$d_i = \frac{d_o f}{d_o - f} \tag{39.2b}$$

In the case of a concave mirror, the focal length is taken to be positive (+); for a convex mirror, the focal length is taken to be negative (−). The object distance d_o is taken to be positive in either case. The sign convention is: If d_i is positive, the image is real; and if d_i is negative, the image is virtual. The **magnification factor** M is given by

$$M = -\frac{d_i}{d_o} \tag{39.3}$$

If M is positive (d_i negative), the image is upright; if M is negative (d_i positive), the image is inverted. The sign convention is summarized in Table 39.1.

Example 39.1 An object is placed 45 cm in front of a concave mirror with a focal length of 15 cm (corresponding to the case in Fig. 39.2a). Determine the image characteristics analytically.

Solution With d_o = 45 cm and f = 15 cm, from Eq. 39.2a,

$$\frac{1}{45} + \frac{1}{d_i} = \frac{1}{15} = \frac{3}{45}$$

By inspection,

$$\frac{1}{d_i} = \frac{2}{45} \quad \text{or} \quad d_i = \frac{45}{2} = 22.5 \text{ cm}$$

Then

$$M = -\frac{d_i}{d_o} = -\frac{22.5 \text{ cm}}{45 \text{ cm}} = -\frac{1}{2}$$

Thus, the image is real (positive d_i), inverted (negative M), and reduced by a factor of $\frac{1}{2}$ (i.e., one-half as tall as the object).

TABLE 39.1 Sign Convention for Spherical Mirrors and Lenses

Quantity	Conditions	Sign
Focal length, f	Concave mirror	+
	Convex mirror	−
	Convex lens	+
	Concave lens	−
Object distance, d_o	Usually* (Always in this experiment)	+
Image distance, d_i	Image real	+
	Image virtual	−
Magnification, M	Image upright	+
	Image inverted	−

* In some cases of lens combinations, d_o may be negative when an image is used as an object.

B. *Spherical Lenses*

The shapes of biconvex and biconcave spherical lenses are illustrated in Fig. 39.3. A radius of curvature is defined for each spherical surface, but only the focal points (one for each spherical surface) are needed for ray diagrams.

A convex lens is called a **converging lens** because rays parallel to the principal axis converge at the focal point. A concave lens is called a **diverging lens** because rays parallel to the principal axis appear to diverge from the focal point.

As with spherical mirrors, the characteristics of the images formed by spherical lenses can be determined graphically or analytically. The chief (1) and parallel (2) rays for the graphical method are illustrated in the ray diagrams in Fig. 39.4. In the case of lenses, the chief ray through the center of a lens is undeviated. A ray parallel to the principal axis is refracted in such a way that it goes through the focal point on transmission through the lens. Also, a focal ray (3) through the near focal point is parallel to the principal axis on transmission. In the case of a concave lens, the ray appears to have passed through the focal point on the object side of the lens.

If the image is formed on the side of the lens opposite to the object, it is real and can be observed on a screen. However, if the image is on the same side of the lens as the object, it is virtual and cannot be seen on a screen.

The spherical **thin-lens equation** and **magnification factor** for analytically determining the image characteristics are identical to the equations for spherical mirrors (Eqs. 39.2 and 39.3). The sign convention is also similar (see Table 39.1). It should be noted that this lens equation applies only to *thin* lenses.

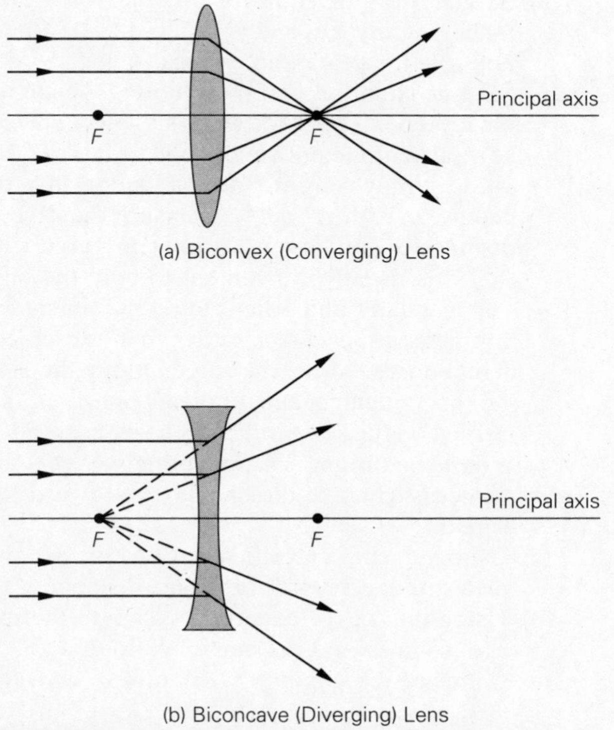

Figure 39.3 Spherical lenses. (a) A biconvex or converging lens and (b) a biconcave or diverging lens showing the refraction of parallel incident rays.

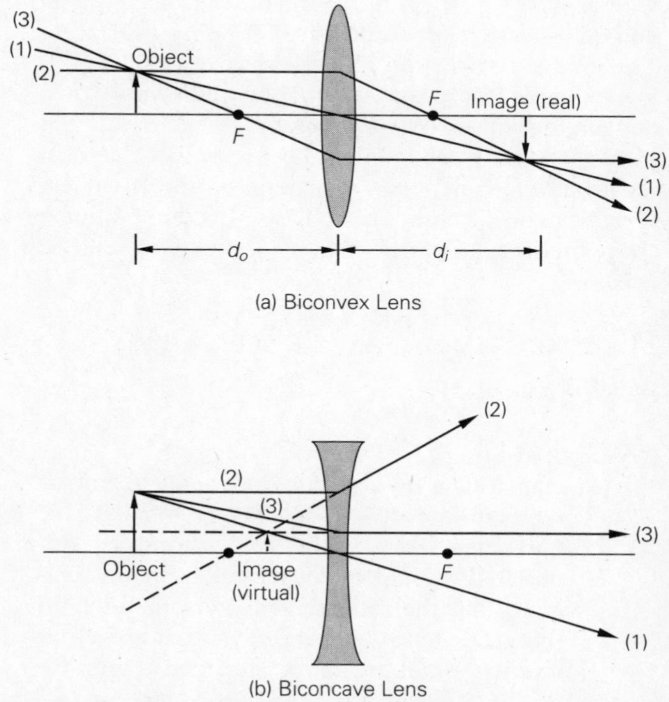

Figure 39.4 Ray diagrams. Examples of the ray method for determining the image characteristics for (a) a biconvex lens and (b) a biconcave lens.

Example 39.2 An object is placed 30 cm from a biconcave lens with a focal length of 10 cm (corresponding to the case in Fig. 39.4b). Determine the image characteristics analytically.

Solution With $d_o = 30$ cm and $f = -10$ cm (negative by convention for a concave lens), using Eq. 39.2b,

$$d_i = \frac{d_o f}{d_o - f} = \frac{(30 \text{ cm})(-10 \text{ cm})}{30 \text{ cm} - (-10 \text{ cm})}$$

$$= \frac{-300 \text{ cm}}{40 \text{ cm}} = \frac{-30 \text{ cm}}{4} = -7.5 \text{ cm}$$

Then,

$$M = -\frac{d_i}{d_o} = \frac{-(-30/4)}{30} = +\frac{1}{4}$$

Thus, the image is virtual (negative d_i), upright (positive M), and reduced by a factor of $\frac{1}{4}$.

However, the relationship between the focal length and the radius of curvature for a spherical lens is not as simple as for that of a spherical mirror (Eq. 39.1). For a lens, the focal length is given by what is known as the *lensmaker's equation*:

$$\frac{1}{f} = (n - 1)\left(\frac{1}{R_1} + \frac{1}{R_2}\right) \qquad \textbf{(39.4)}$$

where n is the index of refraction for the lens material and the R's are taken as positive for *convex* surfaces. The index of refraction of glass varies, $n = 1.5$–1.7. For example, for glass with $n = 1.5$ and symmetrical converging lenses ($R_1 = R$ and $R_2 = R$), Eq. 39.4 yields $f = R$.* Keep in mind, however, that the focal length of a lens depends in general on the R values, which can be different, as well as n. In computations, the experimentally determined value of f will be used.

IV. Experimental Procedure

A. *Spherical Mirrors*

Concave Mirror

1. (a) Construct a ray diagram for a concave mirror with an object located at its focal point. (Drawing provided in the Laboratory Report.) It should be observed from the diagram that the reflected rays are parallel. In this case we say that the rays "converge" at infinity or that the image is formed at infinity.

Inversely, rays coming from an object at infinity converge to form an image at the focal point or in the focal plane (plane perpendicular to the optic axis).

(b) Construct a ray diagram with several rays parallel to the optic axis to show they converge at f.

(c) Using the spherical-mirror equation, determine the image distance for an object at infinity (∞).

2. This focal property permits the experimental determination of the focal length of the mirror. An object a great distance from the mirror is essentially at infinity relative to the dimensions of the mirror.

Take the mirror and screen to a window. Holding the mirror in one hand and the screen in the other, adjust the distance of the screen from the mirror until the image of some outside distant object is observed on the screen (hence a real image).*

Measure the distance f from the mirror vertex to the screen and record in the Laboratory Report. Repeat this procedure twice, and take the average of the three measurements as the focal length of the mirror.

3. *Case 1:* $d_o > R$.

(a) Sketch a ray diagram for an object at a distance slightly beyond R (i.e., $d_o > R$) and note the image characteristics.

(b) Set this situation up on the optical bench as illustrated in Fig. 39.5, with the object placed several centimeters beyond the radius of curvature (known from f determination in procedure 2, with $R = 2f$). Measure the object distance d_o, and record it in Data Table 1.

It is usually convenient to hold the mirror manually and adjust the object distance by moving the mirror rather than the object light source. Move the screen along the side of the optical bench until an image is observed on the screen. This is best observed in a darkened room. The mirror may have to be turned slightly to direct the rays toward the screen.

(c) Estimate the magnification factor M and measure and record the image distance d_i.

(d) Using the mirror equation, compute the image distance and the magnification factor.

(e) Compare the computed value of d_i with the

* For f to be equal to $R/2$ for a symmetrical lens, as for a spherical mirror, requires $n = 2$, which is greater than the index of refraction of glass.

* If a window is not available or it is a dark day, use procedure 4 to determine f experimentally. In this case, show first that $d_i = d_o = R$ and $M = 1$. Then, measuring d_i, the focal length is $f = d_i/2 = R/2$.

Figure 39.5 Experimental arrangements. Arrangements for experimental procedures for (a) spherical mirrors and (b) spherical lenses.

experimental value by computing the percent difference.

4. *Case 2:* $d_o = R$. Repeat procedure 3 for this case.

5. *Case 3:* $f < d_o < R$. Repeat procedure 3 for this case.

6. *Case 4:* $d_o < f$. Repeat procedure 3 for this case.

CONVEX MIRROR

7. Sketch ray diagrams for objects at (1) $d_o > R$, (2) $f < d_o < R$, and (3) $d_o < f$, and draw conclusions about the characteristics of the image of a convex mirror. Experimentally verify that the image of a convex mirror is virtual (i.e., try to locate the image on the screen).

B. Spherical Lenses

CONVEX LENS

8. **(a)** Sketch a ray diagram for a convex lens with the object at its focal point. As with the concave mirror (procedure 1), the image is formed at infinity.
   (b) Using the lens equation, determine the image characteristics for an object at infinity.
   (c) Experimentally determine the focal length of the lens by a procedure similar to that used for the concave mirror. (The lens may be placed in a lens holder and mounted on a meterstick.)*

* In general for a lens, $f \neq R/2$. However, it can be shown for the case of $d_i = d_o$ that $d_o = 2f$. See Question 4 at the end of the experiment.

9. Repeat the four cases for the lens as was done for the concave mirror in procedures 3 to 6, with R replaced by $2f$ (see Fig. 39.5). It is initially instructive to move the lens continuously toward the object light source (decreasing d_o) from a $d_o > 2f$ and to observe the image on the screen, which also must be moved continuously to obtain a sharp image. In particular, notice the change in the size of the image as d_o approaches f.

CONCAVE LENS

10. Repeat the procedures carried out for the convex mirror in procedure 7 for the concave lens, with R replaced by $2f$.

11. It is possible to determine the focal length of a concave lens experimentally by placing it in contact with a convex lens so as to form a lens combination. The combination forms a real image. If two lenses of focal lengths f_1 and f_2 are placed in contact, the lens combination has a focal length f_c given by

$$\frac{1}{f_c} = \frac{1}{f_1} + \frac{1}{f_2} \tag{39.5}$$

Place the concave lens in contact with the convex lens (convex surface to concave surface) in a lens holder and determine the focal length of the lens combination f_c by finding the image of a distant object as in procedure 8. Record in the Laboratory Report.

Using Eq. 39.5 with the focal length of the convex lens determined in procedure 8, compute the focal length of the concave lens.

Name ______________________ Section ______________ Date ______________

Lab Partner(s) ____

EXPERIMENT 39

Spherical Mirrors and Lenses

Laboratory Report

A. Spherical Mirrors

Concave Mirror: Ray diagrams

$d_o = f$

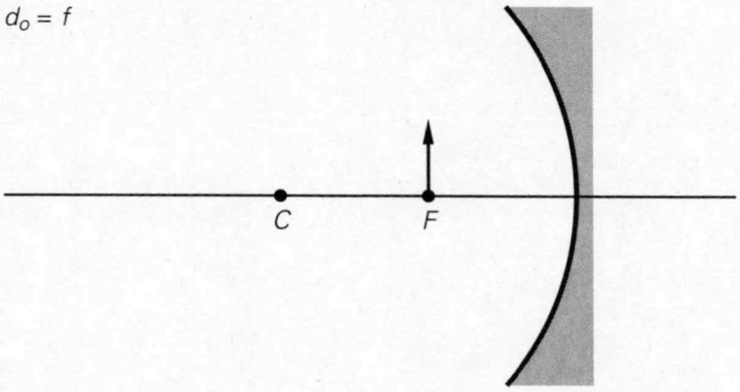

$f < d_o < R$

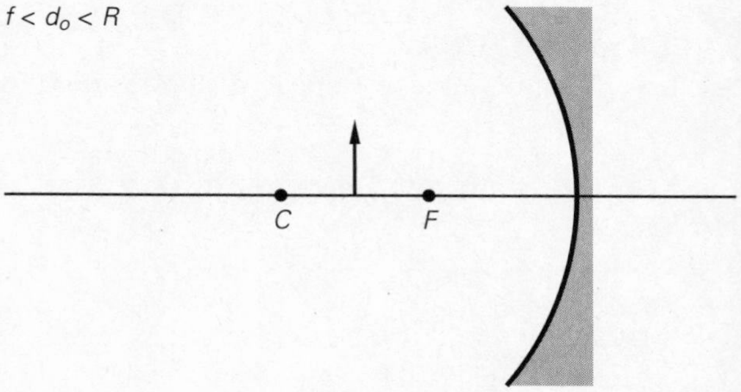

$d_o > R$

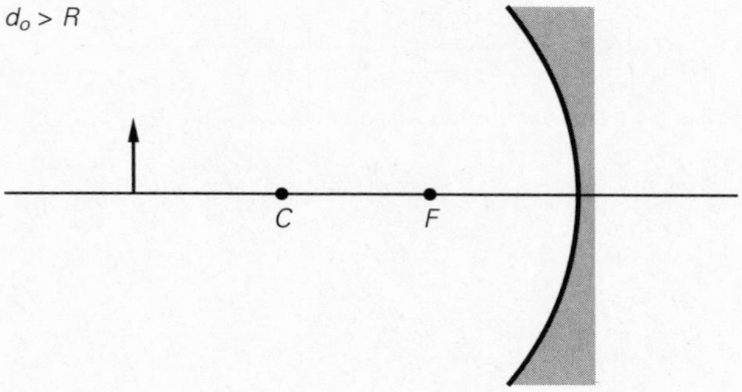

$d_o < f$

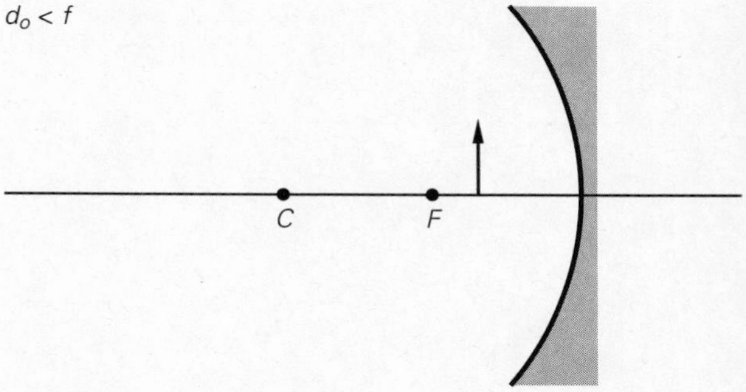

$d_o = R$

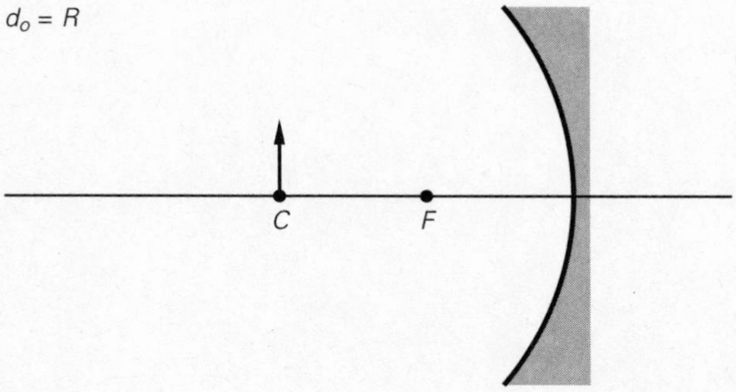

Don't forget units

(continued)

Calculation of d_i for object at ∞

Experimental focal length, f ______

______

______

Average ______

DATA TABLE 1

Purpose: To determine the image distance and magnification.

	Experimental			Computed		d_i percent difference
	d_o ( )	d_i ( )	M factor (estimated)	d_i ( )	M	
$d_o > R$						
$d_o = R$						
$f < d_o < R$						
$d_o < f$						

Calculations
(show work)

Name ______________________ Section ______________ Date ______________
Lab Partner(s) ______________________

EXPERIMENT 39 **Laboratory Report**

Convex mirror: Ray diagrams

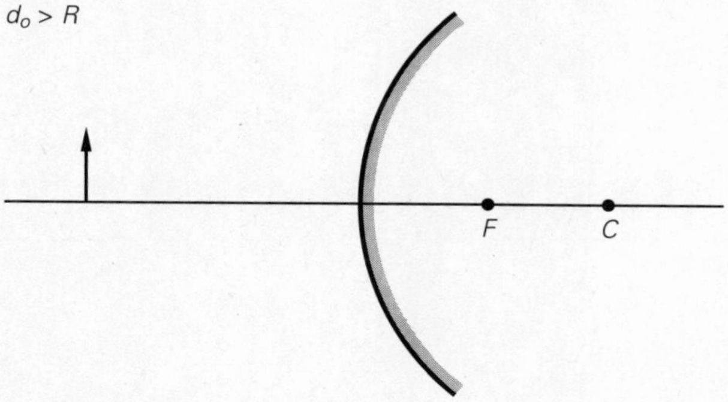

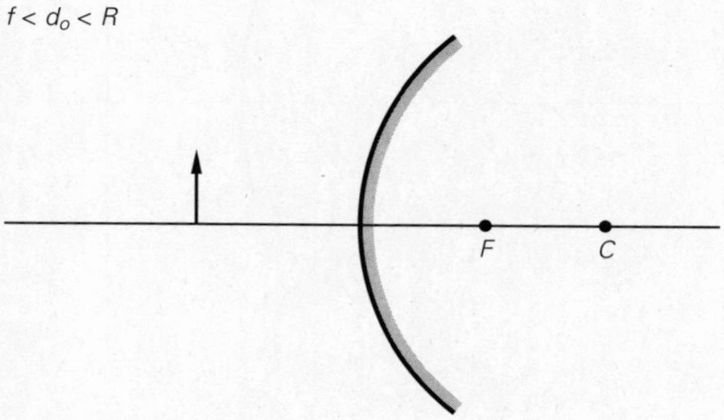

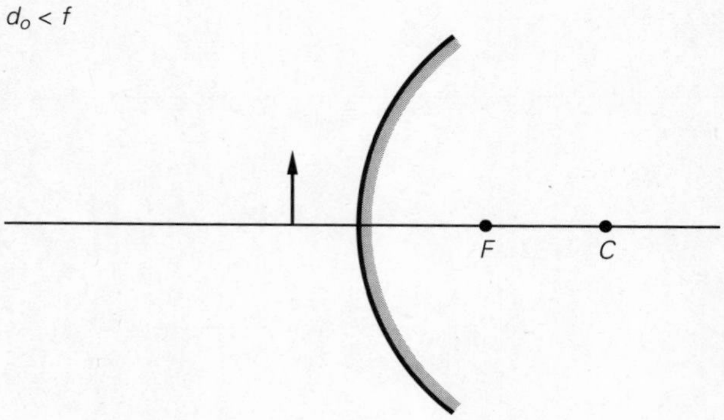

Conclusions

(continued)

B. Spherical Lenses

Convex lens: Ray diagrams

$d_o = f$

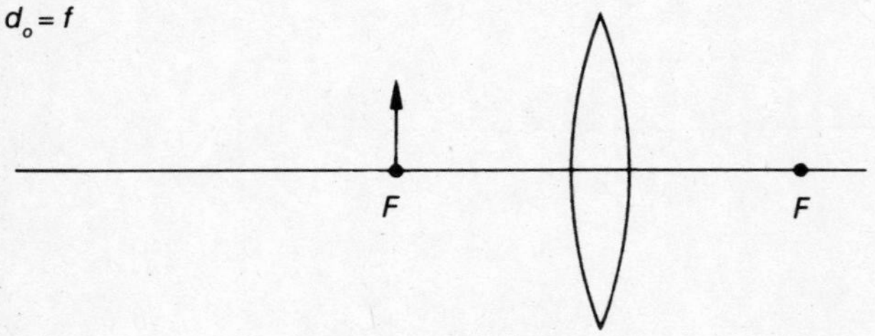

$f < d_o < 2f$

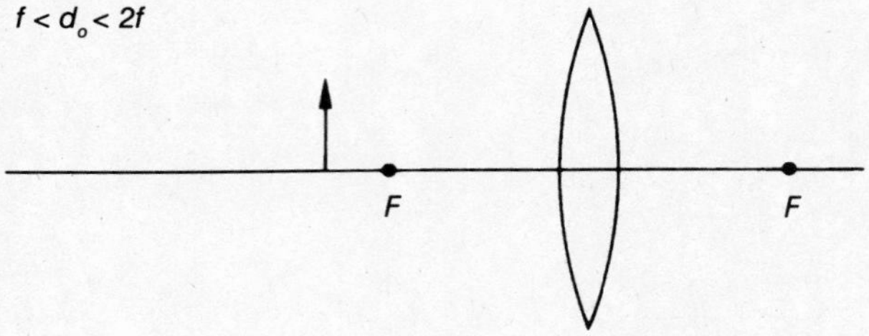

$d_o > 2f$

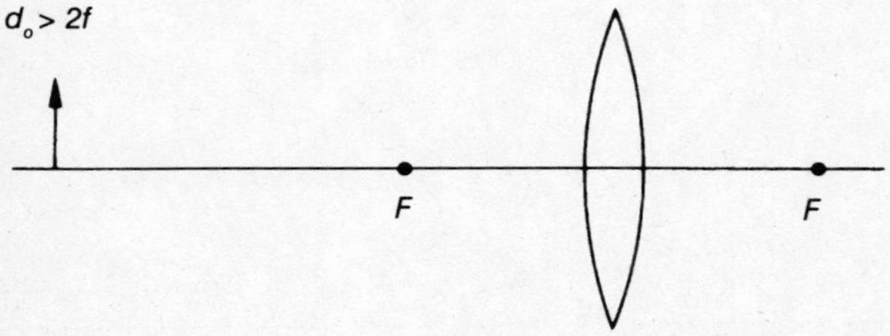

$d_o < f$

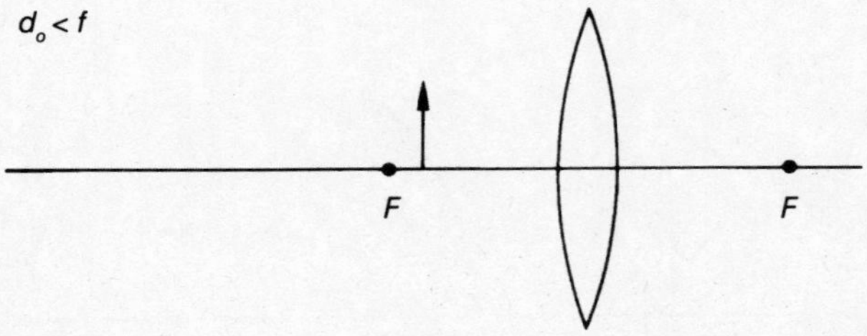

$d_o = 2f$

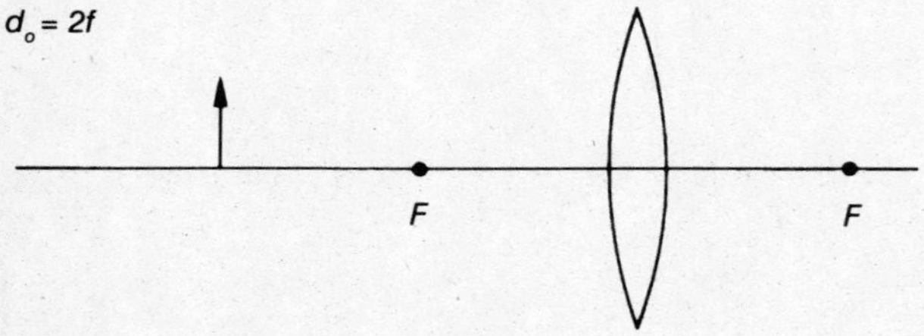

Calculation of d_i for object at ∞

Experimental focal length, f ________________

____

____

Average ________________

Name ______________________ Section ______________ Date ______________

Lab Partner(s) ____

EXPERIMENT 39 **Laboratory Report**

DATA TABLE 2

Purpose: To determine the image distance and magnification.

	Experimental			Computed		d_i percent difference
	d_o ( )	d_i ( )	*M* factor (estimated)	d_i ( )	*M*	
$d_o > 2f$						
$d_o = 2f$						
$f < d_o < 2f$						
$d_o < f$						

Calculations
(show work)

(continued)

Concave lens: Ray diagrams

$d_o > 2f$

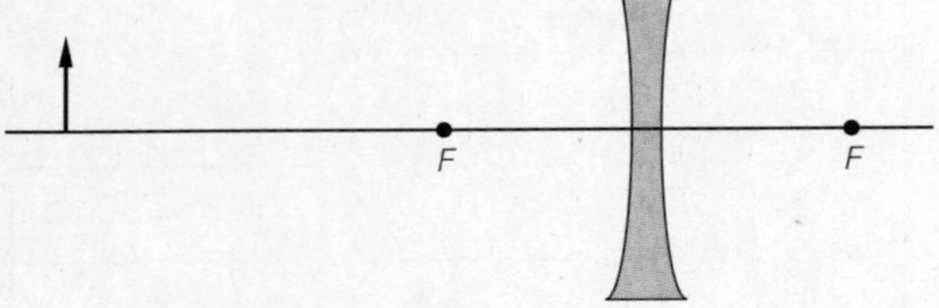

$f < d_o < 2f$

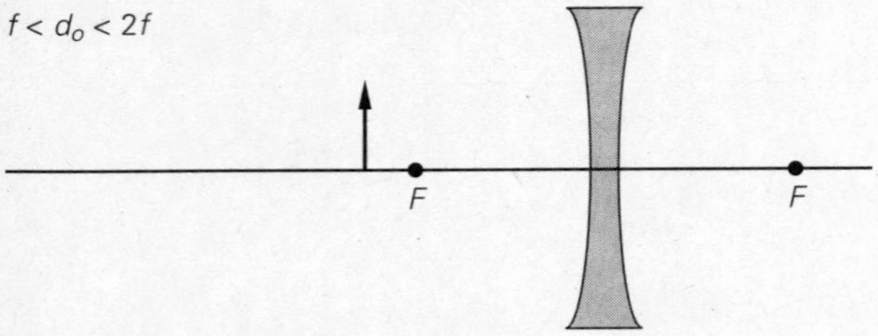

$d_o < f$

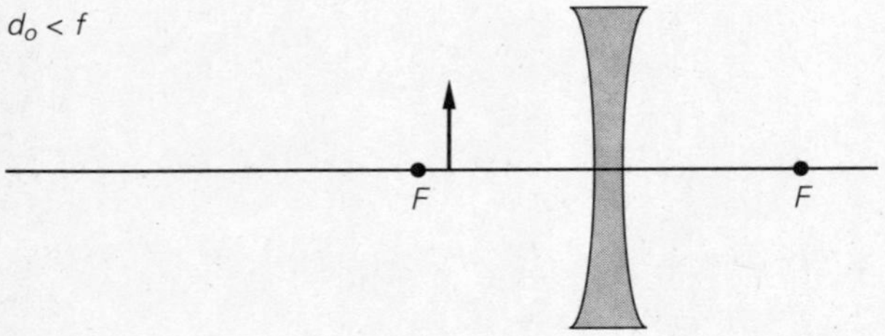

Conclusions

Focal length determination:

f_c, focal length of the combination ______________

f, focal length of concave lens ______________

QUESTIONS

1. A plane mirror essentially has a radius of curvature of infinity. Using the mirror equation, show that (a) the image of a plane mirror is always virtual; (b) the image is "behind" the mirror the same distance as the object is in front of the mirror; and (c) the image is always upright.

Name ______________________ Section ______________ Date ______________

Lab Partner(s) ____

EXPERIMENT 39 **_Laboratory Report_**

2. Show that the magnification factor for a mirror or lens $M = d_i/d_o$ (sign convention omitted) is the lateral magnification or the ratio of the height (lateral size) of the image to that of the object. (*Hint:* Draw a ray diagram.)

3. Explain what characteristics make convex spherical mirrors applicable for store monitoring and concave spherical mirrors applicable as flashlight reflectors.

4. Prove for a converging lens, for the case $d_i = d_o$, that $d_i = d_o = 2f$.

(continued)

5. (a) Using the experimental value of f for the biconvex converging lens and n = 1.5, compute the radius of curvature of the lens's surfaces using the lensmaker's equation. (The radius of curvature for each surface is the same.)

(b) A student incorrectly assumes that $f = R/2$ for the lens and computes f using the value of R found in part (a). Compare this computed value of f with the experimental value.

(c) The index of refraction of the lens could have a different value (n of glass varies generally from 1.5–1.7). Would this make a difference? Explain.

Name ______________________ Section ______________ Date ______________

Lab Partner(s) ____

EXPERIMENT 40

Polarized Light

Advance Study Assignment

Read the experiment and answer the following questions.

1. Is the plane of polarization of a polarizing polymer sheet in the same direction as the molecular chain orientation? Explain.

2. What is the condition for optimum polarization by reflection? Is the polarization angle the same for every material? Explain.

3. Describe how light can be polarized by refraction. Would two images be formed? Explain.

4. Why is sky light partially polarized, and why does it appear blue?

5. What is meant by optical activity?

Polarized Light

I. Introduction and Objectives

When we speak of polarized light, Polaroid sunglasses usually come to mind, as this is one of the most common applications of polarization. However, few people understand how such sunglasses reduce "glare." Since the unaided human eye cannot distinguish between polarized light and unpolarized light, we are not normally aware of the many instances of polarized light around us. Bees, on the other hand, with their many-faceted eyes, can detect polarized light and use scattered polarized sunlight in navigating.

Although the unaided human eye cannot detect polarized light, with a little help polarization can be studied and experimentally investigated. This is the purpose of this experiment, and we will also learn how light is polarized.

After performing this experiment and analyzing the data, you should be able to:

1. Explain what the polarization of light means.
2. Describe several means by which light can be polarized.
3. Explain some practical applications of polarized light.

II. Equipment Needed

- 3 polarizing sheets
- Polarizing sunglasses
- Exposure meter and sheet of Cartesian graph paper (optional)
- Lamp (and converging lens for parallel beam if needed)
- Protractor
- 6–8 glass microscope slides
- Glass plate
- Tripod stand (open ring top)
- Calcite crystal
- Mica sheet
- Cellophane tape
- Lucite or other plastic pieces (e.g., U-shaped, hook, or hollow triangle)
- LCD (on student's wristwatch or hand calculator)

III. Theory

Light, like all electromagnetic radiation, is a **transverse wave**. That is, the directions of the vibrating electric and magnetic field vectors are at right angles to the direction of propagation, as illustrated schematically in Fig. 40.1. (If the vector vibrations were parallel to the direction of propagation, light would be a *longitudinal wave*.) The phenomenon of **polarization** is firm evidence that light is a transverse wave.

Polarization refers to the orientation of the vibrating vectors of electromagnetic radiation. Light from an ordinary light source consists of a large number of waves emitted by the atoms or molecules of the source. Each atom produces a wave with its own orientation of the **E** (and **B**) vibration corresponding to the direction of the atomic vibration.

However, with many atoms, all directions are possible. The result is that the emitted light is **unpolarized**: the vibration vectors are randomly oriented, with all directions equally probable. This is represented schematically in Fig. 40.2a, which views the **E** vectors along the axis of propagation. (**B** vectors are not represented.)

If for some reason the light vectors become preferentially oriented, we say the light is **partially polarized** (Fig. 40.2b). Should there be only one direction of vibration for the **E** vectors (Fig. 40.2c), the light is then **linearly polarized**. This is sometimes called **plane polarized** or simply **polarized** light. The

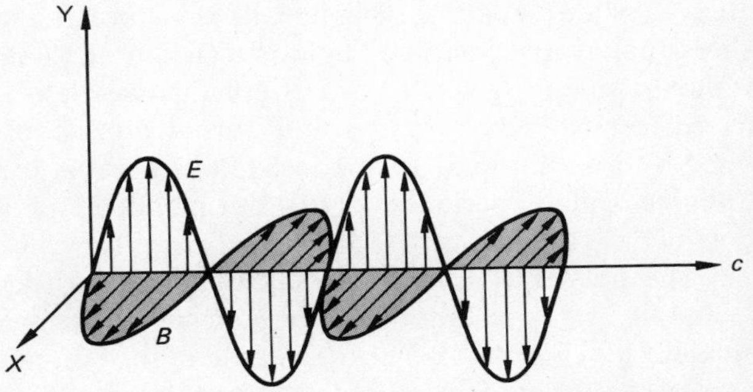

Figure 40.1 Electromagnetic wave. An illustration of an electromagnetic wave. The electric and magnetic field vectors (**E** and **B**) vibrate at right angles to each other and perpendicularly to the direction of propagation.

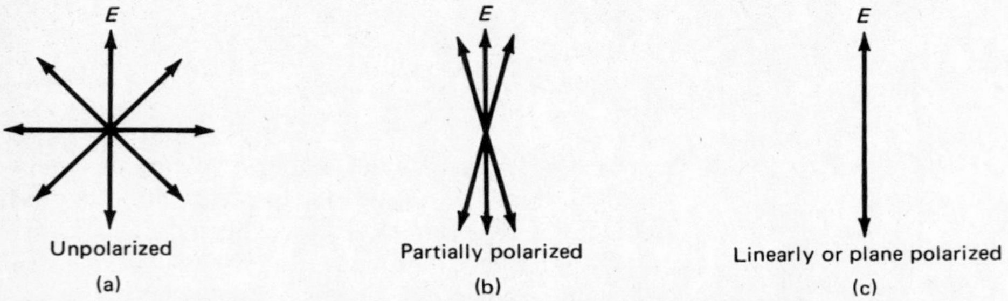

Figure 40.2 Polarization. An illustration of the polarization of light as denoted by the **E** vector viewed along the direction of propagation.

direction of vibration of the **E** vector defines the plane or direction of polarization. The polarization of light may be effected by several means: (a) selective absorption, (b) reflection, (c) refraction, and (d) scattering. Let's take a look at these.

A. Polarization by Selective Absorption

A substance that has the property of transmitting light with the electric field vector in only one direction (linearly polarized light) is said to be **dichroic**. This is the principle of the most common technique for obtaining polarized light. In 1938, E. H. Land developed a material, known by the commercial name of Polaroid, that polarizes light through selective absorption by oriented long-chain polymer molecules. The material is in the form of a thin sheet in which the molecular alignment is produced by stretching during fabrication.

With proper treatment, the outer (valence) molecular electrons can move along the oriented chains. As a result, the molecules readily absorb light with **E** vectors parallel to the oriented chains and transmit light with the **E** vectors perpendicular to the chains.

The direction perpendicular to the oriented molecular chains is commonly called the **transmission axis, plane of polarization,** or **polarization direction**. Hence, when unpolarized light falls on a polarizing sheet (polarizer), polarized light is transmitted. This is illustrated in Fig. 40.3. Various crystals are dichroic. In fact, an early version of Polaroid film developed by Land around 1930 consisted of herapathite (quinine sulfate periodide) crystals imbedded in a polymer sheet.

The polarization of light may be analyzed (detected) by means of another polarizer, which acts as an analyzer (Fig. 40.3). The magnitude of the component of the **E** vector parallel to the transmission axis of the analyzer is $\mathbf{E}_o \cos \theta$. Since the intensity varies as the square of the amplitude, the transmitted intensity of light through the analyzer is

$$I = I_o \cos^2 \theta \qquad \textbf{(40.1)}$$

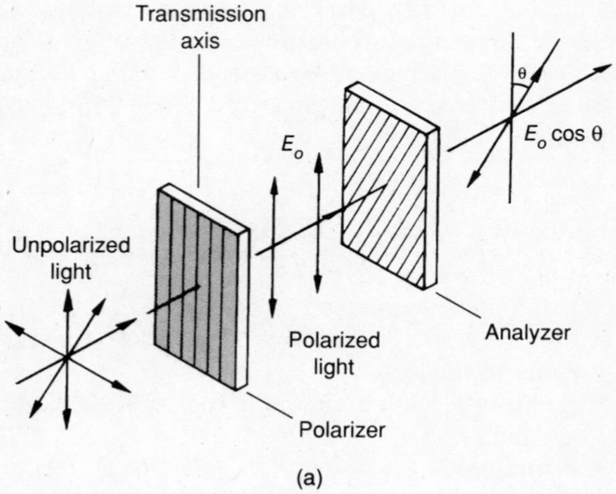

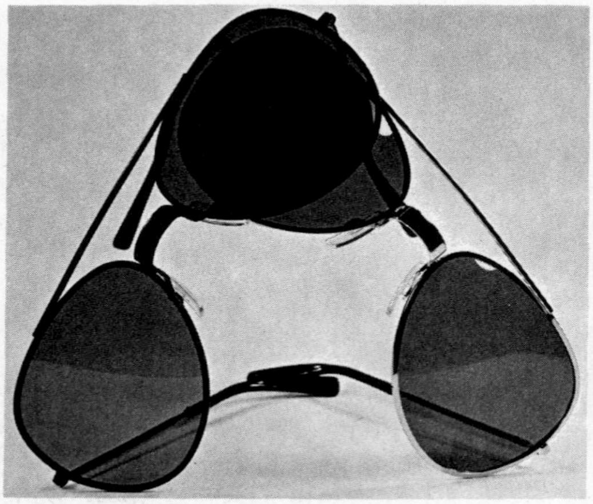

(b)

Figure 40.3 Polarizer and analyzer. (a) The transmission axis (or plane of polarization or polarization direction) is perpendicular to the oriented molecular chains. When the transmission axes of the polarizer and analyzer are not parallel, less light is transmitted. (b) For "crossed polaroids" ($\theta = 90°$), little or no light is transmitted, as shown for the "crossed" polarizing sunglass lenses.

where I_o is the intensity of the polarized light incident on the analyzer. If $\theta = 90°$, we have a condition of cross-polarizers and no light is transmitted through the analyzer.

B. Polarization by Reflection

When light is incident on a material such as glass, some of the light is reflected, and some is transmitted. The reflected light is usually partially polarized, and the degree of polarization depends on the angle of incidence. For angles of incidence of 0° and 90° (grazing and normal angles), the reflected light is unpolarized. However, for intermediate angles, the light is polarized to some extent. Complete polarization occurs at an optimum angle called the **polarization angle** θ_p (Fig. 40.4). This occurs when the reflected and refracted beams are 90° apart, and θ_p is specific for a given material.

Referring to Fig. 40.4, since $\theta_1 = \theta_p$, we have $\theta_1 + 90° + \theta_2 = 180°$. Then, $\theta_1 + \theta_2 = 90°$, or $\theta_2 = 90° - \theta_1$. By Snell's law (Experiment 38),

$$\frac{\sin \theta_1}{\sin \theta_2} = n$$

where n is the index of refraction of the glass and $\sin \theta_2 = \sin (90° - \theta_1) = \cos \theta_1$. Thus,

$$\frac{\sin \theta_1}{\sin \theta_2} = \frac{\sin \theta_1}{\cos \theta_1} = \tan \theta_1 = n$$

or

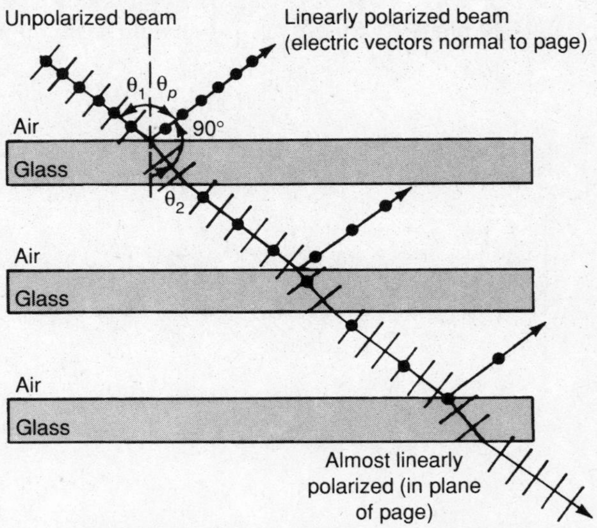

Figure 40.4 Polarization by reflection. Maximum polarization occurs for a particular polarization angle θ_p, which depends on the index of refraction of the material. Notice that the transmitted beam is partially polarized.

$$\tan \theta_p = n \tag{40.2}$$

This expression is sometimes called **Brewster's law**,* and θ_p is called **Brewster's angle**.

Example 40.1 A glass plate has an index of refraction of 1.48. What is the angle of polarization for the plate?

Solution With $n = 1.48$,

$$\theta_p = \tan^{-1}(1.48) = 56°$$

Notice from Fig. 40.4 that the reflected beam is horizontally polarized. Sunlight reflected from water, metallic surfaces (e.g., from a car), etc., is partially polarized; if the surface is horizontal, the reflected light has a strong horizontal component. This fact is used in polarizing sunglasses. The transmission axis of the lenses is oriented vertically so as to absorb the reflected horizontal component and reduce the glare or intensity.

Also notice that the refracted beam is partially polarized. By using a stack of glass plates, the transmitted beam would become almost linearly polarized.

C. Polarization by Refraction

In a sense, the preceding case of a polarized transmitted beam from a stack of glass plates might be thought of as polarization by refraction since the refracted beam is polarized. However, this generally refers to the *double refraction* exhibited by some crystals.

In an optically isotropic medium, such as glass, light travels with the same speed in all directions. As a result, the material is characterized by a single index of refraction. In certain anisotropic crystals, however, the speed of light is not the same in all directions. The crystal calcite ($CaCO_3$, Iceland spar), for example, exhibits double refraction or *birefringence* and is characterized by two indices of refraction.

When an unpolarized beam of light enters a calcite crystal, it splits into two polarized rays with polarizations in mutually perpendicular directions (Fig. 40.5). One beam is called the ordinary (O) ray, and the other, the extraordinary (E) ray. Because of this property, when something (e.g., a printed line) is viewed through a calcite crystal, a double image is seen, corresponding to the two emergent rays.

* After its discoverer, David Brewster (1781–1868), a Scottish physicist.

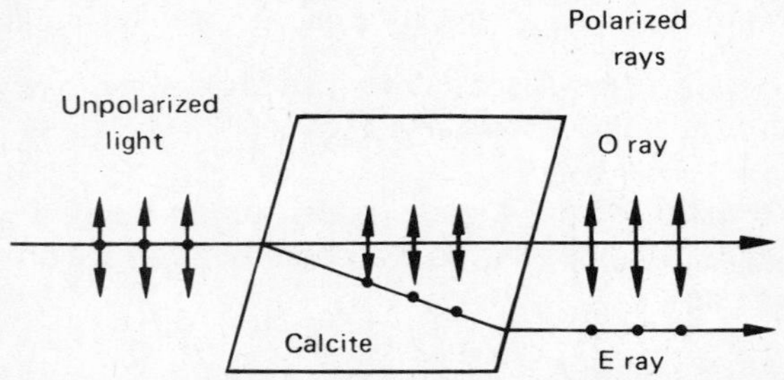

Figure 40.5 Polarization by double refraction or birefringence. An unpolarized beam entering the crystal is split into two polarized beams. (Dots indicate electric field vectors oscillating normal to the page.)

D. Polarization by Scattering

Scattering is the process of a medium absorbing light, then reradiating it. For example, if light is incident on a gas, the electrons in the gas atoms or molecules can absorb and reradiate (scatter) part of the light. In effect, the electrons absorb the light by responding to the electric field of the light wave. Considering an electron as a small antenna, it radiates light in all directions, *except* along its axis of vibration. Hence, the scattered light is partially polarized.

Such scattering of sunlight occurs in the atmosphere and is known as Rayleigh scattering.* The condition for interaction and scattering is that the size d (diameter) of the molecules be much less than the wavelength λ of the light, $d \ll \lambda$. The scattering then varies as $1/\lambda^4$. This condition is satisfied for O_2 (oxygen) and N_2 (nitrogen) molecules in the atmosphere.

Sunlight incident on the atmosphere is white light with a spectrum of wavelength components (or colors). As a result of the $1/\lambda^4$ scattering relationship, the blue end (shorter wavelength) of the spectrum is scattered more than the red end (longer wavelength). The blue light is scattered and rescattered. When looking at the sky, we see this scattered light, and as a result, the sky appears to be blue.

Hence, the blue "sky light" we see is partially polarized, even though we can't visually detect it (without a little help).

* After Lord Rayleigh (1842–1919), a British physicist who described the effect.

E. Optical Activity

Certain substances have the property of being able to rotate the plane of polarization of a beam of polarized light. This rotation, called **optical activity**, is exhibited by crystalline mica, quartz, some sugars, and many long-chain molecular polymers. The principle is illustrated for an optically active crystal in Fig. 40.6.

Notice that the crystal essentially changes the direction of one of the vector components of the polarized light along one of its optical axes. The (vector) resultant is then rotated 90° to the polarization plane of the incoming light and transmitted through the "crossed" analyzer, which would not be the case without rotation.

In traveling through the crystal, the components travel at different speeds. Suppose the thickness of the crystal is such that the vertical component gains (or falls behind) by one-half wavelength compared

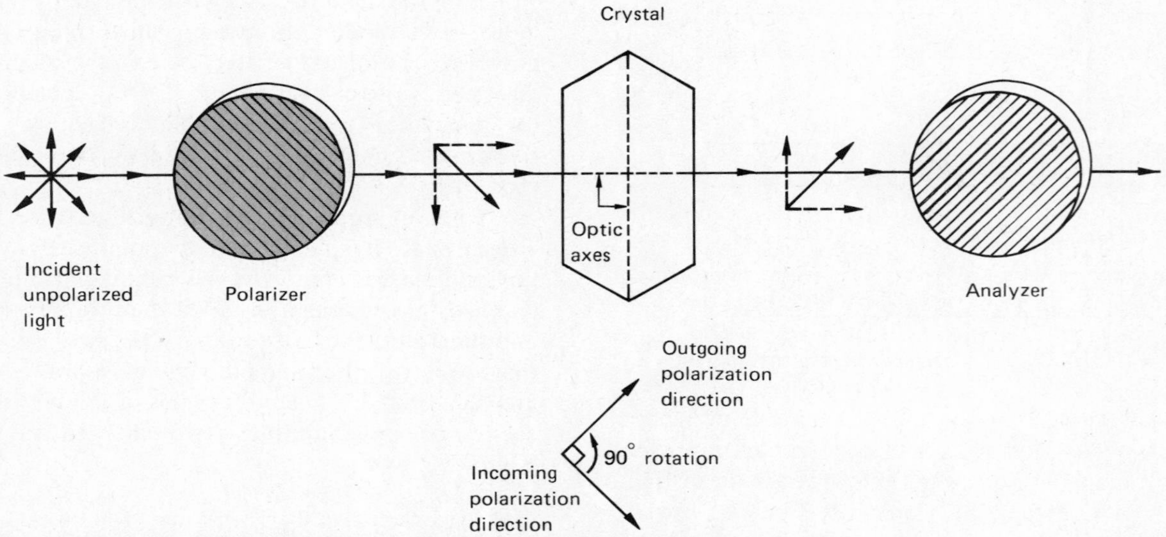

Figure 40.6 Optical activity. Certain substances have the property of being able to rotate the plane of polarization of a beam of linearly polarized light through 90°.

with the horizontal component. The effect is a reversed vertical component and a 90° rotation of the plane of polarization, as shown in the figure.

Only for this particular wavelength of light and this particular crystal thickness (or an appropriate multiple therefore) will a 90° rotation occur, and only this wavelength (color) of light will be transmitted. As a result of nonuniform crystal thickness, a colored pattern is observed when the crystal is viewed through crossed polarizers.

F. Optical Stress Analysis

An important application of polarized light is optical stress analysis of transparent materials. Glasses and plastics are usually optically isotropic. If polarized light is transmitted through an isotropic material and viewed with a crossed polarizer, the transmitted light intensity is minimal.

However, when many materials are mechanically dressed, they become optically anisotropic (indices of refraction vary with direction), and the polarization of the transmitted polarized light is affected. Areas of strain may then be identified and studied through an analyzer (Fig. 40.7). For example, improperly annealed glass may have internal stresses and strains that may later give rise to cracks.

G. Liquid Crystal Displays (LCDs)

LCDs or liquid crystal displays are now commonly used in wristwatches, hand calculators, and even gas pumps. A liquid crystal is a liquid in which the molecules have some order or crystalline nature. Liquid crystals used in LCDs have the ability to rotate or "twist" the plane of polarization of polarized light. In a so-called *twisted nematic display,* a liquid crystal is sandwiched between crossed polarizing sheets and backed by a mirror (Fig. 40.8).

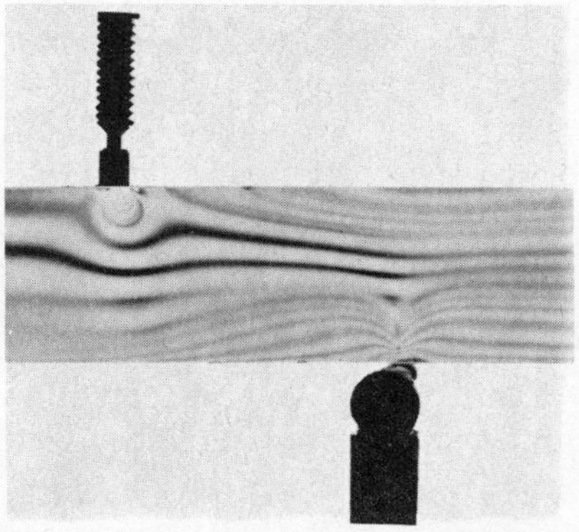

Figure 40.7 Optical stress analysis with polarized light. A transparent bar reveals stress concentrations near the support and loading points because of optical activity.

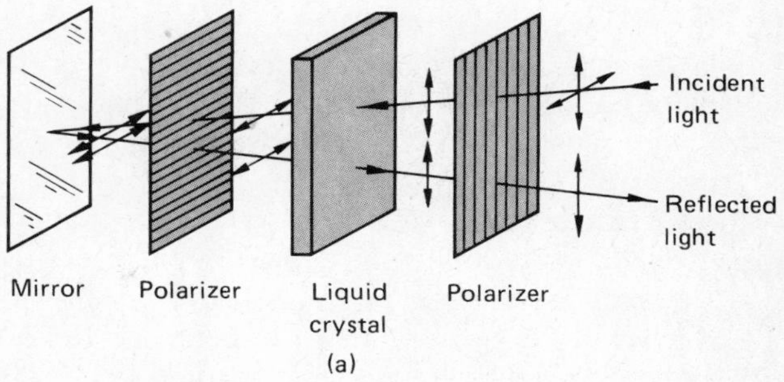

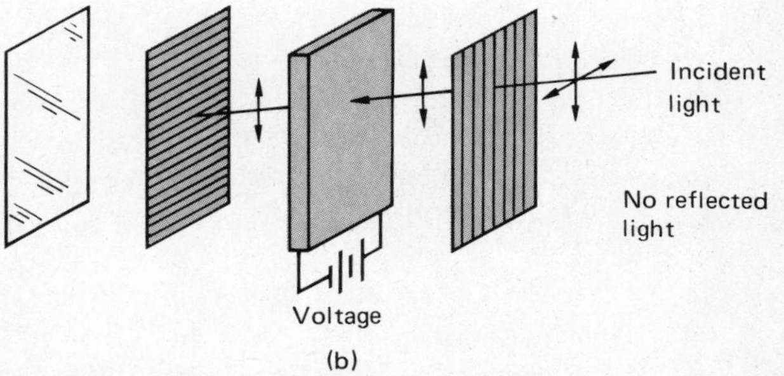

Figure 40.8 LCD (liquid crystal display). (a) A liquid crystal has the property of being able to "twist" or rotate the plane of linearly polarized light by 90°. (b) When a voltage is applied to the crystal, this property is lost. With no light reemerging, the crystal appears dark.

Light falling on the surface of an LCD is polarized, twisted, reflected, and twisted again and then leaves the display. Hence, the display normally appears light because we see the doubly twisted, polarized light coming back from the surface. However, when a voltage is applied to the crystal, the polarized light is not twisted the last time, and hence is absorbed by the final polarizing sheet. Such dark regions of the crystal are used to form numbers and letters in the display.

IV. EXPERIMENTAL PROCEDURE

A. Plane of Polarization (Transmission)

1. Inspect your polarizers to see if the planes of polarization or transmission are indicated on them. If not, these planes need to be determined. (Polarizer and analyzer directions will be needed later.) One method is to use a pair of polarizing sunglasses that has a vertical plane of polarization.

   Determine the planes of polarization for your polarizers by observing the orientations of maximum and minimum transmissions through a polarizer and sunglass lens. Mark the planes of polarization of the polarizers by some means (e.g., a wax pencil or pieces of tape).

2. Investigate the transmission through two polarizers as a function of the angle θ between the planes of polarization (Fig. 40.3). At what angles is the transmission is estimated by brightness or intensity
(a) a maximum,
(b) reduced by one-half, and
(c) a minimum?
Record these angles in the Laboratory Report and show the theoretical prediction (using Eq. 40.1) of the angle for one-half transmission (i.e., $I/I_o = 0.5$).

(Optional) If a light-exposure meter is available, set up an arrangement to measure the intensity through the polarizers as a function of the angle. Plot the intensity (or photocurrent) versus θ on Cartesian graph paper.

3. Orient two polarizers in a crossed position for minimum intensity. Place the third polarizer between these two. Viewing through the polarizer, rotate the middle one (keeping the outer two in a crossed orientation), and observe any intensity changes. As the middle polarizer is rotated, you should observe variations in the transmitted light intensity.

Note the orientation of the plane of polarization of the middle polarizer (relative to the planes of the outer two) for maximum transmission. Make a sketch of the polarizers in the Laboratory Report, and indicate the planes of polarization for the polarizers for this condition.

(*Hint:* Draw three polarizers of different sizes and label the outer two as 1 and 2, and the middle polarizer as 3.) Is there more than one orientation of the middle polarizer for maximum transmission? (Rotate through 360°.) If so, are the angles between the polarization planes different? Explain in the Laboratory Report why this transmission through the outer crossed polarizers is observed.

B. *Polarization by Reflection and Refraction*

4. Using a general value of the index of refraction of glass as $n = 1.6$, compute in the Laboratory Report the reflection polarization angle θ_p.

5. (a) With a single glass microscope slide on the tripod stand positioned near the edge of the table, shine light on the slide at an angle of incidence equal to the computed θ_p. Observe the reflected light through an analyzer at the angle of reflection and examine for polarization. Note the axis of polarization of the reflected light. Observe the reflected light through polarizing sunglasses, and comment.

Observe the light transmitted through the glass slide with an analyzer for any evidence of polarization.

(b) Observe the transmitted light for an increasing number of glass slides, and report and explain any observable differences.

C. *Polarization by Crystal Double Refraction*

6. Place the calcite crystal on some written or printed material and observe the double image. (The images may appear slightly fuzzy owing to small defects in the crystal. Lay the crystal on the side that gives the clearest images.) Notice that when the crystal is rotated the images move, one more than the other. Examine the images with an analyzer.

7. With a pencil or pen, make a linear series of small, heavy dots on a piece of paper. The line of dots should be long enough to extend beyond the edges of the crystal.

Placing the crystal on the line of dots, rotate the crystal. Notice that as the crystal is rotated, one of the dots of a double image remains relatively stationary and the second dot rotates about the first. The image of the nearly stationary dot is formed by the ordinary (O) ray and that of the rotating dot by the extraordinary (E) ray.

Examine a set of dots with an analyzer, and record the polarization direction of each ray.

D. *Polarization by Scattering (Optional)*

8. If it's a sunny day, go outside (with the instructor's permission) and observe the sky light from different portions of the sky with an analyzer. Look in directions away from the sun and at angles of 90°. Once you find a region from which the light shows appreciable polarization, rotate your analyzer to see if there is any preferential direction of polarization. (Should it not be a sunny day, try this with your own polarizing sunglasses some fine day.)

E. *Optical Activity*

9. View a mica sheet between crossed polarizers. Rotate the analyzer and note the change. What changes, the general pattern shape or its colors?

10. Form a pattern or symbol by sticking various layers of cellophane tape on a glass plate or slide. For example, try a "V" or wedge shape with one, two, three, etc., layers of tape in different parts of the "V." Observe the tape symbol between crossed polarizers. Rotate the analyzer. (You may wish to make letters or symbols with pieces of tape cut with a sharp knife or razor blade, for example, your school letters. Could you give the letters your school colors?)

11. Observe the various-shaped pieces of plastic between crossed polarizers. Stress the pieces by pulling or pushing on them (but no so hard as to break them). Can you explain what is observed?

12. View an LCD through an analyzer. Rotate the analyzer. Is the light coming from the lighted portion of the display polarized? (*Note:* You can do this at home using polarizing sunglasses.)

Name ______________________ Section ______________ Date ______________

Lab Partner(s) ____

E X P E R I M E N T 4 0

Polarized Light

Laboratory Report

A. Plane of Polarization (Transmission)

1. Transmission

	Angle θ between polarizer planes
Maximum intensity	______________
One-half intensity	______________
Minimum intensity	______________

Calculation of angle for one-half intensity

2. *(Optional)* Exposure meter readings and angles

3. Three polarizers

Explanation

Sketch

(continued)

B. Polarization by Reflection and Refraction

4. Polarization angle calculation

5. Observations on reflected light

6. Observations on transmitted refracted light

C. Polarization by Crystal Double Refraction

Observations

Name ______________________ Section ______________ Date ______________

Lab Partner(s) ____

EXPERIMENT 40 ***Laboratory Report***

E. Optical Activity

Observations

QUESTIONS

1. In the polarization of light by reflection with a transparent material, would it be possible to have an optimum polarization angle θ_p less than 45°? Justify your answer. (*Hint:* Consider the definition of the index of refraction.)

2. At a sale of polarizing sunglasses, there is a half-price special on some glasses with lenses having a horizontal polarization direction. Would you buy them? If not, why?

(continued)

3. In the procedure using microscope slides, why was the polarization of the transmitted light more observable with an increasing number of slides?

4. The light coming from a liquid crystal display (LCD), as on a watch or calculator, is polarized. How could you conveniently show this to be the case using a commonly available item? (*Hint:* What is a common polarizing material or application of polarization?)

Name ______________________ Section ______________ Date ______________

Lab Partner(s) ____

EXPERIMENT 41

The Prism Spectrometer: Dispersion and the Index of Refraction

Advance Study Assignment

Read the experiment and answer the following questions.

1. What is meant by "dispersion"?

2. Is the index of refraction of a dispersive medium the same for all wavelengths? Explain this in terms of the speed of light in the medium.

3. What is meant by the "angle of deviation" for a prism?

4. What is the condition for the angle of minimum deviation? At this angle, what is the relation of the transmitted ray to the base of the prism?

(continued)

5. What are the four major components of the prism spectrometer and their functions?

The Prism Spectrometer: Dispersion and the Index of Refraction

I. Introduction and Objectives

In vacuum, the speed of light c is the same for all wavelengths or colors of light. However, when a beam of white light falls obliquely on the surface of a glass prism and passes through it, the light is spread out or *dispersed* into a spectrum of colors. This phenomenon led Newton to believe that white light is a mixture of component colors. The dispersion arises in the prism because the wave velocity is slightly different for different wavelengths.

A **spectrometer** is an optical device used to observe and measure the angular deviations of incident light due to refraction and dispersion. Using Snell's law, the index of refraction of the prism glass for a specific wavelength or color can be easily determined.

After performing this experiment and analyzing the data, you should be able to:

1. Explain the dispersion of light in a dispersive medium.
2. Describe the operation of a prism spectrometer.
3. Tell how the index of refraction of a prism can be measured.

II. Equipment Needed

- Prism spectrometer
- Incandescent light source and support stand

III. Theory

A monochromatic (single color or wavelength) light beam in air, obliquely incident on the surface of a transparent medium, is refracted and deviated from its original direction in accordance with Snell's law (see Experiment 38),

$$n = \frac{c}{c_m} = \frac{\sin \theta_1}{\sin \theta_2} \qquad \textbf{(41.1)}$$

where n is the index of refraction, c the speed of light in vacuum (air), c_m the speed of light in the medium, and θ_1 and θ_2 the angles of incidence and refraction, respectively.

If the incident beam is not monochromatic, each component wavelength (color) is refracted differently because the wave speed is slightly different for different wavelengths in a material medium, e.g., a glass prism (Fig. 41.1.). We say that the substance exhibits **dispersion**.

The frequencies of the waves are unchanged, so the greater the wavelength λ_m, the greater the speed of the wave in the material ($c_m = \lambda_m f$). Consequently, the index of refraction is slightly different for different wavelengths ($n = c/c_m = c/\lambda_m f$).*

The dispersion of a beam of white light spreads the transmitted emergent beam into a spectrum of colors, red through violet (see Fig. 41.1). The red component has the longest wavelength, so it is deviated least. The angle between the original direction of the beam and an emergent component of the beam is called the **angle of deviation** D, and is different for each color or wavelength.

As the angle of incidence is decreased from a large value, the angle of deviation of the component colors decreases, then increases, and hence goes through an angle of minimum deviation D_m. The angle of minimum deviation occurs for a particular component when the component ray passes through the prism symmetrically, i.e., parallel to the base of the prism if the prism is isosceles (Fig. 41.2).

* The wavelength of the light in a material λ_m differs from the wavelength of light in vacuum λ, that is, $n = \dfrac{c}{c_m} = \dfrac{\lambda f}{\lambda_m f} = \dfrac{\lambda}{\lambda_m}$.

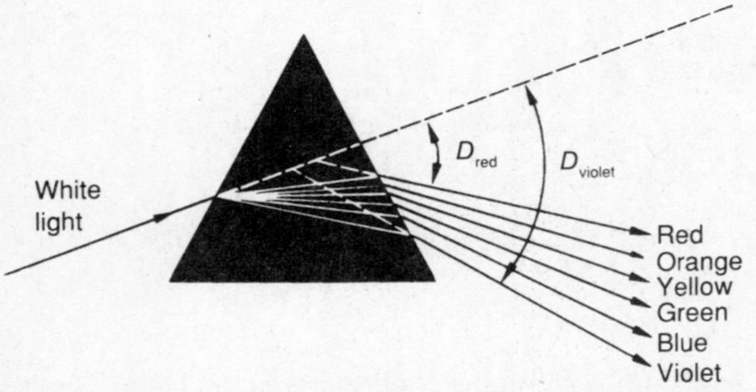

Figure 41.1 Dispersion. The dispersion of light by a glass prism causes white light to be spread out into a spectrum of colors. The angle between the original direction of the beam and an emergent component is called the angle of deviation D for that particular component.

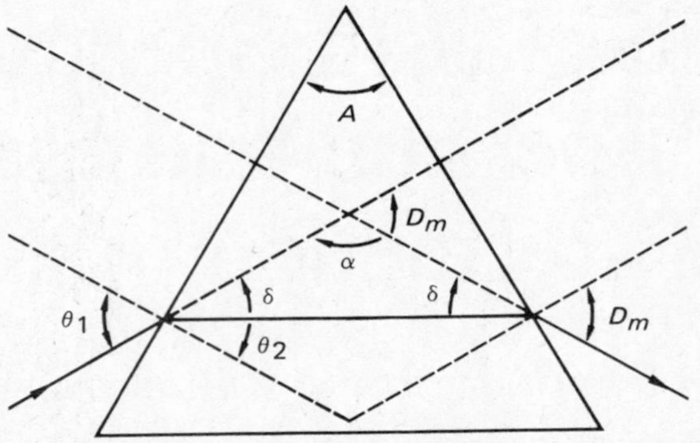

Figure 41.2 Minimum angle of deviation. The geometry for determining the minimum angle of deviation D_m for a light ray. See text for description.

The angle of minimum deviation and the prism angle A are related to the index of refraction of the prism glass (for a particular color component) through Snell's law by the relationship

$$n = \frac{\sin[(A + D_m)/2]}{\sin(A/2)} \qquad \textbf{(41.2)}$$

The derivation of this equation can be seen from the geometry of Fig. 41.2. Note from the top triangle that

$$2(90° - \theta_2) + A = 180°$$

and therefore

$$\theta_2 = \frac{A}{2} \qquad \textbf{(41.3)}$$

Also, for the symmetric case, it can be seen that $D_m = 2\delta$, or

$$\delta = \frac{D_m}{2} \qquad \textbf{(41.4)}$$

(Note the interior triangle, $2\delta + \alpha = 180° = \alpha + D_m$.) Then

$$\theta_1 = \theta_2 + \delta = \frac{A}{2} + \frac{D_m}{2} = \frac{A + D_m}{2} \qquad \textbf{(41.5)}$$

Substituting Eqs. 41.3 and 41.5 into Snell's law (Eq. 41.1) yields Eq. 41.2.

IV. Experimental Procedure*

1. Two types of prism spectrometers are shown in Fig. 41.3, one of which is an adapted force table (see Experiment 5). The four basic parts of a spectrometer are the (a) collimator, (b) prism, (c) telescope, and (d) divided circle.

   The **collimator** is a tube with a slit of adjustable width at one end and a converging lens at the other. Light from a light source enters the collimator. The length of the collimator tube is made equal to the focal length of the lens so as to make the rays of the emerging light beam parallel.

   The **prism** deviates and disperses the beam into a spectrum. The objective of the **telescope** converges the beam and produces an image of the slit, which is viewed through the telescope eyepiece. The eyepiece is fitted with cross hairs, which may be fixed on a particular spectral color. The **divided circle** allows the angle(s) of deviation to be measured.

2. After being given instructions by the instructor, study the various clamps and adjustment screws of your spectrometer. In particular, study the divided circle scale. Some spectrometers are equipped with vernier scales that permit readings to 1 min of arc. Care should be taken, as the adjustments and alignments of the spectrometer are critical and it can be time-consuming to restore proper adjustment.

3. *For spectrometer with telescope.* With the prism not on the spectrometer table, sight the telescope on some distant object and adjust the eyepiece until the cross hairs are in good focus. Then mount the lamp near the collimator slit (adjusted to a small slit width). Move the telescope into the line of sight and adjust so that a sharp image of the illuminated slit is seen focused on the cross hairs.

* Some procedures may not apply to force table apparatus.

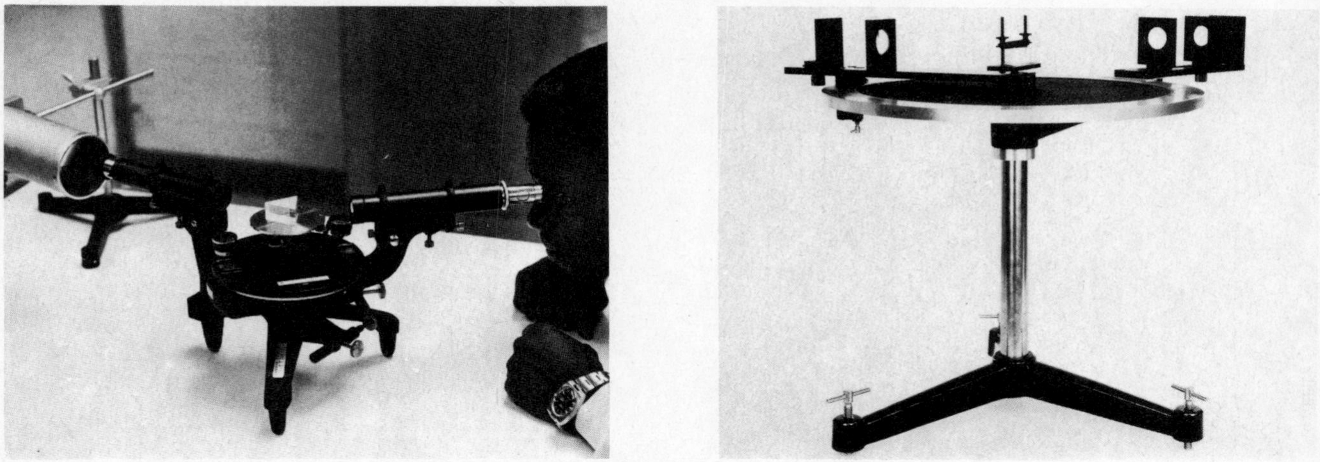

Figure 41.3 **Types of prism spectrometers.** (a) Light from a source goes through the collimator, the prism, and the telescope to the viewer. Magnifying glasses for reading the divided circle graduations are seen on the prism pedestal (in front of the telescope). (b) A force table adapted as a prism spectrometer. (Photo in (b) courtesy of Central Scientific Co., Inc.)

4. *Measurement of the prism angle A.* Mount the prism in the center of the spectrometer table, and orient it as shown in Fig. 41.4. With the unaided eye, locate the white image of the slit reflected from a face of the prism on either side of the prism angle A. The prism may have to be adjusted slightly. (You may also note the color spectrum in the prism face opposite A.)

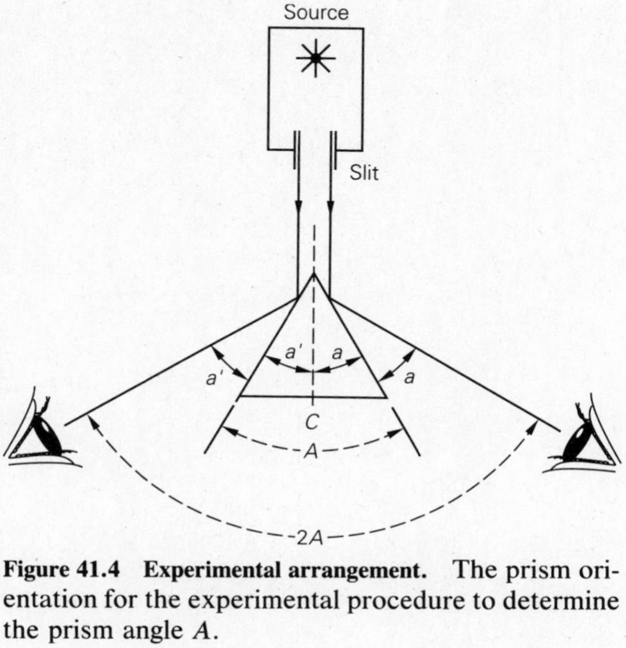

Figure 41.4 Experimental arrangement. The prism orientation for the experimental procedure to determine the prism angle A.

Move the telescope in front of the eye and adjust the cross hairs on the center of the slit image (with the fine-adjustment screw, if available). Make the slit as narrow as possible so that the best setting can be made. On a force table apparatus, adjustment is not required. Read the angle from the divided circle, and record in the Laboratory Report.

Repeat this procedure for the other face of the prism. As shown in Fig. 41.4, the angle between the positions is equal to $2A$. Compute the angle A from the circle readings.

5. *Measurement of the angle of minimum deviation.* Remove the prism and move the telescope into the line of sight of the slit. (It is convenient, but not necessary, to adjust the setup so the telescope has a zero reading on the divided circle. This makes finding the deviation angles easy by reading directly.) Adjust the telescope so that a sharp image of the illuminated slit is seen on the cross hairs. Note and record the reading of the divided circle.

Replace and rotate the prism to a position as shown in Fig. 41.5, and with the unaided eye, locate the emergent spectrum of colors. Move the telescope or slit holder in front of the eye and examine the spectrum. (Change the slit width if applicable and note any difference.) List the sequence of colors, beginning with red, in the Laboratory Report.

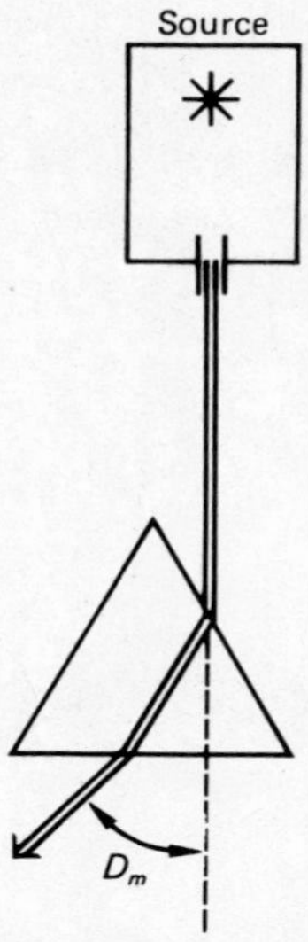

Figure 41.5 Experimental arrangement. The prism orientation for the experimental procedure to determine the angle of minimum deviation.

6. With the slit set as narrow as possible, rotate the prism back and forth slightly, and note the reversal of the direction of motion of the spectrum when the prism is rotated in one direction. Stop rotating the prism at the position of the reversal of motion of the yellow component of the spectrum. This is the position for minimum deviation of this component.

7. Being careful not to disturb the prism, center the telescope cross hairs on the middle of the yellow color band and record the divided circle reading. Also measure the angle readings for each end of the visible spectrum [i.e., the red and blue (violet) ends]. Do this by setting the cross hairs of the telescope at the locations where the spectrum ends are just visible (not at the center of the extreme bands).

8. Compute the index of refraction for yellow light using Eq. 41.2.

Name ______________________ Section ____________ Date ____________

Lab Partner(s) ______________________

EXPERIMENT 41

The Prism Spectrometer: Dispersion and the Index of Refraction

Laboratory Report

Measurement of Prism Angle A

Calculations
(show work)

Circle readings for reflected images ____________

Computation of $2A$ ____________

Prism angle A ____________

Measurement of Angle of Minimum Deviation

Spectrum (sequence) of colors

red	

	Circle reading	*Minimum deviation*
Line of sight		
Yellow		
Red end		
Blue end		

Calculations
(show work)

Index of Refraction for Yellow Light

$n =$ ____________

Don't forget units

(continued)

Calculations
(show work)

QUESTIONS

1. Show that the angle between the two telescope settings of the reflected slit images is equal to $2A$ (procedure 4).

2. What is the speed of yellow light in the prism, based on your experimental results?

3. What is the range of indices of refraction of the prism for the wavelengths of visible light?

Name ______________________ Section ____________ Date ____________

Lab Partner(s) ______________________

EXPERIMENT 42

Line Spectra and the Rydberg Constant

Advance Study Assignment

Read the experiment and answer the following questions.

1. Distinguish between continuous and line spectra, and describe their causes.

2. Why does a gas discharge tube (e.g., a neon light) have a certain color?

3. What are (a) the Balmer series and (b) the Rydberg constant?

(continued)

4. Explain briefly how the prism spectrometer is calibrated.

5. Explain briefly how the Rydberg constant is determined experimentally.

Line Spectra and the Rydberg Constant

I. Introduction and Objectives

In spectroscopic analysis, two types of spectra are observed: continuous spectra and line or discrete spectra. The spectrum of visible light from an incandescent source is found to consist of a **continuous spectrum** or band of merging colors and contains all the wavelengths of the visible spectrum. However, when the light from a gas discharge tube (e.g., mercury or helium) is observed through a spectroscope, only a few colors or wavelengths are observed. The colored images of the spectroscope slit appear as bright lines separated by dark regions; hence the name **line** or **discrete spectra.**

Each gas emits a particular set of spectral lines or has a characteristic spectrum. Thus, spectroscopy (the study of spectra) provides a method of element identification. The discrete lines of a given spectrum depend on the atomic structure of the atoms and are due to electron transitions.

The line spectrum of hydrogen was explained by Bohr's theory of the hydrogen atom. However, before this, the line spectrum of hydrogen was described by an empirical formula involving the Rydberg constant. In this experiment, line spectra will be observed and the relationship of the empirical Rydberg constant to the theoretical quantities of the Bohr theory will be investigated.

After performing this experiment and analyzing the data, you should be able to:

1. Clearly distinguish between continuous and line (discrete) spectra.
2. Explain why gas discharge tubes emit line spectra.
3. Tell what is meant by the Balmer series and the Rydberg constant.

II. Equipment Needed

- Prism spectrometer
- Incandescent light source
- Mercury or helium discharge tube
- Hydrogen discharge tube
- Discharge-tube power supply
- 2 sheets of Cartesian graph paper

III. Theory

The electrons in an incandescent light source undergo thermal agitation and emit electromagnetic radiation (light) of many different wavelengths, hence producing a continuous spectrum. However, when light emitted from excited gases or vaporized liquids or solids is analyzed, line spectra such as those illustrated in Fig. 42.1 are observed.

Modern theory explains spectra in terms of photons of light of discrete wavelengths being emitted as the result of electron transitions between atomic energy levels. Different substances have characteristic spectra—that is, they have a characteristic set of lines at specific wavelengths. In a manner of speaking, the spectrum of a substance acts as a "fingerprint" by which the substance can be identified.

The characteristic color of light from a gas discharge tube is often indicative of the most intense spectral line(s) is the visible region. For example, light from a hydrogen discharge tube has a characteristic red glow resulting from an intense emission line with a wavelength of 656.1 nm (or 6561 Å). Similarly, when table salt (sodium chloride) is vaporized in a flame, yellow light is observed because of

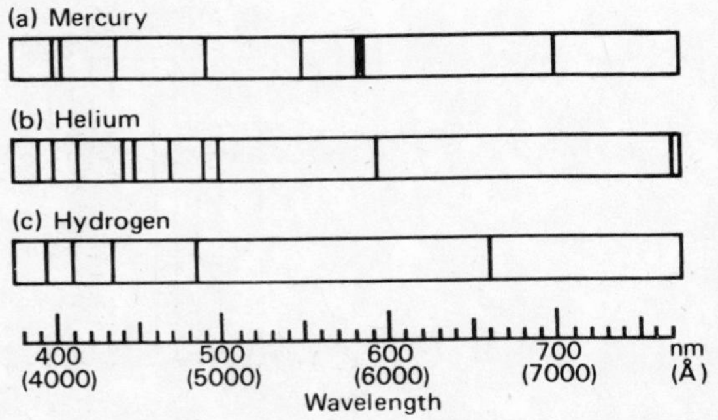

Figure 42.1 Line spectra. Illustrations of visible line spectra for (a) mercury, (b) helium, and (c) hydrogen.

intense emission lines in the region of the sodium spectrum. Wavelengths are commonly measured in nanometer (nm) or angstrom (Å) units:

$$1 \text{ nm} = 10^{-9} \text{ m} = 10^{-7} \text{ cm}$$

and

$$1 \text{ Å} = 10^{-10} \text{ m} = 10^{-8} \text{ cm}$$

so

$$1 \text{ nm} = 10 \text{ Å}$$

The systematic spacing of the spectral lines in the hydrogen spectrum was empirically described by spectroscopists in the late 1800s. For example, the wavelengths of spectral lines in the visible region, called the Balmer series, were found to fit the formula

$$\frac{1}{\lambda} = R\left(\frac{1}{2^2} - \frac{1}{n^2}\right) \qquad n = 3, 4, 5, \ldots \qquad \textbf{(42.1)}$$

where R is the **Rydberg constant,** with a value of 1.097×10^{-2} nm^{-1} (or 1.097×10^{-3} Å^{-1}).

The hydrogen spectrum is of particular theoretical interest because hydrogen, having only one proton and one electron, is the simplest of all atoms. Niels Bohr (1885–1962) developed a theory for the hydrogen atom that explains the spectral lines as resulting from electron transitions between energy levels or discrete electron orbits (Fig. 42.2), with the wavelengths of the spectral lines being given by the theoretical equation

$$\lambda = \frac{hc}{\Delta E} \qquad \textbf{(42.2)}$$

where

$$\Delta E = 13.6\left(\frac{1}{n_f^2} - \frac{1}{n_i^2}\right) \text{ eV}$$

is the energy difference between the initial and final states, n_i and n_f, $h = 6.63 \times 10^{-34}$ J-s $= 4.14 \times 10^{-15}$ eV-s (Planck's constant), and $c = 3.00 \times 10^8$ m/s (speed of light). The values $n = 1, 2, 3, 4, \ldots$ are called the **principal quantum numbers.**

For spectral lines in the visible region, the final state is $n_f = 2$, and

$$\lambda = \frac{hc}{\Delta E} = \frac{hc}{13.6[(1/2^2) - 1/n^2]} \qquad n = 3, 4, 5, \ldots$$

or

$$\frac{1}{\lambda} = \frac{13.6}{hc}\left(\frac{1}{2^2} - \frac{1}{n_i^2}\right) \qquad n = 3, 4, 5, \ldots \qquad \textbf{(42.3)}$$

Comparing this theoretical equation with the empirical equation, Eq. 42.1, it is seen that the forms are identical with the prediction that $R = (13.6 \text{ eV})/hc$.

IV. Experimental Procedure

1. A prism spectrometer will be used to analyze and study spectra in this experiment. The prism spectrometer is illustrated and its use described in Experiment 41. Review the operation of this instrument. Place the incandescent source in front of the collimator slit and observe the continuous spectrum that results from the prism dispersion (c.f. Experiment 41). List the colors of the spectrum in the Laboratory Report, beginning with red.

2. A convenient type of discharge tube and power supply is shown in Fig. 42.3.

   Caution: *Great care should be taken, as the discharge tube operates at high voltage and you could receive an electrical shock.*

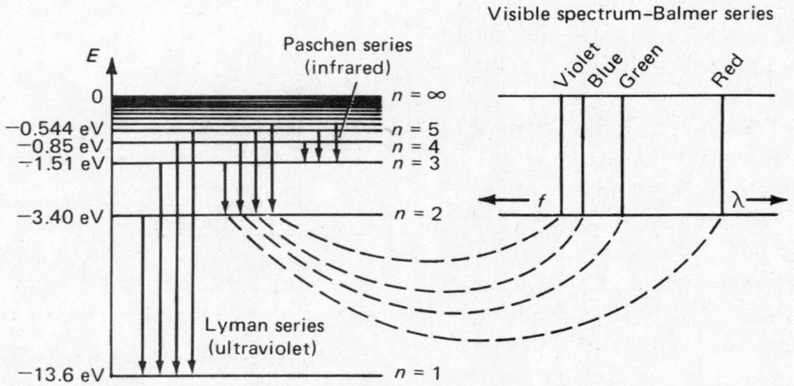

Figure 42.2 Energy level transitions. The energy level transitions for the hydrogen atom. The Balmer series, $n_f = 2$, produces a line spectrum in the visible region.

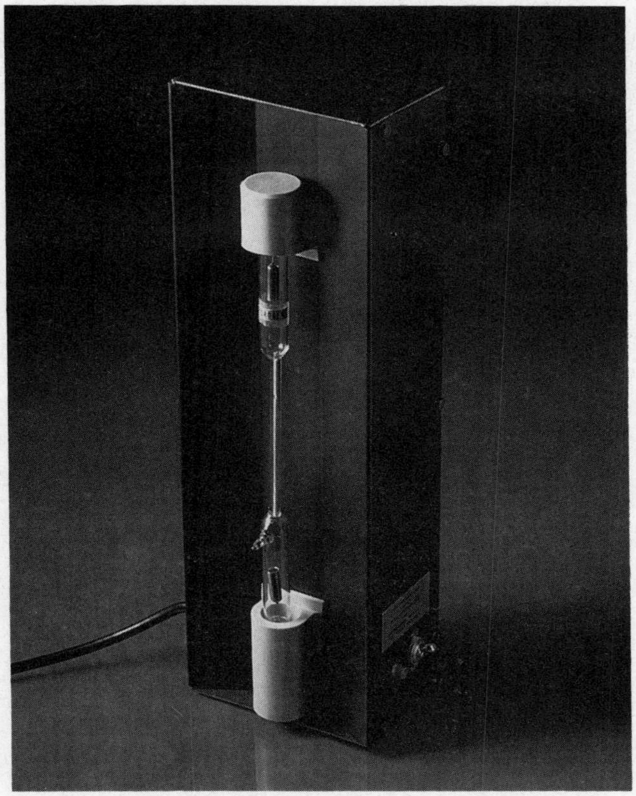

Figure 42.3 Experimental apparatus. A gas discharge tube and power supply. (Photo courtesy of Sargent-Welch Scientific Co.)

Mount a mercury (or helium) discharge tube in the power supply holder and place in front of the collimator slit. ***Caution:*** *If a larger mercury source is used, it should be properly shielded because of the ultraviolet radiation that may be emitted. Consult your instructor.*

Turn on the power supply, observe the mercury (or helium) spectrum through the telescope, and note its line nature.

With the slit as narrow as possible, rotate the prism slightly back and forth and notice the reversal of direction of the motion of the spectrum when the prism is rotated in one direction. Focusing on the yellow line, stop rotating the prism at the position of the reversal of motion of this line. This sets the prism for minimum deviation for the yellow line (Experiment 41), which will be taken as an average for the spectrum. (The other lines have slightly different minimum deviations.)

3. **(a)** Without disturbing the prism, starting at the red end of the spectrum, set the cross hairs of the telescope on the extreme red line and record the color and divided circle reading in the Laboratory Report. Repeat this procedure for each spectral line in order. (Turn off the discharge tube as soon as possible to conserve the life of the tube.)

(b) Find the wavelengths of the spectral lines for the discharge tube gas in Appendix A, Table A8, and match to the line readings.

(c) Using these data, plot the wavelength λ versus the divided circle reading θ. This calibrates the spectrometer, and unknown wavelengths can be determined from divided circle readings from the calibration curve.

4. With the discharge-tube power supply off, replace the mercury (or helium) discharge tube with a hydrogen discharge tube. Turn on the power supply, and starting with the red line of the hydrogen spectrum, determine the divided circle reading for each spectral line with the cross hairs of the telescope positioned on the center of the line. Record in the Laboratory Report.

The red line is referred to as H_α in spectroscopic notation and the other sequential lines as H_β, etc., with subscripts in Greek alphabetical order.

5. Determine the wavelengths of the hydrogen lines from the calibration curve, and plot the reciprocal of the wavelength $1/\lambda$ versus $1/n^2$. (Begin the abscissa scale with zero.) Draw the best straight line that fits the data points and determine the slope of the line.

Note that Eq. 42.1

$$\frac{1}{\lambda} = R\left(\frac{1}{2^2} - \frac{1}{n^2}\right) = \frac{R}{4} - \frac{R}{n^2}$$

has the form of a straight line, $y = mx + b$, with the negative slope equal to the Rydberg constant. Compare the slope of the line with the accepted value of the Rydberg constant by computing the percent error. Compare the intercept of this line with $R/4$.

Name ______________________ Section ______________ Date ______________
Lab Partner(s) ______________________________________

EXPERIMENT 42

Line Spectra and the Rydberg Constant

Laboratory Report

Colors of the Continuous Spectrum

DATA TABLE 1 Mercury (or Helium) Spectrum

Color	Divided circle reading	Wavelength ( ) (from Table A8)

Sequence of colors

red

____
____
____
____
____
____
____
____

Don't forget units

(continued)

DATA TABLE 2 Hydrogen Spectrum

Line	Color	Divided circle reading	Wavelength ( )	$1/\lambda$ ( )	$1/n^2$
H_α, $n = 3$					
H_β, $n = 4$					
H_γ, $n = 5$					
H_δ, $n = 6$					

Calculations (Slope of Graph)
(show work)

R (experimental) ____________

Accepted value ____________

Percent error ____________

$R/4$ from graph ____________

Accepted value ____________

Percent error ____________

QUESTIONS

1. Compute the value of the Rydberg constant from the Bohr theory, and compare it with the accepted empirical value.

Name ______________________ Section ____________ Date ____________

Lab Partner(s) ______________________

EXPERIMENT 42 *Laboratory Report*

2. Why are only four lines seen in the Balmer series? (Transitions for $n_i > 6$ also exist.) Justify your answer mathematically.

3. As n becomes very large, the wavelengths of the Balmer (and other) series approaches a minimum wavelength or series limit (Eq. 42.1). What is the wavelength of the series limit for the Balmer series?

Name ______________________ Section ______________ Date ______________

Lab Partner(s) ____

EXPERIMENT 43

The Transmission Diffraction Grating: Measuring the Wavelengths of Light

Advance Study Assignment

Read the experiment and answer the following questions.

1. What is a diffraction grating? Distinguish between the two types of gratings.

2. What is the grating constant? What would be the grating constant for a grating with 300 lines/mm? (Express the constant in nanometers.)

3. Explain why there is a spectrum for each diffraction order when multicolored light is analyzed.

(continued)

4. Will the red or the violet end of the first-order spectrum be nearest the central maximum? Justify your answer.

5. It will be observed that the second-order spectrum is ''spread out'' more than the first-order spectrum. Why?

The Transmission Diffraction Grating: Measuring the Wavelengths of Light

I. Introduction and Objectives

In Experiment 41 the prism spectrometer had to be calibrated in terms of known wavelengths before we were able to determine unknown wavelengths of light experimentally. How, then, are the wavelengths of spectral lines or colors initially determined? This is most commonly done with a diffraction grating, a simple device that allows for the study of spectra and the measurement of wavelengths.

By replacing the prism with a diffraction grating, a prism spectrometer (Experiments 41 and 42) becomes a grating spectrometer. When using a diffraction grating, the angle(s) at which the incident beam is defracted relate directly to the wavelength(s) of the light. In this experiment the properties of a transmission grating will be investigated and the wavelengths of several spectral lines will be determined.

After performing this experiment and analyzing the data, you should be able to:

1. Describe the principle of a diffraction grating.
2. Explain the operation of a grating spectrometer.
3. Tell how the wavelength of light can be measured with a grating spectrometer.

II. Equipment Needed

- Spectrometer*
- Diffraction grating and holder
- Mercury discharge tube
- Power supply for discharge tube
- Incandescent light source

III. Theory

A **diffraction grating** consists of a piece of metal or glass with a very large number of evenly spaced parallel lines or grooves. This gives two types of gratings: reflection gratings and transmission gratings. **Reflection gratings** are ruled on polished metal surfaces; light is reflected from the unruled areas, which act as a row of "slits." **Transmission gratings** are ruled on glass, and the unruled slit areas transmit incident light.

The transmission type is used in this experiment. Common laboratory gratings have 300 grooves per mm and 600 grooves per mm (about 7500 grooves per in. and 15,000 grooves per in.), and are pressed plastic *replicas* mounted on glass. Glass originals are very expensive.

Diffraction refers to the "bending" or deviation of waves around sharp edges or corners. The slits of a grating give rise to diffraction, and the diffracted light interferes so as to set up interference patterns (Fig. 43.1). Complete constructive interference of the waves occurs when the phase or path difference is equal to one wavelength, and the first-order maximum occurs for

$$d \sin \theta_1 = \lambda \tag{43.1}$$

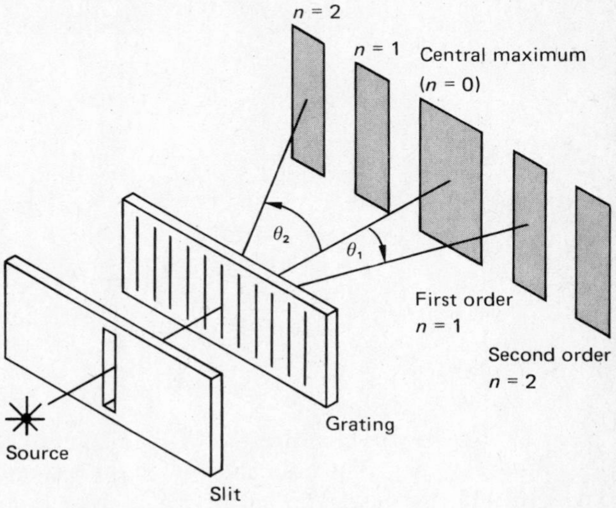

Figure 43.1 Diffraction pattern. A simplistic view of the diffraction pattern (two orders) produced by a diffraction grating. (Patterns and angles are exaggerated for illustration.)

* *Instructor's note:* If a spectrometer is not available, an alternative, inexpensive method is described in the Instructor's Manual.

where d is the grating constant or distance between the grating lines, θ_1 the angle the rays are diffracted from the incident direction, and $d \sin \theta_1$ the path difference between adjacent rays. The **grating constant** is given by

$$d = 1/N \qquad \textbf{(43.2)}$$

where N is the number of lines or grooves per unit length (usually per millimeter or per inch) of the grating.

A second-order maximum occurs for $d \sin \theta_2 = 2\lambda$, and so on, so that in general we may write

$$d \sin \theta_n = n\lambda \qquad n = 1, 2, 3, \ldots \qquad \textbf{(43.3)}$$

where n is the order of the image maximum. The interference is symmetric on either side of an undeviated and undiffracted central maximum of the slit image, so the angle between symmetric image orders is $2\theta_n$ (Fig. 43.2).

In practice, only the first few orders are easily observed, with the number of orders depending on the grating constant. If the incident light is other than monochromatic, each order corresponds to a spectrum. (That is, the grating spreads the light out into a spectrum.) As can be seen from Eq. 43.1, since d is constant, each wavelength (color) is deviated by a slightly different angle, so that the component wavelengths are separated into a spectrum. Each diffraction order in this case corresponds to a spectrum order. (The colorful displays seen on compact disks [CDs] result from diffraction.)

Example 43.1 In an experiment using a diffraction grating with 600 lines/mm, the angle between the corresponding lines of a particular component of the first-order spectrum on either side of the incident beam is 41.30°. What is the wavelength of the spectral line?

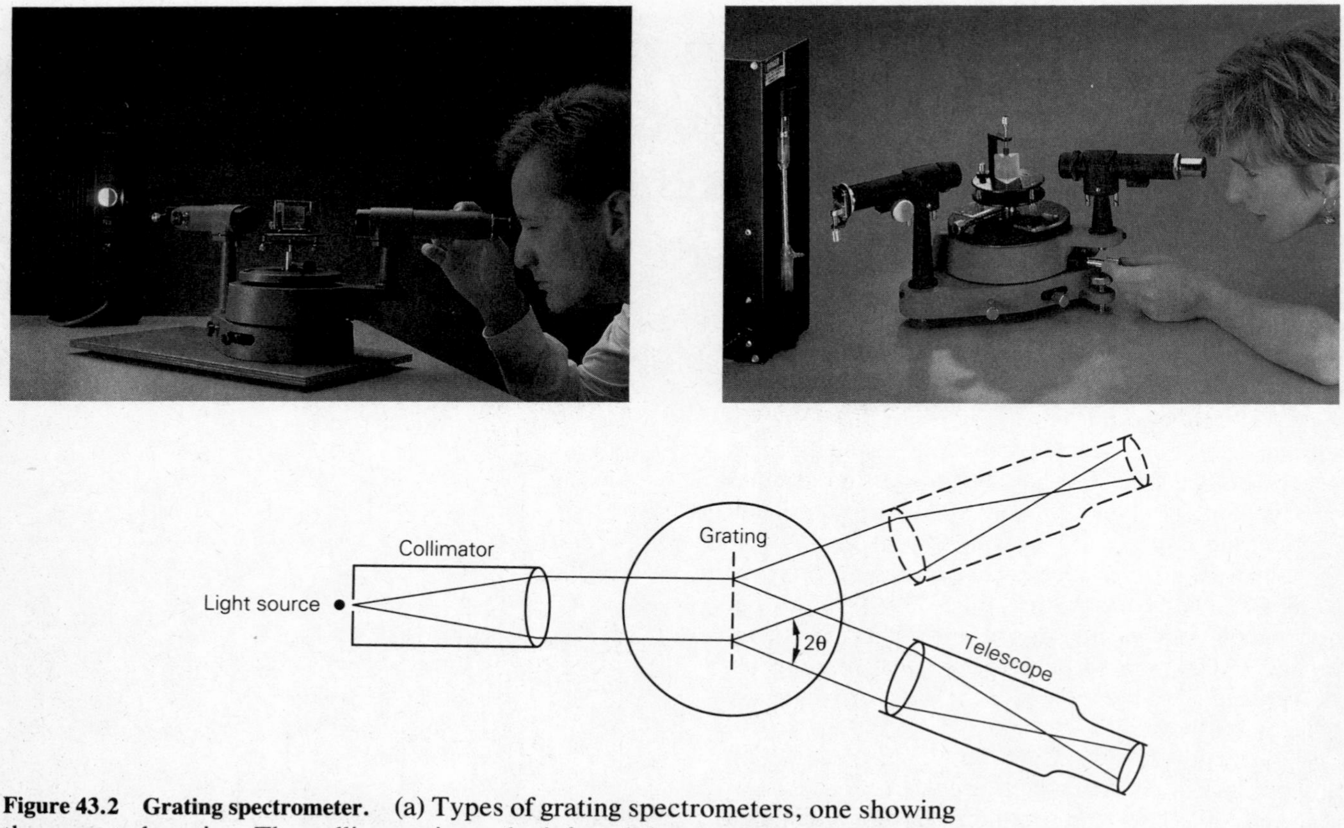

Figure 43.2 Grating spectrometer. (a) Types of grating spectrometers, one showing the mounted grating. The collimator is on the left and the movable telescope that moves to different angles is on the right. (b) An illustration of a top view of a grating spectrometer. When the symmetric images of a particular order n are viewed from both sides of the central maximum, the angle between the two viewing positions is $2\theta_n$. (Photos in (a) courtesy of (left) PASCO Scientific; (right) Sargent-Welch Scientific Co.)

Solution Given $2\theta_1 = 41.30°$ or $\theta_1 = 20.65°$, and with a grating ruling of $N = 600$ lines/mm, the grating constant d is(Eq. 43.2)

$$d = \frac{1}{N} = \frac{1}{600/\text{mm}} = 1.67 \times 10^{-3}\ \text{mm}$$

Then for first-order ($n = 1$) interference by Eq. 43.3,

$$d \sin \theta_1 = \lambda$$

or

$$\begin{aligned} \lambda = d \sin \theta_1 &= (1.67 \times 10^{-3}\ \text{mm})(\sin 20.65°) \\ &= 5.89 \times 10^{-4}\ \text{mm} \end{aligned}$$

Changing to nanometers (1 mm = 10^6 nm),

$$\begin{aligned} \lambda &= 5.89 \times 10^{-4}\ \text{mm}\ (10^6\ \text{nm/mm}) \\ &= 589\ \text{nm} \quad (\text{or } 5890\ \text{Å}) \end{aligned}$$

When doing several calculations, it is convenient to express the grating constant initially in nm.

IV. Experimental Procedure

1. Review the general operation of a spectrometer if necessary (Experiment 41). Record the number of lines per mm of your diffraction grating in part A of the Laboratory Report. Mount the grating on the spectrometer table with the grating ruling parallel to the collimator slit and the plane of the grating perpendicular to the collimator axis.

Determination of the Wavelength Range of the Visible Spectrum

2. Mount an incandescent light source in front of the collimator slit. Move the spectrometer telescope into the line of the slit of the collimator and focus the cross hairs on the central slit image.

   Notice that this central maximum or "zeroth"-order image does not depend on the wavelength of light, so that a white image is observed. Then move the telescope to either side of the incident beam and observe the first- and second-order spectra. Note which is spread out more.

3. **(a)** Focus the cross hairs on the blue (violet) end of the first-order spectrum at the position where you judge the spectrum just becomes visible. Record the divided circle reading (to the nearest minute of arc) in Data Table 1.

   (b) Move the telescope to the other (red) end of the spectrum and record the divided circle reading of its visible limit.

   (c) Repeat this procedure for the first-order spectrum on the opposite side of the central maximum. The angular difference between the respective readings corresponds to an angle of 2θ (Fig. 43.2b).

4. Compute the grating constant d in millimeters, and with the experimentally measured θ's, compute the range of the wavelengths of the visible spectrum in nanometers and angstrom units.

Determination of the Wavelengths of Spectral Lines

5. Mount the mercury discharge tube in its power supply holder and place in front of the collimator slit.

   Caution: *Work very carefully, as the discharge tube operates at high voltage and you could receive an electrical shock. If a large mercury source is used, it should be properly shielded because of the ultraviolet radiation that may be emitted. Consult with your instructor.*

   Turn on the power supply and observe the first- and second-order mercury line spectra on both sides of the central image.

6. Because some of the lines are brighter than others and the weaker lines are difficult to observe in the second-order spectra, the wavelengths of only the brightest lines will be determined. Find the listing of the mercury spectral lines in Appendix A, Table A8, and record the color and wavelength in Data Table 2.

   Then, beginning with either first-order spectra, set the telescope cross hairs on each of the four brightest spectral lines and record the divided circle readings (read to the nearest minute of arc). Repeat the readings for the first-order spectrum on the opposite side of the central image.

7. Repeat the measurement procedure for the four lines in the second-order spectra and, using Eq. 43.2, compute the wavelength of each of the lines for both orders of spectra. Compare with the accepted values by computing the percent error of your measurements in each case.

   Note: In the second-order spectra, two yellow lines—a *doublet*—may be observed. Make certain that you choose the appropriate line. (*Hint:* See the wavelengths of the yellow lines in Appendix A, Table A8. Which is closer to the red end of the spectrum?)

Name ______________________ Section ______________ Date ______________

Lab Partner(s) ____

EXPERIMENT 43

The Transmission Diffraction Grating: Measuring the Wavelengths of Light

Laboratory Report

Number of lines per mm on grating ______________ Grating constant, d ______________ (mm)

DATA TABLE 1

Purpose: To determine the wavelength range of the visible spectrum.

Spectrum limit	Divided circle reading		2θ	θ	$\sin\theta$	Computed wavelength	
	Right	Left				( )	( )
Violet end							
Red end							

Calculations
(show work)

Don't forget units

(continued)

DATA TABLE 2
Purpose: To determine the wavelengths of spectral lines.

Mercury lines		Divided circle reading		2θ	θ	$\sin\theta$	Computed λ ( )	Percent error
Color	Wavelength	Right	Left					
First-order spectrum								
Second-order spectrum								

Calculations
(show work)

QUESTIONS

1. If a grating with more lines per unit length were used, how would the observed angles or spread of the spectra be affected?

Name ______________________ Section ______________ Date ______________

Lab Partner(s) ____

EXPERIMENT 43 *Laboratory Report*

2. Was there any difference in the accuracy of the determination of the wavelengths of the mercury lines for the different-order spectra? If so, give an explanation.

3. Is it possible for the first-order spectrum to overlap the second-order spectrum? Explain, assuming a continuous spectrum.

4. Is there a theoretical limit to the order of the spectrum one would be able to observe with your diffraction grating? Justify your answer mathematically.

Name ______________________ Section ______________ Date ______________

Lab Partner(s) ____

EXPERIMENT 44

The Mass of an Electron: *e/m* Measurement

Advance Study Assignment

Read the experiment and answer the following questions.

1. Why does an electron traveling perpendicular to a uniform magnetic field describe a circular path?

2. What causes the fan-shaped pattern in the vacuum tube?

3. How is the radius of curvature of the electron path measured in the experiment?

(continued)

4. How does changing the current in the solenoid change the curvature of the electron path?

EXPERIMENT 44

The Mass of an Electron: *e/m* Measurement

I. Introduction and Objectives

The mass of an electron, 9.1×10^{-31} kg, is much too small to measure directly. However, using electromagnetic methods involving the charge of the electron in electric and magnetic fields, the electron mass can be determined indirectly. In several situations, the ratio of the electron's charge to its mass (e/m) can be determined in terms of directly measurable parameters. Then, knowing the value of the electron's charge ($e = 1.6 \times 10^{-19}$ C), for example from Millikan's oil-drop experiment, the mass of an electron can be computed. This will be the procedure used in this experiment.

After performing this experiment and analyzing the data, you should be able to:

1. Explain on what the velocity of an electron moving in a magnetic field depends.
2. Explain how the charge/mass (e/m) ratio of an electron can be measured experimentally.

II. Equipment Needed

- Tuning-eye vacuum tube (6AF6)
- Air-core solenoid
- Variable dc power supply (250 V dc)
- ac power supply (6.3 V ac)
- dc power supply (12 V dc)
- Rheostat
- dc ammeter (0 to 5 A)
- Connecting wires
- Vernier calipers and metric ruler
- Wooden dowels of different diameters

III. Theory

An electron traveling with a speed v perpendicular to a uniform magnetic field **B** will experience a force **F** with a magnitude of

$$F = evB \tag{44.1}$$

where e is the charge of the electron.

The direction of the force ($\mathbf{F} = e\mathbf{v} \times \mathbf{B}$) is perpendicular to the plane defined by **v** and **B**. Thus, the force is always at right angles to the direction of the electron's motion. This causes the electron to describe a circular path of radius r, with the magnetic force supplying the required centripetal force of magnitude F_c. That is,

$$F = evB = F_c = \frac{mv^2}{r} \tag{44.2}$$

where m is the mass of the electron. Solving for v, we have

$$v = \frac{eBr}{m} \tag{44.3}$$

The initial electron speed v is normally acquired by accelerating the electron through an electric potential V, and by the work-energy theorem,

$$W = eV = \tfrac{1}{2}mv^2 \tag{44.4}$$

Then, squaring Eq. 44.3 and substituting for v^2, we have, after rearranging,

$$\frac{e}{m} = \frac{2V}{B^2r^2} \tag{44.5}$$

Hence, by knowing or measuring e, V, B, and r, the mass of an electron can be computed.

In this experiment, the electron(s) are produced, accelerated, and deflected in a commercial "tuning-eye" vacuum tube (Fig. 44.1). Such tubes were once commonly used in tuning radios. The magnetic field is supplied by a solenoid. In the tube, the electrons emitted by the cathode are accelerated by the potential difference applied between the center cathode and the outer conical anode (Fig. 44.2).

The electrons move radially outward from the cathode coil, reaching nearly their maximum speed by the time they emerge from beneath the black metal cap covering the center of the tube. The conical anode is coated with a fluorescent material (e.g., zinc sulfide), which emits light when the electrons strike it. Hence, we can visually trace the beam (Fig. 44.3).

The beam pattern in the tube appears fan-shaped owing to two deflecting electrodes in the tube (Fig. 44.2). These electrodes are connected to the cathode,

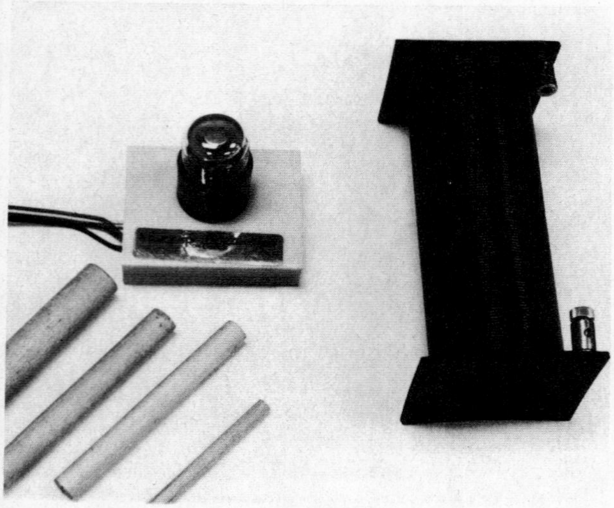

Figure 44.1 Experimental equipment. The "tuning-eye" vacuum tube, air-core solenoid, and wooden dowels used in measuring e/m.

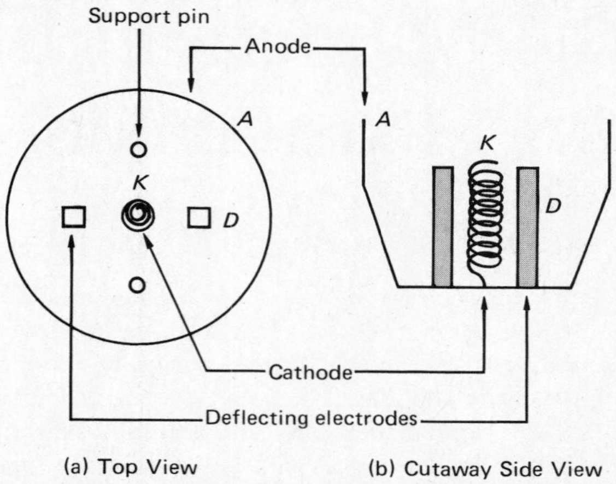

Figure 44.2 Elements of the tuning-eye tube. See text for description.

and therefore are negatively charged and repel electrons moving toward them from the cathode, forming wedge-shaped shadows.

When a uniform magnetic field is applied parallel to the axis of the tube, the electrons are deflected in an almost circular path. This is indicated by the edge of the shadow, from which the radius of curvature can be measured (Fig. 44.3). In the experiment, the magnetic field is produced by the solenoid, which conveniently fits over the tube. The magnitude of the magnetic field at the center of the solenoid coil carrying a current I is given by

$$B = \mu_o nI \quad \textbf{(44.6)}$$

where $n = N/L$ is the turn density (number of turns N per coil length L in meters).

IV. Experimental Procedure

1. Set up the circuits as shown in the schematic diagrams in Fig. 44.4, and place the coil over the tube. Connect the tube leads to the ac and dc power sources and adjust the anode potential to about 150 V dc. Note the fan-shaped tuning-eye pattern. Then connect the solenoid to the 12-V dc power supply, and observe how the electron beam is deflected into a curved path as the coil current is increased from zero to a maximum of about 5.0 A.

2. The radius of curvature is measured by matching it to that of a wooden dowel, a dime, or some other appropriate circular object. The radius of the circular reference object is determined using vernier calipers.

3. With the anode voltage at 150 V dc, adjust the coil current until the curvature of the shadow matches the reference object. Record the ammeter reading in the Laboratory Report. Determine the current value for two more trials. Reverse the connections to the coil so the electron beam bends the other way. Make two more current determinations, and compute the average of all the measurements. Do not watch the ammeter while matching the radii.

4. Repeat procedure 3 for anode voltages of 200 and 250 V.

5. Disconnect the apparatus from the power supplies. Measure the length L of the solenoid and

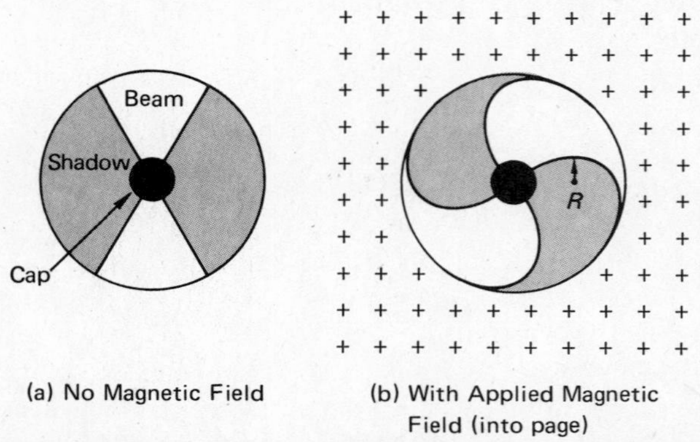

Figure 44.3 Tuning-eye. Illustrations of the observed patterns of the tuning-eye in the tube.

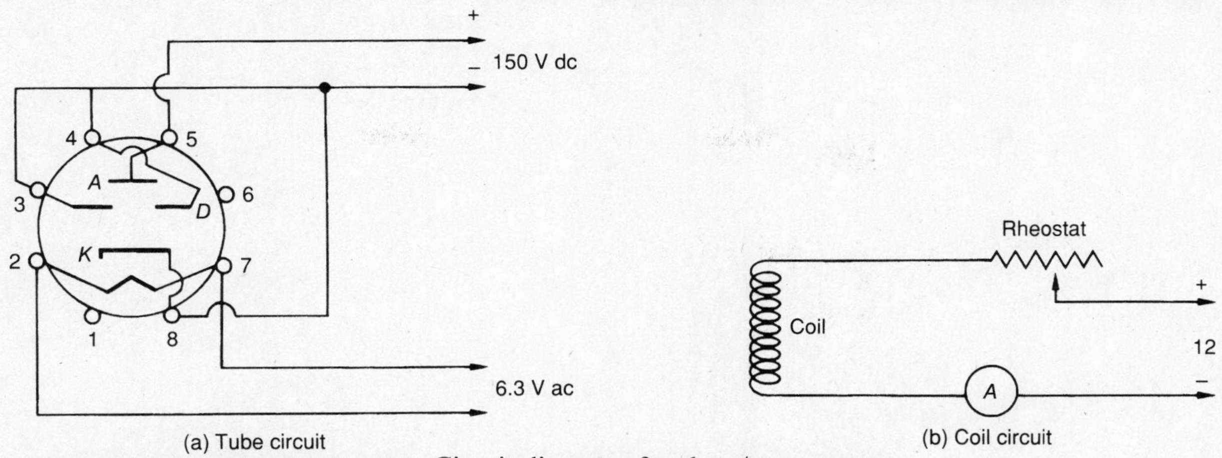

Figure 44.4 Experimental circuits. Circuit diagrams for the e/m apparatus.

count the number of turns N, so as to determine the turn density n if this is not given by the instructor. (The coil usually has 540 turns.)

6. Using the average current in each voltage case, compute the magnitude of the magnetic field B of the solenoid for each set of data.

7. Compute the charge/mass (e/m) ratio of the electron for each set of data and find the average.

8. From the average value of e/m, compute the mass of the electron using $e = 1.6 \times 10^{-19}$ C. Compare this value to the accepted mass value of the electron.

Name ______________________ Section ______________ Date ______________
Lab Partner(s) ____

EXPERIMENT 44

The Mass of an Electron: *e/m* Measurement

Laboratory Report

DATA TABLE
Purpose: To determine the magnitude of B for computation of m_e.

Anode voltage ( )				
Radius, r ( )				
Current ( )	Trial 1			
	2			
	3			
	4			
	5			
Average current				
Magnitude of field, B ( )				
Calculated e/m				

Turn density

N ______________

L ______________

n ______________

Average e/m ______________

Computed m_e ______________

Accepted m_e ______________

Percent error ______________

Calculations
(show work)

Don't forget units

(continued)

QUESTIONS

1. What are the major sources of error in the experiment? Did you expect the percent error that you obtained? Explain.

2. Suppose that protons were emitted in the vacuum tube instead of electrons. How would this affect the experiment?

3. Suppose that only a constant solenoid current were available. Could the mass of an electron still be determined? Explain.

Name ______________________ Section ______________ Date ______________
Lab Partner(s) ____

EXPERIMENT 45

Detection of Nuclear Radiation: The Geiger Counter

Advance Study Assignment

Read the experiment and answer the following questions.

1. What is the principle of the Geiger tube?

2. Define each of the following: (a) threshold voltage; (b) cumulative ionization; (c) plateau; and (d) dead time.

3. Are all radiations counted when the tube voltage is below the threshold voltage? Explain.

(continued)

4. Approximately how many volts above the threshold voltage is the normal operating voltage of the Geiger tube, and why is the operating voltage selected this way?

5. What is background radiation?

6. How does the count rate vary with distance from a point source?

NUCLEAR SAFETY RULES

Radioactive sources will be used in the next few experiments. Some sources are solids and are encapsulated to prevent contact. However, liquid sources may also be used and transferred during an experiment. Some general safety precautions for the use of radioactive materials are:

1. Radioactive materials should be used only by or under the supervision of a person properly informed about the nature of the material.
2. Care should be taken to avoid unnecessary handling or contact with the skin.
3. Mouth pipetting should be strictly prohibited.
4. Eating, drinking, and smoking should not be permitted in any area where radioactive materials are being used.
5. Protective gloves or forceps should be used when the material is handled or transferred.
6. All persons working with radioactive material should thoroughly wash their hands afterward.
7. When not in use, materials should be stored in an appropriately labeled container and in a place of limited access.
8. Should an accident occur (particularly if it involves radioactive materials), it should be reported immediately to the laboratory instructor.

Detection of Nuclear Radiation: The Geiger Counter

I. Introduction and Objectives

Nuclear radiations (alpha, beta, and gamma rays or particles) cannot be detected directly by our senses. Hence, we must use some observable detection method employing the interaction of nuclear decay particles with matter. There are several methods, but the most common is the **Geiger tube**.* In a Geiger tube, the particles from radioactive decay ionize gas molecules, giving rise to electrical pulses that can be amplified and counted. The total instrument is referred to as a Geiger counter.

In this experiment, the characteristics of a Geiger tube and the inverse-square relationship for nuclear radiation will be investigated.

After performing this experiment and analyzing the data, you should be able to:

1. Explain the principle of operations of the Geiger counter and its major disadvantage.
2. Describe how the count rate of a Geiger counter varies with its distance from a radioactive source.

II. Equipment Needed

- Geiger counter (rate meter or scaler type)
- Radioactive source [e.g., Cs-137 (beta-gamma)]
- Laboratory timer or stopwatch
- Calibrated mounting board or meterstick
- 2 sheets of Cartesian graph paper [or 1 sheet of Cartesian and 1 sheet of log (log-log) graph paper (3-cycle)]

III. Theory

The three types of nuclear radiation—alpha, beta, and gamma—are all capable of ionizing a gas. The degree of ionization depends on the energy of the particles and the amount of radiation absorbed by the gas. The ionization of gas molecules by nuclear radiation is the principle of the Geiger tube.

A **Geiger tube** consists of a fine wire running axially through a metal cylinder filled with a gas, usually argon, at a pressure of about 0.1 atm (Fig. 45.1). A potential difference or voltage is maintained between the central wire and the cylinder, the central wire being at a positive potential (+) with respect to the cylinder (−).

Energetic nuclear particles (ionizing radiation) passing through the cylinder and entering the tube ionize the gas molecules. The freed electrons are attracted toward the wire and the positive ions toward the cylinder. If the voltage between the wire and cylinder is great enough, the accelerated electrons acquire enough energy to ionize other gas molecules on their way to the positive wire. The electrons from the secondary ionizations produce additional ionizations. This process is called *cumulative ionization*.

As a result, an "avalanche" discharge sets in, and a current is produced in the resistor. This reduces the potential difference between the wire and cylinder to the point where cumulative ionization does not occur. After the momentary current pulse, which lasts on the order of microseconds, the potential difference between the wire and the cylinder resumes its original value.

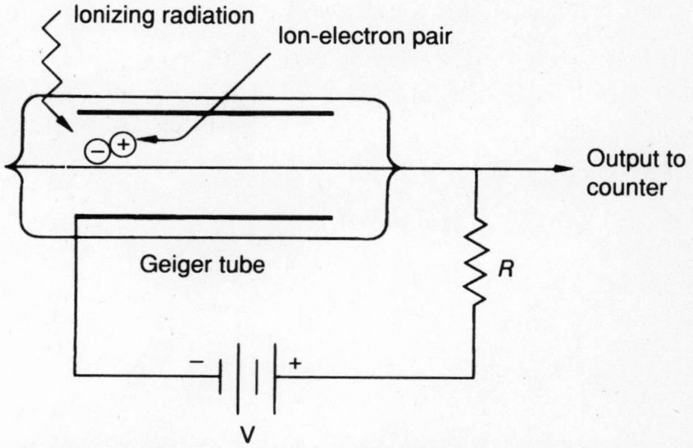

Figure 45.1 Geiger tube. An illustration of the Geiger tube and circuit. See text for description.

* Sometimes referred to as a Geiger-Müller tube (or G-M tube). A prototype was developed in 1913 by the German physicist Hans Geiger (1882–1945), who worked in England on experiments that lead to our present nuclear model of the atom. The tube was improved in 1928 in collaboration with the German physicist S. Müller.

A finite time is required for the discharge to be cleared from the tube. During this time, the voltage of the tube is less than that required to detect other radiation that might arrive. This recovery time is referred to as the *dead time* of the tube. If a large amount of radiation arrives at the tube, the counting rate (counts per minute or cpm) as indicated on the counting equipment will be less than the true value.

There are two common types of Geiger tubes—a "normal" or side-window tube and an "end-window" tube. The side-window tube has a relatively thick wall that may not be penetrated by less penetrating radiation such as alpha particles (Fig. 45.2). The end-window tube has a thin end window, usually of mica, and may be thin enough to be penetrated by very energetic alpha particles.

The brief change in the potential that occurs when a discharge takes place in the tube produces a voltage pulse that can be detected and counted by appropriate instrumentation. Common instruments used for counting are scalers and count-rate meters.

A *scaler* displays the cumulative number of counts on a lighted panel. By using a separate timer, the number of counts per minute (cpm) can be obtained. Some scalers have internal timers that stop the counting after a preset time interval.

A *rate meter* displays the average counting rate directly by means of a dial needle (Fig. 45.2). The needle reading fluctuates back and forth. This is due to the electronic averaging of the number of counts received during a short period of time. A scaler-timer is usually preferred over a rate meter because of this effect.

A. Tube Voltage and Count Rate

When a Geiger tube is in the vicinity of a radiation source with particles of varying energy and there is no voltage on the tube, no counts are observed on the counter. (Counters usually have a loudspeaker circuit so that the counts may also be heard as audible "clicks.") If the tube voltage is slowly increased from zero, at some applied voltage counts will be observed. The lowest applied voltage that will produce a count in the instrument is called the *starting voltage* or **threshold voltage** (Fig. 45.3).

As the tube voltage is increased above the threshold voltage, the number of counts per minute increases rapidly. In this region (about 50 V wide, beginning at about 600 to 700 V, depending on the tube), the count rate is almost linearly proportional to the voltage. This is because as the voltage increases, more of the less energetic particles are counted. Hence, in this region the tube discriminates between particles of different energy. At a given voltage, only particles above a certain energy are detected. The tube then acts as a proportional counter—the voltage being proportional to the energies of the incident particles.

Eventually, as the voltage is increased, the number of counts per minute becomes almost independent of the applied voltage (level region in Fig. 45.3). This region (about 200 V wide) is called the **plateau** of the tube. A change in voltage has little effect on the number of counts detected. Normally, the Geiger tube is operated at a voltage in about the middle of the plateau. Fluctuations in the applied voltage from

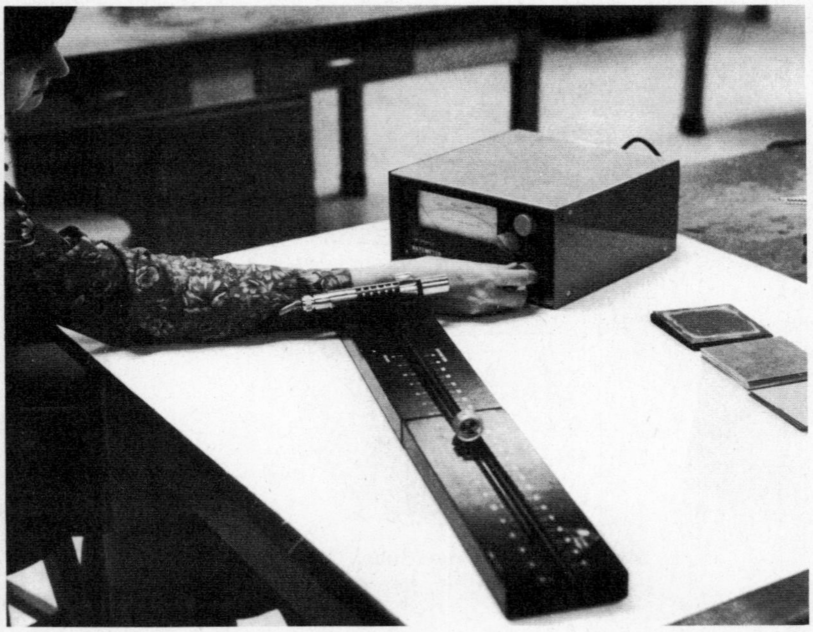

Figure 45.2 Apparatus for radioactive experiments. The standard side-window Geiger tube probe on the mounting board is connected to a count-rate meter. A radioactive source is on the board in the foreground. Notice the radioactivity warning sign on the source. The sheets of material (right) are used in absorption experiments (Experiment 47).

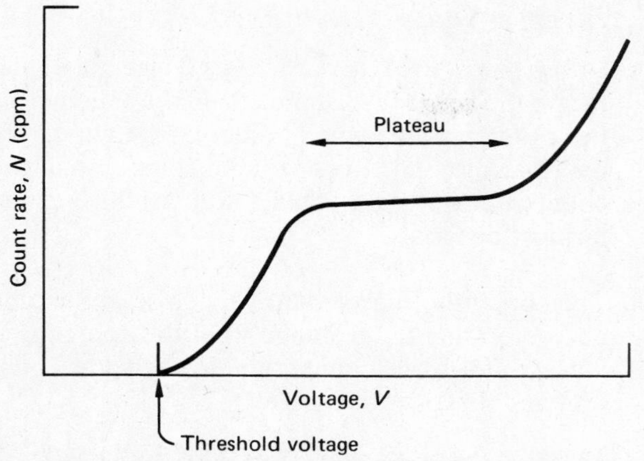

Figure 45.3 Count rate versus tube voltage. A typical graph of how the count rate varies with Geiger tube voltage. Normal operation is in the plateau region. See text for description.

the power supply will then have little effect on the counting rate.

The tube voltage should never be raised to a value far above that of the end of the plateau. At such high voltages, a continuous discharge sets in, and this may destroy the tube if allowed to persist.

B. Inverse-Square Relationship

In normal operation, the count rate depends on the number of particles per unit time entering the Geiger tube. Hence, the count rate depends on the distance of the tube from the source. For a point source emitting a total of N_o particles/min, the particles are emitted in all directions. The number of particles/min N' passing through a unit area of a sphere of radius r is

$$N' = \frac{N_o}{A} = \frac{N_o}{4\pi r^2} \quad \text{(counts/min/area)} \quad \textbf{(45.1)}$$

where $A = 4\pi r^2$ is the area of the sphere.

A Geiger tube with a window area A' at a distance r from a point source then intercepts or receives N counts/min, given by

$$N = N'A' = \frac{N_o A'}{4\pi r^2} \quad \textbf{(45.2)}$$

Although the effective area A' of the Geiger tube is usually not known, the equation shows that the count rate is inversely proportional to r^2 (inverse-square-law form):

$$N \propto \frac{1}{r^2} \quad \textbf{(45.3)}$$

Hence, for a point source, the count rate "falls off" as $1/r^2$ with the distance from the source.

IV. Experimental Procedure

Caution: *Review the radiation safety procedures prior to this experiment.*

1. Connect the Geiger tube probe to the counter by means of the coaxial cable. Before plugging in the counter to an ac outlet, familiarize yourself with the controls, particularly the high-voltage control.

   Scaler: Set the high-voltage control to the minimum setting.

   Rate meter: Set the high-voltage control to the minimum setting. The off-on switch is commonly on the high-voltage control. A selector switch is labeled with volts and counts per minute multiplier positions (× 1, × 10, etc.). When the Geiger tube voltage is adjusted by means of the high-voltage control, the selector switch should *always* be set on "volts." The selector switch is then turned to the appropriate count multiplier range for counting. The meter display scale usually has dual calibrations in volts and counts per minute.

2. Plug in and turn on the counter. Place the radioactive source near the Geiger tube, with the source facing the probe opening as in Fig. 45.2. (A tube mount may be available for an end-window-type tube. The source is placed at the bottom of the tube mount in this case. *Note:* The end window is very fragile and can be punctured easily.)

   Slowly increase the tube voltage by means of the high-voltage control unit the first indication of counting is observed. Then, increase the voltage to about 75 to 100 V above this value.

3. Set the counter to the counting mode, and adjust the distance of the source from the tube (or add aluminum sheets to the end-window tube mount) so that the count rate is several thousand (3000 to 5000) counts per minute. The Geiger tube is then operating normally, and the dead time will not cause serious error.

A. Tube Voltage and Count Rate

4. Lower the high-voltage control to the minimum setting. Then slowly raise the voltage until the first indication of counting is observed (rate meter selector on "volts"). Record this threshold voltage in Data Table 1.

5. Increase the voltage to 25 V above the threshold voltage and record the tube voltage. Measure

and record the number of counts per minute at this voltage setting. (A rate meter is switched to a counting position. Because the meter needle fluctuates, it is best to watch the meter for 30 s and note the highest and lowest meter readings. The count rate is then taken as the mean or average of these readings.)

6. Continue to repeat procedure 5, increasing the voltage by 25 V each time. Record the voltage and the corresponding count rate for each voltage setting. You will notice that the count rate first increases rapidly with voltage. It then levels off, increasing only slightly with increases in voltage. This is the plateau region of the Geiger tube.

   Eventually, with a particular voltage step, a sharp increase in the count rate will be observed. *Do not increase the voltage above this value.* Quickly lower the tube voltage to the minimum setting after this reading to avoid damaging the tube.

7. Plot the count rate N (counts/min) versus voltage V on Cartesian graph paper. Include the threshold voltage. Draw a smooth curve that best fits the data.

B. *Background Radiation*

8. Remove the source several meters (across the room) from the Geiger tube, and apply the mid-plateau voltage to the tube as determined from the graph. (If using an end-window tube with tube mount, remove the tube from the mount and lay the tube on the table.) You will observe an occasional count on the counter. This is due to background radiation arising from cosmic rays and radioactive elements in the environment (e.g., in building materials).

   Let the counter run for a measured time, e.g., 4 to 5 min, and determine the background count rate in counts per minute and record in part B of the Laboratory Report. If the background count rate is small compared to the source count, it may be considered negligible.

C. *Inverse-Square Relationship*

9. Bring the source toward the Geiger tube and locate the source a distance from the tube where the counting rate begins to increase significantly over background. Record the distance r and the count rate N in Data Table 2. Record this r as the farthest distance.

10. Then bring the source relatively close to the tube and determine the distance from the source that gives a full-scale count rate. Record the count rate and distance (closest).

11. Divide the length between the two measured distances into eight intervals or steps. Measure and record the count rate and source distance from the tube for each step as the source is moved away from the tube.

12. The inverse square relationship, $N = A/r^2$ (where A is a constant) can be put into linear form by taking the logarithm of both sides:

$$\log N = \log (Ar^{-2}) = \log r^{-2} + \log A$$

or

$$\log N = -2 \log r + \log A \qquad \textbf{(45.4)}$$

where log is the common logarithm (base 10). Note that Eq. 45.4 has the form of a straight line: $y = mx + b$. (See Experiment 1 for general discussion.)

Take the logs of the N and r values in Data Table 2. (Make two columns for these at the right of the table. See Appendix Table B6 if your calculator does not have a common log function.) On Cartesian graph paper, plot log N versus log r and draw a straight line that best fits the data. Determine the slope of the line and compare it to the theoretical value by finding the percent error.

(Optional) Your instructor may wish to introduce you to log-log graph paper. This special graph paper automatically takes the log values. See Appendix D for a discussion of graphing on log-log and semi-log graph papers. (There is optional use of the latter in Experiments 46 and 47.)

Name ______________________ Section ______________ Date ______________

Lab Partner(s) ____

E X P E R I M E N T 4 5

Detection of Nuclear Radiation: The Geiger Counter

Laboratory Report

A. Tube Voltage and Count Rate

DATA TABLE 1

Purpose: To determine dependence of the count rate on tube voltage.

	Tube voltage	Count rate (cpm)
Threshold voltage		X

B. Background Radiation

Number of counts ______________

Counting time (min) ______________

Counts/min ______________

Don't forget units

(continued)

C. Inverse-Square Relationship

DATA TABLE 2

Purpose: To determine the count rate versus distance from source.

	Source-counter distance ( )	Count rate (cpm)
Closest distance		
Farthest distance		

Calculations
(show work)

Slope of graph ________________

Theoretical value ________________

Percent error ________________

Name ______________________ Section ______________ Date ______________

Lab Partner(s) ____

EXPERIMENT 45 *Laboratory Report*

QUESTIONS

1. What is the average percent increase in the count rate over the voltage range of the Geiger tube plateau? (Obtain from a graph of the data.)

2. If (a) dead time and (b) background radiation corrections were taken into account, how would each affect the graph of N versus V?

3. Give possible reasons why the experimental result of N versus r is not exactly an inverse-square relationship.

4. A count rate of 8000 cpm is recorded at a distance of 5.0 cm from a point source. What would be the observed count rate at a distance of 20 cm?

Name ______________________ Section ______________ Date ______________
Lab Partner(s) ______________________

EXPERIMENT 46

Radioactive Half-life

Advance Study Assignment

Read the experiment and answer the following questions.

1. What is the significance of the half-life of a radioactive isotope in terms of (a) the amount of sample or number of nuclei; and (b) the activity of the sample?

2. How is the half-life related to the decay constant of a radioactive process?

3. Is the activity of a sample of a radioisotope greater after one half-life or one time constant? Explain.

(continued)

4. What is meant by "milking a cow"? Give the technical terms for "milking" and "cow."

5. Ba-137m is a nuclear isomer of Ba-137. Explain what this means.

Radioactive Half-life

I. Introduction and Objectives

The decrease in the activity of a radioactive isotope is characterized by its half-life. This is the time required for one-half of the nuclei of a sample to decay. Of course, the nuclei of a sample cannot be counted directly, but when one-half of the sample has decayed, the activity or the rate of emission of nuclear radiation has also decreased by one-half. Thus, by monitoring the sample with a Geiger counter, when the count rate (counts per minute, cpm) has decreased by one-half, one half-life has elapsed.

In this experiment, the half-life of a radioactive isotope will be determined.

After performing this experiment and analyzing the data, you should be able to:

1. Explain what is meant by the half-life of a radioactive isotope.
2. Distinguish between radioactive half-life and time constant.
3. Describe how the half-life of a short-lived radioactive isotope can be measured.

II. Equipment Needed

- Geiger counter (rate meter with clip mount or scaler type with tube mount)
- Cesium-137/Barium-137m Minigenerator with 0.04 HCl-saline solution
- Laboratory timer or stopwatch
- Disposable planchet (small metal cuplike container to hold radioactive sample)
- 2 sheets of Cartesian graph paper [or 1 sheet of Cartesian and 1 sheet of semi-log graph paper (3-cycle)]

III. Theory

Since the activity of a radioactive isotope is proportional to the quantity of isotope present, the radioactive decay process is described by an exponential function.

$$N = N_o e^{-\lambda t} = N_o e^{-t/\tau} \qquad \textbf{(46.1)}$$

where N is the number of nuclei present at time t, N_0 the original number of nuclei present (at $t = 0$), λ the decay constant of the process, and $\tau = 1/\lambda$ the time constant. The variable N can also represent the activity (cpm) of an isotope sample.

The half-life $t_{1/2}$ is the time it takes for the number of nuclei present or the activity to decrease by one-half ($N = N_o/2$). Hence,

$$\frac{N}{N_o} = \frac{1}{2} = e^{-t_{1/2}/\tau}$$

Since

$$e^{-0.693} = \frac{1}{2}$$

by comparison

$$0.693 = \frac{t_{1/2}}{\tau}$$

and

$$t_{1/2} = 0.693\,\tau = \frac{0.693}{\lambda} \qquad \textbf{(46.2)}$$

Thus, the half-life can be computed if the time constant or the decay constant is known.

Example 46.1 A radioactive sample has an activity of 4000 cpm. What is the observed activity after three half-lives?

Solution After one half-life, the activity decreases by $\frac{1}{2}$, and after another half-life by another $\frac{1}{2}$, and so on. Hence, after three half-lives, the initial activity decreases by a factor of $\frac{1}{2} \times \frac{1}{2} \times \frac{1}{2} = \frac{1}{8}$. With N_o = 4000 cpm,

$$N = \tfrac{1}{8} N_o = \tfrac{1}{8}(4000) = 500 \text{ cpm}$$

Notice that, in general,

$$N = \frac{N_o}{2^n}$$

where n is the number of half-lives.

Theory of Minigenerator

The Cesium-137/Barium-137m Minigenerator* (Fig. 46.1) is an eluting system, in which a short-lived daughter radioactive isotope is eluted (separated by washing) from a long-lived parent isotope. A small "generator" contains radioactive Cs-137, which has

* Registered trademark, Union Carbide.

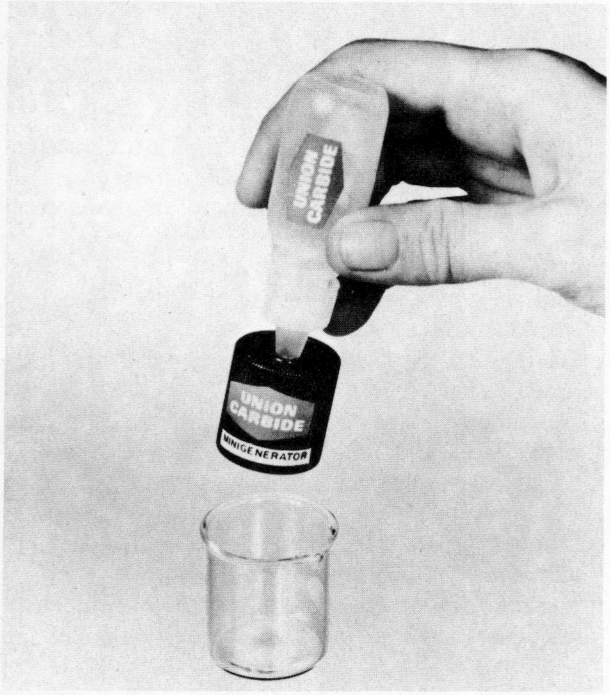

Figure 46.1 The Cesium-137/Barium-137m Minigenerator system. See text for description. (Photo courtesy of Sargent-Welch Scientific Co.)

a half-life of 30 years. Cs-137 beta-decays into Ba-137m, which is an isomeric (excited) state of the stable nucleus Ba-137. The excited isomer Ba-137m has a relatively short half-life and gamma-decays into Ba-137.

The Ba-137m is washed or eluted from the generator by passing a hydrochloric acid–saline solution through the generator. Because of this process, the generator is commonly referred to as a ''cow,'' with the Ba-137m being ''milked'' from the cow. The generator ''cow'' may be milked many times, but like an actual cow, a time interval must elapse between milkings.

Eluting removes the Ba-137m from the generator, and time is required for the ''regeneration'' of Ba-137m from the decay of Cs-137. Normally, the parent and daughter isotopes exist in equilibrium, with equal activities. After eluting (or milking the cow), it takes about 12 min for the Ba-137m to build up and again reach equilibrium with the Cs-137.

IV. Experimental Procedure

Caution: *Review the radiation safety procedures prior to this experiment.*

1. Before the Minigenerator is eluted, turn on the Geiger counter. Apply the appropriate tube voltage for normal operation (see Experiment 45). Over a period of 4 of 5 min measure and record the count of the background radiation as was done in Experiment 45.

2. Mount the Geiger probe so that a planchet with the radioactive Ba-137m sample can be quickly and carefully placed below and near the probe opening at a fixed distance.

3. The counting procedure is as follows. When the sample is in place, the laboratory timer is started ($t = 0$) and allowed to run continuously. Simultaneously with the starting of the timer, the activity is measured on the Geiger counter for 15 s, and the count rate (cpm), together with the time elapsed on the timer, is recorded in the data table.

   Note: If using a rate meter, the average of the high and low meter readings over the 15-s interval is taken as the count rate. If a scaler is used (with or without an internal timer), the count rate in cpm must be computed. For example, suppose that 500 counts are observed for the 15-s ($\frac{1}{4}$-min) interval. The count rate is then 500 counts/$\frac{1}{4}$ min $= 500 \times 4 = 2000$ cpm.

   After 0.5 min has elapsed on the timer, take another 15-s count of the activity. Repeat the 15-s count at the beginning of each elapsed time for 10 to 12 min. A dry run of the counting procedure is helpful.

4. The instructor will ''milk the cow'' or supervise you in doing so. Only a few (2 to 3) drops of the eluate (milk) are needed.

   Caution: *Care should be taken in handling the sample. The milking should be done over a sheet of paper that can be discarded in case of a spill, and* ***if you should come in contact with the sample, immediately wash your hands.***

   The instructor may wish to give you a sample for a trial run of the counting procedure.

5. When given the actual data sample, carry out the counting procedure as described above.

6. Correct for background radiation if necessary. Plot the sample activity (N) in cpm versus the elapsed time (t) in minutes on Cartesian graph paper and note the shape of the curve.

   From the graph, make two determinations of the half-life by finding the time required for the sample activity to decay from its initial value to $\frac{1}{2}$ of the initial value, and from $\frac{1}{2}$ to $\frac{1}{4}$ of the initial value. Average and compare with the half-life for

Ba-137m in Appendix Table A9 by computing the percent error. Also compute the decay constant (λ) from the average value of the half-life.

7. The decay constant may be found graphically by putting the exponential function, $N = N_o e^{-\lambda t}$, into linear form by taking the natural logarithm (base e) of both sides:

$$\ln N = \ln (N_o e^{-\lambda t}) = \ln (e^{-\lambda t}) + \ln N_o$$

or

$$\ln N = -\lambda t + \ln N_o \qquad \textbf{(46.3)}$$

Note that Eq. 46.3 has the form of a straight line: $y = mx + b$. (See Experiment 1 for general discussion.)

Find ln N for each value of N in the Data Table. (Make a column for these to the right of the table. See Appendix Table B7 if your calculator does not have a natural log function.) Plot ln N versus t on Cartesian graph paper and draw a straight line that best fits the data. Determine the slope of the line and compare it to the value of the decay constant computed in the preceding procedure by finding the percent difference.

(*Optional*) Your instructor may wish to introduce you to semi-log graph paper. This special graph paper automatically takes the log values of the variable plotted on the y axis. See Appendix D for a discussion of graphing on semi-log (and log-log) graph paper.

Name ______________________ Section ______________ Date ______________

Lab Partner(s) ____

E X P E R I M E N T 4 6

Radioactive Half-life

Laboratory Report

Background count (cpm) ______________

DATA TABLE

Purpose: To determine the half-life of Ba-137m.

t Elapsed time (min)	N Observed activity (cpm)	Corrected for background radiation (cpm)

Calculations
(show work)

Half-life Measurements for Ba-137m

Time from full to $\frac{1}{2}$ activity ______________

Time from $\frac{1}{2}$ to $\frac{1}{4}$ activity ______________

Average experimental half-life ______________

Accepted half-life ______________

Percent error ______________

Decay constant from average half-life ______________

Decay constant from graph ______________

Percent difference ______________

Don't forget units

(continued)

QUESTIONS

1. In the experiment, if the Ba-137m sample were placed closer to the Geiger tube, the measured activity would be greater (inverse-square relationship). Would this affect the result of the half-life? Explain how this would affect the N versus t graph on Cartesian graph paper (or on semi-log paper).

2. A cobalt-60 source has a measured activity of 12,000 cpm. After how long would the observed activity be 750 cpm? (The half-life of Co-60 is 5.27 yr.)

3. An instructor buys a 10-μCi Cs-137 source for laboratory experiments. After 5 years, what is (a) the strength of the source in μCi; (b) the activity of the source in disintegrations per second? (1 Ci $= 3.70 \times 10^{10}$ disintegrations/s.) (c) What is the strength of the source in becquerels (Bq)? (The becquerel is the official SI unit; 1 Ci $= 3.7 \times 10^{10}$ Bq.)

Name ______________________ Section ____________ Date ____________
Lab Partner(s) ______________________

EXPERIMENT 47

The Absorption of Nuclear Radiation

Advance Study Assignment

Read the experiment and answer the following questions.

1. On what parameters does the absorption of nuclear radiation depend?

2. Do the three types of nuclear radiation have definite ranges of penetration in materials? Explain. What is meant by half-thickness?

3. What is the mass absorption coefficient, and what are its units? Are there any advantages to using the mass absorption coefficient over the linear absorption coefficient? Explain.

(continued)

4. Explain how a source that has only one radioactive isotope can emit both beta and gamma radiation.

5. Why is a beta-gamma source that is shielded with a relatively thin sheet of aluminum effectively a gamma source?

The Absorption of Nuclear Radiation

I. Introduction and Objectives

The observed activity of a radioactive source of a given strength depends on several factors, for example, the distance of the counter from the source. For a point source, the observed activity varies inversely with the distance from the source (inverse-square relationship). This decrease is primarily due to the geometrical spreading of the emitted nuclear radiation outward from the source.

If a Geiger probe is a fixed distance from a long-lived source, the observed activity is relatively constant. However, if a sheet of material is placed between the source and the counter, a decrease in the activity may be observed. That is, the nuclear radiation is absorbed by the material. The amount of absorption depends on the type and energy of the radiation and on the kind and density of the absorbing material.

The absorption or degree of penetration of nuclear radiation is an important consideration in applications such as medical radioisotope treatment and nuclear shielding (e.g., around a nuclear reactor). Also, in industrial manufacturing processes, the absorption of nuclear radiation is used to monitor and control automatically the thickness of metal and plastic sheets and films.

In this experiment, the absorption properties of various materials for different kinds of nuclear radiation will be investigated.

After performing this experiment and analyzing the data, you should be able to:

1. Describe the parameters on which the penetration of nuclear radiation in a material depends.
2. Explain the linear absorption coefficient, "half-thickness," and stopping range.
3. Explain the mass absorption coefficient.

II. Equipment Needed

- Geiger counter (rate meter or scaler type)
- Calibrated mounting board (or meterstick)
- Beta-gamma source (Cs-137 suggested)
- Set of cardboard, aluminum, and lead sheets (about 1 mm thick, 10 sheets of each)
- Laboratory timer or stopwatch
- Micrometer caliper
- 3 sheets of Cartesian graph paper [or 2 sheets of Cartesian graph paper and 1 sheet of semi-log graph paper (3-cycle)]

III. Theory

The three types of nuclear radiation (alpha, beta, and gamma) are absorbed quite differently by different materials. The electrically charged alpha and beta particles interact with the material and produce ionizations along their paths. The greater the charge and the slower the particle, the greater is the linear energy transfer (LET) and ionization along the path, which determines the degree of penetration of the radiation. The absorption or degree of penetration of the radiation also depends on the density of the material.

Alpha particles are easily absorbed. A few centimeters of air and even a sheet of paper will almost completely absorb them. Hence, alpha particles do not generally penetrate the walls or window of an ordinary Geiger tube and so are not counted by this method.

Beta particles can travel a few meters in air or a few millimeters in aluminum before being completely absorbed. Beta radiation, then, does penetrate a Geiger tube. Both alpha and beta particles of a given energy therefore have a definite *range* of penetration in a particular material. Figure 47.1 illustrates the radiation intensity (in cpm) versus absorber thickness for a relatively low density absorber for radiation from a beta-gamma source. The "bend" in the curve indicates the range of the beta radiation. The penetration for thickness beyond this is due to gamma radiation.

Gamma rays, which consist of electromagnetic radiation of very short wavelength, are not readily absorbed. A significant number of high-energy gamma rays can penetrate 1 cm or more of a dense material such as lead. In a given material, a beam of gamma rays is absorbed exponentially. The intensity

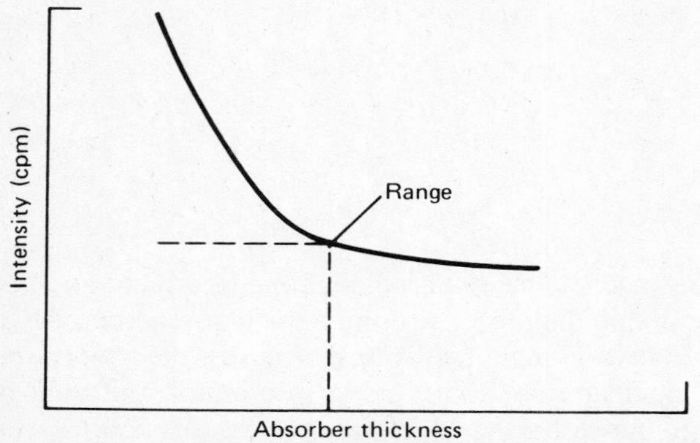

Figure 47.1 Radiation intensity versus absorber thickness. A typical graph of radiation intensity versus absorber thickness for beta-gamma radiation by a low-density absorber. The range is that of the beta radiation.

I (in cpm) of the beam after passing through a certain thickness x of a material is given by

$$I = I_o e^{-\mu x} \quad \textbf{(47.1)}$$

where I_o is the original intensity (at $x = 0$) and the decay constant μ is called the **linear absorption coefficient**. The absorption coefficient is characteristic of the absorbing material (and the wavelength or energy of the gamma radiation). Notice that the unit of μ is inverse length (e.g., 1/cm or cm^{-1}).

Since the gamma intensity decays exponentially, there is no definite penetrating or stopping range as there is in the case of beta radiation. Hence, it is convenient to speak in terms of a **half-thickness** $x_{1/2}$, the material thickness required to reduce the intensity by one-half (i.e., $I_{1/2} = I_o/2$ or $I_{1/2}/I_o = \frac{1}{2}$). Then, by Eq. 47.1,

$$\frac{I_{1/2}}{I_o} = e^{-\mu x_{1/2}} = \frac{1}{2}$$

Taking the logarithm (base e) of both sides of the equation, we have

$$\ln (e^{-\mu x_{1/2}}) = \ln \frac{1}{2}$$

or

$$-\mu x_{1/2} = -\ln 2$$

and

$$x_{1/2} = \frac{\ln 2}{\mu} = \frac{0.693}{\mu} \quad \textbf{(47.2)}$$

Hence, knowing the absorption coefficient of a material, the half-thickness can be calculated.

The absorption of gamma radiation of a given wavelength or energy depends primarily on the density ρ of the material. Thus, it is convenient to define a **mass absorption coefficient** μ_m:

$$\mu_m = \frac{\mu}{\rho} \quad \textbf{(47.3)}$$

The mass absorption coefficient provides a "standardized" coefficient. Samples of a particular absorbing material may have different densities. Each sample would have a different linear absorption coefficient μ, but the mass absorption coefficient μ_m would have the same value for all the samples.

Notice from Eq. 47.3 that the units of μ_m are cm^2/g:

$$\mu_m = \frac{\mu \text{ (1/cm)}}{\rho \text{ (g/cm}^3)} = \frac{\mu}{\rho} \text{ (cm}^2\text{/g)}$$

If μ_m is used in Eq. 47.1 in place of μ, then

$$I = I_o e^{-\mu x} = I_o e^{-(\mu/\rho)(x\rho)} = e^{-\mu_m x'} \quad \textbf{(47.4)}$$

and the absorber thickness $x' = x\rho$ is in g/cm^2. Absorber thicknesses are frequently expressed in these units.

A beta-gamma source will be used to study the absorption of nuclear radiations. The decay scheme of the suggested Cs-137 source is illustrated in Fig. 47.2. The chief decay mode (94%) is beta decay to the excited (isomeric) state of Ba-137. This decays by gamma emission to the stable ground state of Ba-137. Only 6% of the Cs-137 beta decays directly to ground state Ba-137. Hence, for the most part, Cs-137 is a beta-gamma source of 0.511-MeV beta particles and 0.662-MeV gamma rays. (The emitted beta particles actually have a spectrum of energies from 0–0.511 MeV.)

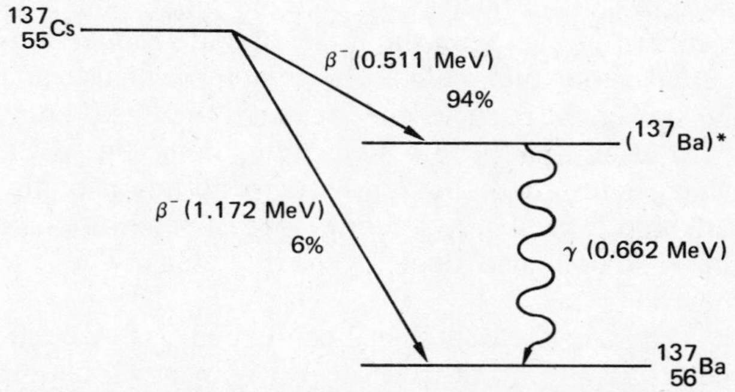

Figure 47.2 Decay scheme of Cs-137. Most of the nuclei (94%) decay to an excited state of barium-137 ($^{137}Ba^*$), which then gamma decays to a stable state.

IV. Experimental Procedure

Caution: *Review the radiation safety procedures prior to this experiment.*

1. First, measure the individual thickness of three different sheets of (a) cardboard, (b) aluminum, and (c) lead with the micrometer, and determine the average sheet thickness of each. Record in Data Table 1.

2. Set up the Geiger counter with the probe on the mounting board (see Fig. 47.2). If an end-window tube is used, lay the tube in the mounting board groove and tape it down to immobilize it (or tape it to a meterstick). Turn on the counter. Place the radioactive source near the probe, and adjust the tube voltage to the plateau operating voltage.

A. Beta Radiation Absorption

3. Adjust the distance of the source from the probe so that the observed count rate is about 8000 cpm. (For a rate meter, the count rate is taken as the average of the high and low meter readings for 30-s time intervals.) Record the count rate I_o in the cardboard column in Data Table 2.

   Place a sheet of cardboard between the source and the probe and measure and record the count rate. (Allow a rate meter to come to equilibrium before taking a 30-s reading.)

4. Add cardboard sheets between the source and the probe one at a time, measuring and recording the count rate after the addition of each sheet. Continue until the count rate is relatively constant with the addition of four successive sheets.

5. Remove the cardboard sheets and repeat the procedure with aluminum sheets.

6. Without recording data, repeat the procedure with lead sheets and mentally note the degree of beta absorption or penetration in lead.

7. Plot the intensity I (in cpm) versus the number n of absorber sheets for both cardboard and aluminum on the same Cartesian graph. Dual-label the ordinate (Y) axis so that the curve for each absorber occupies most of the graph paper.

   Determine the range of beta absorption for each absorber in sheet units from the graph, and record. Multiply each range (in sheet units) by the respective average sheet thickness to determine the range in length units.

B. Gamma Radiation Absorption

8. Using the result of the range of beta absorption in aluminum from procedure 7, place the minimum number of sheets of aluminum in front of the probe that will completely absorb the beta radiation. Then move the source toward the probe until the intensity observed on the Geiger counter is 700 to 800 cpm. Record this intensity I_o in Data Table 3. The observed intensity is then almost solely due to gamma radiation. Why?

9. Leaving the aluminum sheet(s) in place, insert lead sheets one at a time between the aluminum sheets and the source. Measure and record the count rate after each sheet is inserted. Be careful not to move the source. Insert a total of 10 sheets of lead. After the sixth sheet, two sheets may be inserted at a time.

10. Remove all the sheets. Remove the source several meters (across the room) from the probe, and measure the background radiation intensity I_b over a 4- to 5-min interval. (See Experiment 45 for a description of the procedure, if necessary.)

11. Subject the background count rate from each reading for the lead sheets to obtain the corrected intensities. To find the half-thickness, plot the corrected intensity (I_c) versus the number (n) of lead sheets on Cartesian graph paper and note the shape of the curve.

    From the graph, make a determination of the number of sheets ($n_{1/2}$) needed to reduce the intensity from its initial value to $\frac{1}{2}$ of the initial value. (Try to express this number to the nearest 0.05 of a sheet.) The half-thickness is $x_{1/2} = x_i n_{1/2}$, where x_i is the thickness of an individual sheet. From the half-thickness, compute the linear absorption coefficient, μ, from Eq. 47.2 and record this value in Data Table 3.

12. The absorption coefficient may be found graphically by putting the exponential Eq. 47.1 into linear form by taking the natural (base e) logarithm of both sides. But first note that in terms of the number of sheets (n), Eq. 47.1 has the form

$$I = I_o e^{-\mu x} = I_o e^{-\mu(nx_i)} = I_o e^{-(\mu x_i)n} \quad \textbf{(47.5)}$$

where x_i is the individual sheet thickness and the absorber thickness is $x = nx_i$.

Then, taking the natural log of both sides of Eq. 47.5:

$$\ln I = \ln I_o e^{-(\mu x_i)n} = \ln e^{-(\mu x_i)n} + \ln I_o$$

or

$$\ln I = -(\mu x_i)n + \ln I_o \qquad \textbf{(47.6)}$$

Note that Eq. 47.6 has the form of a straight line: $y = mx + b$. (See Experiment 1 for general discussion.)

Find $\ln I_c$ for each value of I_c in Data Table 3. (Make a column for these to the right of the table. See Appendix Table B7 if your calculator does not have a natural log function.)

Plot $\ln I_c$ versus n on Cartesian graph paper and draw a straight line that best fits the data. Determine the slope of the line and compute the linear absorption coefficient μ. (Note from Eq. 47.6 that the slope has a magnitude of μx_i.)

(*Optional*) Your instructor may wish you to use semi-log graph paper. This special graph paper automatically takes in values of the variable plotted on the y axis. See Appendix D for a discussion of graphing on semi-log (and log-log) graph paper.

13. Compute the mass absorption coefficient μ_m for lead ($\rho_{Pb} = 11.3$ g/cm^3). Compare the experimental values to the accepted value of $\mu_m = 0.10$ cm^2/g for gamma rays by computing the percent error for each.

Name ______________________ Section ______________ Date ______________

Lab Partner(s) ____

EXPERIMENT 47

The Absorption of Nuclear Radiation

Laboratory Report

DATA TABLE 1

Purpose: To determine sheet thicknesses.

	Cardboard ( )	Aluminum ( )	Lead ( )
Average sheet thickness			

Calculations
(show work)

Don't forget units

(continued)

A. Beta Radiation Absorption

DATA TABLE 2

Purpose: To determine the relation between intensity and thickness.

Cardboard		Aluminum	
Number of sheets, n	Intensity, I (cpm)	Number of sheets, n	Intensity, I (cpm)
0	(I_o)	0	(I_o)
Range of beta radiation (cm)		Range of beta radiation (cm)	

Calculations
(show work)

Name ______________________ Section ______________ Date ______________

Lab Partner(s) ____

EXPERIMENT 47 **Laboratory Report**

B. Gamma Radiation Absorption

DATA TABLE 3

Purpose: To determine the relationship of intensity and thickness.

Number of lead sheets, n	Intensity, I (cpm)	Corrected intensity, $I_c = I - I_b$
0	(I_o)	

Calculations
(show work)

Background radiation

Number of counts ______________

Time interval ______________

Intensity, I_b (cpm) ______________

(continued)

Absorption Coefficient Measurements for Gamma Rays

Number of sheets to reduce initial intensity to $\frac{1}{2}$, $n_{1/2}$ ________________

Half-thickness, $x_{1/2}$ ________________

Linear absorption coefficient, μ ________________

Mass absorption coefficient, μ_m ________________

Percent error ________________

Slope of graph, x_i ________________

Linear absorption coefficient, μ ________________

Mass absorption coefficient, μ_m ________________

Percent error ________________

QUESTIONS

1. Was there a large difference in the percent error of the experimental mass absorption coefficient? If so, why do you think this was the case?

2. Compute what percent of an incident beam of 0.662-MeV gamma rays is absorbed after passing through 2.5 mm of lead.

3. Would the Cartesian graph of ln I_c versus n (or x) be a straight line if the gamma radiation contained gamma rays of two different energies? Explain.

Name ______________________ Section ______________ Date ______________

Lab Partner(s) ____

4. The mass absorption coefficient of iron is 0.058 for 1.24-MeV gamma rays. What percentage of the beam of such gamma rays is transmitted (if any) through an iron plate 3 cm thick? ($\rho_{Fe} = 7.86\ g/cm^3$.)

APPENDIX A

Material Properties

Table A1 Densities of Materials

Substance	*(g/cm³)*	*(kg/m³)*
Solids		
Aluminum	2.7	2.7×10^3
Brass	8.4	8.4×10^3
Copper	8.9	8.9×10^3
Glass		
crown	2.5–2.7	$2.5\text{–}2.7 \times 10^3$
flint	3.0–3.6	$3.0\text{–}3.6 \times 10^3$
Gold	19.3	19.3×10^3
Iron and steel (general)	7.88	7.88×10^3
Lead	11.3	11.3×10^3
Nickel	8.8	8.8×10^3
Silver	10.5	10.5×10^3
Wood		
oak	0.60–0.90	$0.60\text{–}0.90 \times 10^3$
pine	0.35–0.50	$0.35\text{–}0.50 \times 10^3$
Zinc	7.1	7.1×10^3
Liquids		
Alcohol		
ethyl	0.79	0.79×10^3
methyl	0.81	0.81×10^3
Carbon tetrachloride	1.60	1.60×10^3
Gasoline	0.68–0.75	$0.68\text{–}0.75 \times 10^3$
Glycerine	1.26	1.26×10^3
Mercury	13.6	13.6×10^3
Turpentine	0.87	0.87×10^3
Water	1.00	1.00×10^3
Gases (at STP):		
Air	0.001293	0.001293×10^3
Carbon dioxide	0.001975	0.001975×10^3
Helium	0.000179	0.000179×10^3
Hydrogen	0.000089	0.000089×10^3
Nitrogen	0.000125	0.000125×10^3
Oxygen	0.00143	0.00143×10^3

Table A2 Young's Modulus for Some Metals

Metals	*(N/m²)*	*(dyn/cm²)*
Aluminum	6.5×10^{10}	6.5×10^{11}
Brass	9.0×10^{10}	9.0×10^{11}
Copper	12.0×10^{10}	12.0×10^{11}
Iron		
cast	9.0×10^{10}	9.0×10^{11}
wrought	19.0×10^{10}	19.0×10^{11}
Steel	19.2×10^{10}	19.2×10^{11}

Table A3 Coefficients of Linear Thermal Expansion

Substance	*(1/C°)*
Aluminum	24.0×10^{-6}
Brass	18.8×10^{-6}
Copper	16.8×10^{-6}
Glass	
window	8.5×10^{-6}
Pyrex	3.3×10^{-6}
Iron	11.4×10^{-6}
Lead	29.4×10^{-6}
Nickel	12.8×10^{-6}
Silver	18.8×10^{-6}
Steel	13.4×10^{-6}
Tin	26.9×10^{-6}
Zinc	26.4×10^{-6}

Table A4 Specific Heats

Substance	*(kcal/kg-C°$^{-1}$ or cal/g-C°$^{-1}$)*	*(J/kg-C°$^{-1}$)*
Aluminum	0.22	921
Brass	0.092	385
Copper	0.093	389
Glass	0.16	670
Iron	0.11	460
Lead	0.031	130
Mercury	0.033	138
Nickel	0.11	460
Silver	0.056	234
Steel	0.11	460
Tin	0.054	226
Water	1.00	4186
Zinc	0.093	389

Table A5 Color Code for Resistors (Composition Type)

Bands A and B		*(ohms, Ω) Band C*		*Band D*	
Color	*Significant figure*	*Color*	*Multiplier*	*Color*	*Resistance tolerance (percent)*
Black	0	Black	1	Silver	± 10
Brown	1	Brown	10	Gold	± 5
Red	2	Red	100		
Orange	3	Orange	1,000		
Yellow	4	Yellow	10,000		
Green	5	Green	100,000		
Blue	6	Blue	1,000,000		
Purple (violet)	7				
Gray	8	Silver	0.01		
White	9	Gold	0.1		

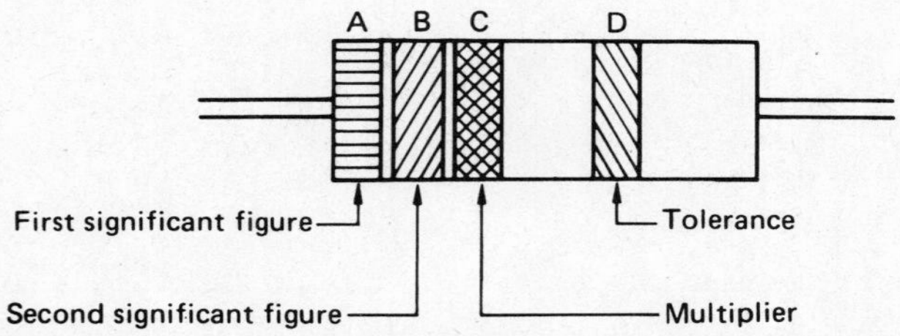

For example, if the bands on a resistor are red (A), black (B), orange (C), the resistance is 20 × 1000 = 20,000 Ω or 20 kΩ.

Table A6 Resistivities and Temperature Coefficients

Substance	*Resistivity*, ρ (Ω-cm)	*Temperature coefficient* (1/C°)
Aluminum	2.8×10^{-6}	0.0039
Brass	7×10^{-6}	0.002
Constantan	49×10^{-6}	0.00001
Copper	1.72×10^{-6}	0.00393
German silver (18% Ni)	33×10^{-6}	0.0004
Iron	10×10^{-6}	0.005
Manganin	44×10^{-6}	0.00001
Mercury	95.8×10^{-6}	0.00089
Nichrome	100×10^{-6}	0.0004
Nickel	7.8×10^{-6}	0.006
Silver	1.6×10^{-6}	0.0038
Tin	11.5×10^{-6}	0.0042

Table A7 Wire Sizes [American Wire Gauge (AWG)]

Gauge No.	*Diameter*	
	in.	*cm*
0000	0.4600	1.168
000	0.4096	1.040
00	0.3648	0.9266
0	0.3249	0.8252
1	0.2893	0.7348
2	0.2576	0.6543
3	0.2294	0.5827
4	0.2043	0.5189
5	0.1819	0.4620
6	0.1620	0.4115
7	0.1443	0.3665
8	0.1285	0.3264
9	0.1144	0.2906
10	0.1019	0.2588
11	0.09074	0.2305
12	0.08081	0.2053
13	0.07196	0.1828
14	0.06408	0.1628
15	0.05707	0.1450
16	0.05082	0.1291
17	0.04526	0.1150
18	0.04030	0.1024
19	0.03589	0.09116
20	0.03196	0.08118
21	0.02846	0.07229
22	0.02535	0.06439
23	0.02257	0.05733
24	0.02010	0.05105
25	0.01790	0.04547
26	0.01594	0.04049
27	0.01419	0.03604
28	0.01264	0.03211
29	0.01126	0.02860
30	0.01003	0.02548
31	0.008928	0.02268
32	0.007950	0.02019
33	0.007080	0.01798
34	0.006304	0.01601
35	0.005614	0.01426
36	0.005000	0.01270
37	0.004453	0.01131
38	0.003965	0.01007
39	0.003531	0.008969
40	0.003145	0.007988

TABLE A8 Major Visible Spectral Lines of Some Elements

Element	*Wavelength* (nm)	(Å)	*Color*	*Relative intensity*
Helium	388.9	3889	Violet	1000
	396.5	3965	Violet	50
	402.6	4026	Violet	70
	438.8	4388	Blue-violet	30
	447.1	4471	Dark blue	100
	471.3	4713	Blue	40
	492.2	4922	Blue-green	50
	501.5	5015	Green	100
	587.6	5876	Yellow	1000
	667.8	6678	Red	100
	706.5	7065	Red	70
Mercury	404.7	4047	Violet	300
	407.8	4078	Violet	150
	435.8	4358	Blue	500
	491.6	4916	Blue-green	50
	546.1	5461	Green	2000
	577.0	5770	Yellow	200
	579.0	5790	Yellow	1000
	690.7	6907	Red	125
Sodium	449.4	4494	Blue	60
	449.8	4498	Blue	70
	466.5	4665	Blue	80
	466.9	4669	Blue	200
	498.3	4983	Green	200
	514.9	5149	Green	400
	515.3	5153	Green	600
	567.0	5670	Green	100
	567.5	5675	Green	150
	568.3	5683	Green	80
	568.8	5688	Green	300
	589.0	5890	Yellow-orange	9000
	589.6	5896	Yellow-orange	5000
	615.4	6154	Orange	500
	616.1	6161	Orange	500

Wavelengths of various colors

Color	*Representative* (nm)	(Å)	*Limits* (nm)	(Å)
Red	650.0	6500	647.0–700.0	6470–7000
Orange	600.0	6000	584.0–647.0	5840–6470
Yellow	580.0	5800	575.0–585.0	5750–5850
Green	520.0	5200	491.2–575.0	4912–5750
Blue	470.0	4700	424.0–491.2	4240–4912
Violet	410.0	4100	400.0–420.0	4000–4200

Visible spectrum ≈ 400.0–700.0 nm = 4000–7000 Å

TABLE A9 Radioisotopes

Isotope	Half-life	Principal Radiations (MeV) Alpha	Beta	Gamma
Barium-133	10.4 years			0.356
Bismuth-210	5.01 days	4.654, 4.691	1.161	
Carbon-14	5730 years		0.156	
Cesium-137	30.1 years		0.512, 1.173	
Barium-137m	2.6 min			0.662
Cobalt-60	5.26 years		0.315	
Iodine-131	8.07 days		0.606	
Lead-210	22.3 years		0.017, 0.061	0.0465
Manganese-54	312.5 days			0.835
Phosphorus-32	14.3 days		1.710	
Polonium-210	138.4 days	5.305		
Potassium-42	12.4 hours		3.52 1.97	
Radium-226	1600 years	4.781 4.598		0.186
Sodium-22	2.60 years	0.545 1.82		1.275
Strontium-90	28.1 years		0.546	
Thallium-204	3.78 years		0.763	
Uranium-238	4.5×10^6 years	4.195		0.48
Yttrium-90	64.0 hours		2.27	
Zinc-65	243.6 days		0.329	1.116

TABLE A10 Elements: Atomic Numbers and Atomic Weights

The atomic weights are based on ^{12}C = 12.0000. If the element does not occur naturally, the mass number of the most stable isotope is given in parentheses.

	Symbol	*Atomic number*	*Atomic weight*		*Symbol*	*Atomic number*	*Atomic weight*
Actinium	Ac	89	(227)	Mercury	Hg	80	200.59
Aluminum	Al	13	26.9815	Molybdenum	Mo	42	95.94
Americium	Am	95	(243)	Neodymium	Nd	60	144.24
Antimony	Sb	51	121.75	Neon	Ne	10	20.179
Argon	Ar	18	39.948	Neptunium	Np	93	(237)
Arsenic	As	33	74.9216	Nickel	Ni	28	58.71
Astatine	At	85	(210)	Niobium	Nb	41	92.9064
Barium	Ba	56	137.34	Nitrogen	N	7	14.0067
Berkelium	Bk	97	(247)	Nobelium	No	102	(253)
Beryllium	Be	4	9.01218	Osmium	Os	76	190.2
Bismuth	Bi	83	208.9806	Oxygen	O	8	15.9994
Boron	B	5	10.81	Palladium	Pd	46	106.4
Bromine	Br	35	79.90	Phosphorus	P	15	30.9738
Cadmium	Cd	48	112.40	Platinum	Pt	78	195.09
Calcium	Ca	20	40.08	Plutonium	Pu	94	(224)
Californium	Cf	98	(251)	Polonium	Po	84	(209)
Carbon	C	6	12.011	Potassium	K	19	39.102
Cerium	Ce	58	140.12	Praseodymium	Pr	59	140.9077
Cesium	Cs	55	132.9055	Promethium	Pm	61	(145)
Chlorine	Cl	17	35.453	Protactinium	Pa	91	(231)
Chromium	Cr	24	51.996	Radium	Ra	88	(226)
Cobalt	Co	27	58.9332	Radon	Rn	86	(222)
Copper	Cu	29	63.545	Rhenium	Re	75	186.2
Curium	Cm	96	(247)	Rhodium	Rh	45	102.9055
Dysprosium	Dy	66	162.50	Rubidium	Rb	37	85.4678
Einsteinium	Es	99	(254)	Ruthenium	Ru	44	101.07
Erbium	Er	68	167.26	Rutherfordium	Rf	104	(257)
Europium	Eu	63	151.96	Samarium	Sm	62	150.4
Fermium	Fm	100	(253)	Scandium	Sc	21	44.9559
Fluorine	F	9	18.9984	Selenium	Se	34	78.96
Francium	Fr	87	(223)	Silicon	Si	14	28.086
Gadolinium	Gd	64	157.25	Silver	Ag	47	107.868
Gallium	Ga	31	69.72	Sodium	Na	11	22.9898
Germanium	Ge	32	72.59	Strontium	Sr	38	87.62
Gold	Au	79	196.967	Sulfur	S	16	32.06
Hafnium	Hf	72	178.49	Tantalum	Ta	73	180.9479
Hahnium	Ha	105	(260)	Technetium	Tc	43	(99)
Helium	He	2	4.00260	Tellerium	Te	52	127.60
Holmium	Ho	67	164.9303	Terbium	Tb	65	158.9254
Hydrogen	H	1	1.0080	Thallium	Tl	81	204.37
Indium	In	49	114.82	Thorium	Th	90	232.0381
Iodine	I	53	126.9045	Thulium	Tm	69	168.9342
Iridium	Ir	77	192.22	Tin	Sn	50	118.69
Iron	Fe	26	55.847	Titanium	Ti	22	47.90
Krypton	Kr	36	83.80	Tungsten	W	74	183.85
Lanthanium	La	57	138.9055	Uranium	U	92	238.029
Lawrencium	Lr	103	(257)	Vanadium	Vy	23	50.9414
Lead	Pb	82	207.12	Xenon	Xe	54	131.30
Lithium	Li	3	6.941	Ytterbium	Yb	70	173.04
Lutetium	Lu	71	174.97	Yttrium	Y	39	88.9059
Magnesium	Mg	12	24.305	Zinc	Zn	30	65.37
Manganese	Mn	25	54.9380	Zirconium	Zr	40	91.22
Mendelevium	Md	101	(256)				

Mathematical and Physical Constants

TABLE B1 Metric Prefixes

Multiple		*Name*	*Abbreviation*
1,000,000,000,000,000,000	10^{18}	exa	E
1,000,000,000,000,000	10^{15}	peta	P
1,000,000,000,000	10^{12}	tera	T
1,000,000,000	10^{9}	giga	G
1,000,000	10^{6}	mega	M
1,000	10^{3}	kilo	k
100	10^{2}	hecto	h
10	10^{1}	deka	da
1	1	—	—
0.1	10^{-1}	deci	d
0.01	10^{-2}	centi	c
0.001	10^{-3}	milli	m
0.000001	10^{-6}	micro	μ
0.000000001	10^{-9}	nano	n
0.000000000001	10^{-12}	pico	p
0.000000000000001	10^{-15}	femto	f
0.000000000000000001	10^{-18}	atto	a

TABLE B2 Physical Constants

Acceleration due to gravity	g	$9.8\ \text{m/s}^2 = 980\ \text{cm/s}^2 = 32.2\ \text{ft/s}^2$
Universal gravitational constant	G	$6.67 \times 10^{-11} \dfrac{\text{N-m}^2}{\text{kg}^2} = 6.67 \times 10^{-8} \dfrac{\text{dyne-cm}^2}{\text{g}^2}$
Electron charge	e	1.60×10^{-19} C
Speed of light	c	3.0×10^{8} m/s $= 3.0 \times 10^{10}$ cm/s $= 1.86 \times 10^{5}$ mi/s
Boltzmann's constant	k	1.38×10^{-23} J/K $= 1.38 \times 10^{-16}$ erg/K
Planck's constant	h	6.63×10^{-34} J-s $= 6.63 \times 10^{-27}$ erg-s $= 4.14 \times 10^{-15}$ eV-s
	$\hbar$	$h/2\pi = 1.05 \times 10^{-34}$ J–s $= 1.05 \times 10^{-27}$ erg–s $= 6.58 \times 10^{-16}$ eV–s
Electron rest mass	m_e	9.11×10^{-31} kg $= 5.49 \times 10^{-4}$ amu $\leftrightarrow$ 0.511 MeV
Proton rest mass	m_p	1.672×10^{-27} kg $=$ 1.00783 amu $\leftrightarrow$ 938.3 MeV
Neutron rest mass	m_n	1.674×10^{-27} kg $=$ 1.00867 amu $\leftrightarrow$ 939.1 MeV
Coulomb's law constant	k	$1/4\pi\varepsilon_o = 9.0 \times 10^{9}\ \text{N-m}^2/\text{C}^2$
Permittivity of free space	ε_o	$8.85 \times 10^{-12}\ \text{C}^2/\text{N-m}^2$
Permeability of free space	μ_o	$4\pi \times 10^{-7} = 1.26 \times 10^{-6}$ Wb/A-m (T-M/A)
Astronomical and earth data		
Radius of earth		
equatorial		3963 mi $= 6.378 \times 10^{6}$ m
polar		3950 mi $= 6.357 \times 10^{6}$ m
Mass of earth		6.0×10^{24} kg
Mass of moon		7.4×10^{22} kg $= \frac{1}{81}$ mass of earth
Mass of sun		2.0×10^{30} kg
Average distance of earth from sun		93×10^{6} mi $= 1.5 \times 10^{8}$ km
Average distance of moon from earth		2.4×10^{5} mi $= 3.8 \times 10^{5}$ km
Diameter of moon		2160 mi $\approx$ 3500 km
Diameter of sun		864,000 mi $\approx 1.4 \times 10^{6}$ km

TABLE B3 Conversion Factors

Mass	1 g = 10^{-3} kg = 6.85 × 10^{-5} slug 1 kg = 10^{3} g = 6.85 × 10^{-2} slug 1 slug = 1.46 × 10^{4} g = 14.6 kg 1 amu = 1.66 × 10^{-24} g = 1.66 × 10^{-27} kg 1 metric ton = 1000 kg
Length	1 cm = 10^{-2} m = 0.394 in. 1 Å = 10^{-10} m = 10^{-8} cm = 10^{-1} nm 1m = 10^{-3} km = 3.28 ft = 39.4 in. 1 km = 10^{3} m = 0.621 mi 1 in. = 2.54 cm = 2.54 × 10^{-2} m 1 ft = 12 in. = 30.48 cm = 0.3048 m 1 mi = 5280 ft = 609 m = 1.609 km
Area	1 cm² = 10^{-4} m² = 0.1550 in.² = 1.08 × 10^{-3} ft² 1 m² = 10^{4} cm² = 10.76 ft² = 1550 in.² 1 in.² = 6.94 × 10^{-3} ft² = 6.45 cm² = 6.45 × 10^{-4} m² 1 ft² = 144 in.² = 9.29 × 10^{-2} m² = 929 cm²
Volume	1cm³ = 10^{-6} m³ = 3.53 × 10^{-5} ft³ = 6.10 × 10^{-2} in.³ 1 m³ = 10^{6} cm³ = 10^{3} liters = 35.3 ft³ = 6.10 × 10^{4} in.³ = 264 gal 1 liter = 10^{3} cm³ = 10^{-3} m³ = 1.056 qt = 0.264 gal 1 in.³ = 5.79 × 10^{-4} ft³ = 16.4 cm³ = 1.64 × 10^{-5} m³ 1 ft³ = 1728 in.³ = 7.48 gal = 0.0283 m³ = 28.3 liters 1 qt = 2 pt = 946.5 cm³ = 0.946 liter 1 gal = 4 qt = 231 in.³ = 3.785 liters
Time	1 h = 60 min = 3600 s 1 day = 24 h = 1440 min = 8.64 × 10^{4} s 1 year = 365 days = 8.76 × 10^{3} h = 5.26 × 10^{5} min = 3.16 × 10^{7} s
Angle	360° = 2π rad 180° = π rad 1 rad = 57.3° 90° = $\pi/2$ rad 60° = $\pi/3$ rad 1° = 0.0175 rad 45° = $\pi/4$ rad 30° = $\pi/6$ rad
Speed	1 m/s = 3.6 km/h = 3.28 ft/s = 2.24 mi/h 1 km/h = 0.278 m/s = 0.621 mi/h = 0.911 ft/s 1 ft/s = 0.682 mi/h = 0.305 m/s = 1.10 km/h 1 mi/h = 1.467 ft/s = 1.609 km/h = 0.447 m/s 60 mi/h = 88 ft/s
Force	1 newton = 10^{5} dynes = 0.225 lb 1 dyne = 10^{-5} N = 2.25 × 10^{-6} lb 1 lb = 4.45 × 10^{5} dynes = 4.45 N Equivalent weight of 1-kg mass = 2.2 lb = 9.8 N
Pressure	1 Pa (N/m²)= 1.45 × 10^{-4} lb/in.² = 7.4 × 10^{-3} torr (mm Hg) = 10 dynes/cm² 1 tor (mm Hg) = 133 Pa (N/m²) = 0.02 lb/in.² = 1333 dynes/cm² 1 atm = 14.7 lb/in.² = 1.013 × 10^{5} N/m² = 1.013 × 10^{6} dynes/cm² = 30 in. Hg = 76 cm Hg 1 bar = 10^{6} dynes/cm² 1 millibar = 10^{3} dynes/cm²
Energy	1 J = 10^{7} ergs = 0.738 ft-lb = 0.239 cal = 9.48 × 10^{-4} Btu = 6.24 × 10^{18} eV 1 kcal = 4186 J = 4.186 × 10^{10} ergs = 3.968 Btu 1 Btu = 1055 J = 1.055 × 10^{10} ergs = 778 ft-lb = 0.252 kcal 1 cal = 4.186 J = 3.97 × 10^{-3} Btu = 3.09 ft-lb 1 ft-lb = 1.356 J = 1.36 × 10^{7} ergs = 1.29 × 10^{-3} Btu 1 eV = 1.60 × 10^{-19} J = 1.60 × 10^{-12} ergs
Power	1 W = 0.738 ft-lb/s = 1.34 × 10^{-3} hp = 3.41 Btu/h 1 ft-lb/s = 1.36 W = 1.82 × 10^{-3} hp 1 hp = 550 ft-lb/s = 745.7 W = 2545 Btu/h
Rest Mass-Energy Equivalents	1 amu = 1.66 × 10^{-27} kg ↔ 931 MeV 1 electron mass = 9.11 × 10^{-31} kg = 5.49 × 10^{-4} amu ↔ 0.511 MeV 1 proton mass = 1.672 × 10^{-27} kg = 1.00728 amu ↔ 938.3 MeV 1 neutron mass = 1.674 × 10^{-27} kg = 1.00867 amu ↔ 939.1 MeV

Table B4 Trigonometric Relationships

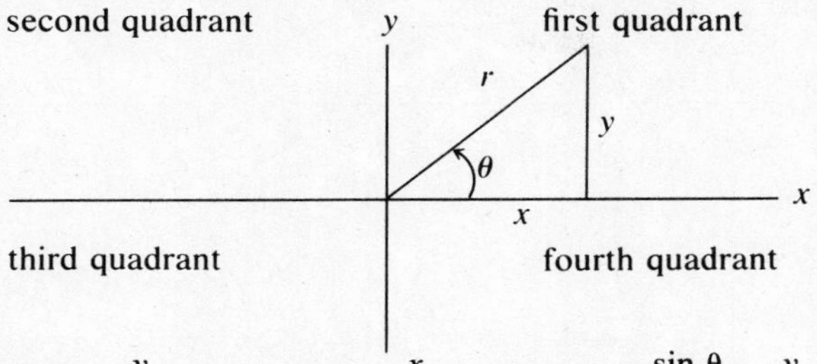

$\sin\theta = \frac{y}{r}$ $\cos\theta = \frac{x}{r}$ $\tan\theta = \frac{\sin\theta}{\cos\theta} = \frac{y}{x}$

θ° (rad)	sin θ	cos θ	tan θ
0° (0)	0	1	0
30° (π/6)	0.500	0.866	0.577
45° (π/4)	0.707	0.707	1.00
60° (π/3)	0.866	0.500	1.73
90° (π/2)	1	0	→ ∞

See Table B5 for other angles.

The sign of trigonometric functions depends on the quadrant, or sign of x and y, e.g., in the second quadrant $(-x,y)$, $-x/r = \cos\theta$ and $y/r = \sin\theta$, or by:

Reduction Formulas

	(θ in second quadrant)		(θ in third quadrant)		(θ in fourth quadrant)
$\sin\theta =$	$\cos(\theta - 90°)$	$=$	$-\sin(\theta - 180°)$	$=$	$-\cos(\theta - 270°)$
$\cos\theta =$	$-\sin(\theta - 90°)$	$=$	$-\cos(\theta - 180°)$	$=$	$\sin(\theta - 270°)$

Fundamental Identities

$\sin^2\theta + \cos^2\theta = 1$

$\sin 2\theta = 2\sin\theta\cos\theta$

$\cos 2\theta = \cos^2\theta - \sin^2\theta = 2\cos^2\theta - 1 = 1 - 2\sin^2\theta$

$\sin^2\theta = \frac{1}{2}(1 - \cos 2\theta)$

$\cos^2\theta = \frac{1}{2}(1 + \cos 2\theta)$

For half angle (θ/2) identities, replace θ with θ/2, e.g.,

$\sin^2\theta/2 = \frac{1}{2}(1 - \cos\theta)$ $\cos^2\theta/2 = \frac{1}{2}(1 + \cos\theta)$

$\sin(\alpha \pm \beta) = \sin\alpha\cos\beta \pm \cos\alpha\sin\beta$

$\cos(\alpha \pm \beta) = \cos\alpha\cos\beta \mp \sin\alpha\sin\beta$

For very small angles:

$\cos\theta \approx 1$

$\sin\theta \approx \theta$ (radians) $\tan\theta = \frac{\sin\theta}{\cos\theta} \approx \theta$

Law of sines:

$$\frac{a}{\sin\alpha} = \frac{b}{\sin\beta} = \frac{c}{\sin\gamma}$$

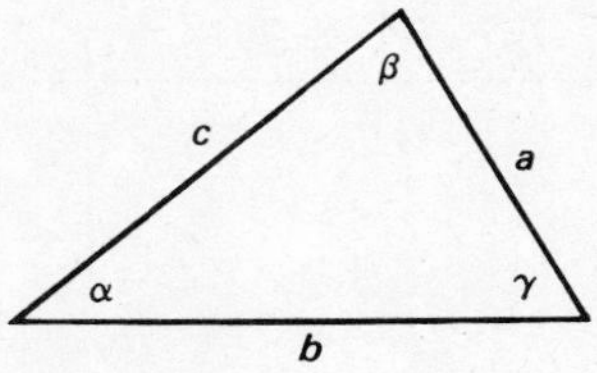

Law of cosines:

$a^2 = b^2 + c^2 - 2bc\cos\alpha$

$b^2 = a^2 + c^2 - 2ac\cos\beta$

$c^2 = a^2 + b^2 - 2ab\cos\gamma$

TABLE B5 Trigonometric Tables

Angle					*Angle*				
Degree	*Radian*	*Sine*	*Cosine*	*Tan-gent*	*Degree*	*Radian*	*Sine*	*Cosine*	*Tan-gent*
0°	.000	0.000	1.000	0.000					
1°	.017	.018	1.000	.018	46°	0.803	0.719	0.695	1.036
2°	.035	.035	0.999	.035	47°	.820	.731	.682	1.072
3°	.052	.052	.999	.052	48°	.838	.743	.669	1.111
4°	.070	.070	.998	.070	49°	.855	.755	.656	1.150
5°	.087	.087	.996	.088	50°	.873	.766	.643	1.192
6°	.105	.105	.995	.105	51°	.890	.777	.629	1.235
7°	.122	.122	.993	.123	52°	.908	.788	.616	1.280
8°	.140	.139	.990	.141	53°	.925	.799	.602	1.327
9°	.157	.156	.988	.158	54°	.942	.809	.588	1.376
10°	.175	.174	.985	.176	55°	.960	.819	.574	1.428
11°	.192	.191	.982	.194	56°	.977	.829	.559	1.483
12°	.209	.208	.978	.213	57°	.995	.839	.545	1.540
13°	.227	.225	.974	.231	58°	1.012	.848	.530	1.600
14°	.244	.242	.970	.249	59°	1.030	.857	.515	1.664
15°	.262	.259	.966	.268	60°	1.047	.866	.500	1.732
16°	.279	.276	.961	.287	61°	1.065	.875	.485	1.804
17°	.297	.292	.956	.306	62°	1.082	.883	.470	1.881
18°	.314	.309	.951	.325	63°	1.100	.891	.454	1.963
19°	.332	.326	.946	.344	64°	1.117	.899	.438	2.050
20°	.349	.342	.940	.364	65°	1.134	.906	.423	2.145
21°	.367	.358	.934	.384	66°	1.152	.914	.407	2.246
22°	.384	.375	.927	.404	67°	1.169	.921	.391	2.356
23°	.401	.391	.921	.425	68°	1.187	.927	.375	2.475
24°	.419	.407	.914	.445	69°	1.204	.934	.358	2.605
25°	.436	.423	.906	.466	70°	1.222	.940	.342	2.747
26°	.454	.438	.899	.488	71°	1.239	.946	.326	2.904
27°	.471	.454	.891	.510	72°	1.257	.951	.309	3.078
28°	.489	.470	.883	.532	73°	1.274	.956	.292	3.271
29°	.506	.485	.875	.554	74°	1.292	.961	.276	3.487
30°	.524	.500	.866	.577	75°	1.309	.966	.259	3.732
31°	.541	.515	.857	.601	76°	1.326	.970	.242	4.011
32°	.559	.530	.848	.625	77°	1.344	.974	.225	4.331
33°	.576	.545	.839	.649	78°	1.361	.978	.208	4.705
34°	.593	.559	.829	.675	79°	1.379	.982	.191	5.145
35°	.611	.574	.819	.700	80°	1.396	.985	.174	5.671
36°	.628	.588	.809	.727	81°	1.414	.988	.156	6.314
37°	.646	.602	.799	.754	82°	1.431	.990	.139	7.115
38°	.663	.616	.788	.781	83°	1.449	.993	.122	8.144
39°	.681	.629	.777	.810	84°	1.446	.995	.105	9.514
40°	.698	.643	.766	.839	85°	1.484	.996	.087	11.43
41°	.716	.658	.755	.869	86°	1.501	.998	.070	14.30
42°	.733	.669	.743	.900	87°	1.518	.999	.052	19.08
43°	.751	.682	.731	.933	88°	1.536	.999	.035	28.64
44°	.768	.695	.719	.966	89°	1.553	1.000	.017	57.29
45°	.785	.707	.707	1.000	90°	1.571	1.000	.000	∞

TABLE B6 Common Logarithms (base 10)

Examples: log 3.12 = 0.4942
log 256 = log (2.56 × 10²) = 2.4082

No.	0	1	2	3	4	5	6	7	8	9	1	2	3	4	5	6	7	8	9
10	0000	0043	0086	0128	0170	0212	0253	0294	0334	0374	4	8	12	17	21	25	29	33	37
11	0414	0453	0492	0531	0569	0607	0645	0682	0719	0755	4	8	11	15	19	23	26	30	34
12	0792	0828	0864	0899	0934	0969	1004	1038	1072	1106	3	7	10	14	17	21	24	28	31
13	1139	1173	1206	1239	1271	1303	1335	1367	1399	1430	3	6	10	13	16	19	23	26	29
14	1461	1492	1523	1553	1584	1614	1644	1673	1703	1732	3	6	9	12	15	18	21	24	27
15	1761	1790	1818	1847	1875	1903	1931	1959	1987	2014	3	6	8	11	14	17	20	22	25
16	2041	2068	2095	2122	2148	2175	2201	2227	2253	2279	3	5	8	11	13	16	18	21	24
17	2304	2330	2355	2380	2405	2430	2455	2480	2504	2529	2	5	7	10	12	15	17	20	22
18	2553	2577	2601	2625	2648	2672	2695	2718	2742	2765	2	5	7	9	12	14	16	19	21
19	2788	2810	2833	2856	2878	2900	2923	2945	2967	2989	2	4	7	9	11	13	16	18	20
20	3010	3032	3054	3075	3096	3118	3139	3160	3181	3201	2	4	6	8	11	13	15	17	19
21	3222	3243	3263	3284	3304	3324	3345	3365	3385	3404	2	4	6	8	10	12	14	16	18
22	3424	3444	3464	3483	3502	3522	3541	3560	3579	3598	2	4	6	8	10	12	14	15	17
23	3617	3636	3655	3674	3692	3711	3729	3747	3766	3784	2	4	6	7	9	11	13	15	17
24	3802	3820	3838	3856	3874	3892	3909	3927	3945	3962	2	4	5	7	9	11	12	14	16
25	3979	3997	4014	4031	4048	4065	4082	4099	4116	4133	2	3	5	7	9	10	12	14	15
26	4150	4166	4183	4200	4216	4232	4249	4265	4281	4298	2	3	5	7	8	10	11	13	15
27	4314	4330	4346	4362	4378	4393	4409	4425	4440	4456	2	3	5	6	8	9	11	13	14
28	4472	4487	4502	4518	4533	4548	4564	4579	4594	4609	2	3	5	6	8	9	11	12	14
29	4624	4639	4654	4669	4683	4698	4713	4728	4742	4757	1	3	4	6	7	9	10	12	13
30	4771	4786	4800	4814	4829	4843	4857	4871	4886	4900	1	3	4	6	7	9	10	11	13
31	4914	4928	4942	4955	4969	4983	4997	5011	5024	5038	1	3	4	6	7	8	10	11	12
32	5051	5065	5079	5092	5105	5119	5132	5145	5159	5172	1	3	4	5	7	8	9	11	12
33	5185	5198	5211	5224	5237	5250	5263	5276	5289	5302	1	3	4	5	6	8	9	10	12
34	5313	5328	5340	5353	5366	5378	5391	5403	5416	5428	1	3	4	5	6	8	9	10	11
35	5441	5453	5465	5478	5490	5502	5514	5527	5539	5551	1	2	4	5	6	7	9	10	11
36	5563	5575	5587	5599	5611	5623	5635	5647	5658	5670	1	2	4	5	6	7	8	10	11
37	5682	5694	5705	5717	5729	5740	5752	5763	5775	5786	1	2	3	5	6	7	8	9	10
38	5798	5809	5821	5832	5843	5855	5866	5877	5888	5899	1	2	3	5	6	7	8	9	10
39	5911	5922	5933	5944	5955	5966	5977	5988	5999	6010	1	2	3	4	5	7	8	9	10
40	6021	6031	6042	6053	6064	6075	6085	6096	6107	6117	1	2	3	4	5	6	8	9	10
41	6128	6138	6149	6160	6170	6180	6191	6201	6212	6222	1	2	3	4	5	6	7	8	9
42	6232	6243	6253	6263	6274	6284	6294	6304	6314	6325	1	2	3	4	5	6	7	8	9
43	6335	6345	6355	6365	6375	6385	6395	6405	6415	6425	1	2	3	4	5	6	7	8	9
44	6435	6444	6454	6464	6474	6484	6493	6503	6513	6522	1	2	3	4	5	6	7	8	9
45	6532	6542	6551	6561	6571	6580	6590	6599	6609	6618	1	2	3	4	5	6	7	8	9
46	6628	6637	6646	6656	6665	6675	6684	6693	6702	6712	1	2	3	4	5	6	7	7	8
47	6721	6730	6739	6749	6758	6767	6776	6785	6794	6803	1	2	3	4	5	5	6	7	8
48	6812	6821	6830	6839	6848	6857	6866	6875	6884	6893	1	2	3	4	4	5	6	7	8
49	6902	6911	6920	6928	6937	6946	6955	6964	6972	6981	1	2	3	4	4	5	6	7	8
50	6990	6998	7007	7016	7024	7033	7042	7050	7059	7067	1	2	3	3	4	5	6	7	8
51	7076	7084	7093	7101	7110	7118	7126	7135	7143	7152	1	2	3	3	4	5	6	7	8
52	7160	7168	7177	7185	7193	7202	7210	7218	7226	7235	1	2	2	3	4	5	6	7	7
53	7243	7251	7259	7267	7275	7284	7292	7300	7308	7316	1	2	2	3	4	5	6	6	7
54	7324	7332	7340	7348	7356	7364	7372	7380	7388	7396	1	2	2	3	4	5	6	6	7

TABLE B6 Common Logarithms (base 10) (continued)

No.	0	1	2	3	4	5	6	7	8	9	1	2	3	4	5	6	7	8	9
55	7404	7412	7419	7427	7435	7443	7451	7459	7466	7474	1	2	2	3	4	5	5	6	7
56	7482	7490	7497	7505	7513	7520	7528	7536	7543	7551	1	2	2	3	4	5	5	6	7
57	7559	7566	7574	7582	7589	7597	7604	7612	7619	7627	1	2	2	3	4	5	5	6	7
58	7634	7642	7649	7657	7664	7672	7679	7686	7694	7701	1	1	2	3	4	4	5	6	7
59	7709	7716	7723	7731	7738	7745	7752	7760	7767	7774	1	1	2	3	4	4	5	6	7
60	7782	7789	7796	7803	7810	7818	7825	7832	7839	7846	1	1	2	3	4	4	5	5	6
61	7853	7860	7868	7875	7882	7889	7896	7903	7910	7917	1	1	2	3	4	4	5	6	6
62	7924	7931	7938	7945	7952	7959	7966	7973	7980	7987	1	1	2	3	3	4	5	6	6
63	7992	8000	8007	8014	8021	8028	8035	8041	8048	8055	1	1	2	3	3	4	5	5	6
64	8062	8069	8075	8082	8089	8096	8102	8109	8116	8122	1	1	2	3	3	4	5	5	6
65	8129	8136	8142	8149	8156	8162	8169	8176	8182	8189	1	1	2	3	3	4	5	5	6
66	8195	8202	8209	8215	8222	8228	8235	8241	8248	8254	1	1	2	3	3	4	5	5	6
67	8261	8267	8274	8280	8287	8293	8299	8306	8312	8319	1	1	2	3	3	4	5	5	6
68	8325	8331	8338	8344	8351	8357	8363	8370	8376	8382	1	1	2	3	3	4	4	5	6
69	8388	8395	8401	8407	8414	8420	8426	8432	8439	8445	1	1	2	2	3	4	4	5	6
70	8451	8457	8463	8470	8476	8482	8488	8494	8500	8506	1	1	2	2	3	4	4	5	6
71	8513	8519	8525	8531	8537	8543	8549	8555	8561	8567	1	1	2	2	3	4	4	5	5
72	8573	8579	8585	8591	8597	8603	8609	8615	8621	8627	1	1	2	2	3	4	4	5	5
73	8633	8639	8645	8651	8657	8663	8669	8675	8681	8686	1	1	2	2	3	4	4	5	5
74	8692	8698	8704	8710	8716	8722	8727	8733	8739	8745	1	1	2	2	3	4	4	5	5
75	8751	8756	8762	8768	8774	8779	8785	8791	8797	8802	1	1	2	2	3	3	4	5	5
76	8808	8814	8820	8825	8831	8837	8842	8848	8854	8859	1	1	2	2	3	3	4	5	5
77	8865	8871	8876	8882	8887	8893	8899	8904	8910	8915	1	1	2	2	3	3	4	4	5
78	8921	8927	8932	8938	8943	8949	8954	8960	8965	8971	1	1	2	2	3	3	4	4	5
79	8976	8982	8987	8993	8998	9004	9009	9015	9020	9025	1	1	2	2	3	3	4	4	5
80	9031	9036	9042	9047	9053	9058	9063	9069	9074	9079	1	1	2	2	3	3	4	4	5
81	9085	9090	9096	9101	9106	9112	9117	9122	9128	9133	1	1	2	2	3	3	4	4	5
82	9138	9143	9149	9154	9159	9165	9170	9175	9180	9186	1	1	2	2	3	3	4	4	5
83	9191	9196	9201	9206	9212	9217	9222	9227	9232	9238	1	1	2	2	3	3	4	4	5
84	9243	9248	9253	9258	9263	9269	9274	9279	9284	9289	1	1	2	2	3	3	4	4	5
85	9294	9299	9304	9309	9315	9320	9325	9330	9335	9340	1	1	2	2	3	3	4	4	5
86	9345	9350	9355	9360	9365	9370	9375	9380	9385	9390	1	1	2	2	3	3	4	4	5
87	9395	9400	9405	9410	9415	9420	9425	9430	9435	9440	0	1	1	2	2	3	3	4	4
88	9445	9450	9455	9460	9465	9469	9474	9479	9484	9489	0	1	1	2	2	3	3	4	4
89	9494	9499	9504	9509	9513	9518	9523	9528	9533	9538	0	1	1	2	2	3	3	4	4
90	9542	9547	9552	9557	9562	9566	9571	9576	9581	9586	0	1	1	2	2	3	3	4	4
91	9590	9595	9600	9605	9609	9614	9619	9624	9628	9633	0	1	1	2	2	3	3	4	4
92	9638	9643	9647	9652	9657	9661	9666	9671	9675	9680	0	1	1	2	2	3	3	4	4
93	9685	9689	9694	9699	9703	9708	9713	9717	9722	9727	0	1	1	2	2	3	3	4	4
94	9731	9736	9741	9745	9750	9754	9759	9763	9768	9773	0	1	1	2	2	3	3	4	4
95	9777	9782	9786	9791	9795	9800	9805	9809	9814	9818	0	1	1	2	2	3	3	4	4
96	9823	9827	9832	9836	9841	9845	9850	9854	9859	9863	0	1	1	2	2	3	3	4	4
97	9868	9872	9877	9881	9886	9890	9894	9899	9903	9908	0	1	1	2	2	3	3	4	4
98	9912	9917	9921	9926	9930	9934	9939	9943	9948	9952	0	1	1	2	2	3	3	4	4
99	9956	9961	9965	9969	9974	9978	9983	9987	9991	9996	0	1	1	2	2	3	3	3	4

TABLE B7 Natural or Naperian Logarithms (base e)

To find the natural logarithm of a number that is $\frac{1}{10}, \frac{1}{100}, \frac{1}{1000}$, etc., of a number whose logarithm is given, subtract from the given logarithm $\log_e 10$, $2 \log_e 10$, $3 \log_e 10$, etc.

To find the natural logarithm of a number that is 10, 100, 1000, etc., times a number whose logarithm is given, add to the given logarithm $\log_e 10$, $2 \log_e 10$, $3 \log_e 10$, etc.

$\log_e 10 = 2.30258\ 50930$
$2 \log_e 10 = 4.60517\ 01860$
$3 \log_e 10 = 6.90775\ 52790$
$4 \log_e 10 = 9.21034\ 03720$
$5 \log_e 10 = 11.51292\ 54650$
$6 \log_e 10 = 13.81551\ 05580$
$7 \log_e 10 = 16.11809\ 56510$
$8 \log_e 10 = 18.42068\ 07440$
$9 \log_e 10 = 20.72326\ 58369$
$10 \log_e 10 = 23.02585\ 09299$

1.00–4.99

N	0	1	2	3	4	5	6	7	8	9
1.0	0.00000	.00995	.01980	.02956	.03922	.04879	.05827	.06766	.07696	.08618
.1	.09531	.10436	.11333	.12222	.13103	.13976	.14842	.15700	.16551	.17395
.2	.18232	.19062	.19885	.20701	.21511	.22314	.23111	.23902	.24686	.25464
.3	.26236	.27003	.27763	.28518	.29267	.30010	.30748	.31481	.32208	.32930
.4	.33647	.34359	.35066	.35767	.36464	.37156	.37844	.38526	.39204	.39878
.5	.40547	.41211	.41871	.42527	.43178	.43825	.44469	.45108	.45742	.46373
.6	.47000	.47623	.48243	.48858	.49470	.50078	.50682	.51282	.51879	.52473
.7	.53063	.53649	.54232	.54812	.55389	.55962	.56531	.57098	.57661	.58222
.8	.58779	.59333	.59884	.60432	.60977	.61519	.62058	.62594	.63127	.63658
.9	.64185	.64710	.65233	.65752	.66269	.66783	.67294	.67803	.68310	.68813
2.0	0.69315	.69813	.70310	.70804	.71295	.71784	.72271	.72755	.73237	.73716
.1	.74194	.74669	.75142	.75612	.76081	.76547	.77011	.77473	.77932	.78390
.2	.78846	.79299	.79751	.80200	.80648	.81093	.81536	.81978	.82418	.82855
.3	.83291	.83725	.84157	.84587	.85015	.85442	.85866	.86289	.86710	.87129
.4	.87547	.87963	.88377	.88789	.89200	.89609	.90016	.90422	.80826	.91228
.5	.91629	.92028	.92426	.92822	.93216	.93609	.94001	.94391	.94779	.95166
.6	.95551	.95935	.96317	.96698	.97078	.97456	.97833	.98208	.98582	.98954
.7	.99325	.99695	*.00063	*.00430	*.00796	*.01160	*.01523	*.01885	*.02245	*.02604
.8	1.02962	.03318	.03674	.04028	.04380	.04732	.05082	.05431	.05779	.06126
.9	.06471	.06815	.07158	.07500	.07841	.08181	.08519	.08856	.09192	.09527
3.0	1.09861	.10194	.10526	.10856	.11186	.11514	.11841	.12168	.12493	.12817
.1	.13140	.13462	.13783	.14103	.14422	.14740	.15057	.15373	.15688	.16002
.2	.16315	.16627	.16938	.17248	.17557	.17865	.18173	.18479	.18784	.19089
.3	.19392	.19695	.19996	.20297	.20597	.20896	.21194	.21491	.21788	.22083
.4	.22378	.22671	.22964	.23256	.23547	.23837	.24127	.24415	.24703	.24990
.5	.25276	.25562	.25846	.26130	.26413	.26695	.26976	.27257	.27536	.27815
.6	.28093	.28371	.28647	.28923	.29198	.29473	.29746	.30019	.30291	.30563
.7	.30833	.31103	.31372	.31641	.31909	.32176	.32442	.32708	.32972	.33237
.8	.33500	.33763	.34025	.34286	.34547	.34807	.35067	.35325	.35584	.35841
.9	.36098	.36354	.36609	.36864	.37118	.37372	.37624	.37877	.38128	.38379
4.0	1.38629	.38879	.39128	.39377	.39624	.39872	.40118	.40364	.40610	.40854
.1	.41099	.41342	.41585	.41828	.42070	.42311	.42552	.42792	.43031	.43270
.2	.43508	.43746	.43984	.44220	.44456	.44692	.44927	.45161	.45395	.45629
.3	.45862	.46094	.46326	.46557	.46787	.47018	.47247	.47476	.47705	.47933
.4	.48160	.48387	.48614	.48840	.49065	.49290	.49515	.49739	.49962	.50185
.5	.50408	.50630	.50851	.51072	.51293	.51513	.51732	.51951	.52170	.52388
.6	.52606	.52823	.53039	.53256	.53471	.53687	.53902	.54116	.54330	.54543
.7	.54756	.54969	.55181	.55393	.55604	.55814	.56025	.56235	.56444	.56653
.8	.56862	.57070	.57277	.57485	.57691	.57898	.58104	.58309	.58515	.58719
.9	.58924	.59127	.59331	.59534	.59737	.59939	.60141	.60342	.60543	.60744

* Starred decimals should be preceded by the integer on the next line.

TABLE B7 Natural or Naperian Logarithms (Continued)

5.00–9.99

N	0	1	2	3	4	5	6	7	8	9
5.0	1.60944	.61144	.61343	.61542	.61741	.61939	.62137	.62334	.62531	.62728
.1	.62924	.63120	.63315	.63511	.63705	.63900	.64094	.64287	.64481	.64673
.2	.64866	.65058	.65250	.65411	.65632	.65823	.66013	.66203	.66393	.66582
.3	.66771	.66959	.67147	.67335	.67523	.67710	.67896	.68083	.68269	.68455
.4	.68640	.68825	.69010	.69194	.69378	.69562	.69745	.69928	.70111	.70293
.5	.70475	.70656	.70838	.71019	.71199	.71380	.71560	.71740	.71919	.72098
.6	.72277	.72455	.72633	.72811	.72988	.73166	.73342	.73519	.73695	.73871
.7	.74047	.74222	.74397	.74572	.74746	.74920	.75094	.75267	.75440	.75613
.8	.75786	.75958	.76130	.76302	.76473	.76644	.76815	.76985	.77156	.77326
.9	.77495	.77665	.77834	.78002	.78171	.78339	.78507	.78675	.78842	.79009
6.0	1.79176	.79342	.79509	.79675	.79840	.80006	.80171	.80336	.80500	.80665
.1	.80829	.80993	.81156	.81319	.81482	.81645	.81808	.81970	.82132	.82294
.2	.82455	.82616	.82777	.82938	.83098	.83258	.83418	.83578	.83737	.83896
.3	.84055	.84214	.84372	.84530	.84688	.84845	.85003	.85160	.85317	.85473
.4	.85630	.85786	.85942	.86097	.86253	.86408	.86563	.86718	.86872	.87026
.5	.87180	.87334	.87487	.87641	.87794	.87947	.88099	.88251	.88403	.88555
.6	.88707	.88858	.89010	.89160	.89311	.89462	.89612	.89762	.89912	.90061
.7	.90211	.90360	.90509	.90658	.90806	.90954	.91102	.91250	.91398	.91545
.8	.91692	.91839	.91986	.92132	.92279	.92425	.92571	.92716	.92862	.93007
.9	.93152	.93297	.93442	.93586	.93730	.93874	.94018	.94162	.94305	.94448
7.0	1.94591	.94734	.94876	.95019	.95161	.95303	.95445	.95586	.95727	.95869
.1	.96009	.96150	.96291	.96431	.96571	.96711	.96851	.96991	.97130	.97269
.2	.97408	.97547	.97685	.97824	.97962	.98100	.98238	.98376	.98513	.98650
.3	.98787	.98924	.99061	.99198	.99334	.99470	.99606	.99742	.99877	*.00013
.4	2.00148	.00283	.00418	.00553	.00687	.00821	.00956	.01089	.01223	.01357
.5	.01490	.01624	.01757	.01890	.02022	.02155	.02287	.02419	.02551	.02683
.6	.02815	.02946	.03078	.03209	.03340	.03471	.03601	.03732	.03862	.03992
.7	.04122	.04252	.04381	.04511	.04640	.04769	.04898	.05027	.05156	.05284
.8	.05412	.05540	.05668	.05796	.05924	.06051	.06179	.06306	.06433	.06560
.9	.06686	.06813	.06939	.07065	.07191	.07317	.07443	.07568	.07694	.07819
8.0	2.07944	.08069	.08194	.08319	.08443	.08567	.08691	.08815	.08939	.09063
.1	.09186	.09310	.09433	.09556	.09679	.09802	.09924	.10047	.10169	.10291
.2	.10413	.10535	.10657	.10779	.10900	.11021	.11142	.11263	.11384	.11505
.3	.11626	.11746	.11866	.11986	.12106	.12226	.12346	.12465	.12585	.12704
.4	.12823	.12942	.13061	.13180	.13298	.13417	.13535	.13653	.13771	.13889
.5	.14007	.14124	.14242	.14359	.14476	.14593	.14710	.14827	.14943	.15060
.6	.15176	.15292	.15409	.15524	.15640	.15756	.15871	.15987	.16102	.16217
.7	.16332	.16447	.16562	.16677	.16791	.16905	.17020	.17134	.17248	.17361
.8	.17475	.17589	.17702	.17816	.17929	.18042	.18155	18267	.18380	.18493
.9	.18605	.18717	.18830	.18942	.19054	.19165	.19277	.19389	.19500	.19611
9.0	2.19722	.19834	.19944	.20055	.20166	.20276	.20387	.20497	.20607	.20717
.1	.20827	.20937	.21047	.21157	.21266	.21375	.21485	.21594	.21703	.21812
.2	.21920	.22029	.22138	.22246	.22354	.22462	.22570	.22678	.22786	.22894
.3	.23001	.23109	.23216	.23324	.23431	.23538	.23645	.23751	.23858	.23965
.4	.24071	.24177	.24284	.24390	.24496	.24601	.24707	.24813	.24918	.25024
.5	.25129	.25234	.25339	.25444	.25549	.25654	.25759	.25863	.25968	.26072
.6	.26176	.26280	.26384	.26488	.26592	.26696	.26799	.26903	.27006	.27109
.7	.27213	.27316	.27419	.27521	.27624	.27727	.27829	.27932	.28034	.28136
.8	.28238	.28340	.28442	.28544	.28646	.28747	.28849	.28950	.29051	.29152
.9	.29253	.29354	.29455	.29556	.29657	.29757	.29858	.29958	.30058	.30158

Method of Least Squares

Let $y' = m'x + b'$ be the predicted equation of the best-fitting straight line for a set of data. The vertical deviation of the ith data point from this line is then $(y_i - y_i')$.

The principle of least squares may be stated as follows: The "best-fitting" straight line is the one that minimizes the sum of the squares of the deviations of the measured y values from those of the predicted equation $y' = m'x + b'$.

The numerical values of the slope m' and intercept b' that minimize the sum of the squares of the deviations, $\sum_{i=1}^{N}(y_i - y_i')^2$, may be found using differential calculus. The results are as follows:

$$m' = \frac{M_{xy}}{M_{xx}} \quad \text{and} \quad b' = \bar{y} - m'\bar{x}$$

where $\bar{x}$ and $\bar{y}$ are the mean values, $\bar{x} = \sum_{i=1}^{N} x_i$ and $\bar{y} = \sum_{i=1}^{N} y_i$, and

$$M_{xy} = \sum_{i=1}^{N}(x_i - \bar{x})(y_i - \bar{y})$$

$$= \sum_{i=1}^{N} x_i y_i - \frac{\left(\sum_{i=1}^{N} x_i\right)\left(\sum_{i=1}^{N} y_i\right)}{N}$$

$$M_{xx} = \sum_{i=1}^{N}(x_i - \bar{x})^2 = \sum_{i=1}^{N} x_i^2 - \frac{\left(\sum_{i=1}^{N} x_i\right)^2}{N}$$

where the sums of the deviations, e.g., $\sum_{i=1}^{N}(x_i - \bar{x})$, are zero.

Exercise

1. Plot the data given in Table 1 on a sheet of graph paper and draw the straight line you judge to best fit the data.

2. Using the method of least squares, find the slope and intercept of the "best-fitting" straight line, and compare with the slope and intercept of the line drawn in (1). Plot this "best-fitting" line on the graph. (Recall that the slope of a line is the change in y for a one-unit increase in x.)

DATA TABLE 1

	y_i	x_i	x_i^2	$x_i y_i$
	25	12		
	44	28		
	78	47		
	80	70		
	43	16		
	58	53		
	95	72		
	67	38		
Sums (Σ)				

Graphing Exponential Functions

In some cases, exponential functions of the form

$$N = N_o e^{\lambda t} \quad \textbf{(D.1)}$$

$$(\text{or } y = Ae^{ax})$$

are plotted on Cartesian coordinates in linear form by first taking the natural or Naperian logarithm (base e) of both sides of the equation, e.g., for $N = N_o e^{\lambda t}$,

$$\ln N = \ln (N_o e^{\lambda t}) = \ln N_o + \ln e^{\lambda t} = \ln N_o + \lambda t$$

or

$$\ln N = \lambda t + \ln N_o \quad \textbf{(D.2)}$$

Similarly, for $y = Ae^{ax}$,

$$\ln y = \ln A + \ln e^{ax} = \ln A + ax$$

or

$$\ln y = ax + \ln A \quad \textbf{(D.3)}$$

These equations have the general form of a straight line when plotted on a Cartesian graph ($y = mx + b$). For example, by plotting ln N versus t as Cartesian coordinates, the slope of the line is λ and the intercept is ln N_o. The value of N_o obtained by taking the *antilog* of the intercept value ln N_o. (For a decaying exponential, $N = N_o e^{-\lambda t}$, the slope would be negative. Note that, before plotting ln N versus t on Cartesian graph paper, ln N must be found for each value of N.)

Because logarithmic functions occur quite often in physics, special graph paper, called *semi-log graph paper*, is printed with graduations along the y or ordinate axis that are spaced logarithmically rather than linearly. The x or abscissa axis is graduated linearly. (Look at a sheet of semi-log graph paper.)

If a quantity is plotted on the ordinate axis of semi-log paper, the logarithmic graduated scale automatically takes the logarithm, so it is not necessary to look up the logarithm for each y value. However, commercial logarithmic graph paper is set up for common (base 10) logarithms rather than natural (base e) logarithms. Exponential functions may be treated as follows. Taking the (common) log of each side of $y = Ae^{ax}$,

$$\begin{aligned} \log y &= \log A + \log e^{ax} \\ &= \log A + ax \log e \\ &= \log A + (0.4343)ax \end{aligned} \quad \textbf{(D.4)}$$

where log e = 0.4343.

Hence, the slope of the resulting straight line is (0.4343)*a* rather than simply *a*.

The logarithmic ordinate scale is called "one cycle," "two-cycle," and so on, depending on the number of powers of 10 covered on the axis. The beginnings of the cycles are consecutively labeled in multiples of 10 (e.g., 0.1, 1.0, 10, or 1.0, 10, 100, etc.), depending on the range (cycles) of the function. (Common logarithms can also be plotted on semi-log paper.)

Care must be taken in determining the slope of the line on a semi-log plot. On an ordinary Cartesian graph, the slope of a line is given by $\Delta y/\Delta x = (y_2 - y_1)/(x_2 - x_1)$. However, on a semi-log graph, the slope of a line is given by

$$\text{slope} = \frac{\Delta \log y}{\Delta x} \quad \left(\text{or } \frac{\Delta \log N}{\Delta t}\right) \quad \textbf{(D.5)}$$

On a semi-log plot, the listed ordinate values are y, not ln y. Hence, one must explicitly take the logs of the ordinate values of the end points of the slope interval, y_2 and y_1, or the log of their ratio:

$$\begin{aligned} \text{slope} &= \frac{\Delta \log y}{\Delta x} = \frac{\log y_2 - \log y_1}{x_2 - x_1} \\ &= \frac{\log y_2/y_1}{x_2 - x_1} \end{aligned} \quad \textbf{(D.6)}$$

The value of N_o can be read directly from the y intercept of the graph.

Another common equation form in physics is

$$y = ax^n \quad \textbf{(D.7)}$$

For example, the electric field, $E = kq/r^2 = kqr^{-2}$, is of this form, with $a = kq$ and $n = -2$. By plotting y versus x^n on Cartesian graph paper, a straight line is obtained with a slope of a. However, in an experiment the measured values are usually y and x, so computation of the x^n's is required.

But in some instances the exponent n may not be known. This constant, along with the constant a, may be found by plotting y versus x on log graph paper. (This is commonly called *log-log graph paper* because of the logarithmic graduations on both axes. Look at a sheet of log-log graph paper.)

The logarithmic graduations on axes again automatically take the logarithms of x and y. Working with common logarithms (base 10) in this instance, the log-log plot of y versus x yields a straight line, as can be seen by taking the (common) log of both sides of Eq. 52.16.

$$\log y = \log (ax^n) = \log a + \log x^n$$
$$= \log a + n \log x$$

or

$$\log y = n \log x + \log a \qquad \textbf{(D.8)}$$

which has the general form of a straight line with a slope of n and an intercept of $\log a$. For the electric field example, this would be

$$E = \frac{kq}{r^2} = kqr^{-2}$$

$$\log E = -2 \log r + \log kq$$

Again, care must be taken in determining the slope of a straight line on a log-log graph. In this case,

$$\text{slope} = \frac{\Delta \log y}{\Delta \log x}$$

$$= \frac{\log y_2 - \log y_1}{\log x_2 - \log x_1} = \frac{\log y_2/y_1}{\log x_2/x_1} \qquad \textbf{(D.9)}$$

and the logs of the end points of the slope interval or their ratio must be found explicitly. (The ordinate and abscissa values on the log-log plot are y and x, *not* $\log y$ and $\log x$.)

As in the case of the semi-log plot, the value of a in $y = ax^n$ can be read directly from the y intercept of the graph. However, in this case, the intercept is not at $x = 0$, *but* at $x = 1$, since the intercept $\log y = \log a$ requires that $\log x = 0$ and $\log 1 = 0$.